HYMNS PSALMS
AND
SPIRITUAL CANTICLES

A Parish Music Manual

HYMNS PSALMS
AND
SPIRITUAL CANTICLES

Compiled, Edited and Arranged by
Theodore Marier

Assisted by the staff of the
Boston Archdiocesan Choir School
at St. Paul Church, Cambridge, MA.

Unison Pew Edition

PUBLISHING CO·

P.O. BOX 167· BELMONT·MASSACHUSETTS· 02178·

Cover design by Paul Fowler

FOREWORD

Liturgically, the great work of the Church in the final quarter of the twentieth century is to bring into practice the changes suggested by the Second Vatican Council. In the *Constitution on the Sacred Liturgy*, the Council called for congregational singing as participation in worship and as something to be encouraged. Subsequent documents from the Sacred Congregation of Rites and from the National Conference of Catholic Bishops have made this call more explicit.

This book represents a carefully researched and experimentally tested response to this call of the Council. Theodore Marier, its compiler, is rightly recognized for his leadership and creativity in religious music. In this volume, he has brought together all that is needed for a complete program of congregational singing. He offers a musical format for the Order of Mass in which the congregation can easily participate. He provides liturgically appropriate musical settings for a wide range of services as well as an excellent selection of hymns.

This book offers much to Catholic worship. It fills the great need for a structured program which can assist in the development of congregations that feel comfortable with sung participation in the Liturgy.

The experience of the materials in this book has greatly enriched the worship at St. Paul's Church in Cambridge, Massachusetts. This community has become more and more aware of how much it is strengthened and enriched in its prayer by the ability of the entire congregation to express its faith and devotion in song.

Hopefully, the wide distribution of *Hymns, Psalms and Spiritual Canticles* will provide similar experiences to great numbers of worshipers. May it open to us something of what St. Paul meant when he exhorted the Colossians to "Let the word of Christ dwell in you abundantly; in all wisdom teach and admonish one another by hymns, psalms and spiritual canticles, singing in your hearts to God by his grace."

Rev. John P. Boles, Pastor
St. Paul Church
Cambridge, Massachusetts

Feast of the Epiphany, 1983

PREFACE

This parish manual has been developed and tested through two decades of continuous daily use at the Church of St. Paul, Cambridge, Mass. The music is designed primarily for singing by cantor, celebrant and congregation with and without choir. When a choir is present, the manual provides numerous optional choral settings as musical enrichments of the liturgical prayers. For example, as options, the choir can sing descants to the gospel and other acclamations; four-part (SATB) settings for psalm verses; through-composed compositions for choir and congregation of the responsorial psalms of major feasts; and parts of the Mass ordinary, some in simple and others in more elaborate settings for choir, congregation and organ.

The grade of difficulty of the music ranges from the very simple to the more complex. For example, there are one-note recitations of the *Glory to God* and *We Believe*, and simple chant-like antiphons and refrains. There are also technically more demanding compositions in contemporary polyphonic style by Anton Heiller, Jean Langlais and Russell Woollen. At whatever level of difficulty, the music includes a part for the people.

For the "core" programs of the Mass, Responsorial Psalms, Morning and Evening Prayer (Service of Light), Compline (Night Prayer) and other services of communal worship, the musical style is consistently homogeneous. Experience has shown that stylistic uniformity builds familiarity and thus eases the day-to-day rendition of new musical settings of liturgical texts. There is, moreover, music provided for every liturgical event indicated in both the *Lectionary* and the *Sacramentary*.

ORDER OF MASS

Simple chant-like melodies with organ accompaniments are provided for all the sung priest-people dialogues, starting with "In the name of the Father . . ." at the beginning of Mass, to "The Mass is ended . . ." The complete setting of the Order of Mass in Latin follows the same style, starting with "In nomine Patris . . ." to the final "Ite, missa est . . . Deo gratias". For the sake of variety, and offering opportunities for expanding the people's repertory of music that is sung during Mass, the manual contains numerous alternate settings of the Mass texts that include unison melodies, polyphonic compositions for choir-organ-congregation, and Gregorian Chants.

HYMNS

From the rich store of classical and contemporary Christian hymnody, the manual offers 370 hymns, providing suitable texts and tunes for all occasions of worship. The harmonizations of many of the traditional chorales are by J.S. Bach, and the hymn tunes of later composers are given either in their traditional arrangements or in carefully prepared settings. Contemporary poets, imbued with a sense of the Church's mainstream theology, have provided texts that are rich in imagery and rhythmic vitality. Along side of such classical texts as *O God, Our Help in Ages Past* by Isaac Watts, *Godhead Here in Hiding* by Gerard Manley Hopkins, and *At the Name of Jesus* by Caroline Noël, the hymn section of the manual offers numerous contemporary texts such as *O God, from Whom Mankind Derives its Name* by Frederick Kaan, *O Lord, You Are My God* by John Dunn, *Think of the Son of God*, an ancient Gaelic poem translated by Douglas Hyde, and *O God of Light* by James Quinn, S.J.

The first lines of hymns as titles are presented in alphabetical sequence to facilitate locating a particular hymn. At the same time, the hymns have been arranged to avoid page turns wherever possible. Many of the hymn texts are metrical paraphrases of psalms. These were carefully researched and selected to offer practical alternatives to the prose psalm settings. Experience has shown that some congregations are more comfortable singing tunes and texts that have a regular recurring pulse than they are when singing tunes and texts in free rhythm. In choosing these metrical settings, care was taken to include all the "common" psalms for the seasons and feasts shown in the *Lectionary*.

PSALMS

The psalms are presented in numerical order. The translations have been drawn from a variety of sources such as the *New American Bible*, the *Revised Standard Version of the Bible, The Psalms* by Mary Perkins Ryan, *The Grail, Psalms for Modern Man*, and the Latin Vulgate. With the permission of the copyright owners, some transpositions of the phrases were made in selected psalms in order to accommodate the musical cadences. In some psalms, also with permission, a non-restrictive language was adopted except where texts are under copyright limitations. The numberings of the psalms and verses are given according to the printed texts of the source books. A psalm with its proper or appropriate antiphon is given for every occasion listed in the *Lectionary*.

MISCELLANEOUS LITURGIES

There is a musical setting in the manual for every rite given in the *Sacramentary*. For ease of rendering by parish groups, both Morning and Evening Prayer are offered in the form of "core" programs. Night Prayer, with psalm options, is presented as in the *Breviary*. The complete texts of all four Passions of Our Lord are given full musical settings, suitable for singing by congregation and three cantors.

READINGS

For private reading or for group recitation, there are some 40 selections from the Old and New Testaments, from the recently discovered *Odes of Solomon*, with their inspiring Christological orientation, together with several quotations from the *Imitation of Christ* by Gerard Groote. Accompanied by soft organ music, these readings serve as excellent Communion meditations, especially when selected to accent the theme of a particular celebration.

INDICES

Fourteen indices expose the content and function of the manual so that the user can readily prepare programs for any worship occasion. A glance at the General Index at the front of the book will reveal the overall layout of the manual. The remaining indices are located at the back of the book. There the musician-liturgist will find listings on easy-to-read charts of the proper responsorial psalms and antiphons for all Sundays of the ABC Years, Solemnities, Feasts, Propers of the Saints, etc., with suggested hymns that reflect the theme of each liturgy. Other lists include titles of hymns, tunes, meters, composers, arrangers, authors, music, and text sources.

APPRECIATION

A word of thanks is hereby expressed to those who contributed support and practical assistance over the past ten years to the organization and preparation of this manual. This list is a long one and many will thus remain anonymous because they participated anonymously in the singing of the congregation with whom the music included in this book was first tried, "as silver is tried by fire!" Without them experimentation with new materials could not have been made nor a synthesis such as this one achieved. We thank them for their patience and support.

But there were individuals whose names ought to be mentioned, persons who brought inspiration and encouragement over a score of years without whom, like the anonymous members of the congregation, neither beginnings could have been made nor the termination of the project realized.

First, there was Edith Alice Marier, whose unabating loving support as wife and choir-mother, gave great and continuing daily impetus to the project until her untimely death in June, 1977; Rev. Joseph I. Collins, Pastor-Emeritus of St. Paul's, whose joy of song and enthusiasm for the sung liturgy provided a spiritual and practical matrix from which the Choir School was formed and thus, too, this manual. With competence and firm dedication to the task, there were others to whom a debt of gratitude is here warmly expressed. John Dunn, for example, whose keen eye for liturgical and musical detail helped to keep the work on course over the entire period of preparation. His assiduous investigation of classical and contemporary hymnody gave the hymn section of the book considerable variety and scope as well as providing suitable or proper selections for all Sundays, Solemnities and Feasts given in the Lectionary. In addition to the numerous original texts and psalm paraphrases he contributed, he is primarily responsible for the alteration of many of the hymn texts in order to make their language more sympathetic to current theological thinking and more comfortable to sing. He, moreover contributed encyclopedic charts of psalms and hymns as they relate to the themes given in the Lectionary.

Our thanks for his hard work, insights and concern. To David Goodine, Sr., and David Goodine, Jr., for their unyielding supervision of production logistics and proof-reading, with strong assists from Elizabeth Stouffer and Martin Stankard. Over the last decade various details of preparation also fell into the competent and willing hands of Rev. Joseph Fratic, Joseph Policelli, Edward and Charlene Haugh, Mary Geiger, Rita Waldron, and Louis Faiola. To them we extend our gratitude for their dedication to this project and their cooperation in its realization.

Theodore Marier
Easter, 1983

COPYRIGHT SOURCES AND ACKNOWLEDGEMENTS

The publishers and individuals who permitted the inclusion of their copyrighted music and texts are listed below. To them we express our thanks. A serious attempt was made to track down every copyrighted text, tune and arrangement. Our apology for any oversight that may have occurred in the process of selection and research.

Unless otherwise indicated below, all the musical settings of the Mass texts, the psalms and their antiphons, and service music, included in this music manual were composed or arranged by the author/editor and are the copyrighted property of the publisher. Included also are his original texts and tunes as indicated on the pages of the Hymns section of the book.

Grateful acknowledgement is hereby expressed for permission to include herein suitable original copyrighted texts and music drawn from existing available sources. Included are the following:

ORDER OF MASS

The International Committee on English in the Liturgy (ICEL), Washington, D.C., for translations from the **Roman Missal**, including texts for the Entrance Rite, the Liturgy of the Word, the Liturgy of the Eucharist, the Communion and Dismissal Rites, Gospel Acclamations, and Blessings, copyrighted in 1970, 1973, 1975, and 1976;

The International Consultation on English Texts (ICET), Washington, D.C., for translations of **Gloria**, **Credo**, Preface Dialogue, **Sanctus**, and **Agnus**. Used with permission.

Summy-Birchard Music, a Division of the Birch Tree Group, Ltd., Princeton, N.J. for Numbers 43, 44, 45, 47, 83, and 84;

Editions Schola Cantorum, Paris, for Number 48.

HYMNS

Geoffrey Chapman, a Division of Cassell, Ltd., London, for texts of Nos. 146, 149, 154, 160, 226, 240, 296, 335, 355, and 596;

The Church Hymnal Corporation, New York, for texts of Nos. 156, 244, 322;

J. Curwen and Sons, c/o G. Schirmer, N.Y., for texts of Nos. 103 and 272;

John Dunn, Arlington, Massachusetts, for texts of Nos. 109, 110, 113(vs. 4), 138, 140(vs. 4), 162, 163(vs. 4), 168, 173(vs. 4), 178, 179, 200(vs. 1), 225, 233(vs. 4), 245, 252, 253, 265, 277, 281(vs. 3), 282(vs. 3), 292, 296(vs. 5), 311(vs. 5), 313, 316(vs. 3), 327, 329, 337, 346(alt.), 353, and 354(vs. 4);

Faber Music, Ltd., London, for texts of Nos. 133, 222, 309, 334;

Fides/Claretian, Notre Dame, Indiana, for texts of Nos. 262, 263 and 264;

Galaxy Music Corp., New York, agents for Galliard, Ltd., for text of No. 238;

John Webster Grant, Canada, for text of No. 354;

H.W. Gray Co., Inc., a subsidiary of Belwin-Mills Publishing Corp., for tunes of Nos. 168, 192, 216, 317, 322;

Frederick Harris & Co., Ltd., Canada, for text of No. 339;

Martin B. Hellriegel, St. Louis, Mo., for texts of Nos. 163(vss. 1-3) and 336;

Hinshaw Music Inc., North Carolina, for musical setting of No. 206;

Hope Publishing Co., Illinois, for texts of Nos. 127, 130, 159, 166, 190, 289, 310, and 311;

Hymn Society of America, Ohio, for texts of Nos. 214, 215, 239, and 362;

International Committee on English in the Liturgy (ICEL), Inc., Washington, D.C., for texts of Nos. 155, 213, 274, 539, and accompaniments of Nos. 118, 340, 341, 342, and 539;

International Consultation on English Texts (ICET) Washington, D.C., for text of No. 361;

A. R. Mowbray & Co., Ltd., Canada, for text of No. 188;

Oxford University Press, London, for texts of Nos. 153 (vss. 4&5), 253, 319, 359, and for tunes of Nos. 116, 133, 157, 178, 179, 249, 277, 286, 289, 313, and 359;

Michael Perry, England, for text of No. 291;

The Pilgrim Press, New York, for texts of Nos. 234 and 243;

Proprietors of Hymns Ancient and Modern, England, for texts of Nos. 217, 321, 333, and for tunes of Nos. 109, 149;

Jeffrey W. Rowthorn, Connecticut, for text of No. 597;

St. Joseph's Abbey, Spencer, Mass., for text of No. 233(vss. 1-3);

St. Mary's Abbey, West Malling, England, for text of No. 348;

Search Press, Ltd., London, for text of No. 173(vss. 1-3);

J. E. Seddon, England, for text of No. 186;

Society of Sacred Mission, England, for text of No. 343;

Summy-Birchard, a Division of Birch Tree Group, Ltd., Princeton, N.J. for English adaptations of Latin texts of Nos. 171, 172, 219, 220; for texts of Nos. 129, 193, 331, 347; and for musical settings of Nos. 135, 285, 330, and 347;

Gordon Truitt, Maryland, for text of No. 293;

Norman Warren, England, for tune of No. 291;

Yale University Press, Connecticut, for text of No. 153(vss. 1-3);

H. F. Yardley, Canada, and F.J. Whitely, Canada, for text of No. 278;

1976 Board of Governors for the 41st Eucharistic Congress, Phila., Pa., for No. 360.

PSALTER

The Confraternity of Christian Doctrine, Washington, D.C., for selected verses from psalms as given in the **New American Bible** and the **Lectionary for Mass**, copyright © 1970. Used by permission. All rights reserved. Included are selections from Psalms 1, 4, 15, 16, 18, 19, 22, 24, 25, 27, 30, 31, 33, 34, 45, 47, 50, 51, 54, 62, 63, 67, 68, 71, 72, 86, 90, 91, 92, 93, 95, 96, 97, 98, 103, 104, 107, 112, 113, 117, 118, 121, 122, 123, 126, 128, 130, 131, 136, 137, 138, 139, 145, 146, 147, and verses from Exodus 15, and Daniel 3;

The International Committee on English in the Liturgy (ICEL), Washington, D.C., for selected texts of antiphons and responses from the **Lectionary for Mass**, copyright © 1970. Used with permission.

The National Council of the Churches of Christ, New York, for selected verses from the psalms as found in the **Revised Standard Version of the Bible**, including Psalms 13, 24, 40, 42-43, 78, 80, 96, 110, 124, 132, and verses from Isaiah 12, copyrighted 1946, 1952, © 1971, 1973;

Fides-Claretian, Notre Dame, Indiana, for selected verses from **The Psalms**, including Psalms 23(22), 29(28), 66(65), 80(79), 84(83), 100(99), 116(115), and 119(118);

Psalms 32, and 65, are from **Psalms for Modern Man** in today's English version. Copyright © American Bible Society, 1970. Used by permission;

GIA Publications, Chicago, Ill., for No. 577;

Paul Manz, Minnesota, for No. 429;

Typis Polyglottis Vaticanis, Italy, for tunes of Nos. 374, 385, 386, 403, 414, 430, 434, 461, 469, and 475, adapted from **Graduale Simplex**;

J. Gerald Phillips, Leominster, Massachusetts, for antiphon at No. 444;

Joseph Policelli, Boston, Massachusetts, for Antiphon A at No. 388.

MISCELLANEOUS LITURGIES AND SCRIPTURE READINGS

The International Committee on English in the Liturgy (ICEL), Washington, D.C. for translations from the **Roman Missal**, antiphons, prayers, introductory rites, litanies, acclamations, **Psalm 95**, and **"Saints of God"** from the **Burial Rite**, copyrighted 1970, 1973, 1975, and 1976. Used with permission.

International Consultation on English Texts (ICET), for translations of **Benedictus** and **Simeon's Canticle**. Used with permission.

The Grail, England, for verses from Psalms 4, 63, 134, and 149;

The Confraternity of Christian Doctrine, Washington, D.C., for selected verses from Daniel 3, Psalms 22, 31, 91, Luke 2, readings from Scripture, and the four Passions, as given in the **New American Bible** and the **Lectionary for Mass**, copyright © 1970. All rights reserved. Used with permission.

Psalms 23 and 141, are from **Psalms for Modern Man**, in today's English version. Copyright © American Bible Society, 1970. Used with permission.

The National Council of the Churches of Christ, New York, for verses from Luke 1, as given in the **Revised Standard Version of the Bible**, copyrighted 1946, 1952, © 1971, 1973;

William Alfred, Cambridge, Mass., for his translation of **Vexilla Regis**, namely, **The Brave Flags of Our King**;

Joseph Policelli, Boston, Mass., for the melody of the antiphon at No. 527;

America Press, N.Y., for selected lines from **The Following of Christ**;

The Trappist Abbey of Our Lady of Gethsemani, Kentucky, for permission to use selected **Odes of Solomon**, in their translation of these poems from the original Greek.

GENERAL INDEX

FOREWORD V

PREFACE VII

COPYRIGHT SOURCES AND ACKNOWLEDGEMENTS IX

ORDER OF MASS - ENGLISH . . . . 1 - 49

Entrance Rite . . . . 1 - 9
Liturgy of the Word . . . . 10 - 15
Liturgy of the Eucharist . . . . 16 - 29
Communion Rite . . . . 30 - 33
Concluding Rite . . . . 34 - 39A
Supplementary Polyphonic Settings . . . . 40 - 49

CANTUS IN ORDINE MISSAE . . . . 50 - 84

Ritus Initiales . . . . 50 - 56
Ad Liturgiam Verbi . . . . 57 - 63
Liturgia Eucharistica . . . . 64 - 68
Ritus Communionis . . . . 69 - 72
Ad Ritus Conclusionis . . . . 73 - 75
Supplementary Mass Chants . . . . 76 - 82
Supplementary Polyphonic Settings . . . . 83 - 84

GOSPEL ACCLAMATIONS . . . . 85 - 98

Sundays and Weekdays of Advent 85
Sundays and Weekdays of Christmastide 86
Sundays and Weekdays of Lent and Holy Week . . . 87 - 90
Lenten Feasts and Solemnities 90A
Eastertide Sundays and Solemnities 91
Sundays of the Year and Solemnities of
the Year . . . . 92 - 93
Proper of the Saints: Solemnities and Feasts 94
Season of the Year: Weekdays, Common,
Votive and Ritual Masses 95
General Use: Choir only . . . . 95A - 95B
Alleluia - Gregorian Chant Mode 2 96
Alleluia - Gregorian Chant Mode 4 97
Alleluia - Gregorian Chant Mode 8 98

HYMNS - Alphabetical by title . . . . 99 - 362

Complete listing 612

RESPONSORIAL PSALMS AND ANTIPHONS . . . . 363 - 477

Complete Listing 603

MISCELLANEOUS LITURGIES . . . . 478 - 554

Morning Prayer - A Core Program 478
Evening Prayer (Service of Light)
A Core Program 490
Night Prayer (Compline) 499
Presentation of the Lord (February 2) 511
Ash Wednesday 515
Passion Sunday 516
Passion According to St. Matthew 520
Passion According to St. Mark 521
Passion According to St. Luke 522
Holy Thursday 523
Holy Thursday - Mass of Chrism 524
Good Friday 526
Passion According to St. John 529
Easter Vigil 533
Rite of Baptism 536
Rite of Confirmation 537
Rite of Christian Burial 538
Rite of Ordinations of Deacons and Priests 550
Sacrament of Reconciliation 552
Ritual for Admitting Choristers into
the Choir 553

SCRIPTURE READINGS AND MEDITATIONS . . . . 555 - 594

SUPPLEMENTARY HYMNS AND CHANTS . . . . 595 - 598

INDICES . . . . 599 - 612

* Responsorial Psalms and Antiphons for:
- ABC Yearly Liturgical Cycles: All Sundays and Solemnities with Selected Appropriate Hymns 599
- Proper of Saints: All Solemnities, Feasts and Memorials 600
- Weekday Liturgical Cycles 601
- Common, Ritual Masses, Masses for Various Occasions, Votive Masses 602

Numerical List of Psalms, Antiphons and
Psalm Hymns 603
Alphabetical List of Hymn Tunes 604
* Metrical Index of Hymn Tunes 605
* Gregorian Chants 606A
* Psalm Tones by Modes and Endings 606B
Readings from Scripture and Other Sources 607
* Authors, Translators and Text Sources 608
* Composers, Arrangers and Music Sources 609
* Topical Index of Seasonal Hymns and Uses 610
* Alphabetical List of Antiphons, Responses,
Responsories, Refrains, Canticles, and
Invitatories 611
Alphabetical List of First Lines of Hymns
and Common Titles 612

*In Organ-Choir Edition only

ORDER OF MASS

Entrance Rite

ENTRANCE SONG *Selections appropriate to the feast or the theme of the celebration will be found listed in the Index.*

The Sign of the Cross

1

At the conclusion of the Entrance Song, *all remain standing and make the sign of the cross as the Celebrant sings the following:*

8
Cel. In the name of the Fa-ther, and of the Son, and of the Ho-ly Spir-it.

All A - men.

Greeting

2

Facing the people with arms extended, the Celebrant sings the following:

8 Cel. The grace and peace of God, our Fa-ther, and the Lord Je-sus Christ be with you.

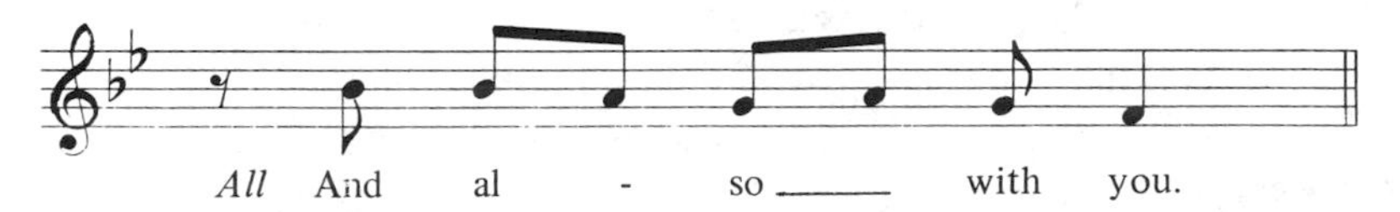
All And al - so with you.

Here follows a brief exposition of the theme of the day's Mass given by the priest or another suitable minister.

Penitential Rite

With "Lord Have Mercy"

8 Cel. My brothers and sisters, to
prepare ourselves to celebrate the
sacred mys-ter-ies, let us call to mind our sins.
Cantor or Choir
You were sent to heal the con - trite:
*You are mighty God and prince of peace:
*You raise the dead to life in the spir - it:
*Lord, Jesus, you raise us to a new life:
Lord, have mer - cy.
All Lord, have mer - cy.
Cantor or Choir
You came to call sin - ners:
*Lord Jesus, you are Son of
God and Son of Mar - y:
*You bring pardon and peace to the sin - ner:
*Lord Jesus, you for - give us our sins:
Christ, have mer - cy.
All Christ, have mer - cy.

**Alternate invocations*

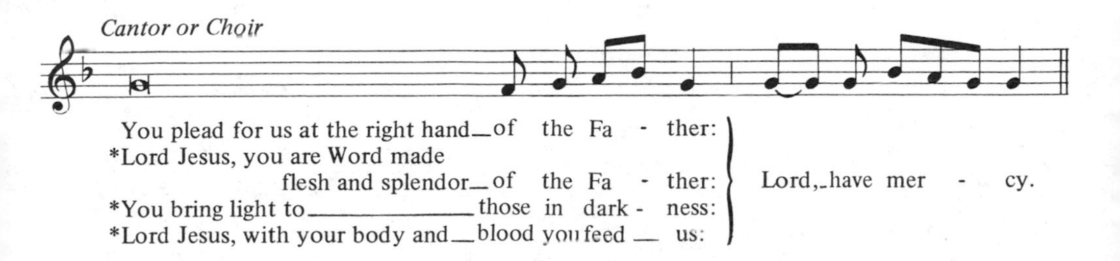
Cantor or Choir
You plead for us at the right hand of the Father:
*Lord Jesus, you are Word made flesh and splendor of the Father:
*You bring light to those in dark - ness:
*Lord Jesus, with your body and blood you feed us:
Lord, have mer - cy.

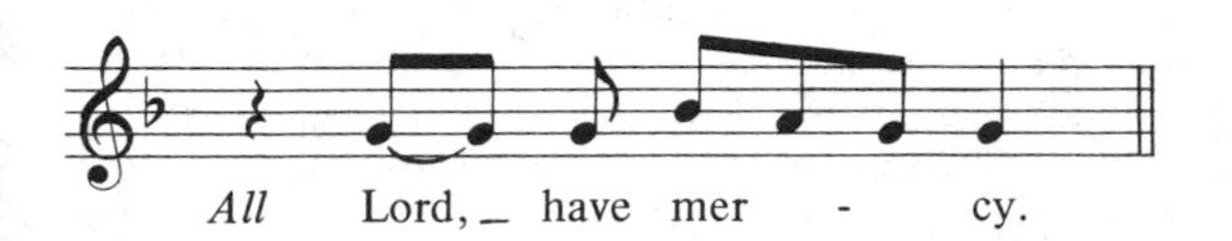
All Lord, have mer - cy.

Cel. May al - might - y God have mer - cy on us, for - give us our sins,

and bring us to ev - er - last - ing life.

All A - men.

4 Penitential Rite

With "I Confess"

Cel. My brothers and sisters, to prepare
ourselves to celebrate the sacred__mys-ter-ies, let us call to mind our sins.__

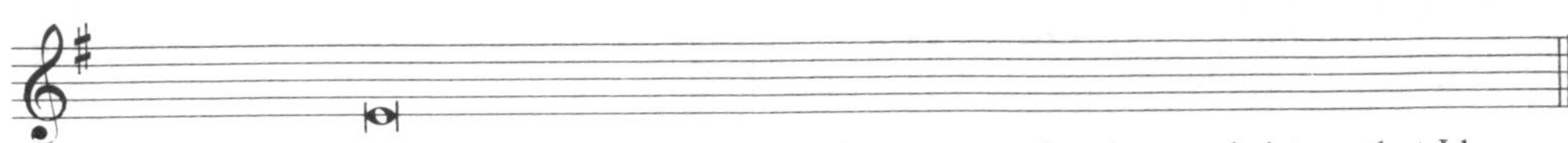

Cel. and People I confess to almighty God, and to you, my brothers and sisters, that I have sinned through my fault in my thoughts and in my words, in what I have done, and in what I have failed to do: and I ask blessed Mary, ever Virgin, all the angels and saints, and you, my brothers and sisters, to pray for me to the Lord our God.

Cel. May al-might-y God have mer-cy on us, for-give__ us our sins, and
bring us to ev-er-last-ing life.__ All A - men.__

5 Lord, Have Mercy

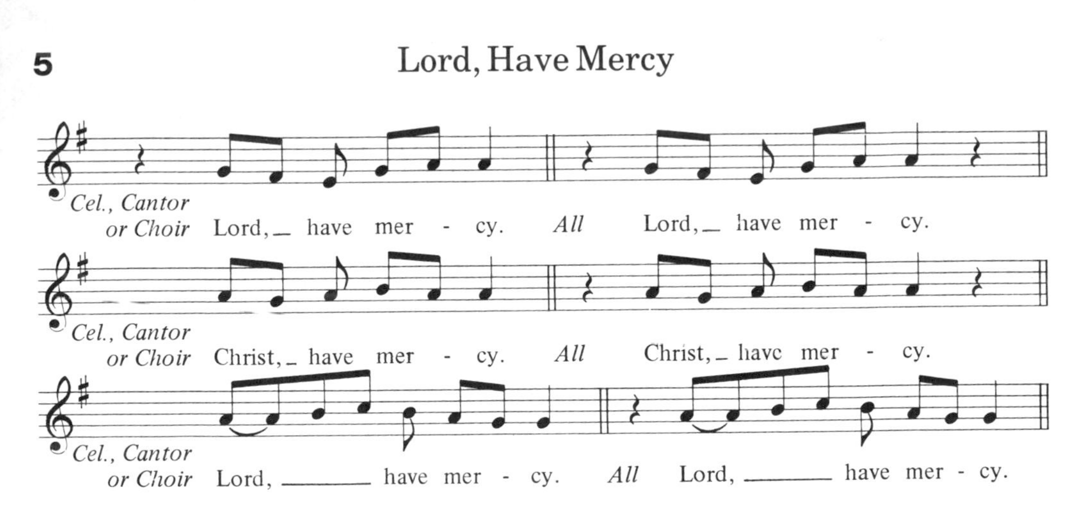
Cel., Cantor or Choir Lord,__ have mer - cy. All Lord,__ have mer - cy.
Cel., Cantor or Choir Christ,__ have mer - cy. All Christ,__ have mer - cy.
Cel., Cantor or Choir Lord, ______ have mer - cy. All Lord, ______ have mer - cy.

Rite of Blessing and Sprinkling Holy Water **6**

This Rite of Blessing and Sprinkling with Holy Water may replace the Penitential Rite at the beginning of Sunday Masses in churches and chapels.

The Celebrant makes the sign of the cross and greets the people as in No. 1, Page 1. *A vessel containing the water to be blessed is placed before him. Facing the people, he invites them to pray, chanting the following:*

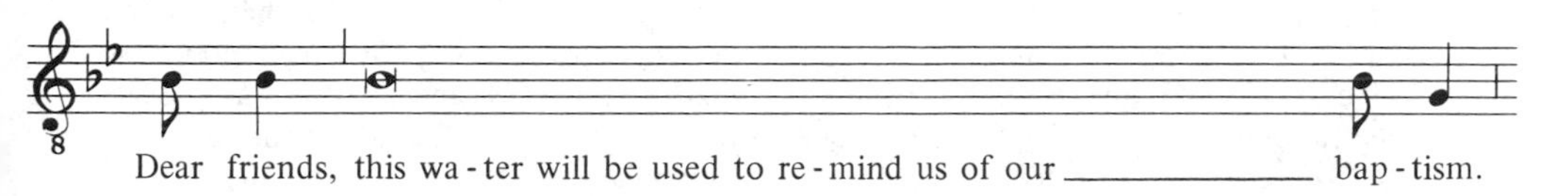
Dear friends, this wa-ter will be used to re-mind us of our bap-tism.

Let us ask God to bless it, and to keep us faith-ful to the

Spir-it he has giv-en us.

After a brief silence, he joins his hands and continues with either A or B below

A *Outside the Easter Season*

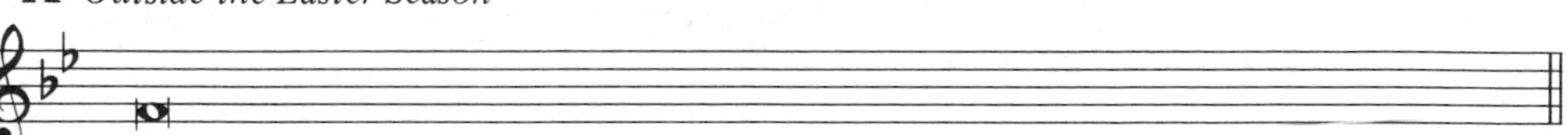

God our Father, your gift of water brings life and freshness to the earth; it washes away our sins and brings us eternal life. We ask you now to bless this water, and to give us your protection on this day which you have made your own. Renew the living spring of your life within us and protect us in spirit and body, that we may be free from sin and come into your presence to receive your gift of salvation. We ask this through Christ our Lord.

B *During the Easter Season*

Lord God almighty, hear the prayers of your people: we celebrate our creation and redemption. Hear our prayers and bless this water which gives fruitfulness to the fields, and refreshment and cleansing to man. You chose water to show your goodness when you led your people to freedom through the Red Sea and satisfied their thirst in the desert with water from the rock. Water was the symbol used by the prophets to foretell your new covenant with man. You made the water of baptism holy by Christ's baptism in the Jordan: by it you give us new birth and renew us in holiness. May this water remind us of our baptism, and let us share the joy of all who have been baptized at Easter. We ask this through Christ our Lord.

When salt is mixed with the water, the Celebrant blesses the salt, chanting as above

Almighty God, we ask you to bless this salt as once you blessed the salt scattered over the water by the prophet Elisha. Wherever this salt and water are sprinkled, drive away the power of evil, and protect us always by the presence of your Holy Spirit. Grant this through Christ our Lord.

Then he pours the salt into the water in silence. Taking the sprinkler, the Celebrant sprinkles himself and his ministers, then the rest of the clergy and the people. He may move through the church for the sprinkling of the people.

During this action, one of the following may be sung:

Outside the Easter Season	No. 476	WITH JOY YOU WILL DRAW WATER and ISAIAH 12
	No. 307	SPRINGS OF WATER, BLESS THE LORD and I SAW WATER
	No. 245	O HOLY SPIRIT, ENTER IN
During the Easter Season	No. 308	ALLELUIA and I SAW WATER
	No. 312	THE CHURCH'S ONE FOUNDATION (Verses 1 and 2)

When he returns to his place and the song is finished, the Celebrant faces the people with joined hands, and sings the following with which the Rite of Sprinkling ends:

May al - might-y God cleanse us of our ____ sins, and through the eucharist we

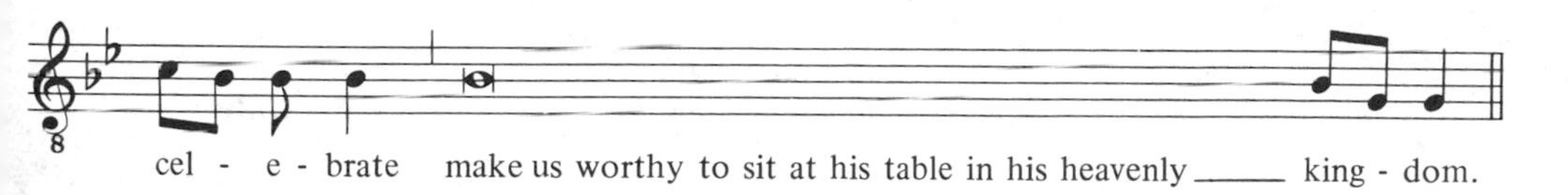
cel - e - brate make us worthy to sit at his table in his heavenly ____ king - dom.

All A - men.

When prescribed, the GLORY TO GOD *follows immediately.*

During Advent and Lent when the GLORY TO GOD *is omitted, the closing prayer of the Rite of Sprinkling (above) is also omitted. Instead, the* OPENING PRAYER *of the Mass (see at* No. 9*) is chanted and the Mass continues as usual.*

7 Glory to God in the Highest

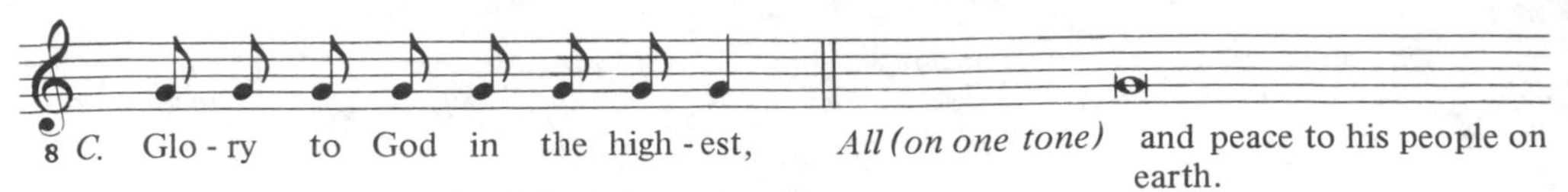
C. Glo - ry to God in the high - est,
All (on one tone)
and peace to his people on earth.

Lord God, heavenly King,
almighty God and Father,
we worship you, we give you thanks,
we praise you for your glory.

Lord Jesus Christ, only Son of the Father,
Lord God, Lamb of God,
you take away the sin of the world:
have mercy on us;
you are seated at the right hand of the Father:
receive our prayer.

For you alone are the Holy One,
you alone are the Lord,
you alone are the Most High,
Jesus Christ,
with the Holy Spirit,
in the glory of God the Father. Amen.

8 Glory to God in the Highest

T.M.
Cel., Cantor or Choir Glo - ry to God in the high - est,
All and peace to his peo - ple on earth.
Lord, God, heav - en - ly King, al - might-y God and Fa - ther,
we wor - ship you, we give you thanks, we praise you for your glo - ry.

Lord Je - sus Christ, on - ly Son of the Fa - ther, Lord_God, Lamb_of
God, you take a - way the sin_ of the world: have mer - cy on us;
you are seat - ed at the right_ hand_ of the Fa - ther:
re - ceive_ our prayer. For_ you a - lone are the Ho - ly One,
you a - lone_ are the Lord,_ you a - lone are the Most_
High, Je - sus Christ, with the Ho - ly Spir - it, in the glo - ry
of God_ the Fa - ther. A - men, a - men._

Opening Prayer **9**

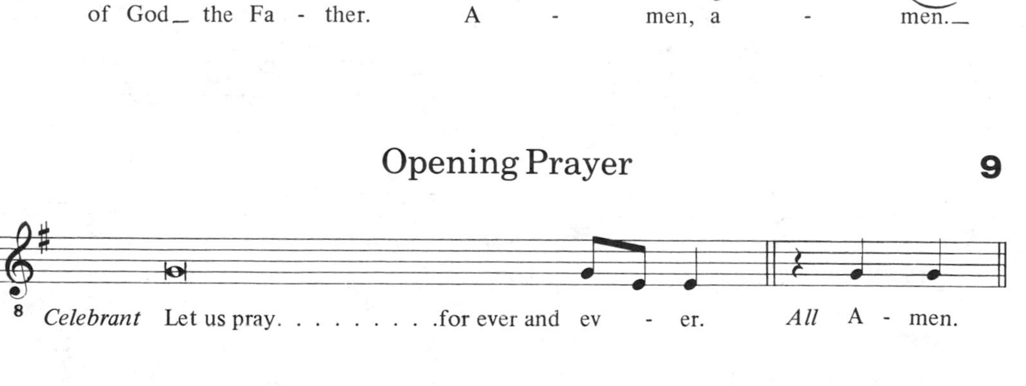
8 *Celebrant* Let us pray. . . . . .for ever and ev - er. *All* A - men.

Liturgy of the Word

FIRST READING Old Testament.

At the conclusion – Reader This is the word of the Lord
All Thanks be to God

RESPONSORIAL PSALM *For appropriate psalm or psalm hymn, see Index*

SECOND READING New Testament Epistle

At the conclusion – Reader This is the word of the Lord
All Thanks be to God

GOSPEL ACCLAMATION *See* Nos. 85 *to* 98 *inclusive*

THIRD READING Gospel *If sung, responses and formula for chanting are given below*

10 Gospel Responses

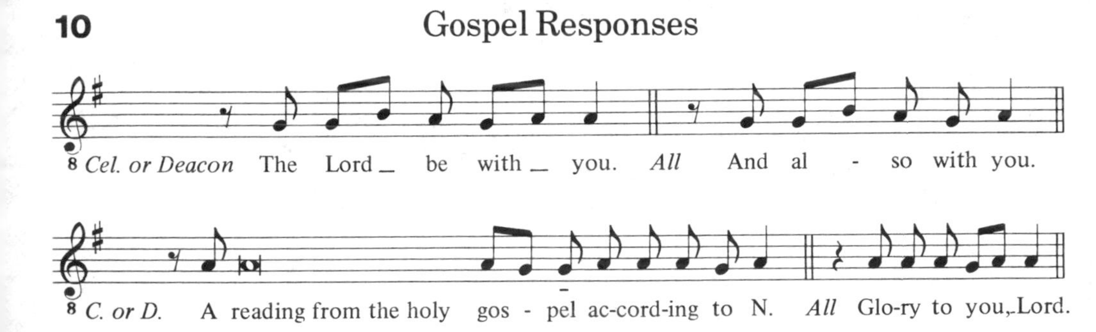

8 Cel. or Deacon The Lord be with you. All And al - so with you.
8 C. or D. A reading from the holy gos - pel ac-cord-ing to N. All Glo-ry to you, Lord.

11 Gospel Chant and Conclusion

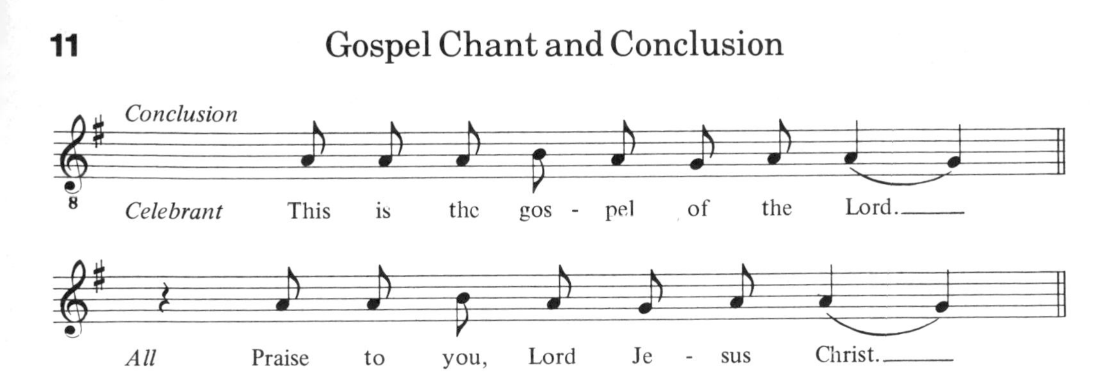

Conclusion
8 Celebrant This is the gos - pel of the Lord.
All Praise to you, Lord Je - sus Christ.

Profession of Faith - I

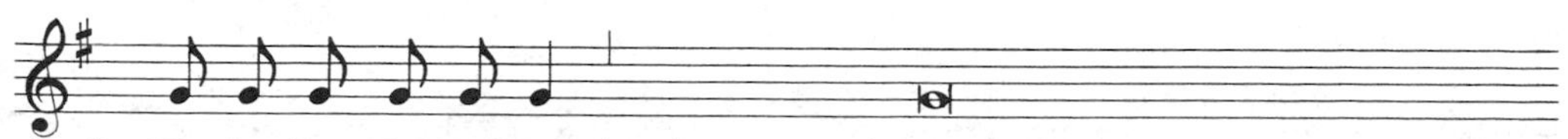

C. We be - lieve in one God, / *All (on one tone)* the Father, the Almighty,/
maker of heaven and earth,
of all that is seen and unseen.
We believe in one Lord, Jesus Christ,
the only Son of God,
eternally begotten of the Father,
God from God, Light from Light,
true God from true God,
begotten, not made,/one in Being with the Father.
Through him all things were made.
For us men and for our salvation
he came down from heaven:

All bow during these two lines:

by the power of the Holy Spirit
he was born of the Virgin Mary, and became man.

For our sake he was crucified under Pontius Pilate;
he suffered, died, and was buried.
On the third day he rose again
in fulfillment of the Scriptures;
he ascended into heaven
and is seated at the right hand of the Father.
He will come again in glory/to judge the living and the dead,
and his kingdom will have no end.
We believe in the Holy Spirit,/the Lord, the giver of life,
who proceeds from the Father and the Son.
With the Father and the Son he is worshipped and glorified.
He has spoken through the Prophets.
We believe in one holy catholic and apostolic Church.
We acknowledge one baptism for the forgiveness of sins.
We look for the resurrection of the dead,
and the life of the world to come. Amen.

13 Profession of Faith - II

T.M.
Cantor or Celebrant
All
We be-lieve in one _ God, the Fa - ther, the Al - might - y,
mak - er of heav - en and earth, of all _ that is seen _ and _
un - seen. We be-lieve in one _ Lord, Je - sus _ Christ, the on - ly _ Son _ of
God, e - ter - nal - ly be - got - ten of the Fa - ther, God _ from _ God, _
Light _ from _ Light, true God _ from true God, _ be - got - ten, not made,
one in Be - ing with the Fa - ther. Through _ him all things _ were _ made.
For us men _ and for our sal - va - tion he came down _ from _ heav - en:

All bow to . . . "became man."
by the pow'r of the Ho-ly Spir - it he was born _ of the Vir-gin Mar - y,
and be-came_man. For our sake _ he was cru-ci-fied un-der Pon-tius Pilate; he___ suf - fered,_ died,_ and was bur - ied. On the third _
day___ he___ rose _______ a - gain__ in ful-fill-ment of the Scrip-tures;
he as-cend-ed in-to heav - en and is seat-ed at the right hand of the
Fa - ther. He will come_a-gain in glo - ry to judge the liv-ing
and the dead,_ and his king - dom will have _ no __ end. We be-lieve

in the Ho - ly Spir - it, the Lord, _ the giv - er of life, who pro - ceeds _

from the Fa - ther and the Son. With the Fa-ther and the Son he is

wor - shipped and glo - ri - fied. He has spo - ken through the Proph - ets.

We be - lieve in one, ho - ly, cath - o - lic, and ap - os - tol - ic Church.

We ac-knowl-edge one bap - tism ___ for the for - give - ness _ of ___ sins.

We look _ for the res - ur - rec - tion of the dead, ___ and the life _ of the

world _ to _ come. A - men, _ a - men. _

Prayer of the Faithful

14

Two Settings

A. Byzantine B. Psalm Tone 8G

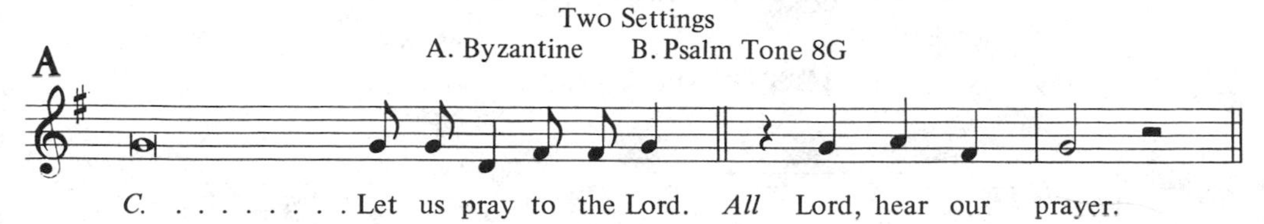
A
C. . . . . Let us pray to the Lord. All Lord, hear our prayer.

CONCLUDING ORATION

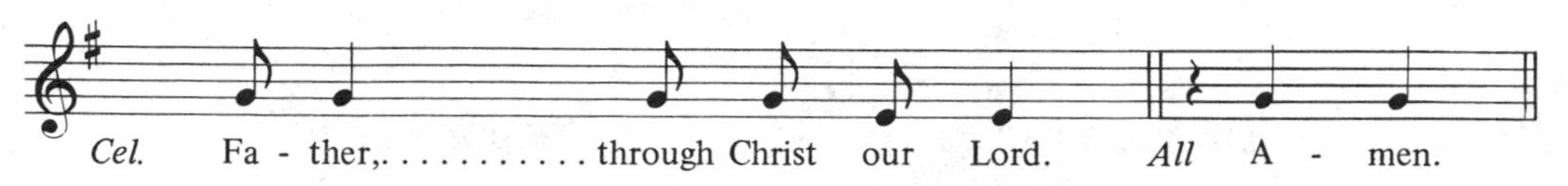
Cel. Fa - ther,. . . . . through Christ our Lord. All A - men.

B
C. That the holy Church of God be a most visible sign of the grace
of the Resur - rec - tion.

Line given serves as a model

All. We pray to the Lord.

Concluding oration same as above.

Choir Responses to the Prayer of the Faithful

15

Liturgy of the Eucharist

16 Prayer over the Gifts

Cel. . . . . through Christ our Lord. All A - men.

17 Eucharistic Prayer - Preface Responses I

Cel. The Lord_ be with_ you. All And al - so with you.

Cel. Lift ___ up your hearts. All We lift_them up to the Lord. Cel.: Let us

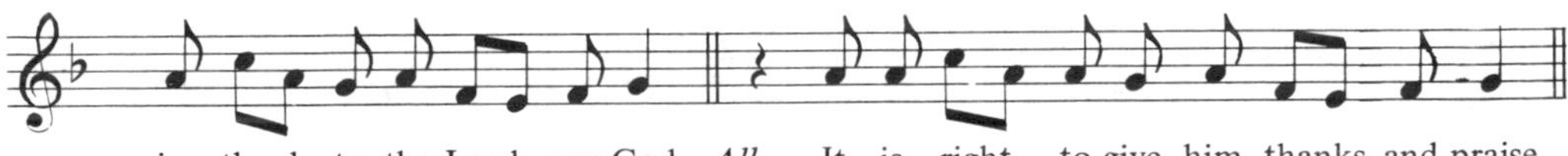
give thanks_to the Lord_our God. All It is right_ to give him thanks_and praise.

18 Eucharistic Prayer - Preface Responses II

Cel. The Lord_ be with you. All And al - so with you.

Cel. Lift _ up _ your hearts. _ All We lift _ them up to the Lord. _ Cel. Let us

give thanks to the Lord _ our God. All It is right to give him thanks _ and praise. _

Eucharistic Prayer - Preface Responses III **19**

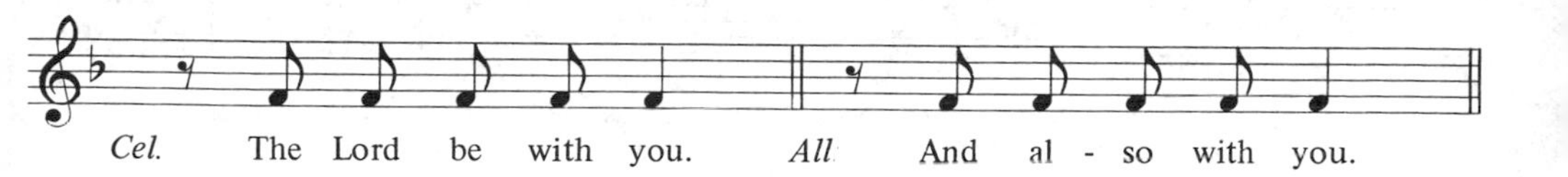
Cel. The Lord be with you. All And al - so with you.

Cel. Lift up your hearts. All We lift them up to the Lord.

Cel. Let us give thanks to the Lord our God. ___

All It is right to give him thanks and praise.

20 Chanting Formula for Preface I

For Celebrant

21 Holy, Holy, Holy - I

Major Mode

T.M.

All Ho - ly, ho - ly,__ ho - ly Lord,_ God _ of pow'r __ and might,

heav'n __ and earth are full __ of your glo - ry. Ho - san - na,

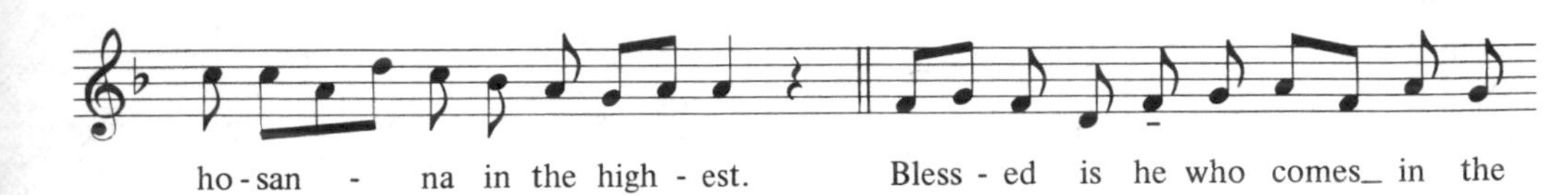

ho - san - na in the high - est. Bless - ed is he who comes_ in the

name _ of the Lord. Ho - san - na, ho - san - na in the high - est.

22 Chanting Formula for Preface II

23 Holy, Holy, Holy II

Minor Mode

T.M.

All Ho - ly, ho - ly, ho - ly Lord, God of pow'r and might,

heav'n and earth are full of your glo - ry. Ho - san - na
in the high - est. Bless - ed is he who comes in the name
of the Lord. Ho - san - na in the high - est.
Holy, Holy, Holy III
24
T.M.
All
Ho - ly, ho - ly, ho - ly Lord, God of pow'r and might,
heav'n and earth are full of your glo - ry. Ho -
san - na in the high - est. Bless - ed is
he who comes in the name of the Lord. Ho -
san - na in the high - est.

25 Eucharistic Prayer II

Celebrant

Cel. Lord, you are holy indeed,. . . . . Do this in memory of me.

26 Memorial Acclamations

Cel.
Let us pro - claim the mys - ter - y of faith.

A

All
Christ has died, Christ is ris - en, Christ will come a - gain.

B

All
Dy - ing you de - stroyed our death, ris - ing you re - stored
our life, Lord Je - sus, come in glo - ry.

C

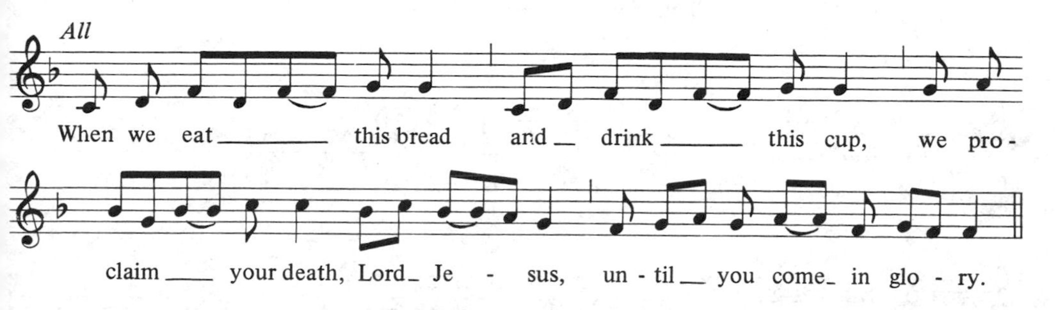
All
When we eat this bread and drink this cup, we pro-
claim your death, Lord Je - sus, un - til you come in glo - ry.

D

All
Lord, by your cross and res - ur - rec - tion you have
set us free. You are the Sav - ior of the world.

Cel. In memory of his death and resurrection. . . . . .
. . . . . .and give you glory through your Son, Jesus Christ.

27

Eucharistic Prayer - Conclusion I

Major Mode

Cel. Through him, with him, in him, in the u - ni - ty of the Ho-ly

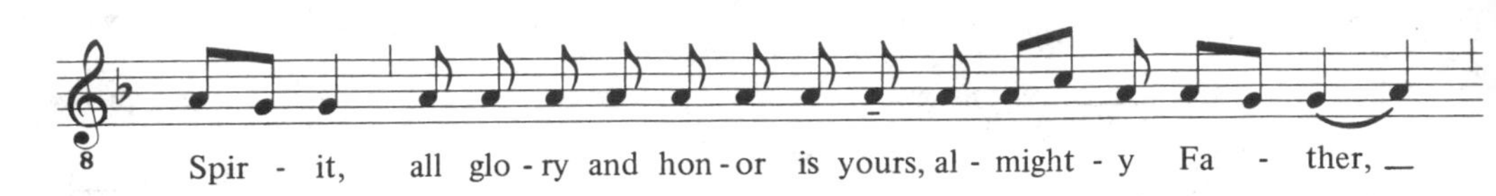
Spir - it, all glo - ry and hon - or is yours, al - might - y Fa - ther,

for ev - er and ev - er. All A - men, a - men.

28

Eucharistic Prayer - Conclusion II

Minor Mode

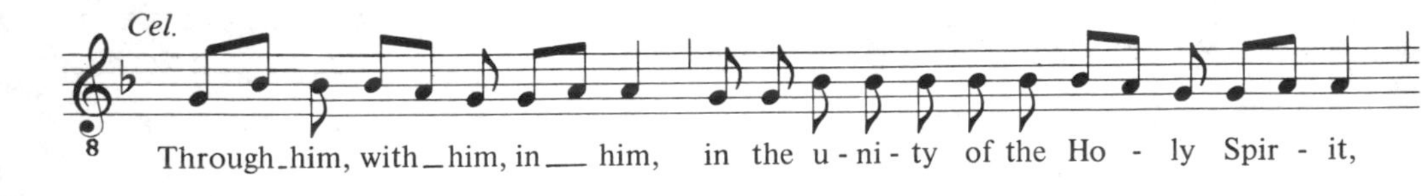
Cel.
Through him, with him, in him, in the u - ni - ty of the Ho - ly Spir - it,

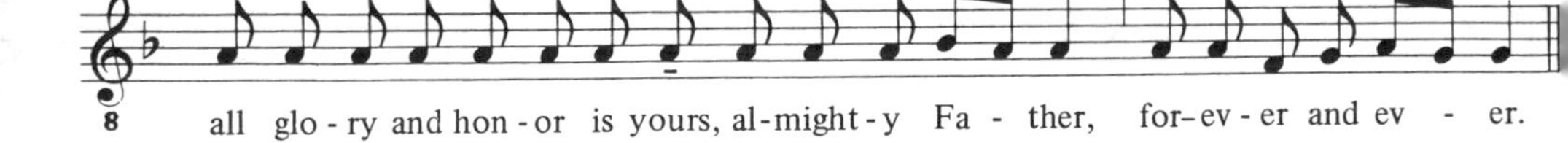
all glo - ry and hon - or is yours, al-might - y Fa - ther, for-ev - er and ev - er.
All A - men.

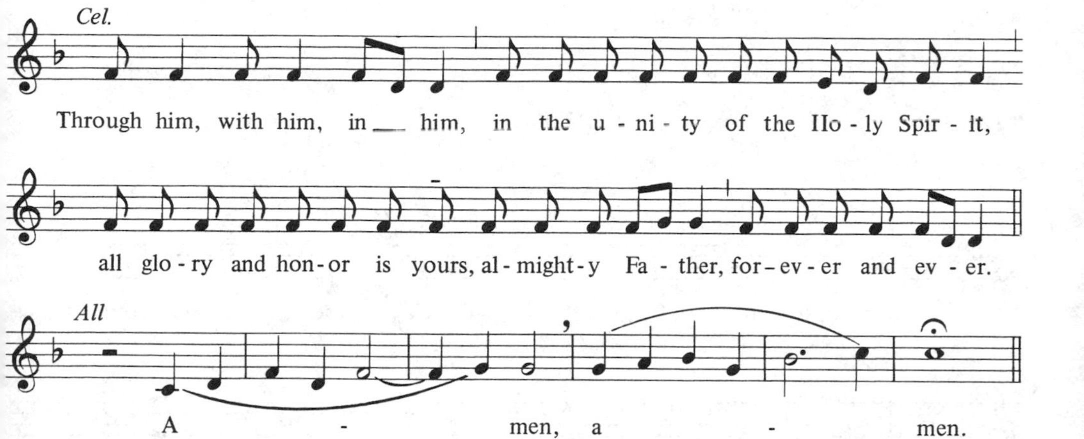
Cel.
Through him, with him, in __ him, in the u - ni - ty of the Ho - ly Spir - it,
all glo - ry and hon - or is yours, al - might - y Fa - ther, for - ev - er and ev - er.
All
A - men, a - men.

Communion Rite

30

Our Father I

T.M.

Cel. Let us pray with confidence to the Fa - ther in the words our Sav - ior gave — us: *All* Our Fa - ther, who art in heav - en, hal - lowed be thy name; thy king-dom come; thy will be done on earth as it is in heav - en. Give us this day our dai - ly bread; and — for - give us our tres - pass - es as we for - give — those who tres - pass a-gainst us; and lead us not in - to temp-ta - tion, but — de - liv - er us

EMBOLISM

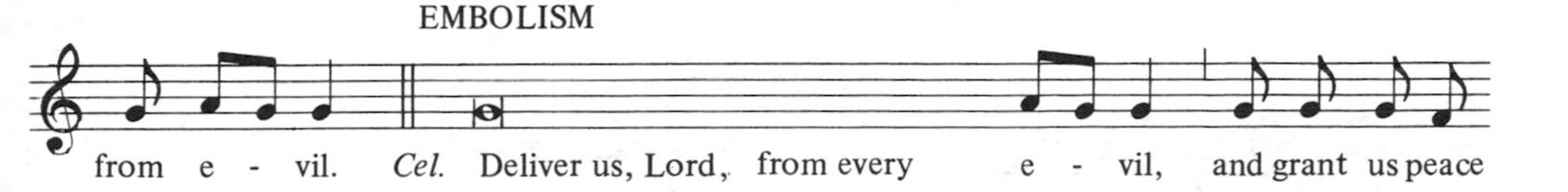
from e - vil. Cel. Deliver us, Lord, from every e - vil, and grant us peace

in our_ day. In your mer-cy keep us free_from sin and pro-tect us from all anx -

i - et-y as we wait in joy - ful hope for the com-ing of our Sav - ior, Je - sus Christ.

ACCLAMATION

All For the king-dom, the pow'r_and the glo - ry are yours, now and for-ev - er.

RITE OF PEACE

Celebrant: Lord Jesus Christ, you said to your apostles: I leave you peace, my peace I give you. Look not on our sins, but on the faith of your Church, and grant us the peace and unity of your kingdom where you live for ever and ever.

All Amen.

Cel. The peace of the Lord_ be with you al - ways. All And al - so with you._

SIGN OF PEACE *Celebrant or Deacon (spoken):*

Let us offer each other the sign of peace.

Our Father II

Sacramentary

8
Cel. Let us pray with confidence to the Fa - ther in the words our Savior gave_us.
All Our Fa - ther who art in heav - en, hal-lowed be thy name; thy king-dom come;
thy will be done on earth as it is in heav - en. Give us this day our dai - ly bread;
and for-give us our tres-pass - es as we for-give those who tres-pass a - gainst _ us;
and lead us not in - to temp - ta - tion, but de-liv - er us from e - vil.

EMBOLISM

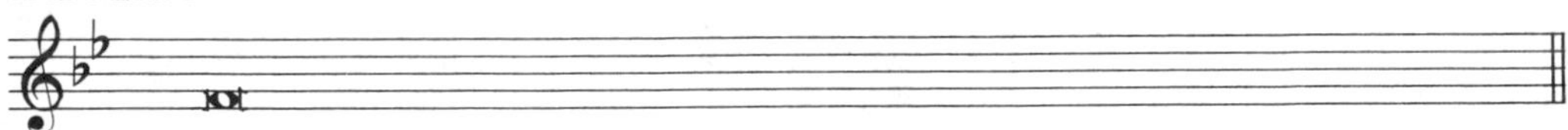

Cel. Deliver us, Lord, from every evil, and grant us peace in our day. In your mercy keep us free from sin and protect us from all anxiety as we wait in joyful hope for the coming of our Savior, Jesus Christ.

ACCLAMATION

All For the king-dom, the pow'r and the glo - ry are yours, now and for - ev - er.

RITE OF PEACE *See preceding page*

Lamb of God I **32**

Major Mode

T.M.

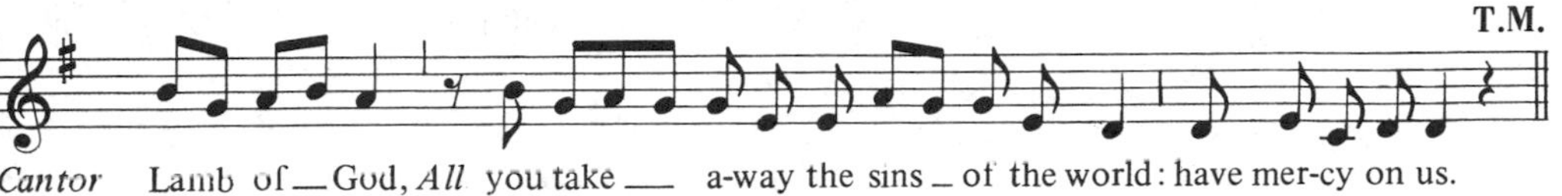
Cantor Lamb of — God, All you take — a-way the sins — of the world: have mer-cy on us.

C. Lamb — of — God, All you take — a-way the sins — of the world: have mer-cy on us.

C. Lamb — of — God, All you take — a-way the sins — of the world: grant — us — peace.

Lamb of God II **33**

Minor Mode

T.M.

Cantor Lamb — of God, All you take a-way the sins — of the world: have mer - cy on us.

C. Lamb — of God, All you take a-way the sins — of the world: have mer - cy on us.

C. Lamb — of God, All you take a-way the sins — of the world: grant — us peace. —

COMMUNION SONG *See Index*

PRAYER AFTER COMMUNION

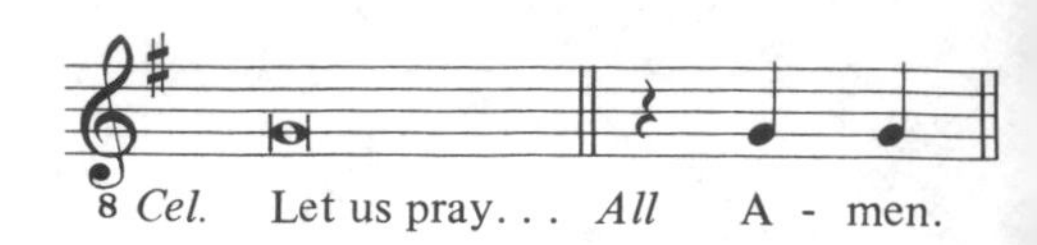
8 Cel. Let us pray... All A - men.

Concluding Rite

34

Blessing at the End of Mass I

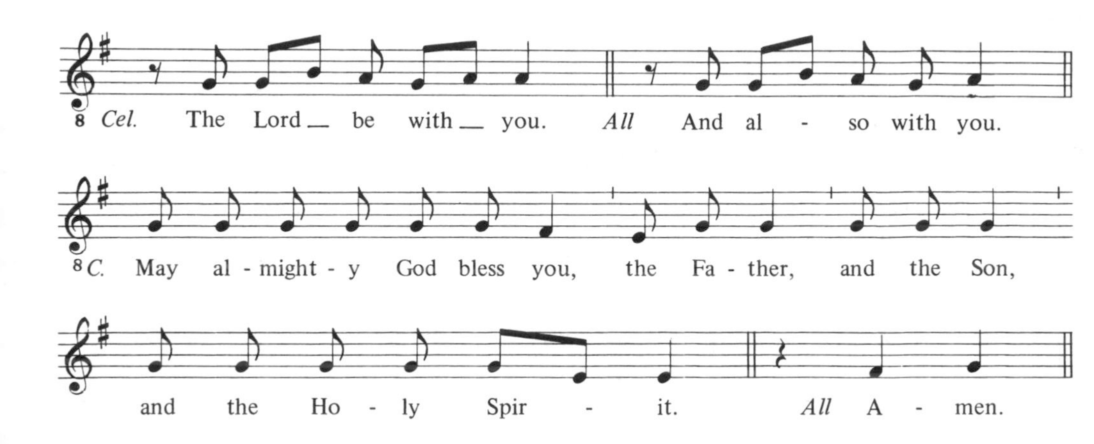
8 Cel. The Lord _ be with _ you. All And al - so with you.
8 C. May al - might - y God bless you, the Fa - ther, and the Son,
and the Ho - ly Spir - it. All A - men.

35

Blessing at the End of Mass II

8 Cel. The Lord be with you. All And al - so with you.

8 C. May al-might - y God bless you, the Fa-ther, and the Son, and the Ho - ly Spir - it.

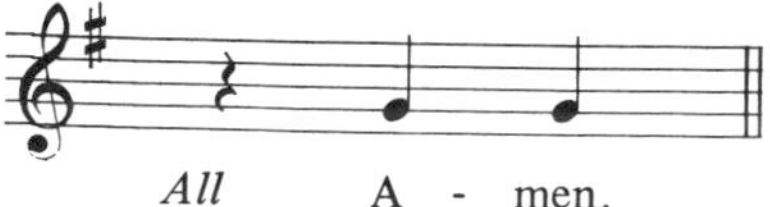
All A - men.

Blessing at the End of Mass III (Solemn) **36**

Cel. or Deacon
Bow your heads and pray for God's bless - ing.

The following is a model formula for chanting the blessings. Additional blessings appropriate for celebrations during the Proper of the Seasons or as Prayers over the People, are given in the Sacramentary

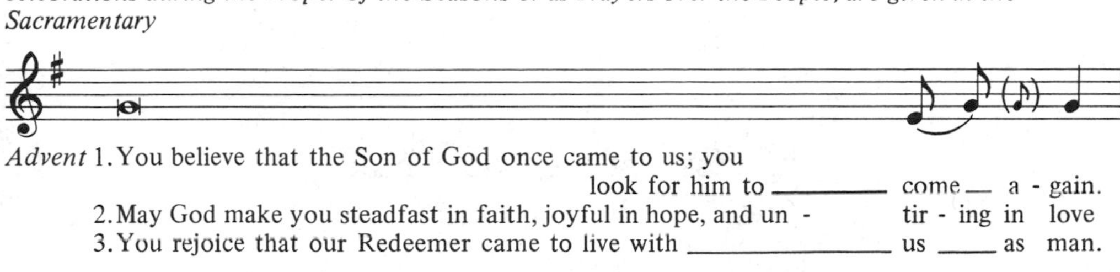
Advent 1. You believe that the Son of God once came to us; you look for him to come a - gain.
2. May God make you steadfast in faith, joyful in hope, and un - tir - ing in love
3. You rejoice that our Redeemer came to live with us as man.

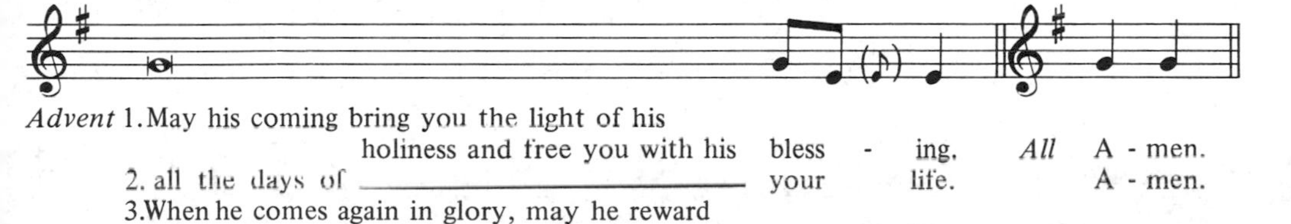
Advent 1. May his coming bring you the light of his holiness and free you with his bless - ing. All A - men.
2. all the days of your life. A - men.
3. When he comes again in glory, may he reward you with end - less life. A - men.

Last blessing

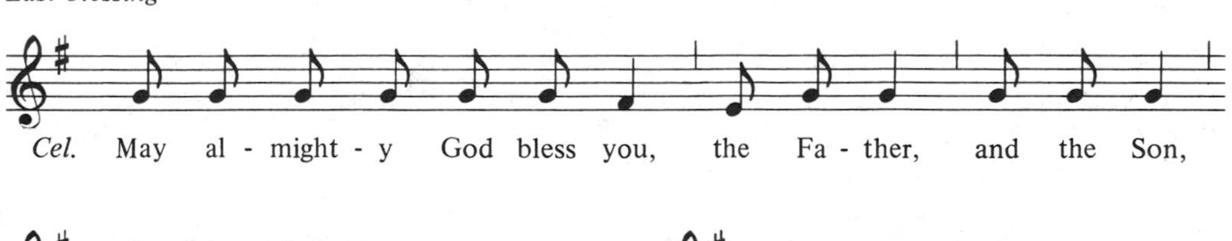
Cel. May al - might - y God bless you, the Fa - ther, and the Son,

and the Ho - ly Spir - it. All A - men.

37 Dismissal Rite with Bishop

Bishop The Lord be with you. All And al - so with you.
Bishop Blessed be the name of the ___ Lord. All Now and for ev - er.
Our help is in the name of the ___ Lord. Who made heaven and ___ earth.
May almighty. . . Same as at No. 34

38 Dismissal at the End of Mass

One of the following may be used

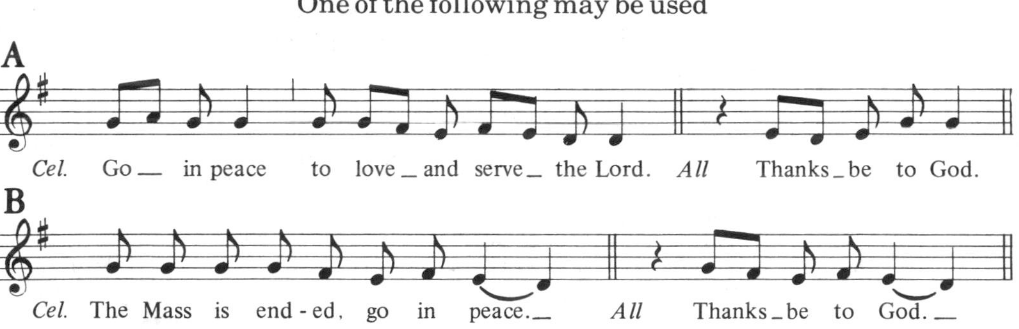
A
Cel. Go _ in peace to love _ and serve _ the Lord. All Thanks _ be to God.
B
Cel. The Mass is end - ed, go in peace. _ All Thanks _ be to God. _

39 / 39A Dismissal During Eastertide
Tempore Paschali

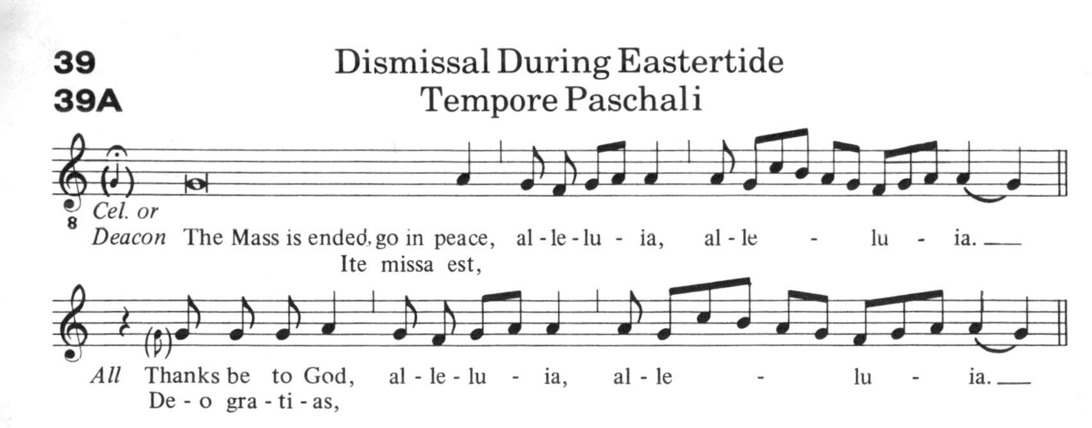
Cel. or Deacon The Mass is ended, go in peace, al - le - lu - ia, al - le - lu - ia. _
Ite missa est,
All Thanks be to God, al - le - lu - ia, al - le - lu - ia. _
De - o gra - ti - as,

Missa Brevis

Theodore Marier

Lord, Have Mercy
40
May be used with Penitential Rite at No. 3.
C. Lord, — have mer - cy. All Lord, — have mer - cy. Choir Lord, have mercy.
C. Christ, — have mer - cy. All Christ, — have mer - cy. Choir Christ, have mercy.
C. Lord, — have mer - cy. All Lord — have mer - cy. Choir Lord, have mercy.
Holy, Holy, Holy
41
C.
All
Ho - ly, ho - ly, — ho - ly Lord, God of pow - er and might, —
Choir
All
heaven and earth are full of your glory. Ho - san - na in — the high - est.
Choir
All
Blessed is he who comes in the name of the Lord. Ho - san - na in — the high - est.

42 Lamb of God

C.
All
Lamb of God, you take away the sins of the
world, have mer - cy on us.
Choir
Lamb of God, you take away
the sins of the world, have mercy on us.
C.
Lamb of God,
All
you take away the sins of the world, grant us peace.
Allegro
f
Choir Lord, have mer - cy. All Lord, have mer - cy.
Choir Lord, have mer - cy. All Christ, have

English Mass

Anton Heiller

43 Lord, Have Mercy

mer - cy. *Choir* Christ, have mer - cy.

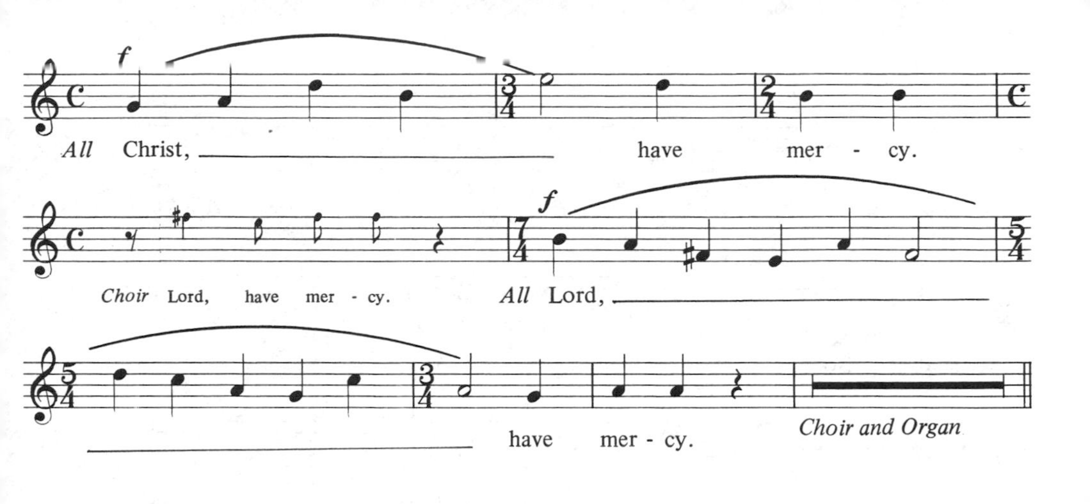
f
All Christ, have mer - cy.
Choir Lord, have mer - cy.
f
All Lord, have mer - cy.
Choir and Organ

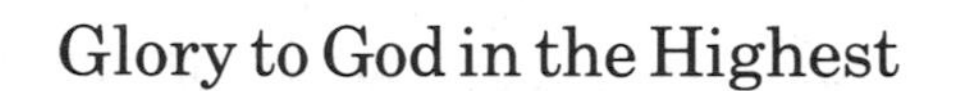

Glory to God in the Highest

44

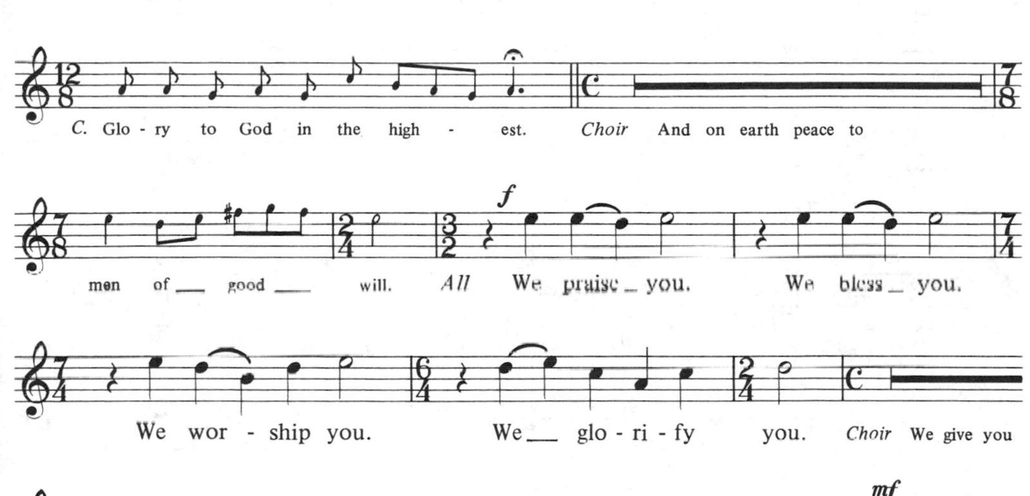
C. Glo - ry to God in the high - est.
Choir And on earth peace to men of good will.
f
All We praise you. We bless you.
We wor - ship you. We glo - ri - fy you.
Choir We give you

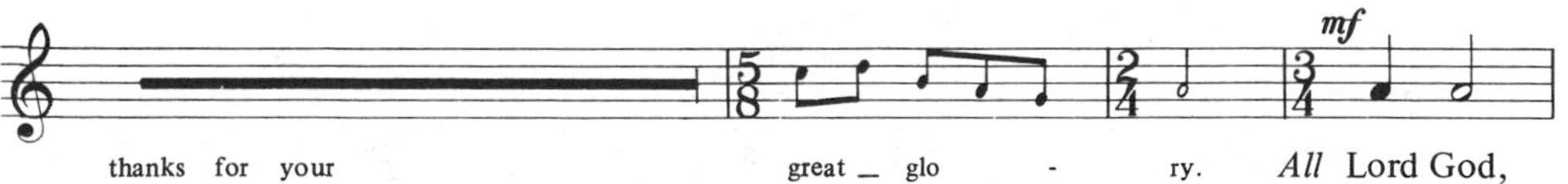
thanks for your great glo - ry.
mf
All Lord God,

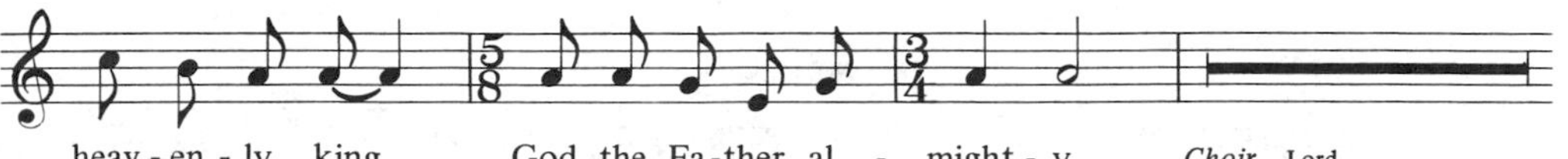
heav - en - ly king, God the Fa - ther al - might - y.
Choir Lord,

mf
Jesus Christ, the only be - got - ten Son. All Lord God,
Lamb of God, Son of the Fa - ther. Choir You, who take
away the sins of the world, All have mer - cy on us.
Choir You who take a - way the sins of the world All re -
p
ceive our prayer. Choir You who sit at the right hand of
the Fa - ther, All have mer - cy on us.
mp
Organ:
Choir For you alone are holy.
f
All You a - lone are Lord. Choir You alone, O Jesus
Organ
Christ, are most high,

ff
All With the Ho - ly Spir - it in the glo - ry of
God the Fa - ther. A - men.
Rit.

Holy, Holy, Holy **45**

Organ:
f
All Ho - ly, ho - ly, ho - ly Lord God of
hosts.
Choir Heaven and earth are filled with your glory.
Organ:
f
All Ho-san - na in the high - est.
Choir Blessed is he who comes in the name of the Lord.
Organ
All Ho - san - na in the high - est.

46 Holy, Holy, Holy

Theodore Marier

2
Choir
A
All
Ho - ly, Ho -
ly, ho - ly, ho - ly Lord God of pow'r and might.
Organ:
2
B
f
Heav - en and earth ___ are
full ___ of your glo - ry
Choir
full of your glory.
C
Choir
All f
Ho - san - na, Ho - san -
na in the high - est. ______
Organ
D
p
All Bless-ed is
he who comes _ in the name of the Lord,
Choir
in the name of the
All p
. . . . Lord, ___ who comes _ in the name of the Lord.

E
Organ
Choir
Ho - san - na,
All
ho - san - na in the high - est.
Holy, Holy, Holy
47
Hermann Schroeder
Organ
Choir
All
Ho - ly, Ho - ly, ho - ly
Organ
Choir
Lord God of hosts.
Heaven and earth are filled with your glory.
All
Ho - san - na, ho - san - na in the high -
est.
Blessed is he who comes in the name of the Lord.
Organ
All
Ho-san - na,
ho - san - na in the high - est.

48 Holy, Holy, Holy - Sanctus

Jean Langlais
Organ
10
All
ff
Ho - ly,
San - ctus,
A Organ
6
All
ff
ho - ly, ho - ly,
san - ctus, san - ctus,
Choir
5
holy Lord, God of might and power.
Dóminus, Deus Sábaoth.
B All
Heav'n and
Ple - ni
earth are full of your glo - ry.
sunt cae - li et ter - ra.
Choir
7
Hosanna in the highest.
Hosánna in excélsis.
C All
Ho - san -
Ho - sán -
2
na in the high - est.
na in ex - cél - sis.
Organ
3
Organ
5
D Choir
21
Blessed is he who comes in the name of the Lord.
Benedíctus qui venit in nómine Dómini.
Organ
2
E
5
Choir Hosanna in the highest.
Hosánna in excélsis.
All Ho - san -
Ho - sán -
2
na in the high - est.
na in ex - cél - sis.
Organ
3

Glory to God in the Highest

T. M.

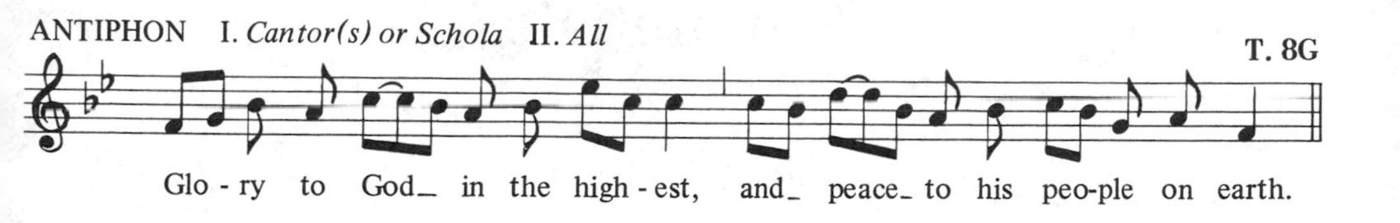
ANTIPHON I. *Cantor(s) or Schola* II. *All*
T. 8G
Glo - ry to God_ in the high - est, and_ peace_ to his peo-ple on earth.

Cantor/Choir

Lord God, heavenly King,
Almighty God and Father,
We worship you, we give you thanks,
We praise you for your glory.

All repeat ANTIPHON

Lord Jesus Christ, only Son of the Father,
Lord God, Lamb of God,
You take away the sin of the world:
have mercy on us;
You are seated at the right hand of the Father:
Receive our prayer.

All repeat ANTIPHON

For you alone are the Holy One,
You alone are the Lord,
You alone are the Most High Jesus Christ,
With the Holy Spirit, in the glory of
God the Father. Amen.

All repeat ANTIPHON

50 # CANTUS IN ORDINE MISSAE

Ritus Initiales

51 Signum Crucis

Sacerdos In nó - mi - ne Pa - tris, et Fí - li - i, et Spí- ri - tus San - cti.
In the name of the Father, the Son, and the Holy Spirit.

All A - men.

52 Formula Salutationis

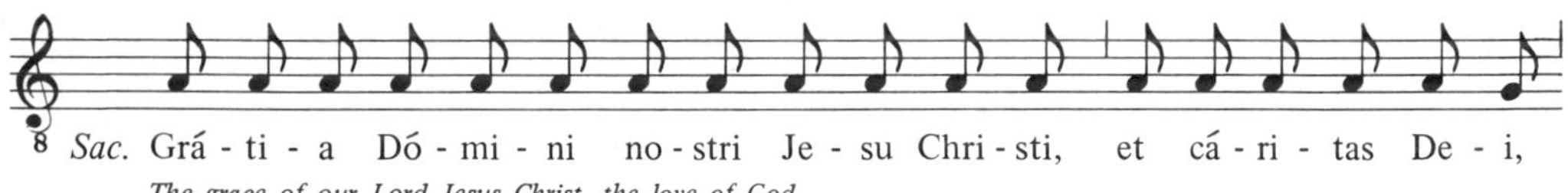
Sac. Grá - ti - a Dó - mi - ni no - stri Je - su Chri - sti, et cá - ri - tas De - i,
The grace of our Lord Jesus Christ, the love of God,

et com-mu - ni - cá - ti - o San - cti Spí - ri - tus sit cum ó - mni- bus vo - bis.
and the fellowship of the Holy Spirit be with all of you.

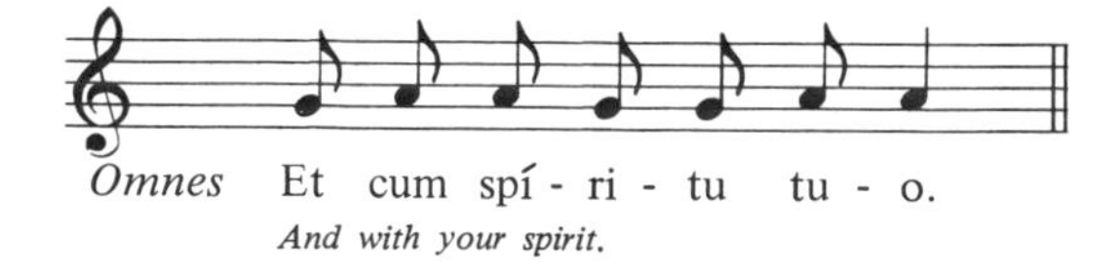
Omnes Et cum spí - ri - tu tu - o.
And with your spirit.

Ad Ritum Paenitentialem

Sac. Fra - tres, a - gno - scá - mus pec - cá - ta no - stra, ut a - pti si - mus

Brethren, let us call to mind our sins so that we might

ad sa - cra my - sté - ri - a ce - le - brán - da.

prepare ourselves to celebrate the sacred mysteries.

Sac. ℣. Mi - se - ré - re no - stri, Dó - mi - ne. *Omnes* ℟. Qui - a pec - cá - vi - mus ti - bi.

Have mercy on us, Lord. Because we have sinned against you.

℣. O - stén - de no - bis, Dó - mi - ne, mi - se - ri - cór - di - am tu - am.

Show us, Lord, your clemency.

℟. Et sa - lu - tá - re tu - um da no - bis.

And grant us your salvation.

℣. Mi - se - re - á - tur no - stri o - mní - po - tens De - us, et di - mís - sis

May the almighty and omnipotent God have mercy on us, forgive us our sins

pec - cá - tis no - stris, per - dú - cat nos ad vi - tam ae - tér - nam.
and lead us to life everlasting.

Omnes ℟. A - men.

54

Kyrie XI

Orbis Factor

I. *Cantores* II. *Omnes*

Ký - ri - e, e - lé - i - son.
Lord, have mercy.

Chri - ste, e - lé - i - son.
Christ, have mercy.

C.
Ký - ri - e, e - lé - i - son.

O.
Ký - ri - e, e - lé - i - son.

Gloria VIII

55

De Angelis

Gló - ri - a in ex - cél - sis De - o. Et in ter - ra pax ho - mi - ni - bus bo-nae vo-lun-

Glory to God in the highest. And peace to men of good will.

tá - tis. Lau-dá - mus te. Be-ne - dí-ci-mus te. _ Ad-o-rá - mus te.

We praise you. We bless you. We adore you.

Glo - ri - fi - cá-mus te. Grá-ti-as á - gi-mus ti - bi pro-pter ma-gnam gló-ri-am tu-am.

We glorify you. We give you thanks for your great glory.

Dó-mi-ne De-us, Rex cae-lé - stis, De - us_Pa - ter_ o - mní - po - tens. Dó - mi -

Lord God, heavenly King, God the Father almighty.

ne Fi - li u - ni - gé - ni - te, Je - su_Chri ste. Dó-mi-ne De-us, _ A-gnus De - i,

Lord, only begotten Son, Jesus Christ. Lord God, Lamb of God,

Fí - li - us __ Pa - tris. Qui tol - lis pec-cá-ta mun - di, __ mi-se-ré - re_no-bis.

Son of the Father. You take away the sins of the world, have mercy on us.

Qui tol-lis pec-cá-ta mun-di, sú-sci-pe de-pre-ca-ti-ó-nem no - stram.
You take away the sins of the world, receive our prayer.
Qui se-des ad déx-te-ram Pa-tris, mi-se-ré-re no-bis. Quó-ni-am tu so-lus
You sit at the right hand of the Father, have mercy on us. For you alone
san-ctus. Tu so-lus Dó-mi-nus. Tu so-lus Al-tís-si-mus, Je - su
are holy. You alone are Lord. You alone are Most High, Jesus Christ.
Chri-ste. Cum San-cto Spí-ri-tu in gló-ri-a De-i Pa - tris. A - men.
With the Holy Spirit in the glory of God the Father. Amen.

56 Post Collectam

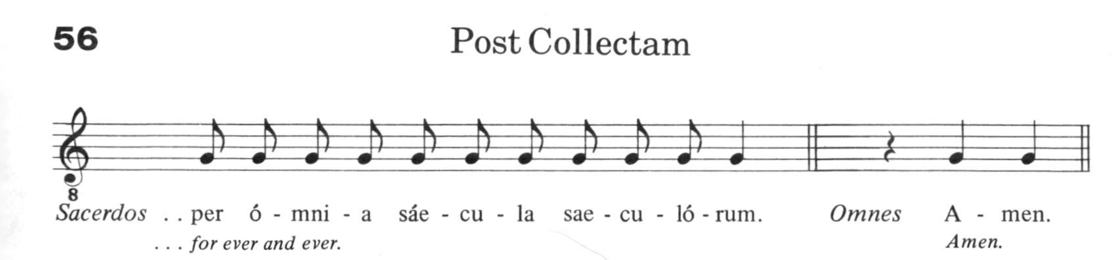
Sacerdos . . per ó-mni-a sáe-cu-la sae-cu-ló-rum. Omnes A-men.
. . . for ever and ever. Amen.

Ad Liturgiam Verbi

57

Post Lectionem I   Post Lectionem II

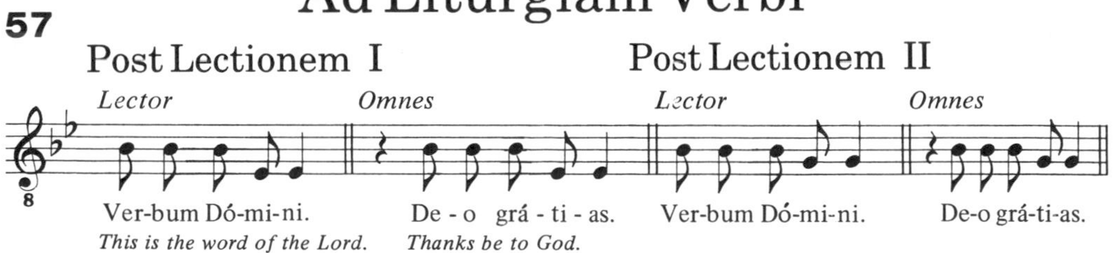
Lector Omnes Lector Omnes
Ver-bum Dó-mi-ni. De-o grá-ti-as. Ver-bum Dó-mi-ni. De-o grá-ti-as.
This is the word of the Lord. Thanks be to God.

Alleluia - Tempore Per Annum et Tempore Paschali **58**

I *Cantor vel Schola* II *Omnes*

Al - le - lu - ia, Al - le - lu - ia, ___ Al - le - lu - ia.

Acclamatio - Tempore Quadragesimae **59**

I *Cantor vel Schola* II *Omnes*

Par-ce Dó-mi-ne, _ par-ce pó-pu-lo__ tu - o: _ ne in ae-tér-num i-ra-scá-ris no-bis.

Spare us, O Lord, spare thy people: *let not your wrath be upon us forever.*

Ante Evangelium **60**

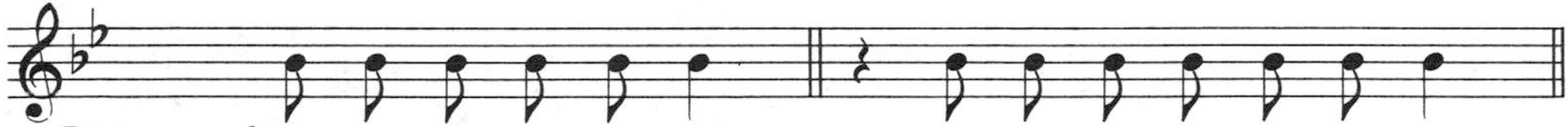

Diaconus vel Sacerdos ℣. Dó - mi - nus vo - bís - cum. ℟. Et cum spí - ri - tu tu - o.

The Lord be with you. *And also with you.*

℣. Lec-ti - o sanc-ti E-van-gél- i - i se-cun-dum Mar - cam: / Mat-té-um: / Lu - cam: / Jo-án-nem: ℟. Gló-ri-a ti - bi, Dó-mi - ne.

A reading from the Gospel according to *Glory to you, O Lord.*

Post Evangelium **61**

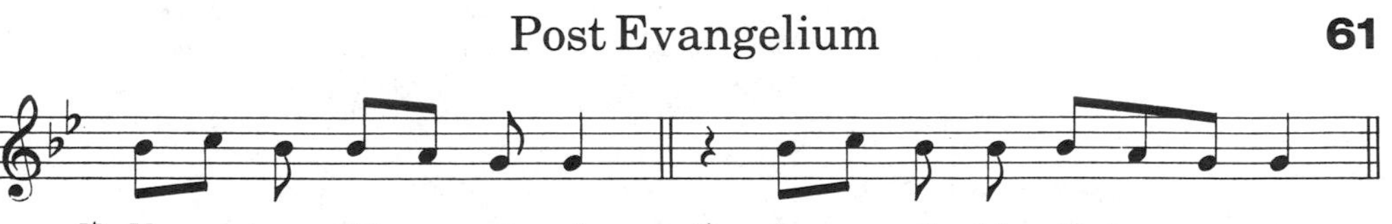
℣. Ver - bum Dó - mi - ni. ℟. Laus_ ti - bi, Chri - ste.
This is the word of the Lord.
Praise to you, O Christ.

62

Credo III

Cel., Cantor, vel Schola
Omnes

Cre-do in u-num De - um. Pa - trem o-mni - po-tén - tem, fa - ctó-rem
I believe in one God, The Father, the almighty, maker

cae - li et ter-rae, vi - si - bí - li - um ó - mni-um, et in - vi - si - bí - li-um.
of heaven and earth, of all that is seen and unseen.

Et in u-num Dó-mi-num Je-sum Chri-stum, Fí - li-um De - i u - ni - gé - ni-tum.
And in one Lord, Jesus Christ, only Son of God,

Et ex Pa - tre na - tum an-te ó-mni - a saé - cu-la. De-um de De - o,
eternally begotten of the Father, God from God,

lu-men de lú-mi - ne, De - um ve-rum de De - o ve - ro. Gé - ni-tum, non
Light from Light, true God from true God, begotten, not made,

fa - ctum, con-sub-stan - ti - á - lem Pa - tri: per quem ó-mni - a fa - cta sunt.
one in being with the Father: through whom all things were made.

Qui pro-pter nos hó-mi-nes, et pro-pter no-stram sa-lú-tem de-scén-dit de___
For us men and for our salvation he came down from

cae-lis. Et in-car-ná-tus est de Spí-ri-tu San-cto ex Ma-rí-a
heaven. He was born by the power of the Holy Spirit of the Virgin Mary,

Vír-gi-ne: Et ho-mo fa-ctus est. Cru-ci-fí-xus é-ti-am pro no-bis:
and became man. He was crucified for our sake:

sub Pón-ti-o Pi-lá-to pas-sus, et se-púl-tus est. Et re-sur-ré-xit
under Pontius Pilate he suffered, died and was buried. And he rose again

tér-ti-a di-e, se-cún-dum Scri-ptú-ras. Et a-scén-dit in cae-lum:
on the third day, according to the Scriptures. And he ascended into heaven:

se-det ad déx-te-ram Pa-tris. Et í-te-rum ven-tú-rus est cum gló-ri-a,
he is seated at the right hand of the Father. And he will come again in glory,

ju - di - cá - re vi - vos et mór - tu - os: cu - jus re - gni non e - rit fi - nis.
to judge the living and the dead: whose kingdom will have no end.

Et in Spí - ri - tum San-ctum, Dó-mi-num, et vi - vi - fi - cán - tem: qui ex Pa - tre
And in the Holy Spirit, Lord, and giver of life: who from the Father

Fí - li - o - que pro - cé-dit. Qui cum Pa-tre et Fí - li - o si-mul ad - o - rá-tur,
and the Son proceeds. Who with the Father and the Son is worshipped,

et con-glo - ri - fi - cá-tur: qui lo - cú-tus est per Pro - phé-tas. Et u - nam
and glorified: who spoke through the Prophets. And in one

san-ctam ca-thó - li-cam et a - po - stó - li-cam Ec - clé - si - am. Con - fí - te - or
holy catholic and apostolic Church. I confess

u-num ba - ptí - sma in re-mis - si - ó - nem pec - ca - tó - rum. Et ex - spé -
one baptism for the remission of sins. And I look for

cto re - sur - re - cti - ó-nem mor-tu - ó-rum. Et vi - tam ven-tú - ri saé - cu-li.

the resurrection of the dead. *And the life of the world to come.*

A - - - - men.

So be it.

Ad Orationem Universalem **63**

Diaconus vel Cantor . . . .ex - au - dí - re di - gné - ris. *Omnes* ℟. Te ro - gá - mus, au - di nos.

. . . .vouchsafe graciously to hear (us). *We beseech you, hear us.*

Liturgia Eucharistica

Post Orationem Super Oblata **64**

Sac. *Omnes*

Per Chri - stum Do - mi - num no - strum. A - men.

Through Christ, our Lord.

Ante Prefationem **65**

Sac. *Omnes* *Sac.*

Dó-mi-nus vo - bís - cum. Et cum spí - ri - tu tu - o. Sur - sum cor - da.

The Lord be with you. *And also with you.* *Lift up your hearts.*

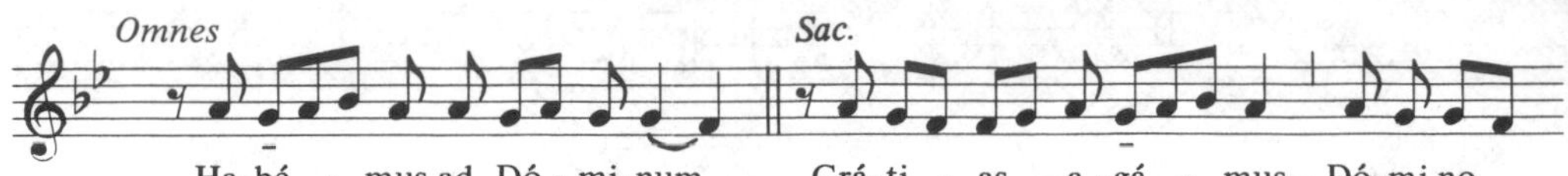
Omnes
Sac.
Ha-bé - mus ad Dó - mi-num.
Grá-ti - as a - gá - mus Dó-mi-no
We lift them up to the Lord.
Let us give thanks to the Lord,

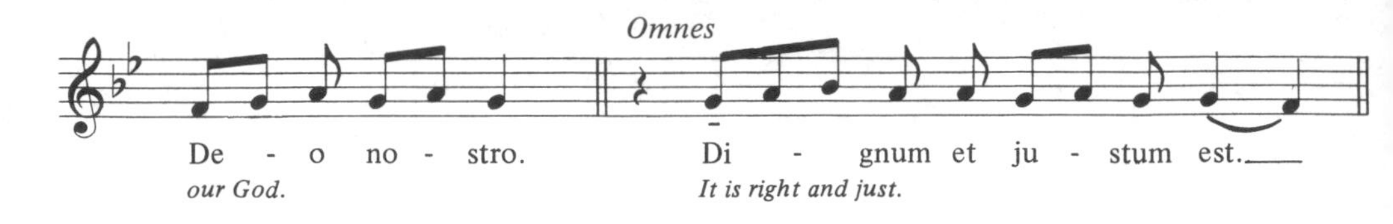
Omnes
De - o no - stro.
Di - gnum et ju - stum est.
our God.
It is right and just.

66 Sanctus XIII

Stelliferi Conditor Orbis

Cantor (es)
Omnes
San - ctus,* San - ctus, San - ctus Dó - mi - nus De - us Sá - ba - oth.
Holy, holy, holy Lord, God of power and might.

Ple - ni sunt cae - li et ter - ra gló - ri - a tu - a. Ho - sán -
Heaven and earth are full of your glory.

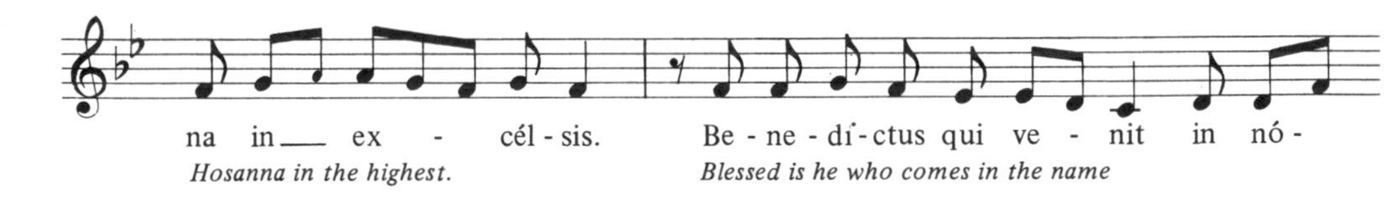
na in ex - cél - sis. Be - ne - dí - ctus qui ve - nit in nó -
Hosanna in the highest.
Blessed is he who comes in the name

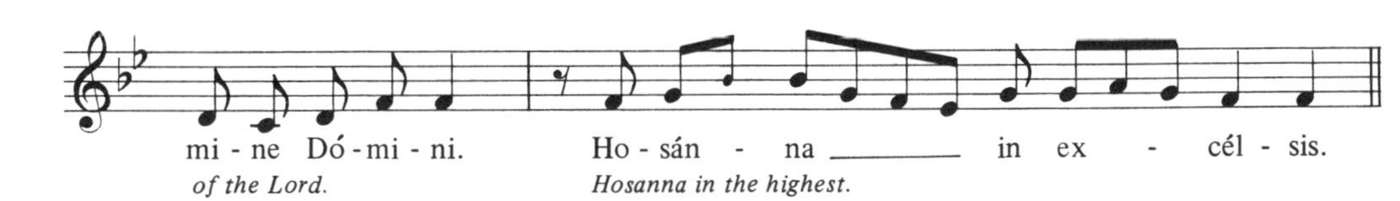
mi - ne Dó - mi - ni. Ho - sán - na in ex - cél - sis.
of the Lord.
Hosanna in the highest.

Post Consecrationem

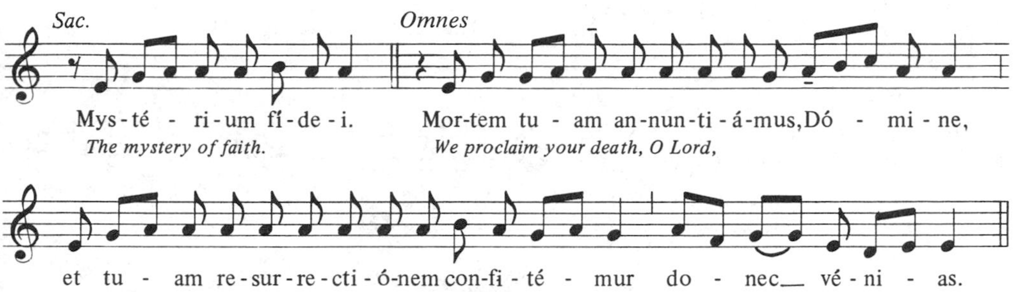
Sac.
Omnes
Mys-té - ri-um fí-de-i.
The mystery of faith.
Mor-tem tu - am an-nun-ti-á-mus, Dó - mi-ne,
We proclaim your death, O Lord,
et tu - am re-sur-re-cti-ó-nem con-fi-té - mur do - nec__ vé-ni - as.
and confess your resurrection until you shall come again.

Post Doxologiam

68

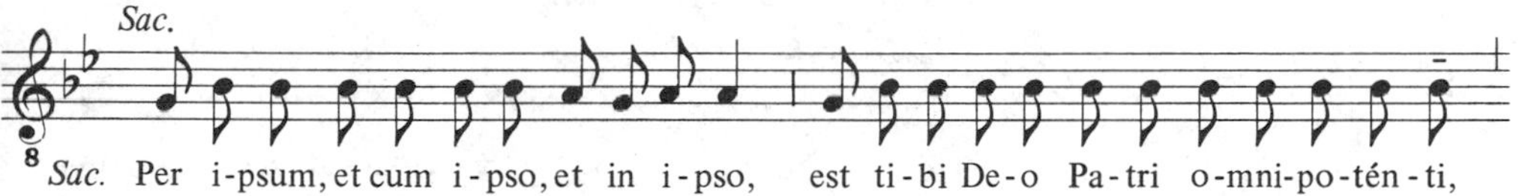
Sac.
Sac. Per i-psum, et cum i-pso, et in i-pso, est ti-bi De-o Pa-tri o-mni-po-tén-ti,
Through him, with him, and in him, is to you God Father almighty,

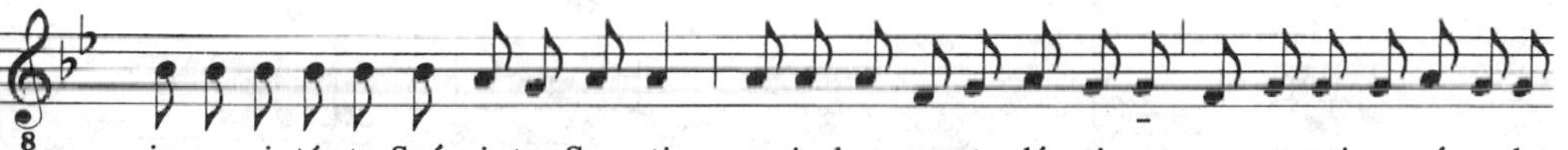
in u-ni-tá-te Spí-ri-tus San-cti, omn-is hon-or et gló-ri-a per o-mni-a saé-cu-la
in the unity of the Holy Spirit, all honor and glory for ever and ever.

Omnes
sae-cu-ló - rum. ℟. A-men.__

Omnes
Vel
A - men.__

Ritus Communionis

Pater Noster

Sac.
8
Prae - cé - ptis sa - lu - tá - ri - bus mó - ni - ti, et di - ví - na in - sti - tu - ti - ó - ne
Directed by saving precepts, and by divine instruction

Omnes
for - má - ti, au - dé - mus dí - ce - re: Pa-ter no-ster, qui es in cae - lis:
formed, we dare to say: Our Father, who art in heaven:

san - cti - fi - cé - tur___ no - men tu - um: ad -vé - ni - at re-gnum tu-um:
hallowed be thy name: thy kingdom come:

fi - at vo - lún - tas tu - a, sic - ut in cae - lo___ et___ in ter - ra.
thy will be done, on earth as it is in heaven.

Pa-nem no-strum co - ti - di - á - num da no - bis hó - di - e; et di - mít -
Give us this day our daily bread:

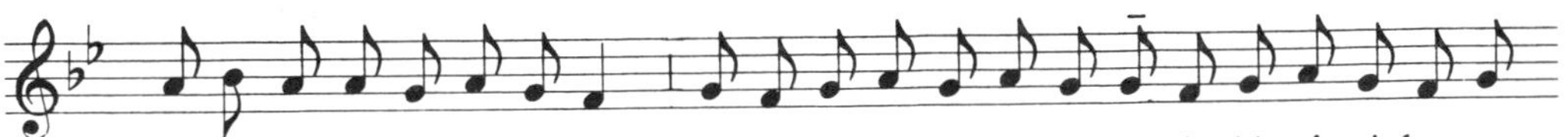
te no-bis dé - bi - ta no-stra, sic - ut et nos di - mít - ti - mus de - bi - tó - ri - bus no -
and forgive us our trespasses as we forgive those who trespass against us.

stris; et ne nos in-dú-cas in ten-ta - ti - ó - nem; sed lí - be - ra nos a ma - lo.

And lead us not into temptation, but deliver us from evil.

Sac.

Líbera nos, quaésumus, Dómine, ab ómnibus ma - lis, da propítius pacem in di - é - bus

Deliver us, Lord, from every evil, and grant us peace in our day.

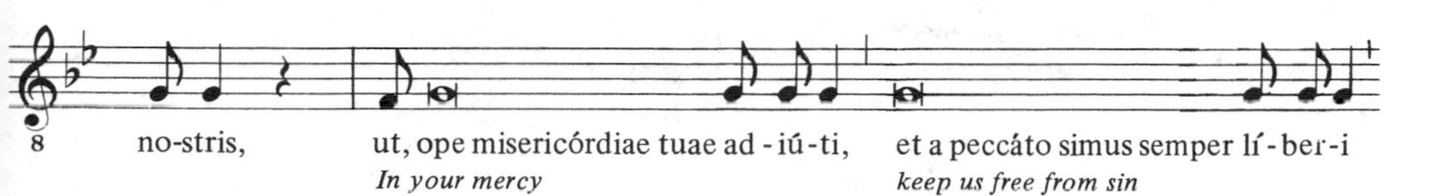

no-stris, ut, ope misericórdiae tuae ad - iú - ti, et a peccáto simus semper lí - ber - i

In your mercy *keep us free from sin*

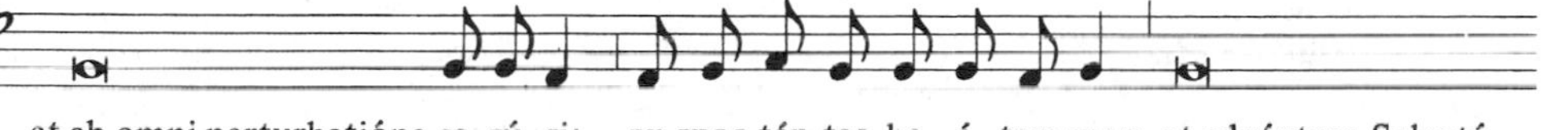

et ab omni perturbatióne se - cú - ri: ex-spec-tán-tes be - á - tam spem et advéntum Salvató -

and protect us from all anxiety *as we wait in joyful hope for the coming*

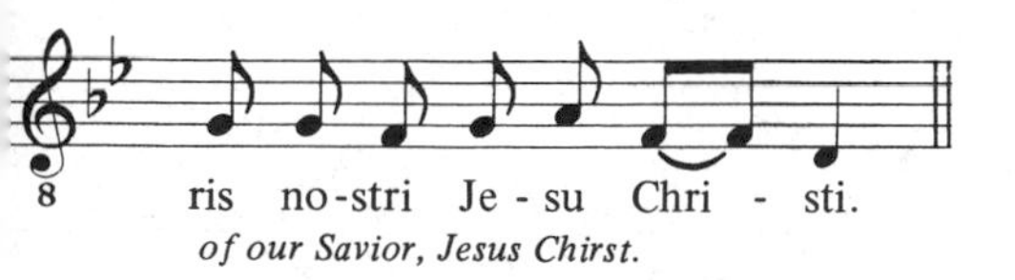

ris no - stri Je - su Chri - sti.

of our Savior, Jesus Chirst.

Omnes

Qui-a ___ tu - um est re-gnum, et po - té - stas, ___ et gló - ri - a in saé - cu - la.

For the kingdom, the power and glory are yours, now and forever.

70 Ad Pacem

Sac.
Omnes
...qui vi - vis et re - gnas in saé - cu - la sae - cu - ló - rum. ℟. A - men.
... You live and reign for ever and ever.

Sac.
Omnes
Pax Dó - mi - ni sit sem - per vo - bís - cum. ℟. Et cum spí - ri - tu tu - o.
The peace of the Lord be with you always.
And with your spirit.

71 Agnus Dei IX

Cum Jubilo

Cantor(es)
Omnes
A - gnus De - i, qui tol - lis pec - cá - ta
Lamb of God, you take away the sins of the world:

Cantor(es)
mun - di: mi - se - ré - re no - bis. A - gnus De -
have mercy on us.

Omnes
i, qui tol - lis pec-cá - ta mun - di: mi - se - ré - re no - bis.

Cantor(es)
Omnes
A - gnus De - i, qui tol - lis

pec - cá - ta mun - di: do - na no - bis pa - cem.
grant us peace.

Ad Orationem Post Communionem **72**

Sac.
Omnes
Per Chri - stum Dó - mi - num no - strum. ℟. A - men.
Through Christ our Lord.

Ad Ritus Conclusionis

Ad Benedictionem **73**

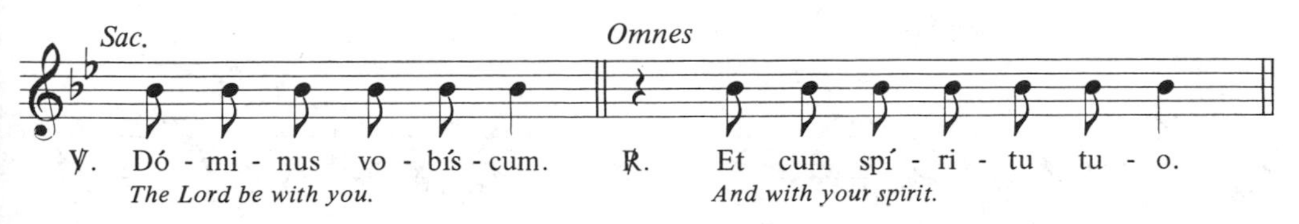
Sac.
Omnes
℣. Dó - mi - nus vo - bís - cum. ℟. Et cum spí - ri - tu tu - o.
The Lord be with you.
And with your spirit.

Sac.
Be - ne - dí - cat vos o - mní - po - tens De - us, Pa - ter, et Fí - li - us, et Spí - ri - tus
May the blessing of almighty God, Father, and Son, and Holy Spirit

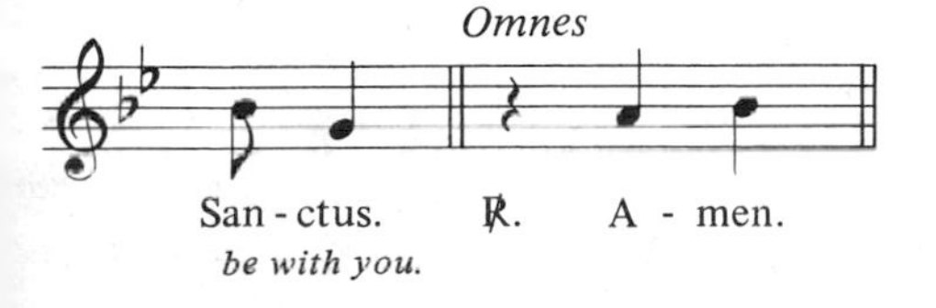
Omnes
San - ctus. ℟. A - men.
be with you.

Ad Benedictionem Episcopalem **74**

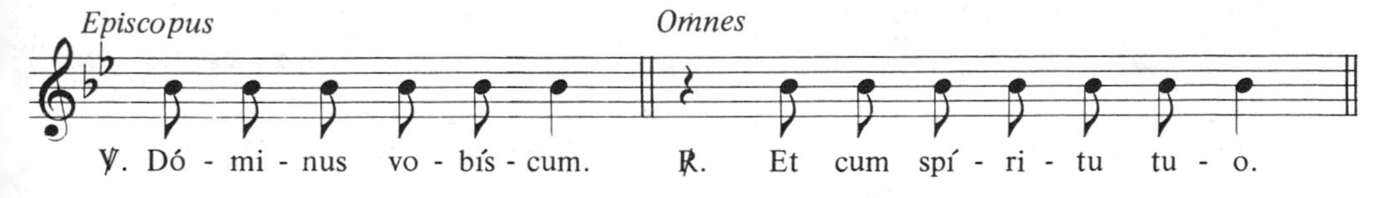
Episcopus
Omnes
℣. Dó - mi - nus vo - bís - cum. ℟. Et cum spí - ri - tu tu - o.

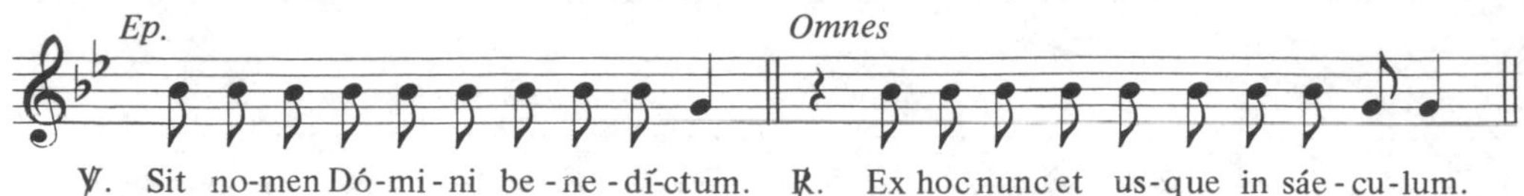
Ep.
Omnes

℣. Sit no-men Dó-mi-ni be-ne-dí-ctum. ℟. Ex hoc nunc et us-que in sáe-cu-lum.
Blessed be the name of the Lord. *Now and forever.*

Ep.
Omnes

℣. Ad-ju-tó-ri-um no-strum in nó-mi-ne Dó-mi-ni. ℟. Qui fe-cit cae-lum et ter-ram.
Our help is in the name of the Lord. *Who made heaven and earth.*

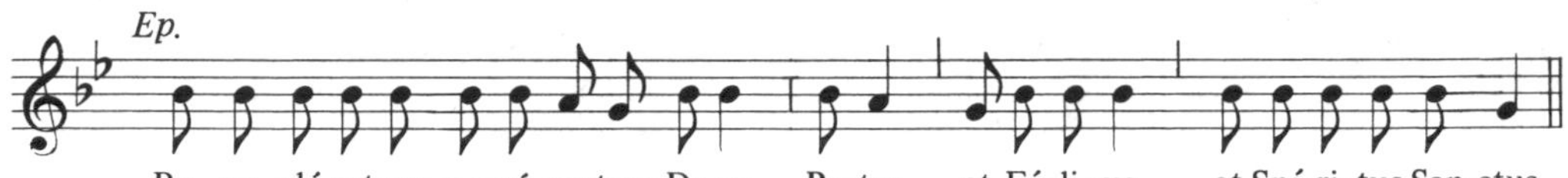
Ep.

Be-ne-dí-cat vos o-mní-po-tens De-us, Pa-ter, et Fí-li-us, et Spí-ri-tus San-ctus.
May the blessing of almighty God be upon you, Father, Son and Holy Spirit.

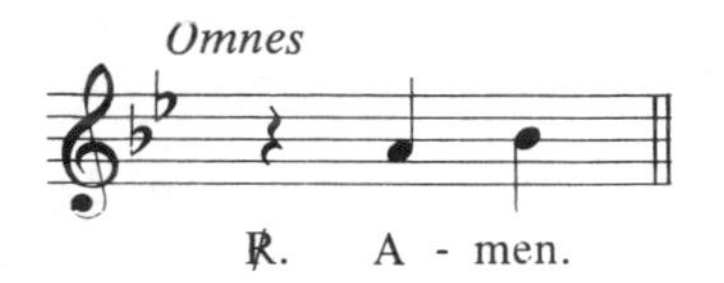
Omnes

℟. A - men.

75 Ad Dimittendum Populum

Sac.
Omnes

I - te, ___ mis - sa est. ℟. De - o ___ grá - ti - as.
Go, the Mass is ended. *Thanks be to God.*

Alleluia Tempore Paschali - No. 39A

Kyrie XVI

76

In Feriis per Annum

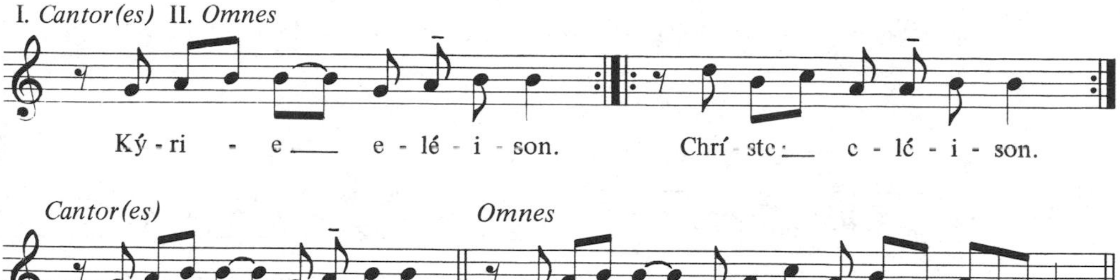
I. *Cantor(es)* II. *Omnes*
Ký - ri - e — e - lé - i - son. Chrí - ste — e - lé - i - son.

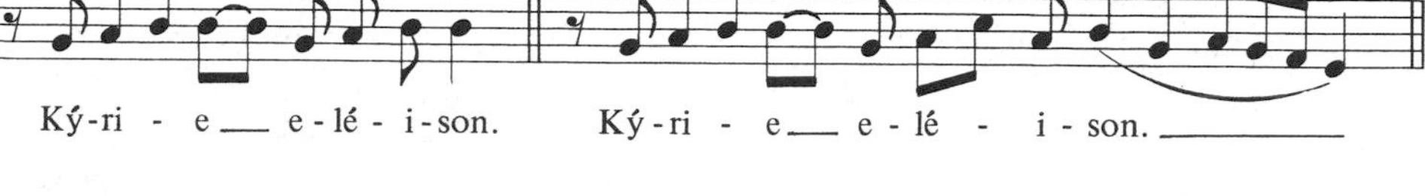
Cantor(es)
Omnes
Ký-ri - e — e - lé - i-son. Ký-ri - e — e - lé - i - son. —

Gloria XV

77

Dominator Deus

Sac. vel Cantor
Omnes
Gló-ri - a — in ex-cél-sis Dé - o. Et in ter-ra pax ho-mí-ni-bus bo-nae

vo-lun-tá-tis. Lau-dá-mus te. Be-ne - dí-ci-mus te. Ad-o - rá-mus te.

Glo-ri-fi-cá-mus te. Grá-ti-as á-gi-mus ti-bi prop-ter mag-nam gló-ri-am tu-am.

Dó-mi-ne De-us, Rex cae-lé-stis, De-us Pa-ter o-mní-po-tens. Dó - mi - ne Fi - li

u - ni - gé - ni - te, Je - su Chri-ste. Dó-mi-ne De-us, A-gnus De-i, Fí- li - us Pa-tris.

Qui tol-lis pec-cá-ta mun-di, mi - se - ré -re no-bis. Qui tol-lis pec-cá - ta mun-di,

sú - sci - pe de-pre - ca - ti - ó-nem no-stram. Qui se-des ad déx - te-ram Pa - tris,

mi-se - ré-re no-bis. Quó-ni-am tu so - lus san-ctus. Tu so-lus Dó-mi-nus.

Tu so-lus Al - tís - si-mus, Je - su Chri - ste. Cum San-cto Spí-ri - tu

in gló - ri - a De - i Pa - tris. A - men.

Sanctus XVIII — 78

In Feriis - Missa pro Defunctis

Cantor
Omnes

San - ctus,__ * San - ctus,__ San-ctus Dó - mi-nus De - us Sá - ba - oth.

Ple - ni sunt cae - li et ter - ra gló - ri - a tu - a. Ho-sán-na in ex-cél-sis.

Be-ne-dí-ctus qui ve-nit in nó-mi-ne Dó-mi-ni. Ho-sán - na in ex-cél - sis.__

Agnus Dei XVIII — 79

In Feriis Adventus et Quadragesimae

Cantor
Omnes

A - gnus De - i, * qui tol-lis pec-cá - ta mun-di: mi - se - ré - re no - bis.

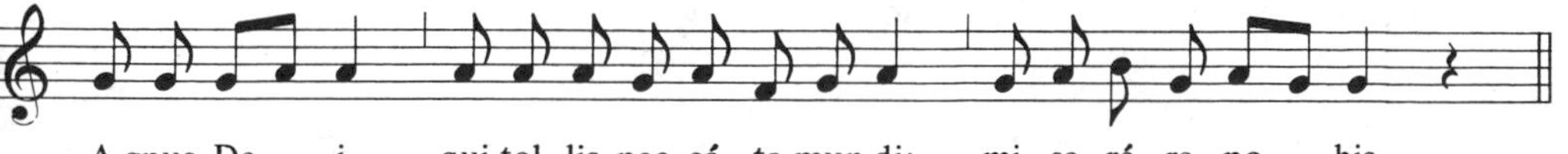

A-gnus De - i, qui tol - lis pec-cá - ta mun-di: mi - se - ré - re no - bis.

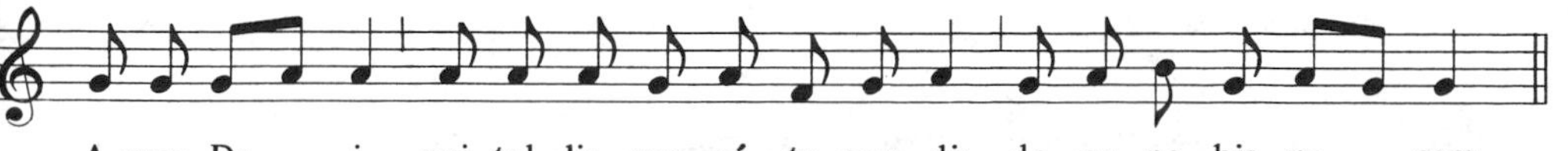

A-gnus De - i, qui tol - lis pec - cá - ta mun - di: do - na no - bis pa - cem.

80 Kyrie XVII

In Dominicis Adventus et Quadragesimae

I. Cantor(es) II. Omnes
Ký - ri - e e - lé - i - son.
Chrí - ste e - lé - i - son.
Cantor(es)
Ký - ri - e e - lé - i - son.
Omnes
Ký-ri - e c - lé - i - son.

81 Sanctus XVII

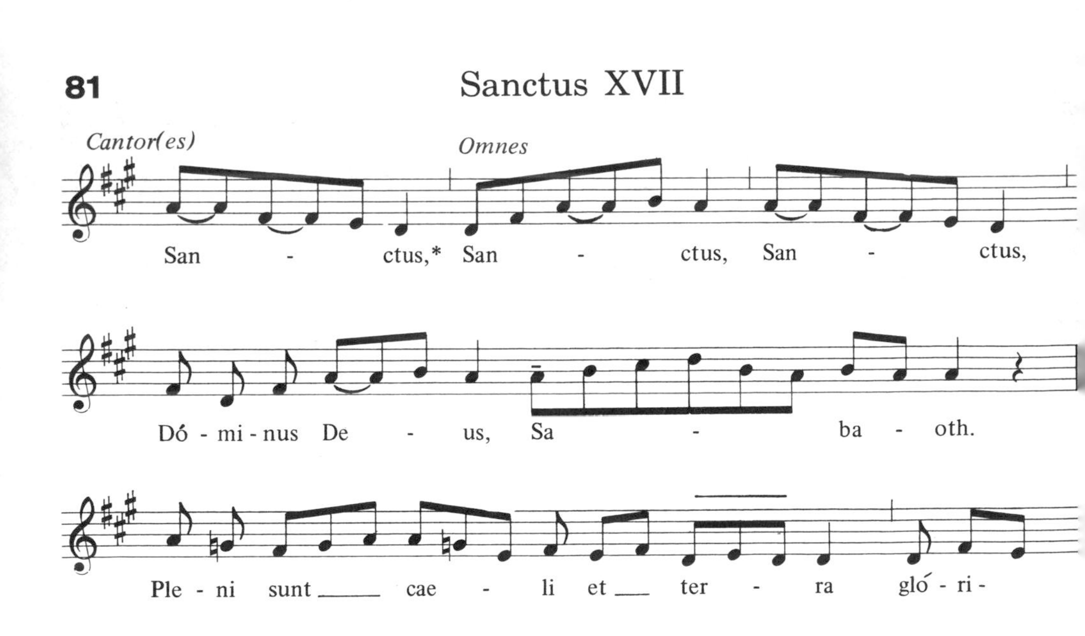
Cantor(es)
Omnes
San - ctus,* San - ctus, San - ctus,
Dó - mi - nus De - us, Sa - ba - oth.
Ple - ni sunt cae - li et ter - ra gló - ri -

a — tu - a. Ho - sán - na — in ex - cél - sis.
Be - ne - dí - ctus qui ve - nit in nó - mi - ne Dó - mi - ni.
Ho - sán - na — in ex - cel - sis.

Agnus Dei XVII **82**

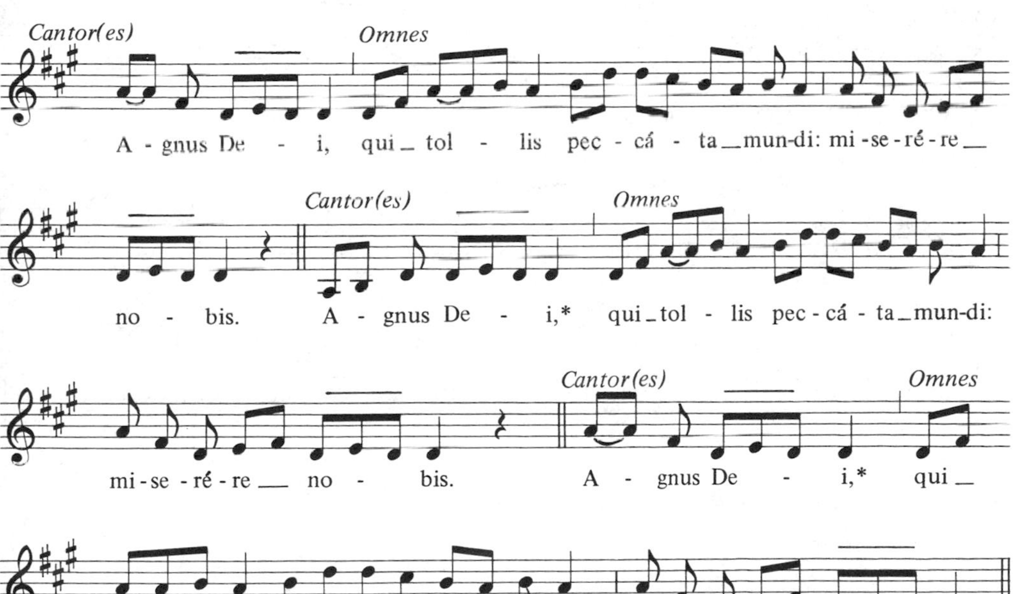
Cantor(es)
Omnes
A - gnus De - i, qui — tol - lis pec - cá - ta — mun-di: mi - se - ré - re —
no - bis.
Cantor(es)
Omnes
A - gnus De - i,* qui — tol - lis pec - cá - ta — mun-di:
mi - se - ré - re — no - bis.
Cantor(es)
Omnes
A - gnus De - i,* qui —
tol - lis pec - cá - ta — mun-di: do - na no - bis — pa - cem.

83

Mass in the Major Modes

Russell Woollen

Sanctus

Choir
All
San - ctus, San - ctus,
Choir
All
San - ctus, — Dó-mi-nus De-us Sá - ba-oth.
Choir
All
Ple - ni sunt ——— cae - li et ter - ra gló - ri - a
tu - a. Ho - sán - na ———
in ex - cél - sis, ——— ho - sán -
rit
Fine
Choir
na — in ex - cél - sis.
Benedíctus qui venit in nómine Dómini.
All Repeat Hosanna from 𝄋 above.

Choir
All
mp
Ag - nus De - i, qui tol - lis pec - cá - ta mun - di,
mi - se - ré - re
no - bis.
Organ
Choir
All
ff
Agnus Dei, qui tollis peccáta
mun - di,
mi-se-
ré - re no - bis, mi - se - ré - re no - bis.
Organ and Choir
Agnus Dei, qui tollis peccáta mundi,
Agnus Dei, qui tollis peccáta mundi,
Agnus Dei, qui tollis
pec - cá - ta mun - di,
All f
do-na no - bis pa - cem,
Choir
p All
do - na no - bis
pa - cem, pa - cem.

GOSPEL ACCLAMATIONS

For the Liturgical Year

85

Advent

T.M.
Al - le - lu - ia, al - le - lu - ia,__ al - le - lu - ia.

86

Christmastide

T.M.
Al - le - lu - ia, al - le - lu - ia, al - le - lu - ia.

87

Lent I

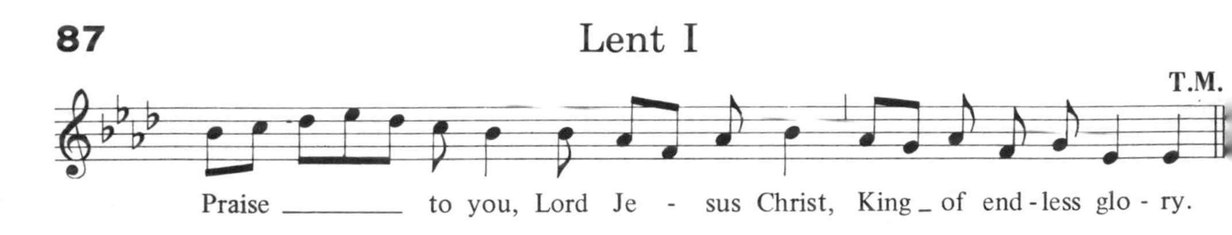
T.M.
Praise ________ to you, Lord Je - sus Christ, King _ of end - less glo - ry.

88

Lent II

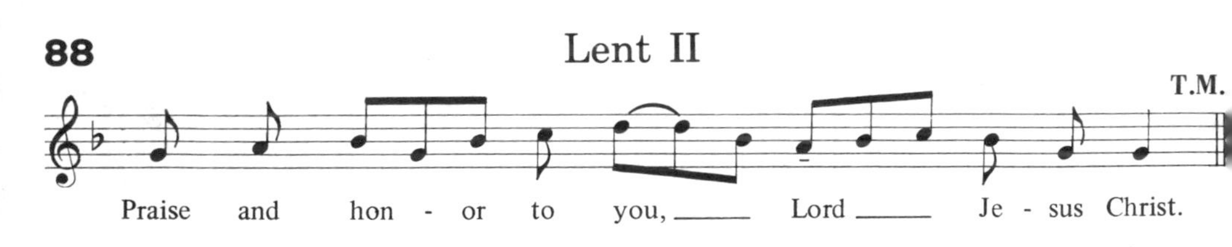
T.M.
Praise and hon - or to you, _____ Lord _____ Je - sus Christ.

89

Lent III

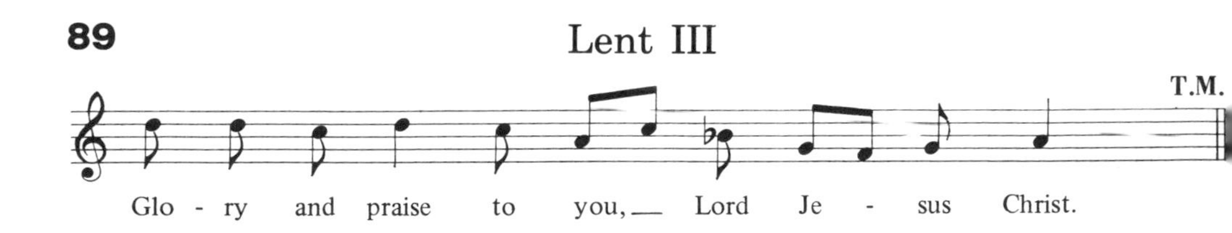
T.M.
Glo - ry and praise to you, __ Lord Je - sus Christ.

Lent IV

90

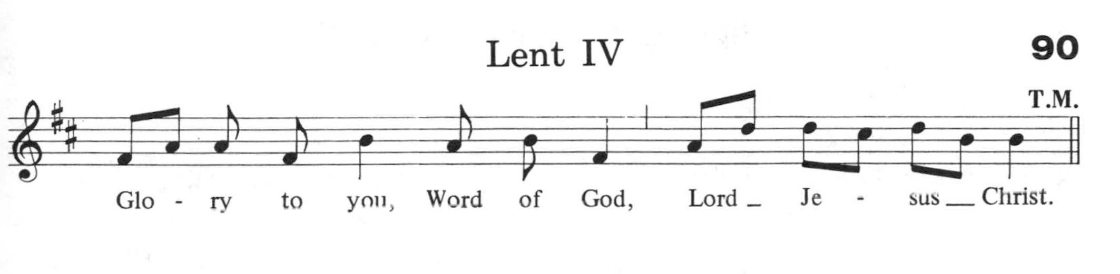
T.M.
Glo - ry to you, Word of God, Lord _ Je - sus __ Christ.

Eastertide Sundays

91

Al - le - lu - ia, al - le - lu - ia, al - le - lu - ia.

Season of the Year - Sundays (1)

92

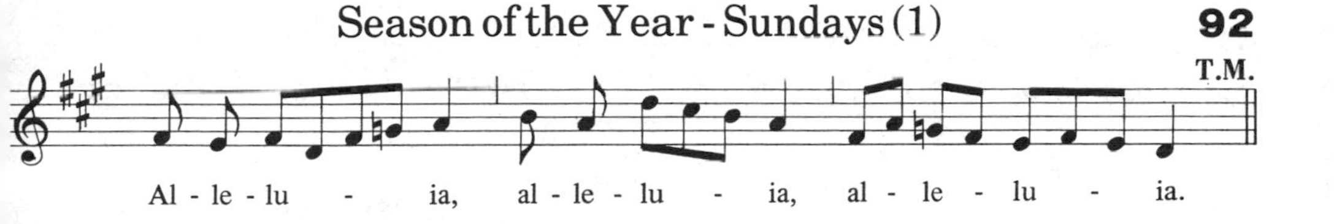
T.M.
Al - le - lu - ia, al - le - lu - ia, al - le - lu - ia.

Season of the Year - Sundays (2)

93

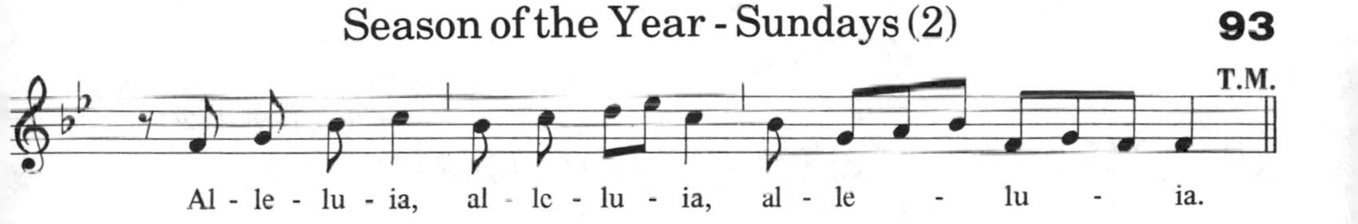
T.M.
Al - le - lu - ia, al - le - lu - ia, al - le - lu - ia.

Solemnities and Feasts of Saints

94

Te Deum
Al - le - lu - ia, al - le - lu - ia, ___ al - le - lu - ia.

Weekdays of the Year, Eastertide, Commons, Votive

95

Gregorian

Al - le - lu - ia, al - le - lu - ia, ___ al - le - lu - ia.

96 Alleluia - Gregorian Mode 2

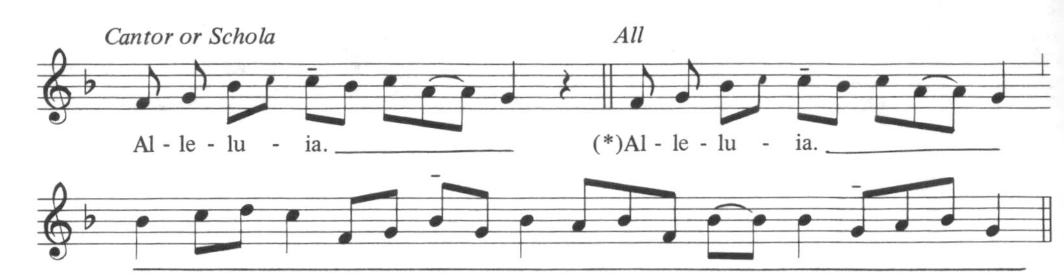
Cantor or Schola
All
Al - le - lu - ia.
(*)Al - le - lu - ia.

Cantor or Schola sings appropriate sentence.
All repeat from asterisk (*).

97 Alleluia - Gregorian Mode 4

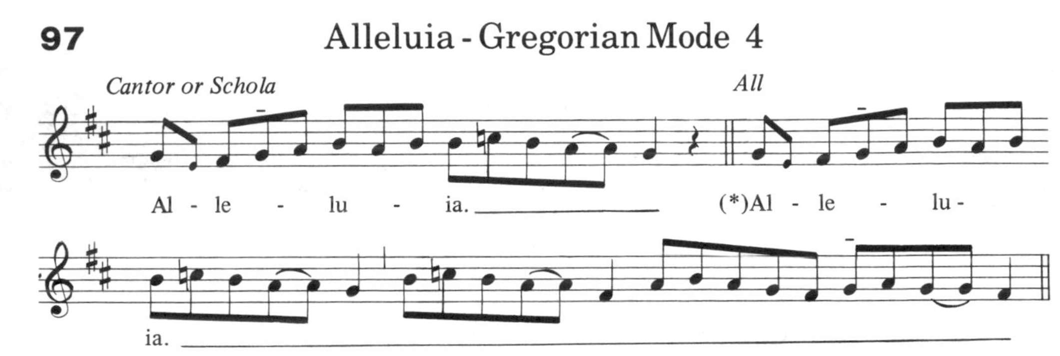
Cantor or Schola
All
Al - le - lu - ia.
(*)Al - le - lu -
ia.

Cantor or Schola sings appropriate sentence.
All repeat from asterisk (*).

98 Alleluia - Gregorian Mode 8

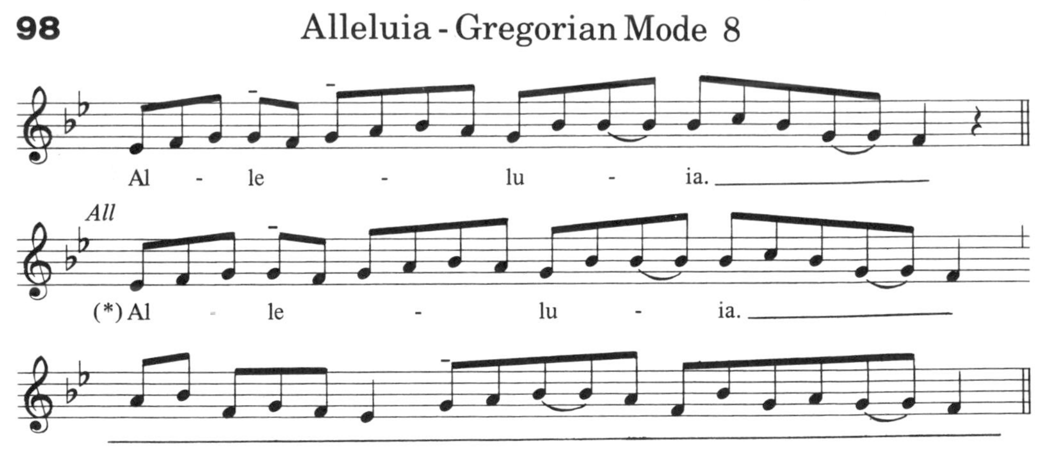
Al - le - lu - ia.
All
(*) Al - le - lu - ia.

Cantor or Schola sings appropriate sentence.
All repeat from asterisk (*).

A Boy Is Born in Bethlehem

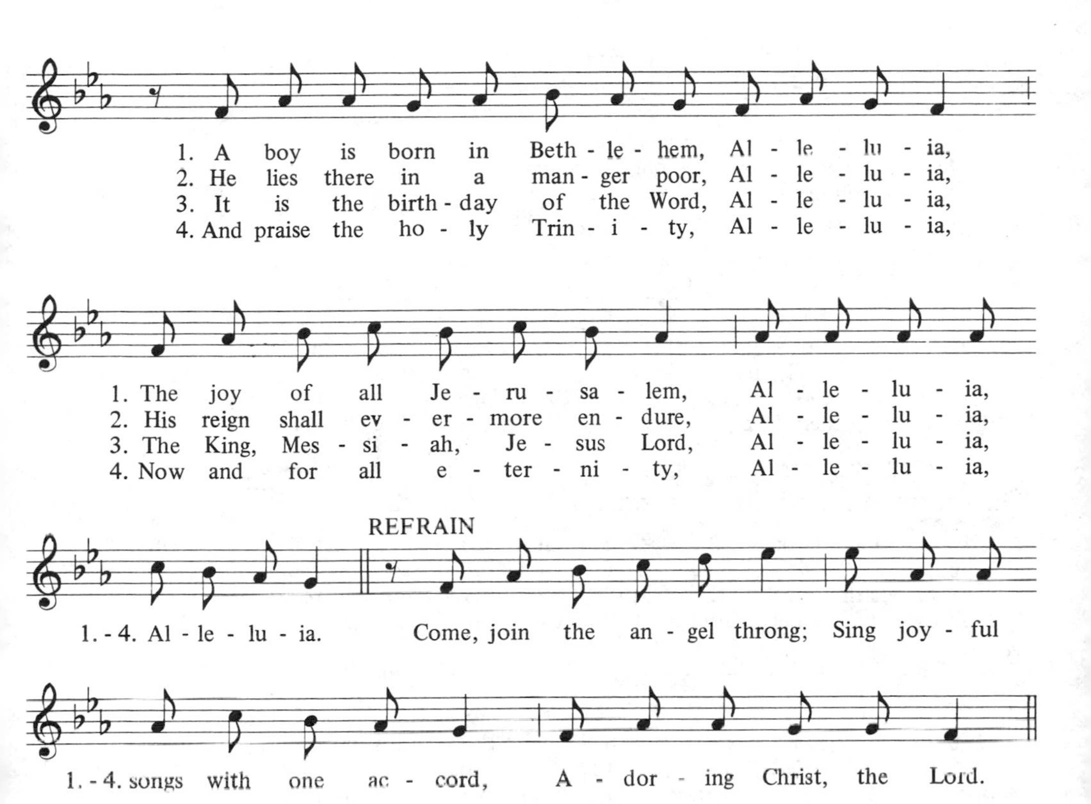
1. A boy is born in Beth - le - hem, Al - le - lu - ia,
2. He lies there in a man - ger poor, Al - le - lu - ia,
3. It is the birth - day of the Word, Al - le - lu - ia,
4. And praise the ho - ly Trin - i - ty, Al - le - lu - ia,
1. The joy of all Je - ru - sa - lem, Al - le - lu - ia,
2. His reign shall ev - er - more en - dure, Al - le - lu - ia,
3. The King, Mes - si - ah, Je - sus Lord, Al - le - lu - ia,
4. Now and for all e - ter - ni - ty, Al - le - lu - ia,
REFRAIN
1. - 4. Al - le - lu - ia. Come, join the an - gel throng; Sing joy - ful
1. - 4. songs with one ac - cord, A - dor - ing Christ, the Lord.

Text: 4th Century anon. Trans. anon.
Tune: *Puer natus in Bethlehem*, Plainchant, Mode 1.

100 A Mighty Fortress Is Our God

1. A might - y for - tress is our God, A
2. Did we in our own strength con - fide Our
3. And though this world, with dev - ils filled, Should
4. That word a - bove all earth - ly powers, No
1. bul - wark nev - er fail - ing; Our help - er he a -
2. striv - ing would be los - ing, Were not the right man
3. threat - en to un - do us; We will not fear, for
4. thanks to them a - bid - eth; The Spir - it and the
1. mid the flood Of mor - tal ills pre - vail - ing; For
2. on our side, The man of God's own choos - ing; Dost
3. God hath willed His truth to tri - umph through us; The
4. gifts are ours Through him who with us sid - eth; Let
1. still our an - cient foe Doth seek to work us
2. ask who that may be? Christ Je - sus it is
3. prince of dark - ness grim, We trem - ble not for
4. goods and kin - dred go, This mor - tal life al -
1. woe; His craft and power are great, And
2. he; Lord Sa - ba - oth his name, From
3. him; His rage we can en - dure, For
4. so; The bod - y they may kill; God's
1. armed with cru - el hate, On earth is not his e - qual.
2. age to age the same, And he must win the bat - tle.
3. lo! his doom is sure, One lit - tle word shall fell him.
4. truth a - bid - eth still; His king - dom is for - ev - er.

Text: Martin Luther, +1546. Trans. F. Hedge, +1890.
Tune: *Ein' feste Burg,* Martin Luther, +1546.

Accept, Almighty Father

101

1. Ac - cept, Al - might - y Fa - ther, This gift of ___ bread and
2. Je - sus, by this com - min - gling, Of wa - ter ___ and of
1. wine, Which ___ soon your priest will of - fer To
2. wine, May ___ you who took our na - ture, Give
1. you, O ___ God be - nign, In hum - ble rep - a -
2. us your ___ life di - vine. Come, Lord, and make us
1. ra - tion For sins and fail - ings dread, To
2. ho - ly, With faith our lives im - bue. Grant
1. win life ev - er - last - ing For liv - ing and for dead.
2. un - to us sal - va - tion, Our hope and love re - new.

Text: Verse 1, Anonymous.
Verse 2, T. Marier.
Tune: *Munich*, Meiningen Gesangbuch, 1693.

102

Adeste, Fideles

1. Ad - é - ste, fi - dé - les Lae - ti, tri - um - phán - tes,
2. De - um de De - o, Lu - men de lú - mi-ne,
3. Can - tet nunc i - o! Cho - rus an - ge - ló - rum,
4. Er - go qui na - tus Di - e ho - di - ér - na,

1. Ve - ní - te, ve - ní - te in Béth - le - hem; Na - tum vi - dé - te
2. Ges-tant pu - él - lae ví - sce - ra; De - um ve - rum,
3. Can-tet nunc au - la coe - lés - ti - um: Gló - ri - a
4. Je - su ti - bi sit gló - ri - a; Pa - tris ae - tér - ni

REFRAIN

1. Re - gem an - ge - ló - rum: Ve - ní - te, ad - o - ré - mus. Ve - ní - te, ad - o -
2. Gé - ni - tum non fac - tum:
3. In ex - cél - sis De - o.
4. Ver - bum ca - ro fac - tum:

ré - mus. Ve - ní - te, ad - o - ré - mus, Dó - mi - num.

For setting in English, see "O Come, All Ye Faithful".

Text: Attributed to J.F. Wade, +1786.
Tune: *Adeste fideles,* J.F. Wade, +1786.

All Creatures of Our God and King

1. All crea - tures of our God and King, Lift
2. Thou rush - ing wind that art so strong, Ye
3. Thou flow - ing wa - ter, pure and clear, Make
4. And all ye men of ten - der heart, For -
5. Let all things their cre - a - tor bless, And
1. up your voice and with us sing Al - le - lu - ia,
2. clouds that sail in heav'n a - long, O praise him,
3. mu - sic for thy Lord to hear, Al - le - lu - ia,
4. giv - ing oth - ers, take your part, O sing ye,
5. wor - ship him in hum - ble - ness, O praise him,
1. al - le - lu - ia! Thou burn - ing sun with gold - en
2. al - le - lu - ia! Thou ris - ing morn, in praise re -
3. al - le - lu - ia! Thou fire so mas - ter - ful and
4. al - le - lu - ia! Ye who long pain and sor - row
5. al - le - lu - ia! Praise, praise the Fa - ther, praise the
1. beam, Thou sil - ver moon with soft - er gleam, O
2. joice, Ye lights of eve - ning, find a voice, O
3. bright, That giv - est man both warmth and light, O
4. bear, Praise God and on him cast your care, O
5. Son, And praise the Spir - it, Three in One. O
1-5. praise him, O praise him! Al - le - lu - ia,
1-5. Al - le - lu - ia, Al - le - lu - ia, Al - le - lu - ia.

Text: St. Francis of Assisi, +1229. Trans. W.H. Draper, +1933.

Tune: *St. Francis,* T. Marier.

104 All Glory Be to God on High

1. All glo - ry be to God on high, The
2. To Je - sus Christ, our Lord and light, E -
3. O Ho - ly Spir - it, wel - come guest, Source
4. O ho - ly Fa - ther, thine al - ways Be
1. Lord of all cre - a - tion, Who
2. ter - nal vi - sion glo - rious, The
3. of life's quick - 'ning pow - ers; Con -
4. thanks and ad - o - ra - tion; To
1. fash - ioned earth, and sea and sky, And
2. hope of ev - 'ry heart con - trite, O'er
3. sol - er, Fa - ther, kind - est, best, Thy
4. Je - sus Lord, be end - less praise For
1. wrought man - kind's sal - va - tion; Sus -
2. death and sin vic - to - rious; To
3. sev'n - fold gift be ours. From
4. this thy great sal - va - tion; O
1. tain - ing life by his com - mand, He gives to all with
2. thee, whose mer - cies all di - vine With grace and love for
3. thee come strength, and peace and light; In - crease in us thy
4. Par - a - clete, we thee a - dore, And sing thy prais - es
1. gen - 'rous hand. To God be praise and glo - ry!
2. us com - bine, Be praise and thanks and glo - ry!
3. ra - diance bright. All laud to thee and glo - ry!
4. ev - er - more: One God of all cre - a - tion.

Text: Verses 1-3, T. Marier.
Verse 4, F.B. MacNutt, +1949, alt.
Tune: *Allen Gott,* N. Decius, +c. 1546.

All Glory Laud and Honor

105

REFRAIN
All glo - ry, laud and hon - or To thee, Re - deem - er,
King! To whom the lips of chil - dren Made
Fine
sweet ho - san - nas ring.
1. Thou art the King of
2. The peo - ple of the
3. To thee be - fore thy
4. Thou didst ac - cept their
1. Is - ra - el, Thou Da - vid's Roy - al Son, Who
2. He - brews With palms be - fore thee went; Our
3. Pas - sion They sang their hymns of praise; To
4. prais - es, Ac - cept the pray'rs we bring, Who
1. in the Lord's name com - est, The
2. praise and pray'r and an - thems Be -
3. thee, now high ex - alt - ed, Our
4. in all good de - light - est, Thou
1. King and Bless - ed One.
2. fore thee we pre - sent.
3. mel - o - dy we raise.
4. kind and gra - cious King.
Repeat Refrain

Text: St. Theodulph, +821. Trans. J.M. Neale, +1866, alt.
Tune: *St. Theodulph,* M. Teschner, +1635.

106 All Nations Clap Your Hands

Ps. 47

1. All na - tions, clap your hands, Let shouts of tri-umph ring,
2. A - bove our might-y foes He gave us pow'r to stand,
3. With shouts as-cends our King, With tri - umph's stir - ring call;
4. O sing in joy - ful strains And make his glo - ry known;
1. For might - y o - ver all the lands The Lord, Most High is King.
2. And as our her - i - tage he chose The rich and prom-ised land.
3. Praise God, praise God, his prais - es sing, For God is Lord of all.
4. God o - ver all the na - tions reigns, And ho - ly is his throne.

Text: Psalm 47 paraphrase, anon., "Psalter Hymnal", 1959 alt.
Tune: *St. Thomas New,* Aaron Williams, +1763.

All People That on Earth Do Dwell 107

Ps. 100

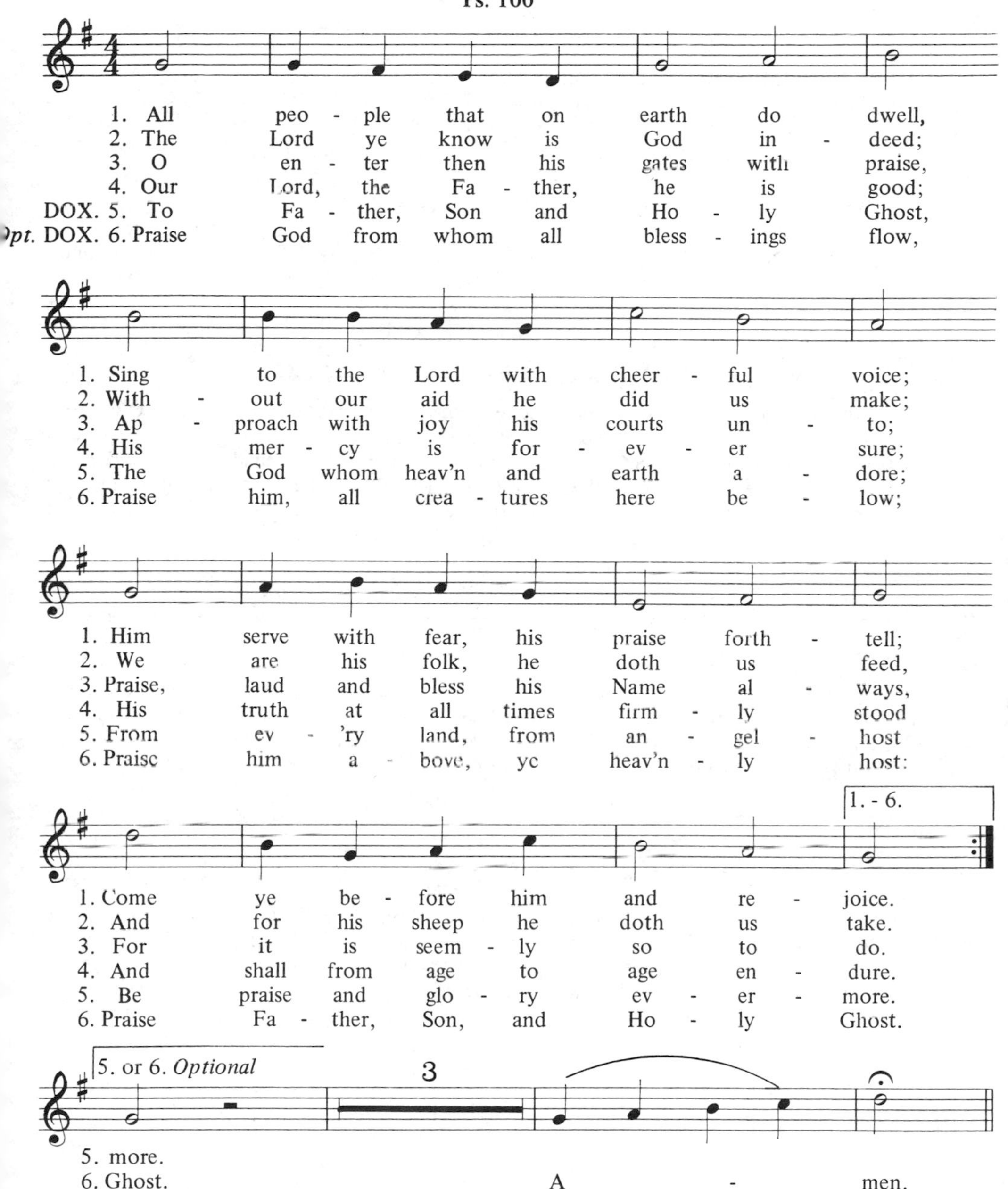
1. All peo - ple that on earth do dwell,
2. The Lord ye know is God in - deed;
3. O en - ter then his gates with praise,
4. Our Lord, the Fa - ther, he is good;
DOX. 5. To Fa - ther, Son and Ho - ly Ghost,
Opt. DOX. 6. Praise God from whom all bless - ings flow,
1. Sing to the Lord with cheer - ful voice;
2. With - out our aid he did us make;
3. Ap - proach with joy his courts un - to;
4. His mer - cy is for - ev - er sure;
5. The God whom heav'n and earth a - dore;
6. Praise him, all crea - tures here be - low;
1. Him serve with fear, his praise forth - tell;
2. We are his folk, he doth us feed,
3. Praise, laud and bless his Name al - ways,
4. His truth at all times firm - ly stood
5. From ev - 'ry land, from an - gel - host
6. Praise him a - bove, ye heav'n - ly host:
1. - 6.
1. Come ye be - fore him and re - joice.
2. And for his sheep he doth us take.
3. For it is seem - ly so to do.
4. And shall from age to age en - dure.
5. Be praise and glo - ry ev - er - more.
6. Praise Fa - ther, Son, and Ho - ly Ghost.
5. or 6. Optional
3
5. more.
6. Ghost. A - men.

Text: Verses 1-4, Psalm 100 paraphrase, W. Keth, +1593, alt.
Verse 5, anon.
Verse 6, T. Ken, +1711.
Tune: *Old Hundredth,* "Genevan Psalter", 1551.

108 All Who Keep the Faith of Jesus

1. All who keep the faith of Je - sus, Sing the won - ders
2. Bless - éd were the cho - sen peo - ple Out of whom the
3. Where - fore let all faith - ful peo - ple Tell the hon - or
4. May the Moth - er's in - ter - ces - sions On our homes a
5. For the sick and for the a - ged, For our dear ones
1. that were done, When the love of God the Fa - ther O'er our
2. Lord did come, Bless - éd was the land of prom - ise Fa - shioned
3. of her name, Let the Church in her fore - shad - owed Part in
4. bless - ing win, That the chil - dren all be pros - pered, Strong and
5. far a - way, For the hearts that mourn in se - cret, All who
1. sin the vic - t'ry won, When he made the Vir - gin
2. for his earth - ly home; But more bless - éd far the
3. her thanks - giv - ing claim; What Christ's Moth - er sang in
4. fair and pure with - in, Fol - low - ing our Lord's own
5. need our prayers to - day, For the faith - ful gone be -
1. Mar - y Moth - er of his on - ly Son. Hail Mar-y, full of grace!
2. Moth - er, She who bare him in her womb. Hail Mar-y, full of grace!
3. glad - ness Let Christ's peo - ple sing the same. Hail Mar-y, full of grace!
4. foot - steps, Firm in faith and free from sin. Hail Mar-y, full of grace!
5. fore us, May the ho - ly Vir - gin pray. Hail Mar-y, full of grace!

Text: V.S.S. Coles, +1929.
Tune: *Den des Vaters Sinn geboren,* J.A. Freylinghausen, +1739.

All Ye Peoples, Bless the Lord

Ps. 66

1. All ye peo - ples, bless the Lord; Al - le - lu - ia!
2. Praise the Lord with joy - ful cry. Al - le - lu - ia!
3. Praise the Lord, the might - y one! Al - le - lu - ia!
4. All who know and love the Lord, Al - le - lu - ia!
5. O be joy - ful in the Lord; Al - le - lu - ia!

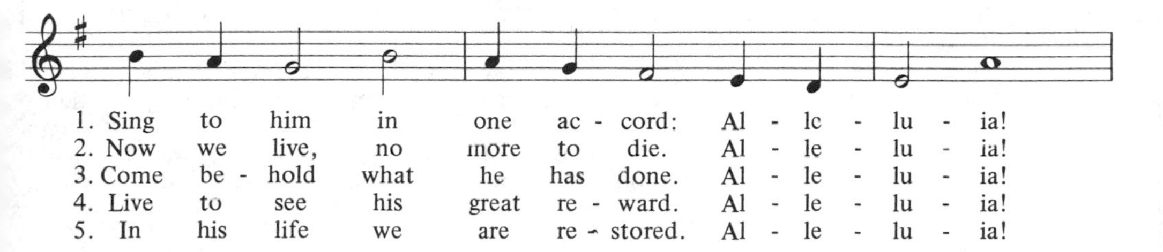
1. Sing to him in one ac - cord: Al - le - lu - ia!
2. Now we live, no more to die. Al - le - lu - ia!
3. Come be - hold what he has done. Al - le - lu - ia!
4. Live to see his great re - ward. Al - le - lu - ia!
5. In his life we are re - stored. Al - le - lu - ia!

1. All the earth his pow'r pro-claim; Shout the glo - ries of his name.
2. His ma - jes - tic strength re - vere; See his foes all bow in fear.
3. By the pow - ers of his hand Sea was changed in - to dry land.
4. In his love he hears our pray'r That his grace, with us, he'll share.
5. All ye thank - ful na - tions raise Hymns and psalms of glo - rious praise.

1-5. Al - le - lu - ia! Al - le - lu - ia! Al - le - lu - ia!

Text: Psalm 66 paraphrase, J. Dunn.
Tune: *Chislehurst,* S.H. Nicholson, +1947.

Alleluia, Alleluia! Sing a New Song to the Lord

Ps. 98

1. Al - le - lu - ia, Al - le - lu - ia! Sing a new song
2. Al - le - lu - ia, Al - le - lu - ia! He has made sal -
3. Al - le - lu - ia, Al - le - lu - ia! Psalms of cel - e -
4. Al - le - lu - ia, Al - le - lu - ia! Riv - ers, seas and
5. Al - le - lu - ia, Al - le - lu - ia! Glo - ry to th'In -

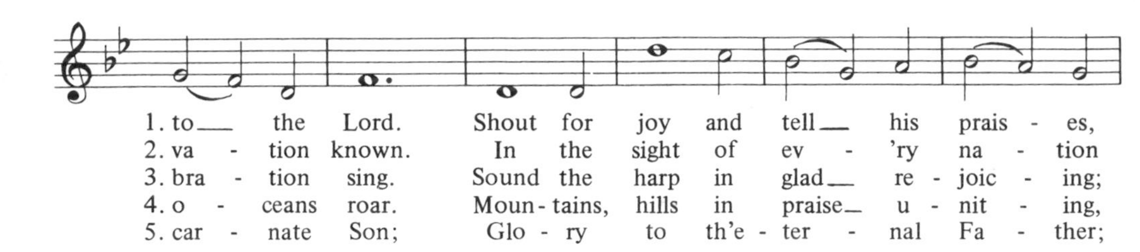
1. to__ the Lord. Shout for joy and tell__ his prais - es,
2. va - tion known. In the sight of ev - 'ry na - tion
3. bra - tion sing. Sound the harp in glad__ re - joic - ing;
4. o - ceans roar. Moun - tains, hills in praise__ u - nit - ing,
5. car - nate Son; Glo - ry to th'e - ter - nal Fa - ther;

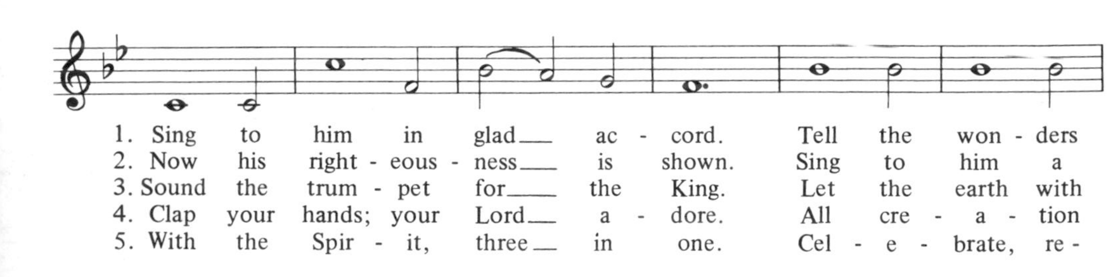
1. Sing to him in glad__ ac - cord. Tell the won - ders
2. Now his right - eous - ness__ is shown. Sing to him a
3. Sound the trum - pet for__ the King. Let the earth with
4. Clap your hands; your Lord__ a - dore. All cre - a - tion
5. With the Spir - it, three__ in one. Cel - e - brate, re -

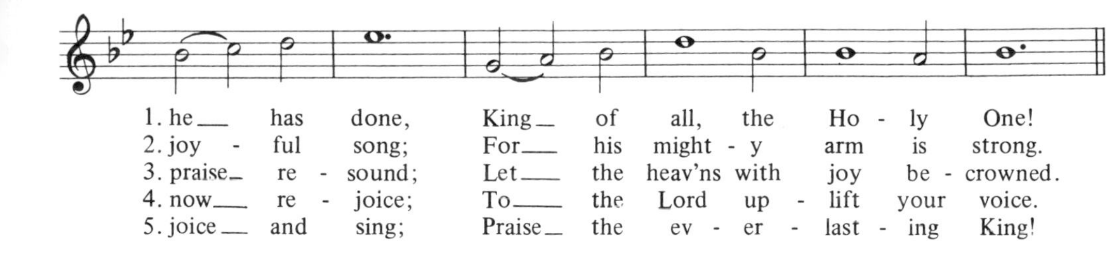
1. he__ has done, King__ of all, the Ho - ly One!
2. joy - ful song; For__ his might - y arm is strong.
3. praise__ re - sound; Let__ the heav'ns with joy be - crowned.
4. now__ re - joice; To__ the Lord up - lift your voice.
5. joice__ and sing; Praise__ the ev - er - last - ing King!

Text: Psalm 98 paraphrase, J. Dunn.
Tune: *Bryn myrddin,* J. Morgan Nicholas.

Alleluia! Sing to Jesus

First Tune
1. Al - le - lu - ia! Sing to Je - sus! His the scep - ter, his the
2. Al - le - lu - ia! Not as or - phans Are we left in sor - row
3. Al - le - lu - ia! Bread of heav - en, Thou on earth our food and
4. Al - le - lu - ia! King e - ter - nal, Thee the Lord of lords we
1. throne; Al - le - lu - ia! His the tri - umph, His the vic - to -
2. now. Al - le - lu - ia! He is near us, Faith be - lieves, nor
3. stay! Al - le - lu - ia! Here the sin - ful Call on thee from
4. own. Al - le - lu - ia! Born of Mar - y, Earth thy foot - stool,
1. ry a - lone. Hark! the songs of peace - ful Si - on Thun - der
2. ques - tions how; Though the cloud from sight re - ceived him When the
3. day to day. In - ter - ces - sor, friend of sin - ners, Earth's Re -
4. heav'n thy throne. Thou with - in the veil hast en - tered, Robed in
1. like a might - y flood: Je - sus out of ev - 'ry
2. for - ty days were o'er, Shall our hearts for - get his
3. deem - er, hear our cry, That we dwell with thee for -
4. flesh, our great High Priest, Thou on earth both Priest and
1. na - tion Hath re - deemed us by his blood.
2. prom - ise, "I am with you ev - er - more"?
3. ev - er, Thou the Lord of Hosts, Most High.
4. Vic - tim In the Eu - cha - ris - tic feast.

Text: W. Chatterton Dix, +1898, alt.
Tune: *Rustington,* Sir C.H.H. Parry, +1918.

112 Alleluia! Sing to Jesus

Second Tune
1. Al - le - lu - ia! Sing to Je - sus! His the
2. Al - le - lu - ia! Not as or - phans Are we
3. Al - le - lu - ia! Bread of heav - en, Thou on
4. Al - le - lu - ia! King e - ter - nal, Thee the
1. scep - ter, his the throne; Al - le - lu - ia! His the
2. left in sor - row now. Al - le - lu - ia! He is
3. earth our food and stay. Al - le - lu - ia! Here the
4. Lord of lords we own. Al - le - lu - ia! Born of
1. tri - umph, His the vic - to - ry a - lone. Hark! the
2. near us, Faith be - lieves, nor ques - tions how; Though the
3. sin - ful Call on thee from day to day. In - ter -
4. Mar - y, Earth thy foot - stool, heav'n thy throne. Thou with-
1. songs of peace - ful Si - on Thun - der like a
2. cloud from sight re - ceived him When the for - ty
3. ces - sor, friend of sin - ners, Earth's Re - deem - er,
4. in the veil hast en - tered, Robed in flesh, our
1. might - y flood: Je - sus out of ev - 'ry
2. days were o'er, Shall our hearts for - get his
3. hear our cry, That we dwell with thee for
4. great High Priest: Thou on earth both Priest and
1. na - tion Hath re - deemed us by his blood.
2. prom - ise, "I am with you ev - er - more"?
3. ev - er, Thou the Lord of Hosts, Most High.
4. Vic - tim In the Eu - cha - ris - tic Feast.

Text: W. Chatterton Dix, +1898, alt.
Tune: *Hyfrydol*, R.H. Prichard, +1887.

Angels We Have Heard on High

1. An - gels we have heard on high,
2. Shep - herds, why this ju - bi - lee?
3. Come to Beth - le - hem and see
4. See him in a man - ger laid,
1. Sweet - ly sing - ing o'er the plains, And the moun - tains
2. Why your glad - some strain pro - long? Say what may the
3. Him, whose birth the an - gels sing; Come, a - dore on
4. Whom the choirs of an - gels praise. Mar - y, Jo - seph,
1. in re - ply, Ech - o still their joy - ous strains.
2. ti - dings be, Which in - spire your heav'n - ly song?
3. bend - ed knee, Th'In - fant Christ, the new - born King.
4. lend your aid, While our hearts in love we raise.
REFRAIN
1.-4. Glo - - - - - - - - - - ri - a in ex - cel - sis De - o!
Glo - - - - - - - - - - ri - a in ex - cel - sis De - o!

Text: Verses 1-3, anon. Traditional French Carol.
Verse 4, J. Dunn. © by author. Used with permission.
Tune: *Gloria,* French Noel.

114 As With Gladness Men of Old

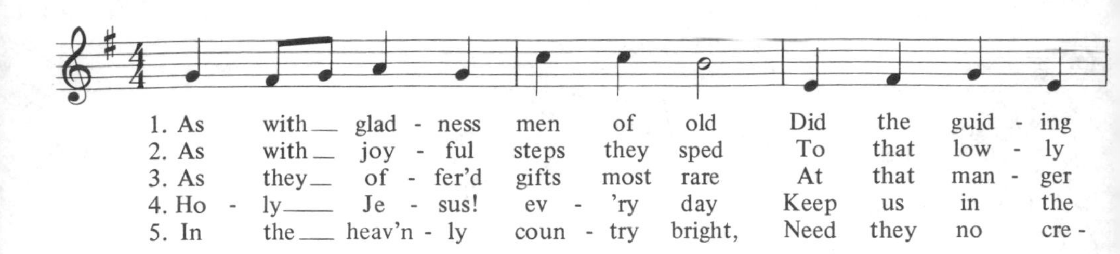
1. As with glad - ness men of old Did the guid - ing
2. As with joy - ful steps they sped To that low - ly
3. As they of - fer'd gifts most rare At that man - ger
4. Ho - ly Je - sus! ev - 'ry day Keep us in the
5. In the heav'n - ly coun - try bright, Need they no cre -

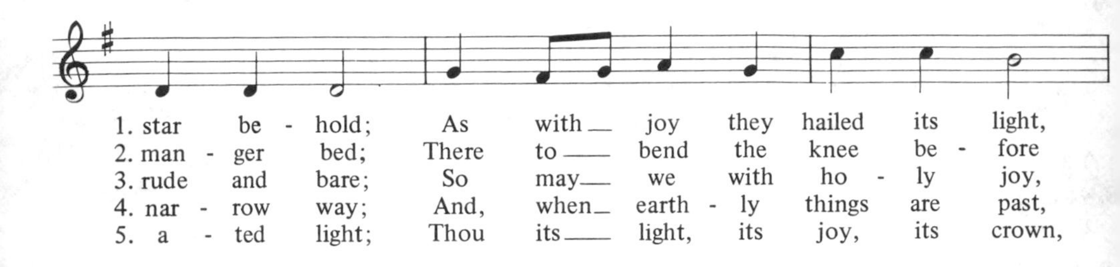
1. star be - hold; As with joy they hailed its light,
2. man - ger bed; There to bend the knee be - fore
3. rude and bare; So may we with ho - ly joy,
4. nar - row way; And, when earth - ly things are past,
5. a - ted light; Thou its light, its joy, its crown,

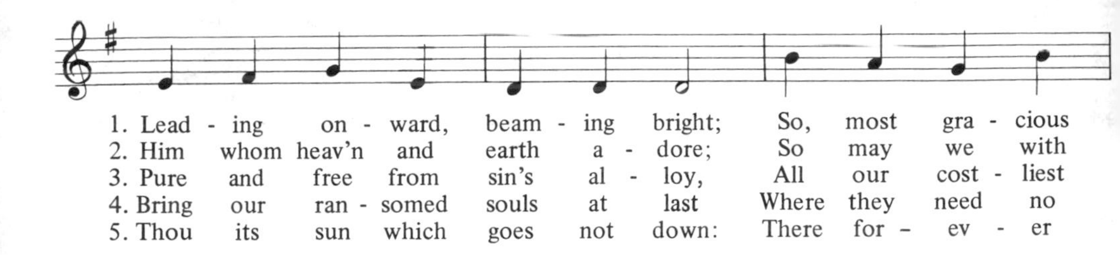
1. Lead - ing on - ward, beam - ing bright; So, most gra - cious
2. Him whom heav'n and earth a - dore; So may we with
3. Pure and free from sin's al - loy, All our cost - liest
4. Bring our ran - somed souls at last Where they need no
5. Thou its sun which goes not down: There for - ev - er

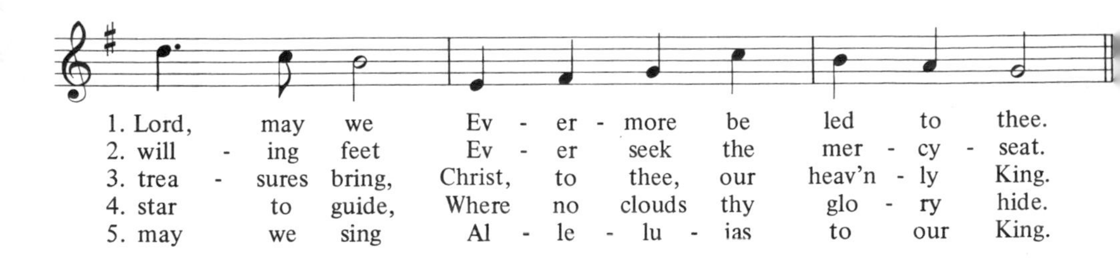
1. Lord, may we Ev - er - more be led to thee.
2. will - ing feet Ev - er seek the mer - cy - seat.
3. trea - sures bring, Christ, to thee, our heav'n - ly King.
4. star to guide, Where no clouds thy glo - ry hide.
5. may we sing Al - le - lu - ias to our King.

Text: W. Chatterton Dix, +1898.
Tune: *Dix*, C. Kocher, +1872.

At the Cross Her Station Keeping **115**

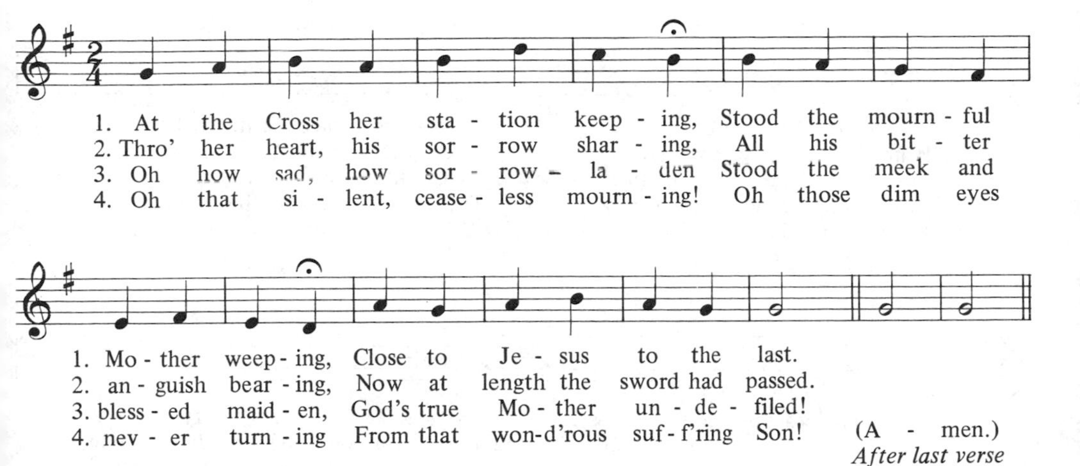
1. At the Cross her sta - tion keep - ing, Stood the mourn - ful
2. Thro' her heart, his sor - row shar - ing, All his bit - ter
3. Oh how sad, how sor - row – la - den Stood the meek and
4. Oh that si - lent, cease - less mourn - ing! Oh those dim eyes
1. Mo - ther weep - ing, Close to Je - sus to the last.
2. an - guish bear - ing, Now at length the sword had passed.
3. bless - ed maid - en, God's true Mo - ther un - de - filed!
4. nev - er turn - ing From that won-d'rous suf - f'ring Son!
(A - men.)
After last verse

5. For the sins of his own nation,
Saw him hang in desolation,
Bleed in torments, bleed and die!

6. Saw the Lord's Anointed taken;
Saw her child in death forsaken;
Heard his last expiring cry.

7. Those Five Wounds of Jesus smitten,
Mother, in my heart be written,
Deeply as in thine they be.

8. Thou, my Savior's cross who bearest,
Thou, thy Son's rebukes who sharest,
Let me share them both with thee.

9. In the Passion of my Maker
Be my sinful soul partaker,
Weep till death, and weep with thee.

10. Mine with thee be that sad station,
There to watch the great salvation
Wrought upon th'atoning Tree.

11. Virgin thou of virgins fairest,
May the bitter woe thou sharest
Make on me impression deep.

12. Thus Christ dying may I carry,
With him in his Passion tarry,
And his wounds in mem'ry keep.

13. May his wounds transfix me wholly,
May his cross and life-blood holy
Ebriate my heart and mind.

14. Thus inflam'd with pure affection
In the Virgin's Son protection
May I at the Judgment find.

15. When in death my limbs are failing,
Let his Mother's pray'r prevailing
Lift me, Jesus, to thy throne.

16. To my parting soul be given
Entrance through the gate of Heaven,
There confess me for thine own. A-men.

Text: *Stabat Mater,* ascribed to Jacopone da Todi, +1306. Trans. E. Caswall, +1878.
Tune: *Mainz,* anon., 1661.

116 At the Name of Jesus

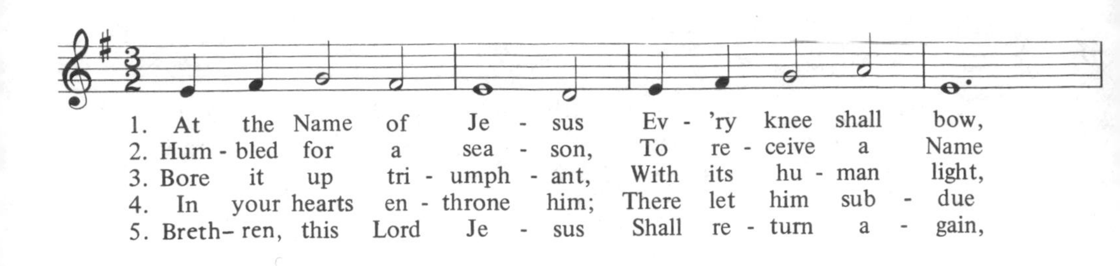
1. At the Name of Je - sus Ev - 'ry knee shall bow,
2. Hum - bled for a sea - son, To re - ceive a Name
3. Bore it up tri - umph - ant, With its hu - man light,
4. In your hearts en - throne him; There let him sub - due
5. Breth- ren, this Lord Je - sus Shall re - turn a - gain,

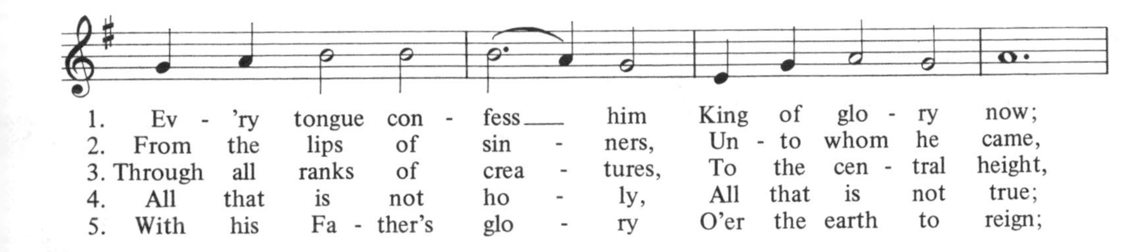
1. Ev - 'ry tongue con - fess___ him King of glo - ry now;
2. From the lips of sin - ners, Un - to whom he came,
3. Through all ranks of crea - tures, To the cen - tral height,
4. All that is not ho - ly, All that is not true;
5. With his Fa - ther's glo - ry O'er the earth to reign;

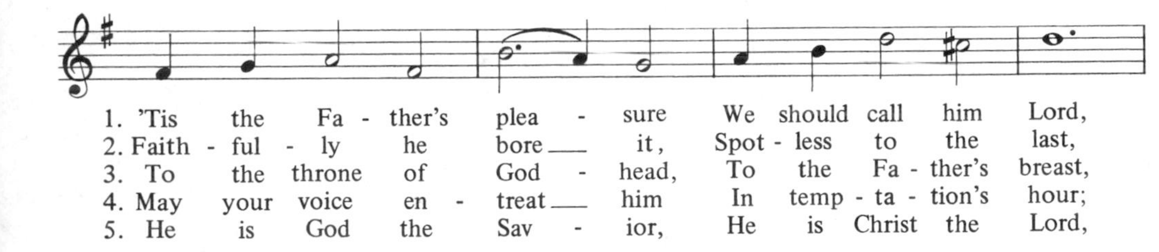
1. 'Tis the Fa - ther's plea - sure We should call him Lord,
2. Faith - ful - ly he bore___ it, Spot - less to the last,
3. To the throne of God - head, To the Fa - ther's breast,
4. May your voice en - treat___ him In temp - ta - tion's hour;
5. He is God the Sav - ior, He is Christ the Lord,

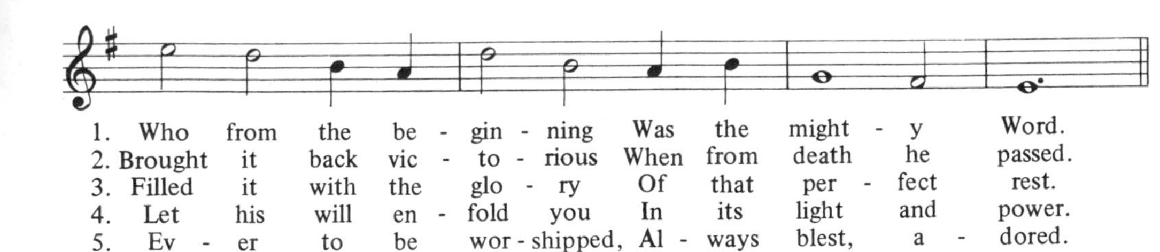
1. Who from the be - gin - ning Was the might - y Word.
2. Brought it back vic - to - rious When from death he passed.
3. Filled it with the glo - ry Of that per - fect rest.
4. Let his will en - fold you In its light and power.
5. Ev - er to be wor - shipped, Al - ways blest, a - dored.

Text: C. Noel, +1877, alt.
Tune: *King's Weston*, R. Vaughan Williams, +1958. From "Enlarged Songs of Praise", Oxford University Press. Used by permission.

Ave Maria

117

A - ve Ma - rí - a,* grá - ti - a ple - na, Dó - mi - nus te - cum,
Hail Mary, full of grace, the Lord is with thee,

be - ne - dí - cta tu in mu - li - é - ri - bus, et be -
blessed art thou among women, and

ne - dí - ctus fru - ctus ven - tris tu - i, Je - sus. San - cta Ma -
blessed is the fruit of thy womb, Jesus. Holy Mary,

rí - a, Ma - ter De - i, o - ra pro no - bis pec - ca - tó - ri - bus,
Mother of God, pray for us sinners,

nunc et in ho - ra mor - tis no - strae. A - men.
now and at the hour of our death. Amen.

Text: St. Luke's Gospel and tradition.
Tune: Plainchant, Mode 1.

118 Ave Verum Corpus

1.
2.

A - ve ve-rum Cor-pus na-tum de Ma-rí - a Vír - gi - ne:__
Ve - re pas-sum, im-mo-lá-tum in cru-ce pro hó - mi - ne:__

Hail, true body, born of the Virgin Mary:
Truly suffered, died on the cross for mankind:

1.
2.

Cu-jus la-tus per - fo- rá - tum flu - xit __ a - qua_ et _ sán - gui-ne.__
Es-to no-bis prae-gu-stá - tum mor - tis __ in _ ex - á - mi - ne:_

From whose pierced side flowed water and blood!
Be for us a foretaste of death in the last hour!

O____ Je - su dul - cis! O____ Je - su pi - e!

O gentle Jesus! *O holy Jesus!*

O________ Je - su, fi - li __ Ma - rí - ae!___

O Jesus, Son of Mary!

Text: Ascribed to Innocent VI, +1362.
Tune: Plainchant, Mode 6.

Baptized into Your Name Most Holy

1. Bap - tized in - to your Name most_ ho - ly, O Fa - ther, Son, and
2. My lov - ing Fa - ther, here you_ take me Hence-forth to be your
3. O faith - ful God, you nev - er___ fail me; Your cov-'nant sure - ly
4. All that I am and love most_ dear - ly, Re - ceive it all, O

1. Ho - ly Ghost, I claim a place, though weak and___ low - ly,
2. child and heir; My faith - ful Sav - ior, here you___ make me
3. will a - bide. Let not e - ter - nal death as - sail me
4. Lord, from me. O let me make my vows sin - cere - ly,

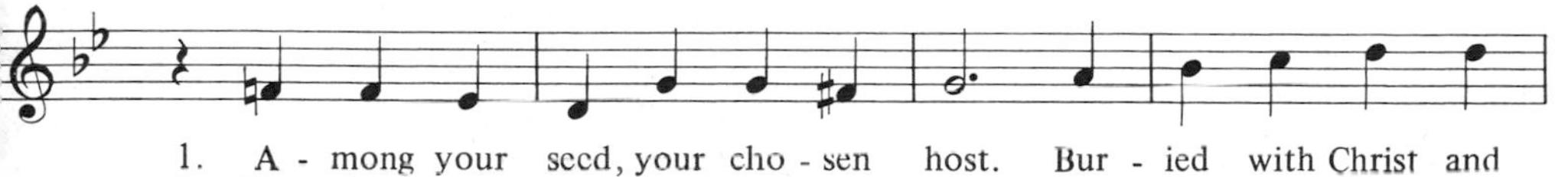
1. A - mong your seed, your cho - sen host. Bur - ied with Christ and
2. The fruit of all your sor - rows share; O Ho - ly Ghost, you
3. Should I trans - gress it on my side! Have mer - 'cy when I
4. And help me your own child to be! Let noth - ing that I

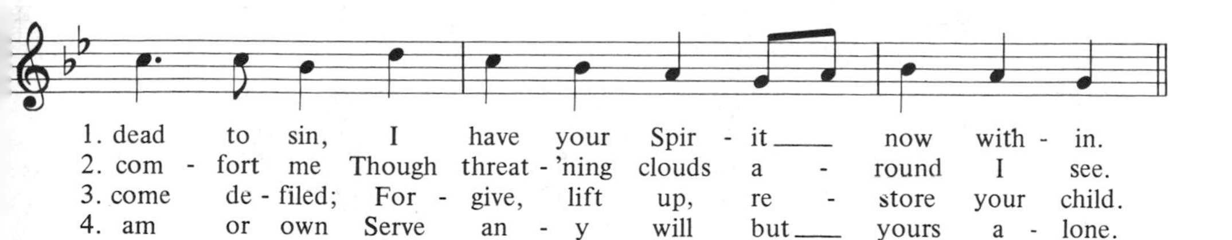
1. dead to sin, I have your Spir - it___ now with - in.
2. com - fort me Though threat - 'ning clouds a - round I see.
3. come de - filed; For - give, lift up, re - store your child.
4. am or own Serve an - y will but___ yours a - lone.

Text: J.J. Rambach, +1735. Trans. C. Winkworth, +1878, alt.
Tune: *Wer nur den lieben Gott, G.* Neumark, +1681.

120 Before the Lord We Bow

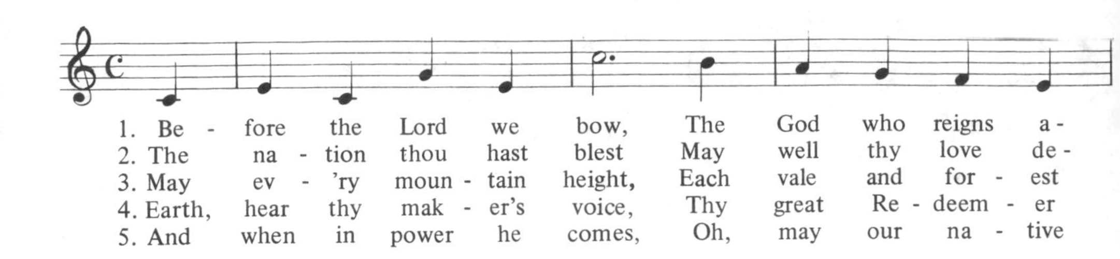
1. Be - fore the Lord we bow, The God who reigns a -
2. The na - tion thou hast blest May well thy love de -
3. May ev - 'ry moun - tain height, Each vale and for - est
4. Earth, hear thy mak - er's voice, Thy great Re - deem - er
5. And when in power he comes, Oh, may our na - tive

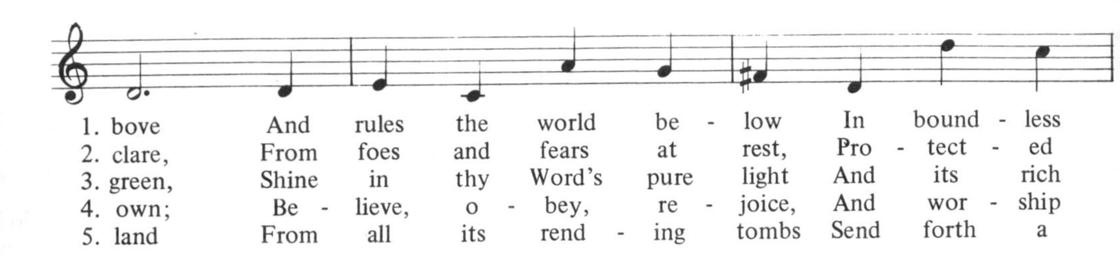
1. bove And rules the world be - low In bound - less
2. clare, From foes and fears at rest, Pro - tect - ed
3. green, Shine in thy Word's pure light And its rich
4. own; Be - lieve, o - bey, re - joice, And wor - ship
5. land From all its rend - ing tombs Send forth a

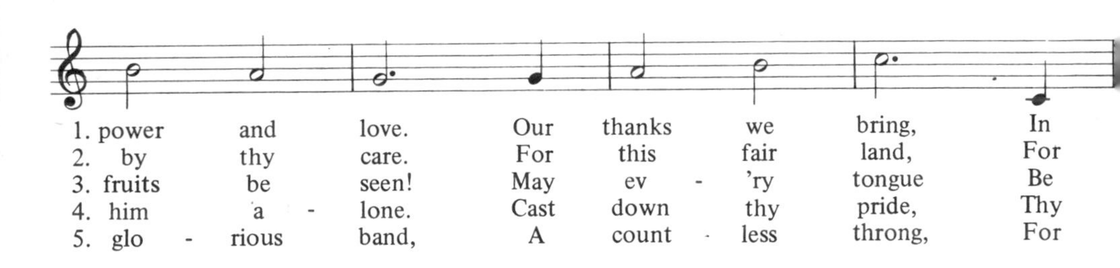
1. power and love. Our thanks we bring, In
2. by thy care. For this fair land, For
3. fruits be seen! May ev - 'ry tongue Be
4. him a - lone. Cast down thy pride, Thy
5. glo - rious band, A count - less throng, For

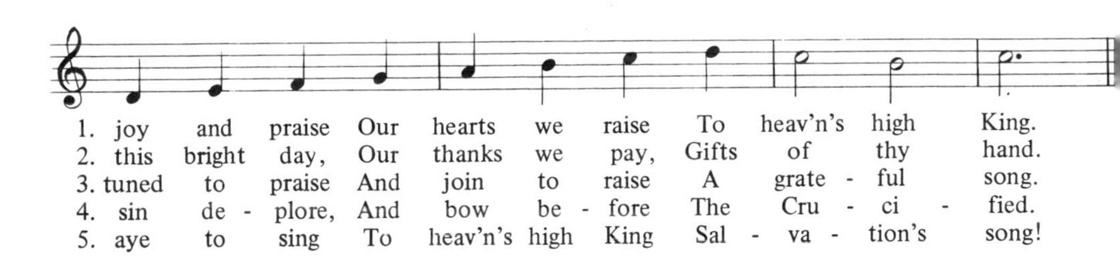
1. joy and praise Our hearts we raise To heav'n's high King.
2. this bright day, Our thanks we pay, Gifts of thy hand.
3. tuned to praise And join to raise A grate - ful song.
4. sin de - plore, And bow be - fore The Cru - ci - fied.
5. aye to sing To heav'n's high King Sal - va - tion's song!

Text: Francis Scott Key, +1843.
Tune: *Darwall's 148th,* J. Darwall, +1789.

Be Thou My Vision

1. Be thou my vi - sion,___ O Lord of my heart;
2. Be thou my wis - dom,_______ thou, my true Word;
3. Be thou my bat - tle - shield,__ sword for the fight.
4. Rich - es I need not____ nor man's emp - ty praise,
5. Heart of my own heart,___ what - ev - er be - fall,

1. Naught is all else to me___ save that thou art.
2. I ev - er with thee,_______ thou with me, Lord.
3. Be thou my dig - ni - ty,___ thou my de - light.
4. Thou my in - her - i - tance,__ now and al - ways.
5. Still be my vi - sion,___ O Rul - er of all.

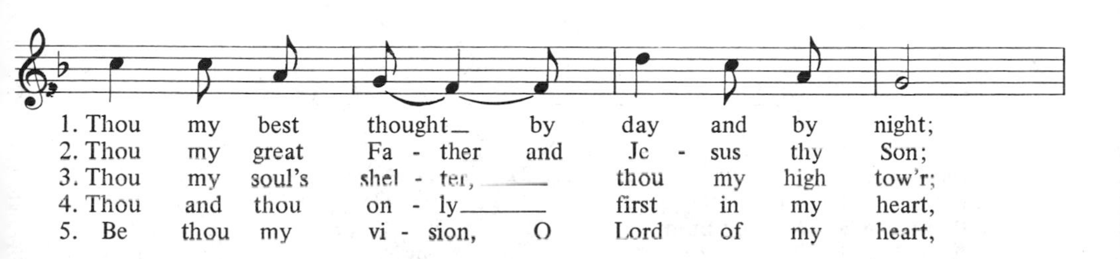
1. Thou my best thought__ by day and by night;
2. Thou my great Fa - ther and Je - sus thy Son;
3. Thou my soul's shel - ter,____ thou my high tow'r;
4. Thou and thou on - ly______ first in my heart,
5. Be thou my vi - sion, O Lord of my heart,

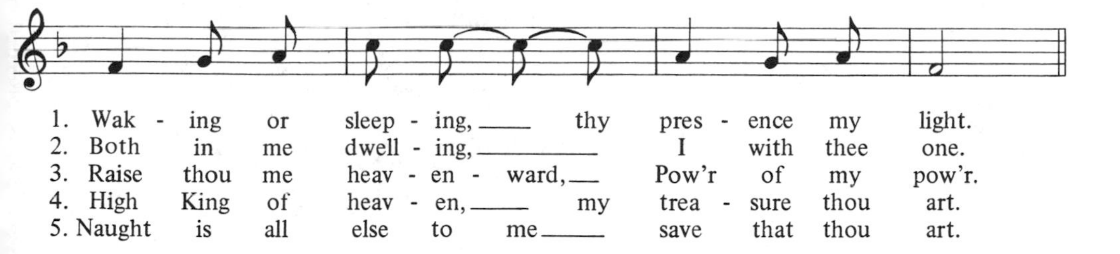
1. Wak - ing or sleep - ing,___ thy pres - ence my light.
2. Both in me dwell - ing,_______ I with thee one.
3. Raise thou me heav - en - ward,__ Pow'r of my pow'r.
4. High King of heav - en,_____ my trea - sure thou art.
5. Naught is all else to me_____ save that thou art.

Text: Ancient Gaelic, trans. E. Hull, +1935, alt.
Tune: *Desrocquettes,* J.H. Desrocquettes, +1974.

122

Blessed Be God

Divine Praises

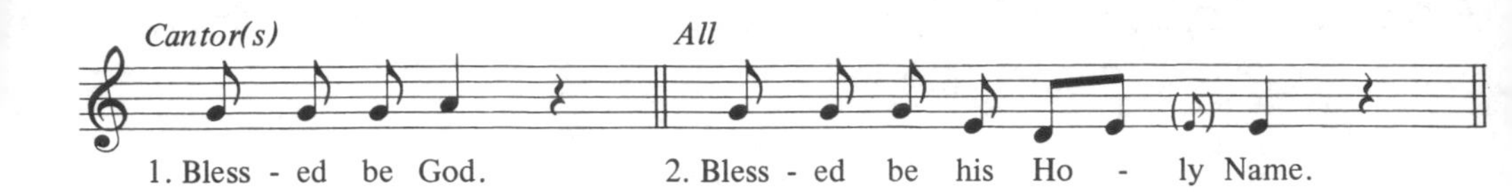

Cantor(s)
All
1. Bless - ed be God.
2. Bless - ed be his Ho - ly Name.

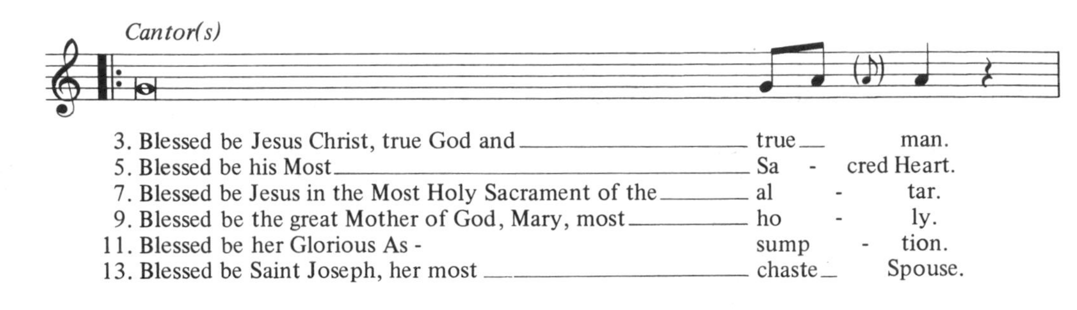

Cantor(s)
3. Blessed be Jesus Christ, true God and true man.
5. Blessed be his Most Sa - cred Heart.
7. Blessed be Jesus in the Most Holy Sacrament of the al - tar.
9. Blessed be the great Mother of God, Mary, most ho - ly.
11. Blessed be her Glorious As - sump - tion.
13. Blessed be Saint Joseph, her most chaste Spouse.

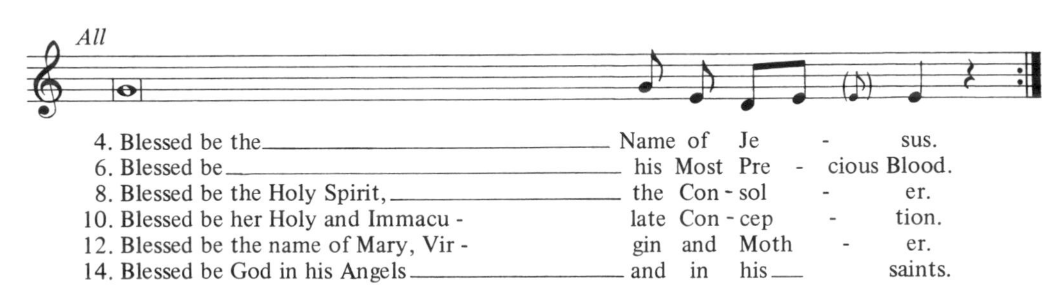

All
4. Blessed be the Name of Je - sus.
6. Blessed be his Most Pre - cious Blood.
8. Blessed be the Holy Spirit, the Con - sol - er.
10. Blessed be her Holy and Immacu - late Con - cep - tion.
12. Blessed be the name of Mary, Vir - gin and Moth - er.
14. Blessed be God in his Angels and in his saints.

Text: Anon.
Tune: *Divine Praises,* T. Marier.

Blest Are the Pure in Heart **123**

1. Blest are the pure in heart, For they shall see our God;
2. The Lord, once left the throne Our life and peace to bring,
3. Still to the hum - ble soul He will him - self im - part,
4. We seek thy pres - ence, Lord, May ours this bless - ing be:

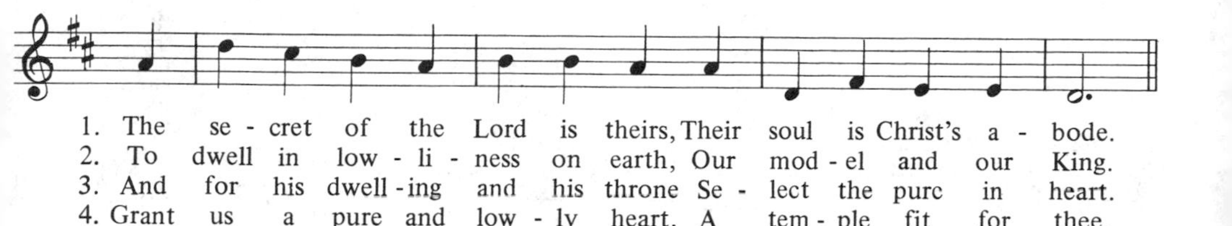
1. The se - cret of the Lord is theirs, Their soul is Christ's a - bode.
2. To dwell in low - li - ness on earth, Our mod - el and our King.
3. And for his dwell - ing and his throne Se - lect the pure in heart.
4. Grant us a pure and low - ly heart, A tem - ple fit for thee.

Text: J. Keble, +1866, alt.
Tune: *Franconia,* J. Koenig, +1759, from "Choralbuch" of 1738.

Bread of Heav'n, on Thee We Feed

1. Bread of heav'n, on thee we feed,
2. Vine of heav'n, thy Blood sup - plies
1. For thy Flesh brings life in - deed;
2. This blest cup of Sac - ri - fice;
1. Ev - er may our souls be fed
2. Lord, thy wounds our heal - ing give,
1. With this true and liv - ing Bread,
2. To thy Cross we look and live:
1. Day by day with strength sup - plied
2. Je - sus, may we ev - er be
1. Through the life of him who died.
2. Thine in love e - ter - nal - ly.

Text: J. Conder, +1855, alt.
Tune: *Gott des Himmels und der Erden*, H. Albert, +1642.

Breathe on Me, Breath of God

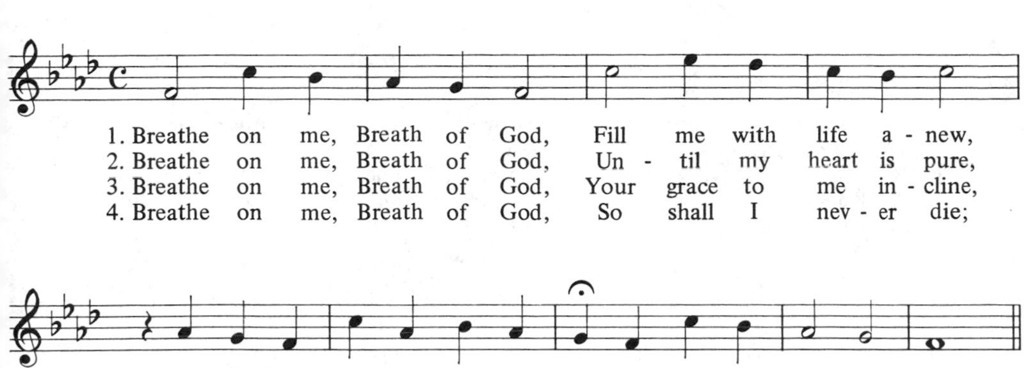
1. Breathe on me, Breath of God, Fill me with life a - new,
2. Breathe on me, Breath of God, Un - til my heart is pure,
3. Breathe on me, Breath of God, Your grace to me in - cline,
4. Breathe on me, Breath of God, So shall I nev - er die;
1. That I may love all that you love, And do what you would do.
2. Un - til with you I have one will To do and to en - dure.
3. Till all this earth - ly part of me Glows with your fire di - vine.
4. But live with you the per - fect life Of your e - ter - ni - ty.

Text: E. Hatch, +1889, alt.
Tune: *Aylesbury*, J. Chetham, +1746, in "Psalms", 1718.

Break Forth, O Beauteous Heav'nly Light

1. Break forth, O beau - teous heav'n - ly light, And ush - er in the
2. O won-drous work,_ O won-drous night, All else so far ex -
3. O Je - su, wel - come gra - cious name, All hail, blest King of
4. My heart is full__ and I must sing, My heart with praise is
1. morn - ing; Ye shep - herds, shrink_ not with af - fright, But
2. cel - ling; The Sav - ior now,__ un - veiled to sight, On
3. glo - ry! O Je - su, wel - come, Ho - ly Lamb, With
4. swell - ing; And I must sing__ un - to the King A
1. hear the an - gel's warn - ing. This Child now weak in
2. earth as man is dwell - ing: That man to whom a -
3. praise I will a - dore thee. To thee my praise I
4. song his hon - or tell - ing. O fair - er thou than
1. in - fan - cy, Our con - fi - dence_ and joy shall be, The
2. lone__ is giv'n Pow'r o'er the lights,_ the clouds of heav'n, The
3. will__ pro - long, To thee my ev - er thank - ful song; Who
4. mor - tal race, Thy lips o'er - flow__ with heav'n - ly grace, And
1. pow'r of Sa - tan break - ing, Our peace e - ter - nal__ mak - ing.
2. trem-bling heav'ns a - dore him! The moun-tains shake be - fore him.
3. hast our na - ture tak - en, Else of all hope for - sak - en.
4. so thou art con - fess - ed Of God for - ev - er__ bless - ed.

Text: Verse 1, J. Rist, +1667. Trans. J.J. Troutbeck, +1889.
Verses 2-4, A.T. Russell, +1874.
Tune: *Ermuntre dich,* J. Schop, +1664.

Christ Be My Leader

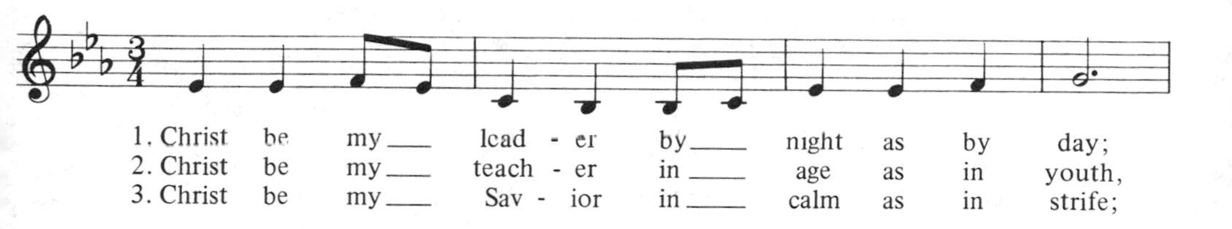
1. Christ be my leader by night as by day;
2. Christ be my teacher in age as in youth,
3. Christ be my Savior in calm as in strife;

1. Safe through the darkness for he is the way.
2. Drifting or doubting, for he is the truth.
3. Death cannot hold me for he is the life. Nor

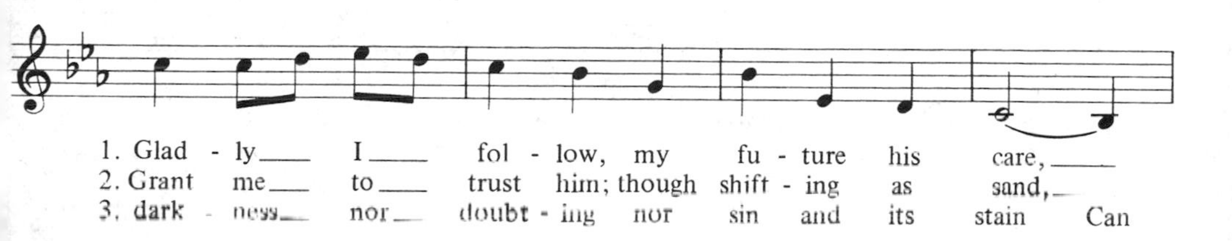
1. Gladly I follow, my future his care,
2. Grant me to trust him; though shifting as sand,
3. darkness nor doubting nor sin and its stain Can

1. Darkness is daylight when Jesus is there.
2. Doubt cannot daunt me in Jesus I stand.
3. touch my salvation: with Jesus I reign.

Text: T. Dudley Smith.
Tune: *Slane,* Irish Folk Melody.

128 Christ Is Made the Sure Foundation

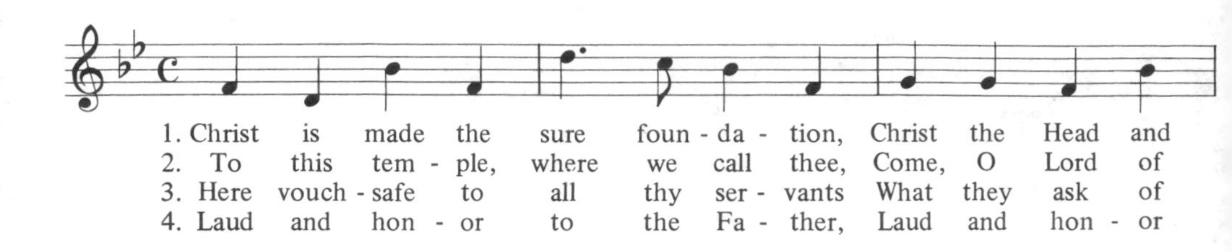
1. Christ is made the sure foun - da - tion, Christ the Head and
2. To this tem - ple, where we call thee, Come, O Lord of
3. Here vouch - safe to all thy ser - vants What they ask of
4. Laud and hon - or to the Fa - ther, Laud and hon - or

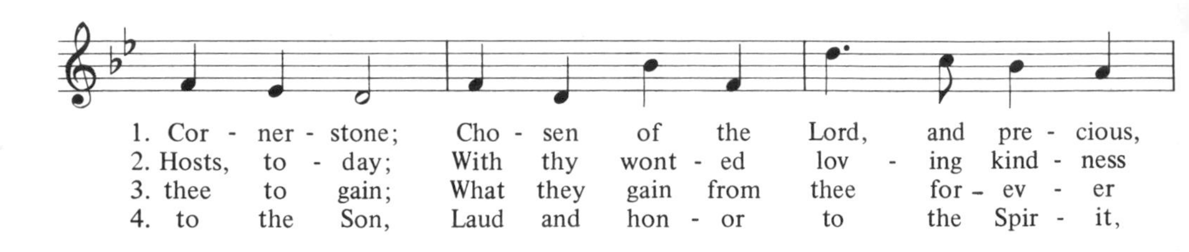
1. Cor - ner - stone; Cho - sen of the Lord, and pre - cious,
2. Hosts, to - day; With thy wont - ed lov - ing kind - ness
3. thee to gain; What they gain from thee for - ev - er
4. to the Son, Laud and hon - or to the Spir - it,

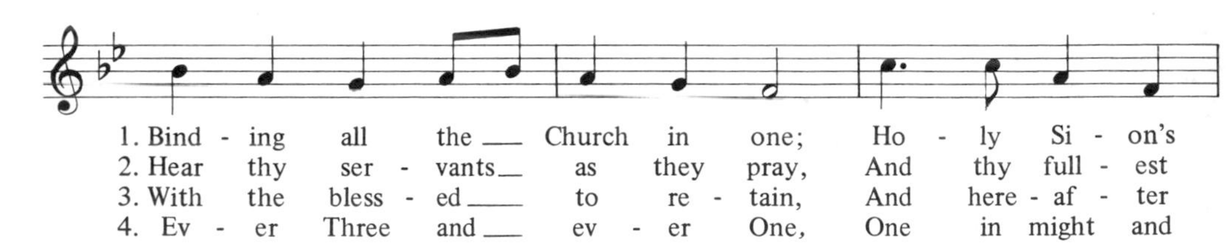
1. Bind - ing all the __ Church in one; Ho - ly Si - on's
2. Hear thy ser - vants __ as they pray, And thy full - est
3. With the bless - ed __ to re - tain, And here - af - ter
4. Ev - er Three and __ ev - er One, One in might and

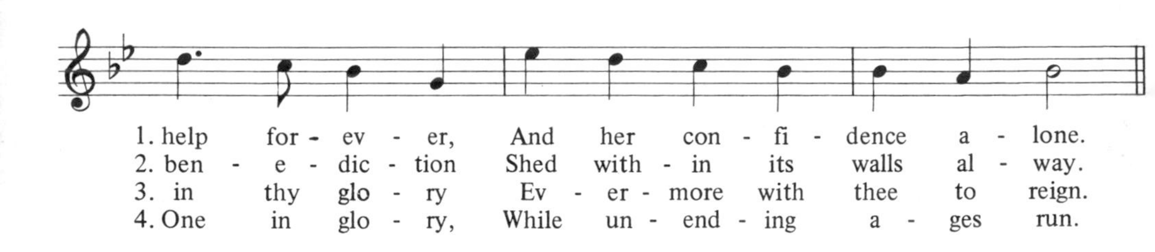
1. help for - ev - er, And her con - fi - dence a - lone.
2. ben - e - dic - tion Shed with - in its walls al - way.
3. in thy glo - ry Ev - er - more with thee to reign.
4. One in glo - ry, While un - end - ing a - ges run.

Text: *Angelarius fundamentum,* 7th Century, anon. Trans. J.M. Neale, +1866, alt.
Tune: *Regent Square,* H. Smart, +1879.

Christ, Lord of Glory

Schola Christ, Lord of glo - ry.
All Christ, Prince of na - tions. Christ, our King of kings!
Schola Christ Je - sus, hear us.
All Per - pet - ual safe - ty and wel - fare to the Church of God.
Schola Re - deem - er, Sav - ior.
All As - sist and strength - en her.
1.2.
3.
Schola
All
1. Mar - y, bless - ed Moth - er, As - sist and strength - en her.
2. Jo - seph, ho - ly guard - ian, As - sist and strength - en her.
3. Bless - ed Mi - chael, pa - tron, As - sist and strength - en her.
Schola Christ, Lord of glo - ry.

Continued on next page

All Christ, Prince of na - tions. Christ, our King of kings!
Schola To him on - ly is vic - to - ry, all praise and ju - bi - la - tion
through all the end - less a - ges of e - ter - ni - ty.
All A - men.
Schola A - bun-dance of good things be ours.
All The peace of Christ_ be ours.
Schola Re - deemed by the blood of Je - sus.
All Pro - claim_our joy. Pro - claim_our joy. Pro - claim_our joy.
Schola
May his ho - ly king - dom come.
All
Praise be to our God!_ A - men.

Text: 8th Century Acclamations. Trans. C.J. McNaspy and J. Nolan.

Tune: *Christus Rex*, 9th Century Ambrosian Chant.

Christ Is the World's Light

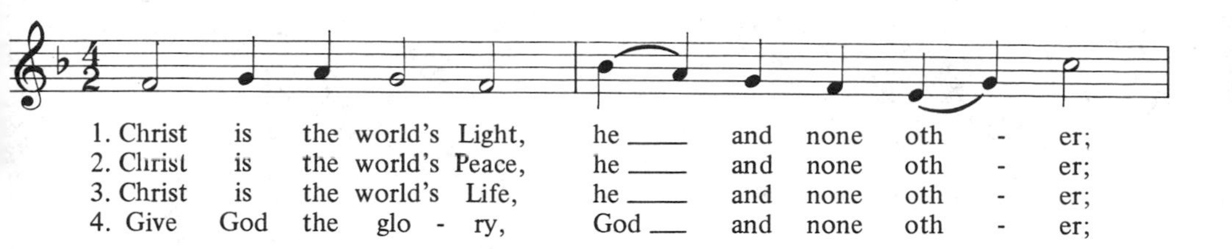
1. Christ is the world's Light, he ___ and none oth - er;
2. Christ is the world's Peace, he ___ and none oth - er;
3. Christ is the world's Life, he ___ and none oth - er;
4. Give God the glo - ry, God ___ and none oth - er;

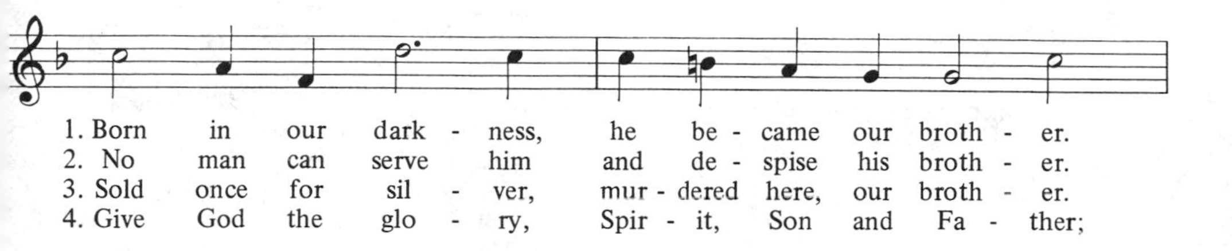
1. Born in our dark - ness, he be - came our broth - er.
2. No man can serve him and de - spise his broth - er.
3. Sold once for sil - ver, mur - dered here, our broth - er.
4. Give God the glo - ry, Spir - it, Son and Fa - ther;

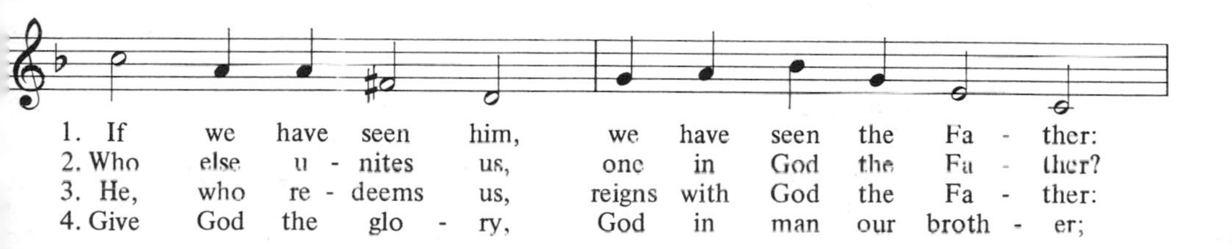
1. If we have seen him, we have seen the Fa - ther:
2. Who else u - nites us, one in God the Fa - ther?
3. He, who re - deems us, reigns with God the Fa - ther:
4. Give God the glo - ry, God in man our broth - er;

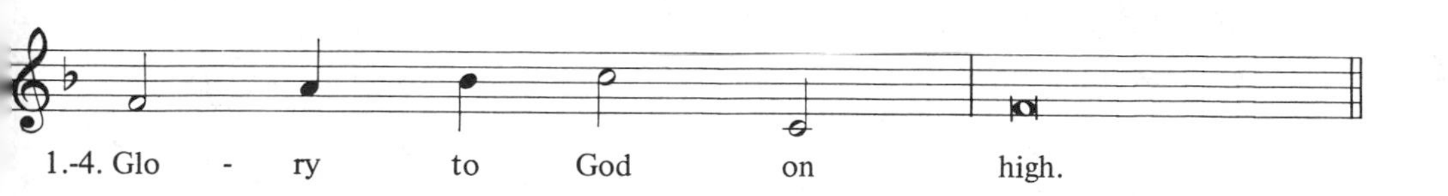
1.-4. Glo - ry to God on high.

Text: F.P. Green.
Tune: *Scientia salutis,* J. Stainer, +1901.

131 Christ the Lord Is Ris'n Today

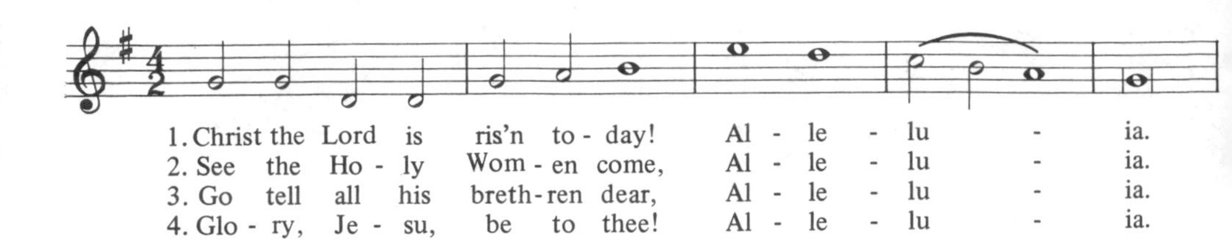
1. Christ the Lord is ris'n to - day! Al - le - lu - ia.
2. See the Ho - ly Wom - en come, Al - le - lu - ia.
3. Go tell all his breth-ren dear, Al - le - lu - ia.
4. Glo - ry, Je - su, be to thee! Al - le - lu - ia.

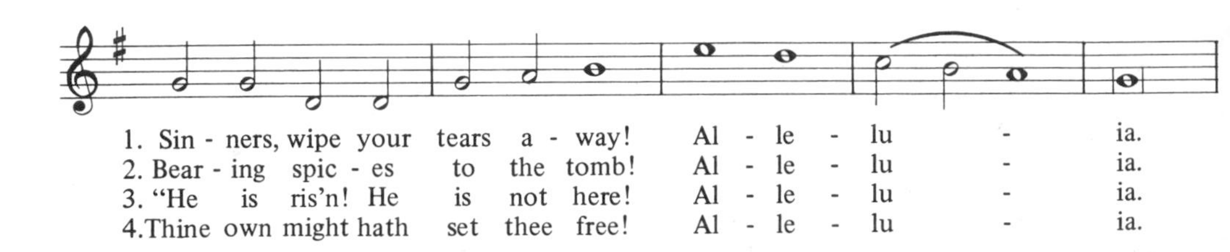
1. Sin - ners, wipe your tears a - way! Al - le - lu - ia.
2. Bear - ing spic - es to the tomb! Al - le - lu - ia.
3. "He is ris'n! He is not here! Al - le - lu - ia.
4. Thine own might hath set thee free! Al - le - lu - ia.

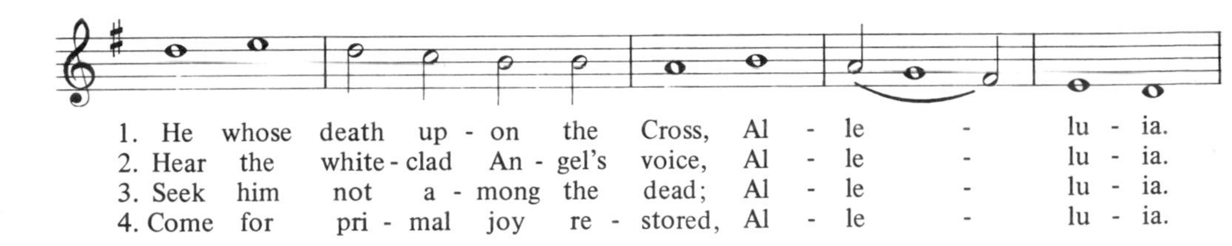
1. He whose death up - on the Cross, Al - le - lu - ia.
2. Hear the white - clad An - gel's voice, Al - le - lu - ia.
3. Seek him not a - mong the dead; Al - le - lu - ia.
4. Come for pri - mal joy re - stored, Al - le - lu - ia.

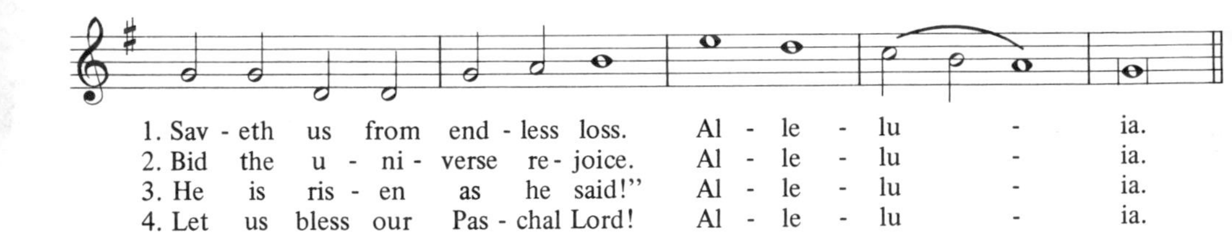
1. Sav - eth us from end - less loss. Al - le - lu - ia.
2. Bid the u - ni - verse re - joice. Al - le - lu - ia.
3. He is ris - en as he said!" Al - le - lu - ia.
4. Let us bless our Pas - chal Lord! Al - le - lu - ia.

Text: 14th Century, anon. Trans. J. O'Connor, +1870.
Tune: *Gaudeamus pariter,* J. Horn, +1547.

Christ, Whose Glory Fills the Skies

132

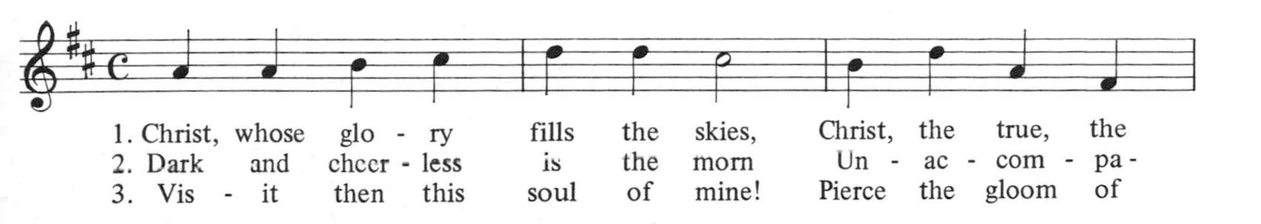
1. Christ, whose glo - ry fills the skies, Christ, the true, the
2. Dark and cheer - less is the morn Un - ac - com - pa -
3. Vis - it then this soul of mine! Pierce the gloom of

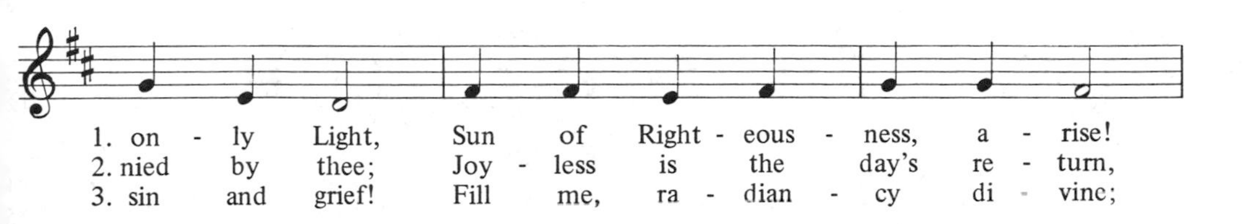
1. on - ly Light, Sun of Right - eous - ness, a - rise!
2. nied by thee; Joy - less is the day's re - turn,
3. sin and grief! Fill me, ra - dian - cy di - vine;

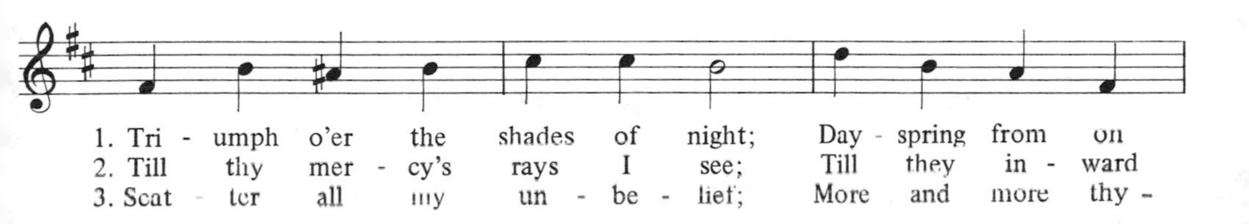
1. Tri - umph o'er the shades of night; Day - spring from on
2. Till thy mer - cy's rays I see; Till they in - ward
3. Scat - ter all my un - be - lief; More and more thy -

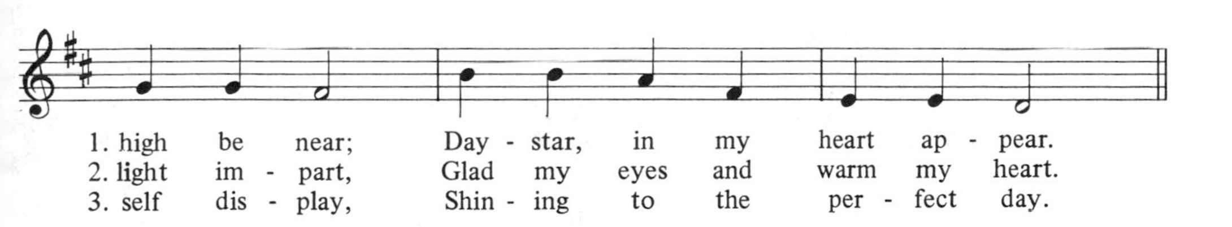
1. high be near; Day - star, in my heart ap - pear.
2. light im - part, Glad my eyes and warm my heart.
3. self dis - play, Shin - ing to the per - fect day.

Text: C. Wesley, +1788.
Tune: *Ratisbon,* J.G. Werner, +1822, "Choralbuch".

133 Come Down, O Love Divine

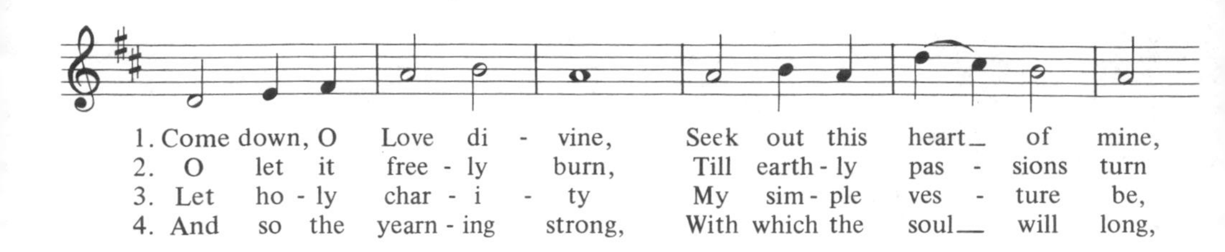
1. Come down, O Love di - vine, Seek out this heart_ of mine,
2. O let it free - ly burn, Till earth - ly pas - sions turn
3. Let ho - ly char - i - ty My sim - ple ves - ture be,
4. And so the yearn - ing strong, With which the soul_ will long,

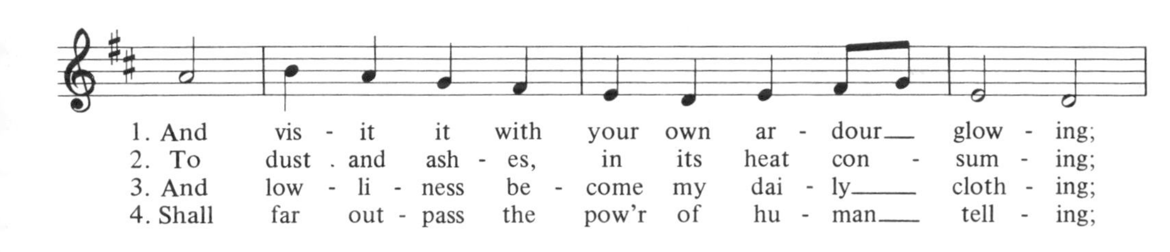
1. And vis - it it with your own ar - dour_ glow - ing;
2. To dust and ash - es, in its heat con - sum - ing;
3. And low - li - ness be - come my dai - ly_ cloth - ing;
4. Shall far out - pass the pow'r of hu - man_ tell - ing;

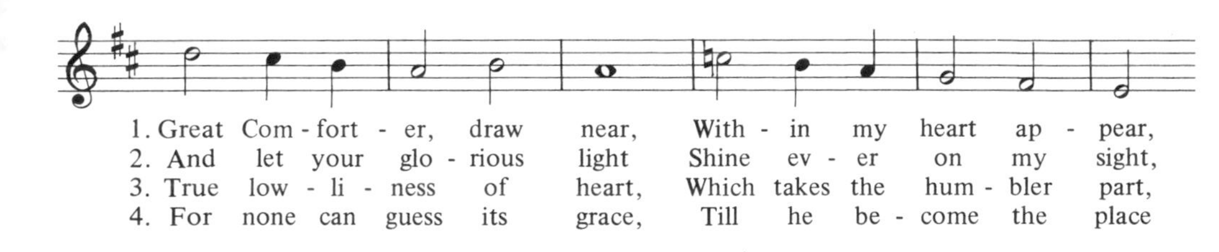
1. Great Com - fort - er, draw near, With - in my heart ap - pear,
2. And let your glo - rious light Shine ev - er on my sight,
3. True low - li - ness of heart, Which takes the hum - bler part,
4. For none can guess its grace, Till he be - come the place

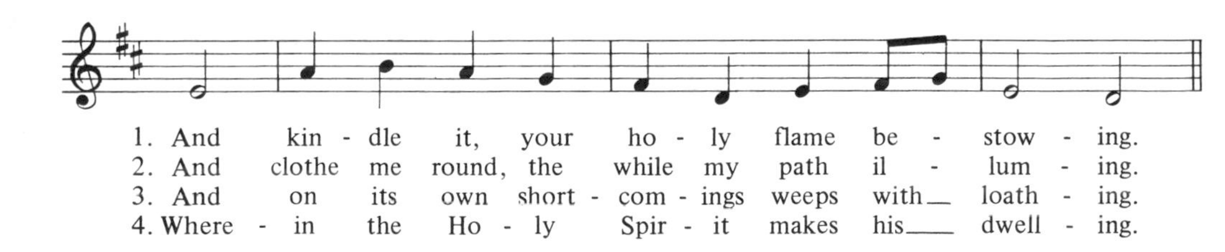
1. And kin - dle it, your ho - ly flame be - stow - ing.
2. And clothe me round, the while my path il - lum - ing.
3. And on its own short - com - ings weeps with_ loath - ing.
4. Where - in the Ho - ly Spir - it makes his_ dwell - ing.

Text: *Discendi, amor santo,* Bianco da Siena, +1434. Trans. R.F. Littledale, +1890.
Adapted by A.G. Petti in "New Catholic Hymnal",

Tune: *Down Ampney,* R. Vaughan Williams, +1958, from the "English Hymnal",
Oxford University Press. Used with permission.

Come, Follow Me

1. "Come, fol - low me," says Christ the Lord, "All in my way a -
2. "I am the light; I light the way, A god - ly life dis -
3. "Re - form your lives, come af - ter me; I am your soul's sal -
4. Then let us fol - low Christ, our Lord, And take the cross ap -
1. bid - ing; De - ny your - selves, and hear my word, O -
2. play - ing; I bid you walk as in the day; I
3. va - tion; Your heart from ev - ery guile be free From
4. point - ed, And firm - ly cling - ing to his Word, In
1. bey my call and guid - ing. O bear the cross, what -
2. keep your feet from stray - ing. I am the way and
3. sin and its temp - ta - tion. I am the ref - uge
4. suf - fering be un - daunt - ed. For those who bear the
1. e'er be - tide; Take my ex - am - ple for your guide.
2. well I show How you should live while here be - low".
3. of the soul And lead you to your heav'n - ly goal".
4. bat - tle's strain The crown of heav'n - ly life ob - tain.

Text: Johann Scheffer, +1677. Translation by C.W. Schaeffer, +1896, alt.
Tune: *Eisenach,* B. Gesius, +1613.

135 Come, Holy Ghost, Creator Blest

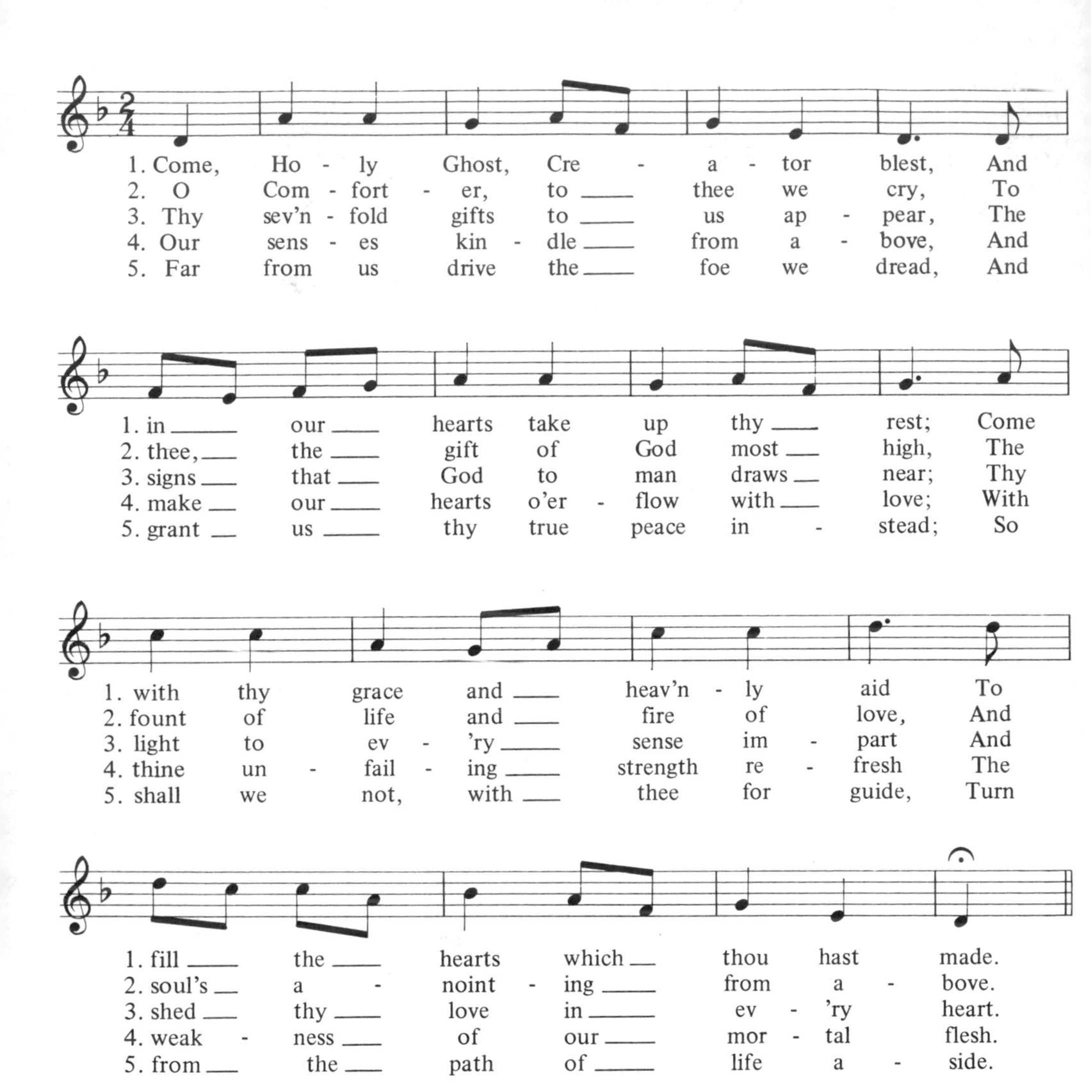

1. Come, Ho - ly Ghost, Cre - a - tor blest, And
2. O Com - fort - er, to thee we cry, To
3. Thy sev'n - fold gifts to us ap - pear, The
4. Our sens - es kin - dle from a - bove, And
5. Far from us drive the foe we dread, And
1. in our hearts take up thy rest; Come
2. thee, the gift of God most high, The
3. signs that God to man draws near; Thy
4. make our hearts o'er - flow with love; With
5. grant us thy true peace in - stead; So
1. with thy grace and heav'n - ly aid To
2. fount of life and fire of love, And
3. light to ev - 'ry sense im - part And
4. thine un - fail - ing strength re - fresh The
5. shall we not, with thee for guide, Turn
1. fill the hearts which thou hast made.
2. soul's a - noint - ing from a - bove.
3. shed thy love in ev - 'ry heart.
4. weak - ness of our mor - tal flesh.
5. from the path of life a - side.

6. Make thou to us the Father known,
Teach us th'eternal Son to own,
Be this our never changing creed:
That thou dost from them both proceed.

7. To God the Father let us sing,
To God the Son, our risen King,
And equally let us adore
The Spirit God forevermore.

Text: *Veni Creator,* Rabanus Maurus, +856. Trans. E. Caswall, +1878, alt.
Tune: *Mount Auburn,* T. Marier. From "Pius X Hymnal",

Come, Holy Spirit, Ever One

100

1. Come, Ho - ly Spir - it, ev - er one With God the Fa -
2. Let flesh and heart and lips and mind Sound forth our wit -
3. Al - might - y Fa - ther, hear our cry, Thro' Je - sus Christ

1. ther and the Son: It is the hour our souls pos - sess
2. ness to man - kind: And love light up our mor - tal frame
3. our Lord most high, And with the Spir - it Par - a - clete,

1. - 2.
3.

1. With your full flood of ho - li - ness.
2. Till oth - ers catch the liv - ing flame.
3. Whose reign the end - less a - ges greet. A - men.

Text: *Nunc, sancte nobis,* attributed to St. Ambrose, +397. Trans. J.H. Newman, +1890, alt.
Tune: *Ferial Day,* Ambrosian Chant.

137 Come, Let Us Sing unto the Lord

Ps. 95

1. Come, let us sing un - to the Lord,
2. Let us be - fore his pres - ence come
3. Our God is great and he is King,
4. To him the spa - cious sea be - longs,
5. O come, and let us wor - ship him,
1. To him our voic - es raise;
2. With praise and thank - ful voice;
3. A - bove all gods he is;
4. For he the same did make;
5. Praise him with one ac - cord.
1. With joy - ful noise let us the Rock
2. Let us sing psalms to him with grace
3. The depths of earth are in his hand;
4. The dry land al - so from his hands
5. He is our Shep - herd, we his flock;
1. Of our sal - va - tion praise.
2. And make a joy - ful noise.
3. The heights of hills are his.
4. Its form at first did take.
5. He is our God and Lord.

Text: Psalm 95 paraphrase, "Scottish Psalter", 1650, alt.
Tune: *Nun danket all und bringet Ehr,* J. Crüger, +1662.

Come, Show Us Your Salvation, Lord **138**

Ps. 85

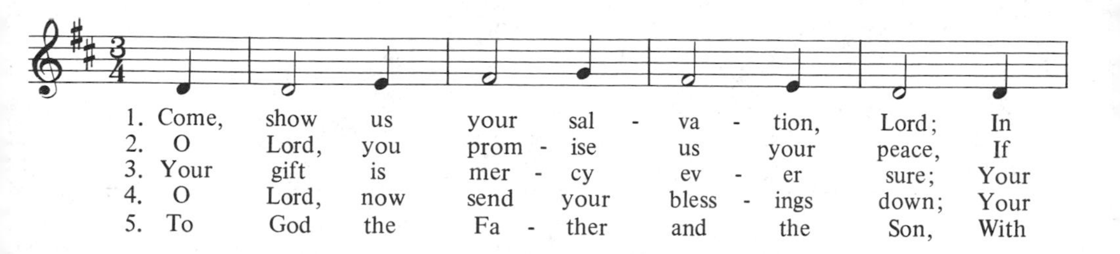
1. Come, show us your sal - va - tion, Lord; In
2. O Lord, you prom - ise us your peace, If
3. Your gift is mer - cy ev - er sure; Your
4. O Lord, now send your bless - ings down; Your
5. To God the Fa - ther and the Son, With

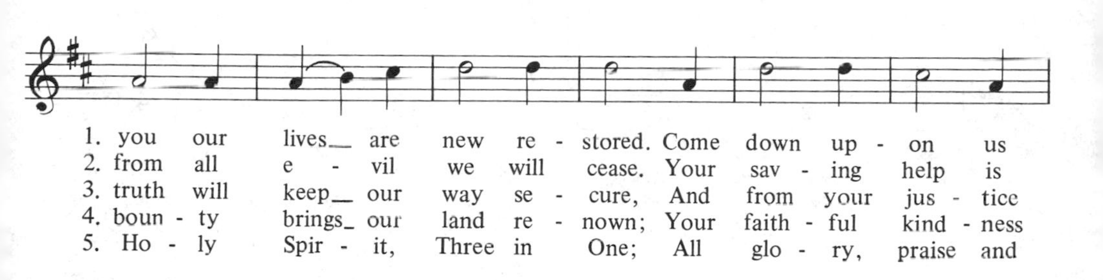
1. you our lives_ are new re - stored. Come down up - on us
2. from all e - vil we will cease. Your sav - ing help is
3. truth will keep_ our way se - cure, And from your jus - tice
4. boun - ty brings_ our land re - nown; Your faith - ful kind - ness
5. Ho - ly Spir - it, Three in One; All glo - ry, praise and

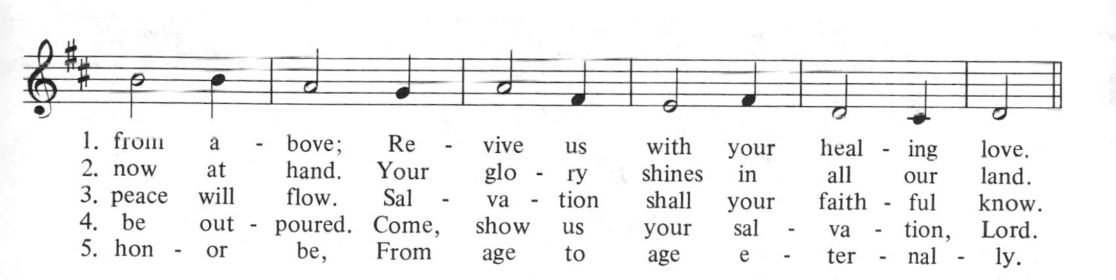
1. from a - bove; Re - vive us with your heal - ing love.
2. now at hand. Your glo - ry shines in all our land.
3. peace will flow. Sal - va - tion shall your faith - ful know.
4. be out - poured. Come, show us your sal - va - tion, Lord.
5. hon - or be, From age to age e - ter - nal - ly.

Text: Psalm 85 paraphrase, J. Dunn.
Tune: *Puer nobis,* attributed to M. Praetorius, +1609. Harm. anon.

139 Come, Take the Body of the Savior

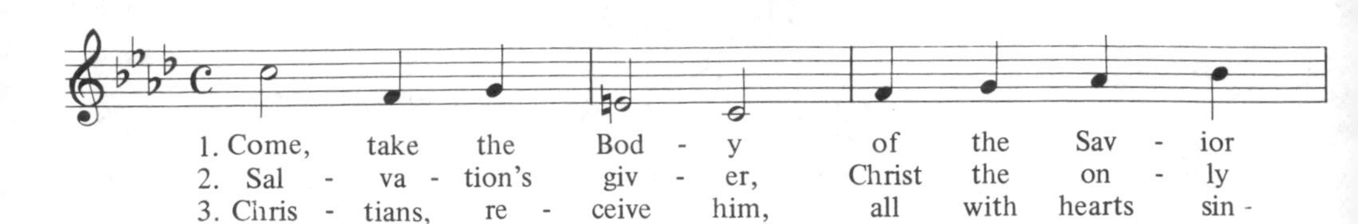
1. Come, take the Bod - y of the Sav - ior
2. Sal - va - tion's giv - er, Christ the on - ly
3. Chris - tians, re - ceive him, all with hearts sin -

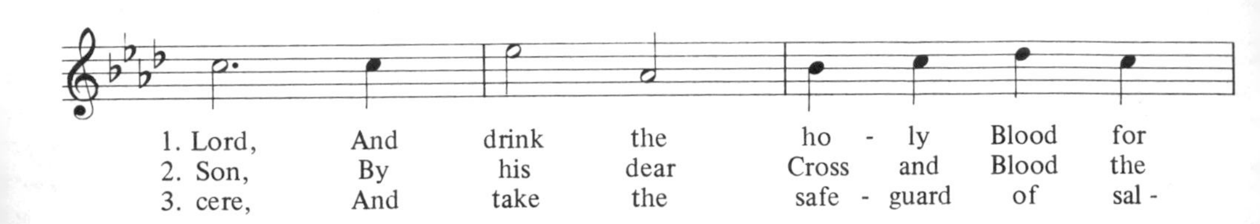
1. Lord, And drink the ho - ly Blood for
2. Son, By his dear Cross and Blood the
3. cere, And take the safe - guard of sal -

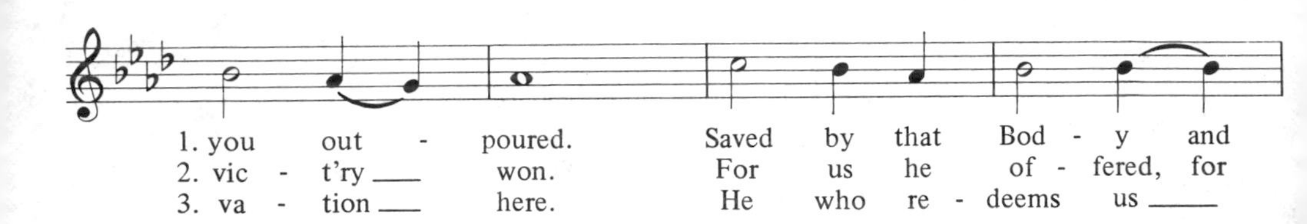
1. you out - poured. Saved by that Bod - y and
2. vic - t'ry won. For us he of - fered, for
3. va - tion here. He who re - deems us

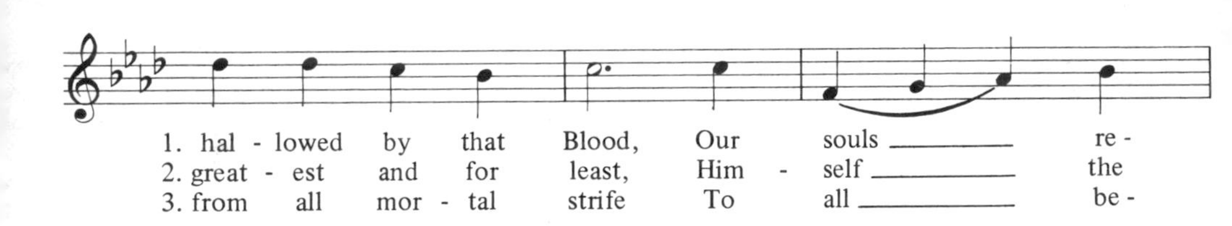
1. hal - lowed by that Blood, Our souls re -
2. great - est and for least, Him - self the
3. from all mor - tal strife To all be -

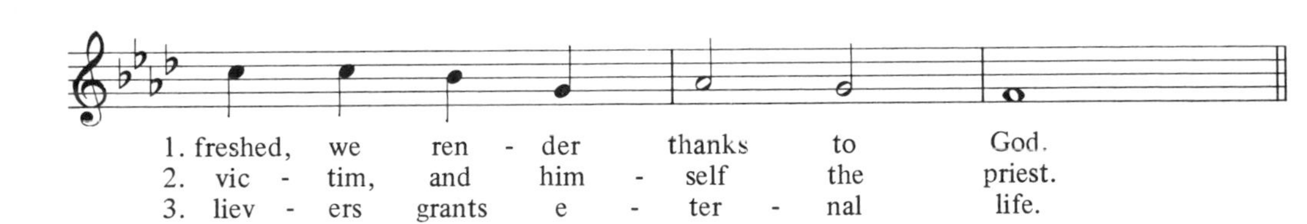
1. freshed, we ren - der thanks to God.
2. vic - tim, and him - self the priest.
3. liev - ers grants e - ter - nal life.

Text: Latin, 7th Century. Trans. J.M. Neale, +1866, alt.
Tune: *Schönster Herr Jesu,* anon., 1677.

Come, Thou Long-Expected Jesus

1. Come, thou long - ex - pect - ed Je - sus, Born to set thy
2. Born thy peo - ple to de - liv - er, Born a child and
3. Love di - vine, all loves ex - cell - ing, Joy of heav'n to
4. Come to us, Re - deem - er, Sav - ior, Come, O Lord of
1. peo - ple free; From our fears and sins re - lease us,
2. yet a king. Born to reign in us for - ev - er,
3. earth come down, Fix in us thy hum - ble dwell - ing,
4. hosts, to - day. Fill us with thy lov - ing kind - ness,
1. Let us find our rest in thee. Is - rael's strength and
2. Now thy gra - cious king - dom bring. By thine own e -
3. All thy faith - ful mer - cies crown. Je - sus, thou art
4. Hear thy peo - ple as they pray. Je - sus, Lord of
1. con - so - la - tion, Hope of all the earth thou art:
2. ter - nal Spir - it Rule in all our hearts a - lone.
3. all com - pas - sion, Pure, un - bound - ed love thou art.
4. our sal - va - tion, Hope of all the earth thou art.
1.-4. Al - le - lu - ia, Al - le - lu - ia.
1. Joy of ev - 'ry lov - ing heart.
2. Raise us to thy glo - rious throne.
3. En - ter ev - 'ry lov - ing heart.
4. En - ter ev - 'ry lov - ing heart.

Text: Verses 1-3, C. Wesley, +1788, alt.
Verse 4, J. Dunn. © by author. Used with permission.
Tune: *Hyfrydol,* R.H. Prichard, +1887.

Come, Thou Redeemer of the Earth

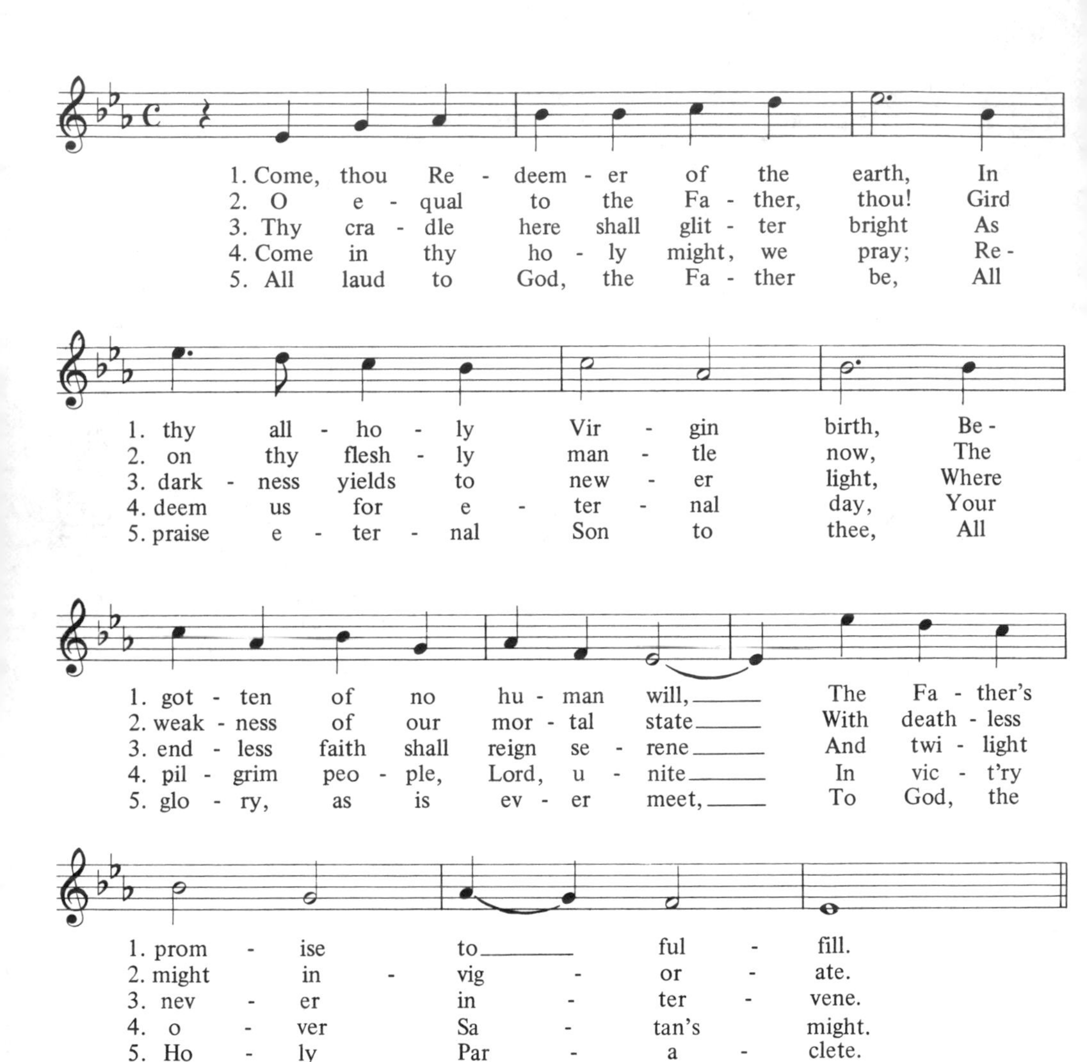
1. Come, thou Re - deem - er of the earth, In
2. O e - qual to the Fa - ther, thou! Gird
3. Thy cra - dle here shall glit - ter bright As
4. Come in thy ho - ly might, we pray; Re -
5. All laud to God, the Fa - ther be, All
1. thy all - ho - ly Vir - gin birth, Be -
2. on thy flesh - ly man - tle now, The
3. dark - ness yields to new - er light, Where
4. deem us for e - ter - nal day, Your
5. praise e - ter - nal Son to thee, All
1. got - ten of no hu - man will, The Fa - ther's
2. weak - ness of our mor - tal state With death - less
3. end - less faith shall reign se - rene And twi - light
4. pil - grim peo - ple, Lord, u - nite In vic - t'ry
5. glo - ry, as is ev - er meet, To God, the
1. prom - ise to ful - fill.
2. might in - vig - or - ate.
3. nev - er in - ter - vene.
4. o - ver Sa - tan's might.
5. Ho - ly Par - a - clete.

Text: St. Ambrose, +397. Trans. J.M. Neale, +1866, alt.
Tune: *Andernach,* anon., 1608.

Come unto Me, Ye Weary

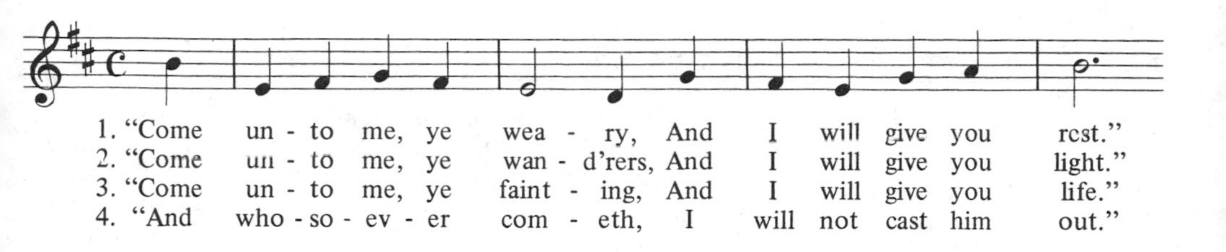
1. "Come un - to me, ye wea - ry, And I will give you rest."
2. "Come un - to me, ye wan - d'rers, And I will give you light."
3. "Come un - to me, ye faint - ing, And I will give you life."
4. "And who - so - ev - er com - eth, I will not cast him out."

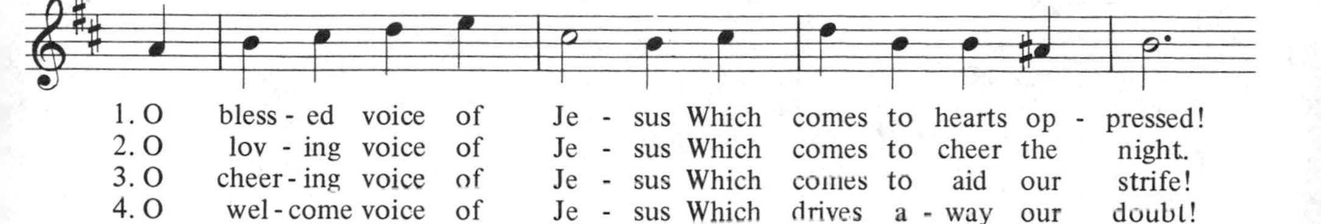
1. O bless - ed voice of Je - sus Which comes to hearts op - pressed!
2. O lov - ing voice of Je - sus Which comes to cheer the night.
3. O cheer - ing voice of Je - sus Which comes to aid our strife!
4. O wel - come voice of Je - sus Which drives a - way our doubt!

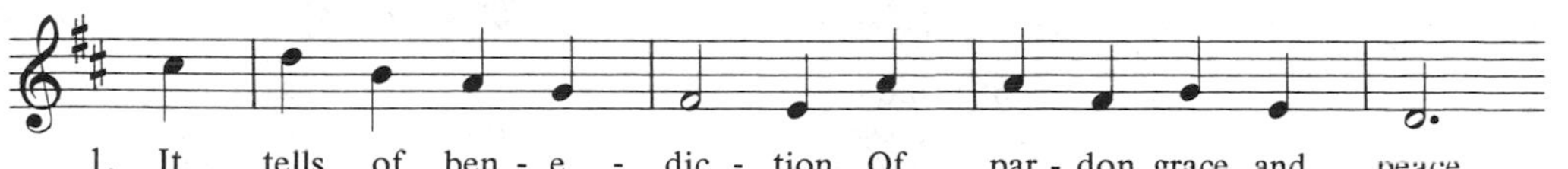

1. It tells of ben - e - dic - tion, Of par - don, grace and peace,
2. Our hearts were filled with sad - ness And we had lost our way;
3. The foe is stern and ea - ger, The fight is fierce and long;
4. Which calls us ver - y sin - ners, Un - wor - thy though we be

1. Of joy that has no end - ing, Of love which can - not cease.
2. But he has brought us glad - ness And songs at break of day.
3. But he has made us might - y And strong - er than the strong.
4. Of love so free and bound - less, To come, dear Lord, to thee.

Text: W. Chatterton Dix, +1898.
Tune: *Old 130th*, French "Psalter", Strassburg, 1539.

143 Come, Ye Thankful People, Come

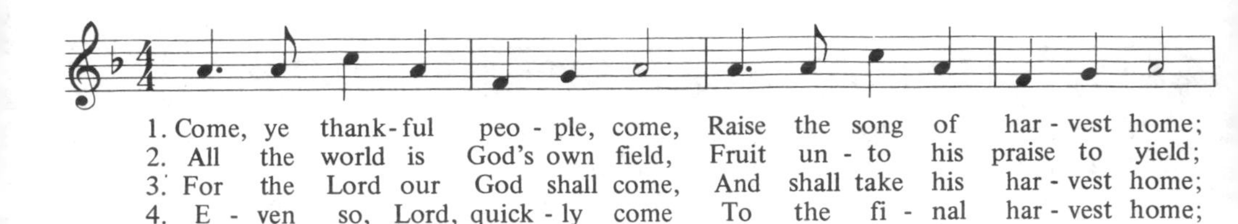

1. Come, ye thank-ful peo - ple, come, Raise the song of har - vest home;
2. All the world is God's own field, Fruit un - to his praise to yield;
3. For the Lord our God shall come, And shall take his har - vest home;
4. E - ven so, Lord, quick - ly come To the fi - nal har - vest home;

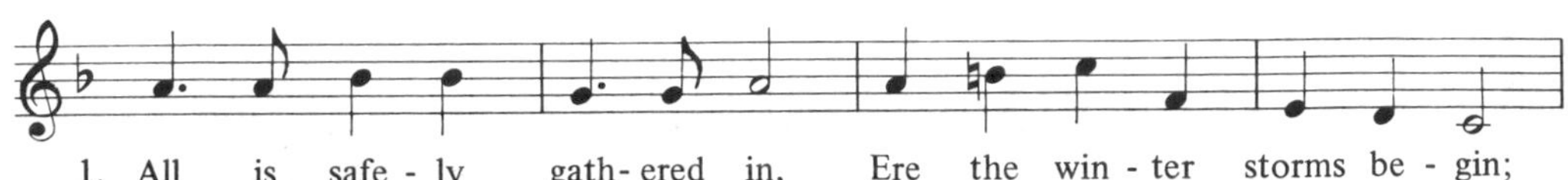

1. All is safe - ly gath- ered in, Ere the win - ter storms be - gin;
2. Wheat and tares to - geth - er sown, Un - to joy or sor - row grown;
3. From his field shall in that day All of - fens - es purge a - way,
4. Gath - er thou thy peo - ple in, Free from sor - row, free from sin;

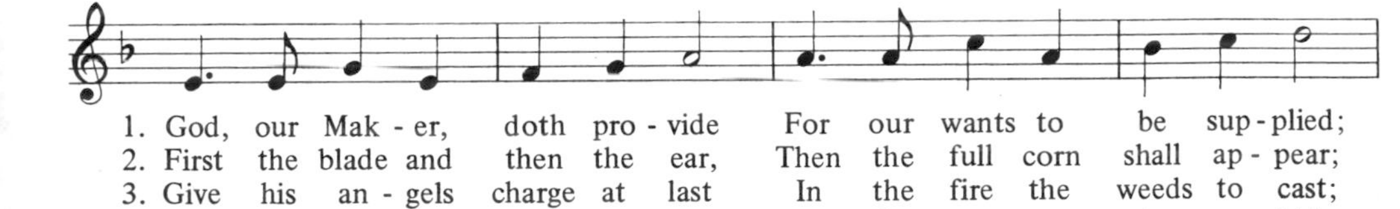

1. God, our Mak - er, doth pro - vide For our wants to be sup - plied;
2. First the blade and then the ear, Then the full corn shall ap - pear;
3. Give his an - gels charge at last In the fire the weeds to cast;
4. There for - ev - er pu - ri - fied, In thy pres - ence to a - bide;

1. Come to God's own tem - ple, come, Raise the song of har - vest home.
2. Lord of har - vest, grant that we Whole - some grain and pure may be.
3. But the fruit - ful ears to store In his gar - ner ev - er - more.
4. Come with all thine an - gels, come, Raise the glo - rious har - vest home.

Text: H. Alford, +1871, alt.
Tune: *St. George's Windsor,* G.J. Elvey, +1893.

Comfort, Comfort Ye, My People

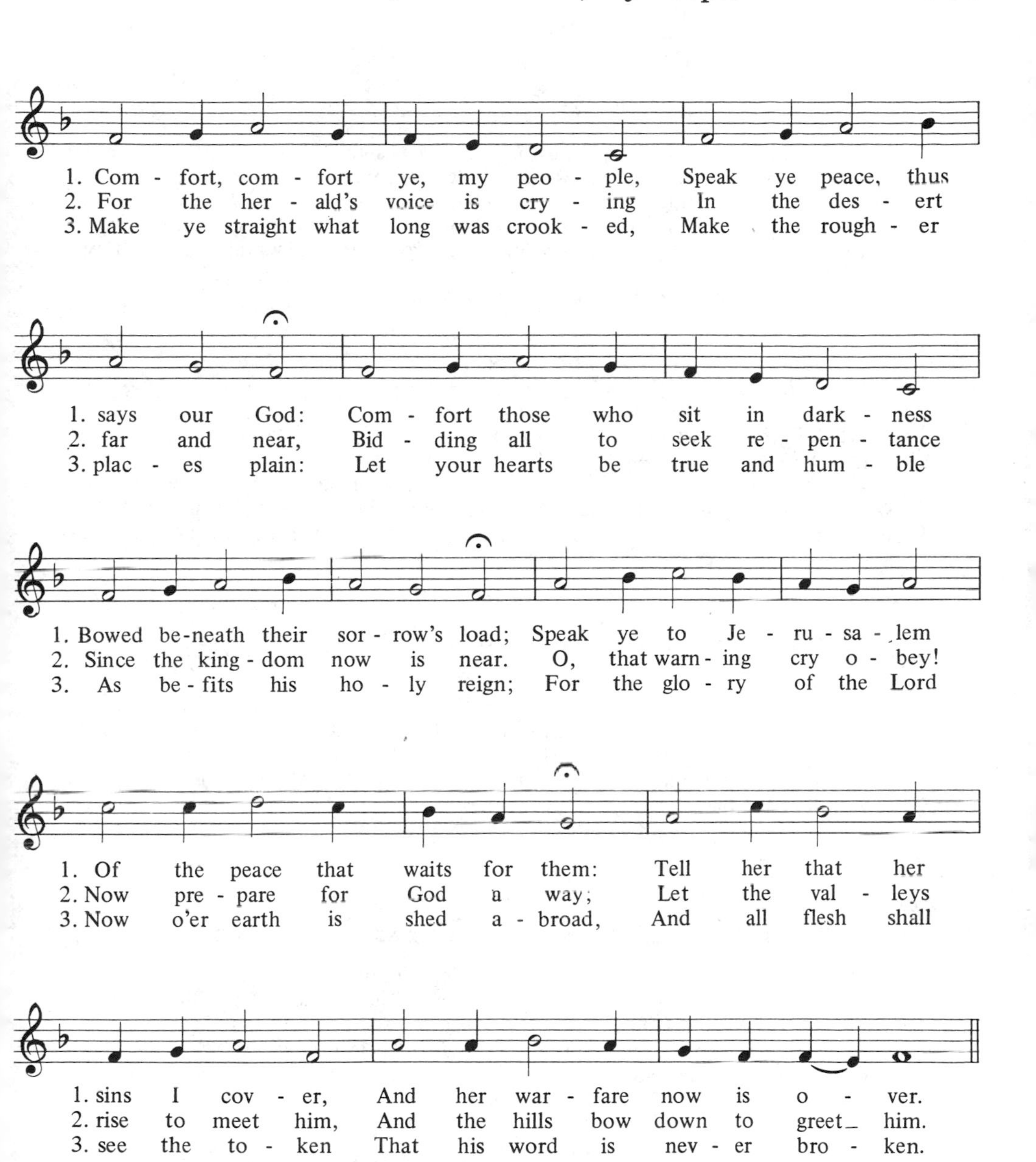
1. Com - fort, com - fort ye, my peo - ple, Speak ye peace, thus
2. For the her - ald's voice is cry - ing In the des - ert
3. Make ye straight what long was crook - ed, Make the rough - er
1. says our God: Com - fort those who sit in dark - ness
2. far and near, Bid - ding all to seek re - pen - tance
3. plac - es plain: Let your hearts be true and hum - ble
1. Bowed be-neath their sor - row's load; Speak ye to Je - ru - sa - lem
2. Since the king - dom now is near. O, that warn - ing cry o - bey!
3. As be - fits his ho - ly reign; For the glo - ry of the Lord
1. Of the peace that waits for them: Tell her that her
2. Now pre - pare for God a way; Let the val - leys
3. Now o'er earth is shed a - broad, And all flesh shall
1. sins I cov - er, And her war - fare now is o - ver.
2. rise to meet him, And the hills bow down to greet_ him.
3. see the to - ken That his word is nev - er bro - ken.

Text: Isaiah 40: 1-8 paraphrase, J. Olearius, +1684. Trans. C. Winkworth, +1878.
Tune: *Freu dich sehr,* "Genevan Psalter", 1551.

145 Crown Him with Many Crowns

1. Crown him with man - y crowns, The Lamb up - on his throne;
2. Crown him the Son of God Be - fore the worlds be - gan,
3. Crown him the Lord of life, Who tri-umphed o'er the grave,
4. Crown him of lords the Lord Who o - ver all doth reign,
5. Crown him the Lord of heav'n, En - throned in worlds a - bove;

1. Hark! how the heav'n-ly an - them_ sounds With praise to him a - lone;
2. And ye, who walk where he hath_ trod, Crown him the Son of man,
3. And rose vic - to - rious in the_ strife For those he came to save;
4. Who once on earth th'In - car - nate_ Word, For ran-somed sin - ners slain,
5. Crown him the King to whom is_ giv'n The won-drous name of Love.

1. A - wake, my soul, and sing Of him who died for thee,
2. Who ev - 'ry grief hath known That pains the hu - man breast,
3. His glo - ries now we sing Who died, and rose on high,
4. Now lives in realms of light Where saints with an - gels sing
5. Crown him with man - y crowns As thrones be - fore him fall,

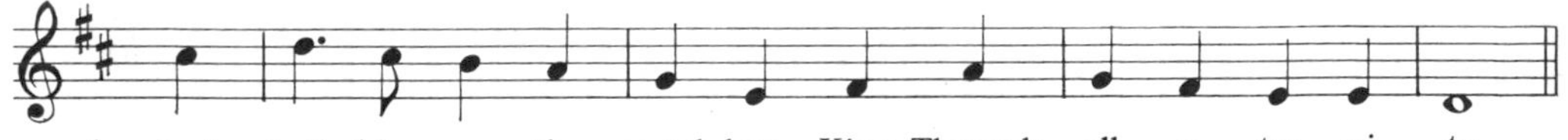

1. And hail him as thy match-less King Through all e - ter - ni - ty.
2. And takes and bears them for his own, That all in him may rest.
3. Who died, e - ter - nal life to bring, And lives that death may die.
4. Their songs be - fore him day and night, Their God, Re - deem - er, King.
5. Crown him, ye kings, with man - y crowns, For he is King of all.

Text: M. Bridges, +1894, alt.
Tune: *Diademata,* G.J. Elvey, +1893.

Day Is Done

1. Day is done, but Love un - fail - ing Dwells ev - er here;
2. Dark de - scends, but Light un - end - ing Shines through our night;
3. Eyes will close, but you, un - sleep - ing, Watch by our side;

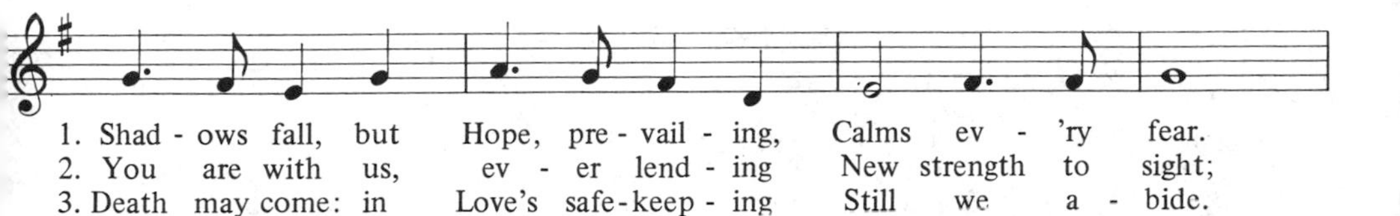
1. Shad - ows fall, but Hope, pre - vail - ing, Calms ev - 'ry fear.
2. You are with us, ev - er lend - ing New strength to sight;
3. Death may come: in Love's safe - keep - ing Still we a - bide.

1. Lov - ing Fa - ther, none for - sak - ing, Take our hearts of Love's own mak - ing,
2. One in love, your truth con - fess - ing, One in hope of heav - en's bless - ing,
3. God of love, all e - vil quell - ing, Sin for - giv - ing, fear dis - pell - ing,

1. Watch our sleep - ing, guard our wak - ing, Be al - ways near!
2. May we see, in love's pos - sess - ing, Love's end - less light!
3. Stay with us, our hearts in - dwell - ing, This e - ven - tide!

Text: J. Quinn, S.J.,
Tune: *Ar hyd y nos,* Welsh Folk Melody.

147 Dear Maker of the Starry Skies

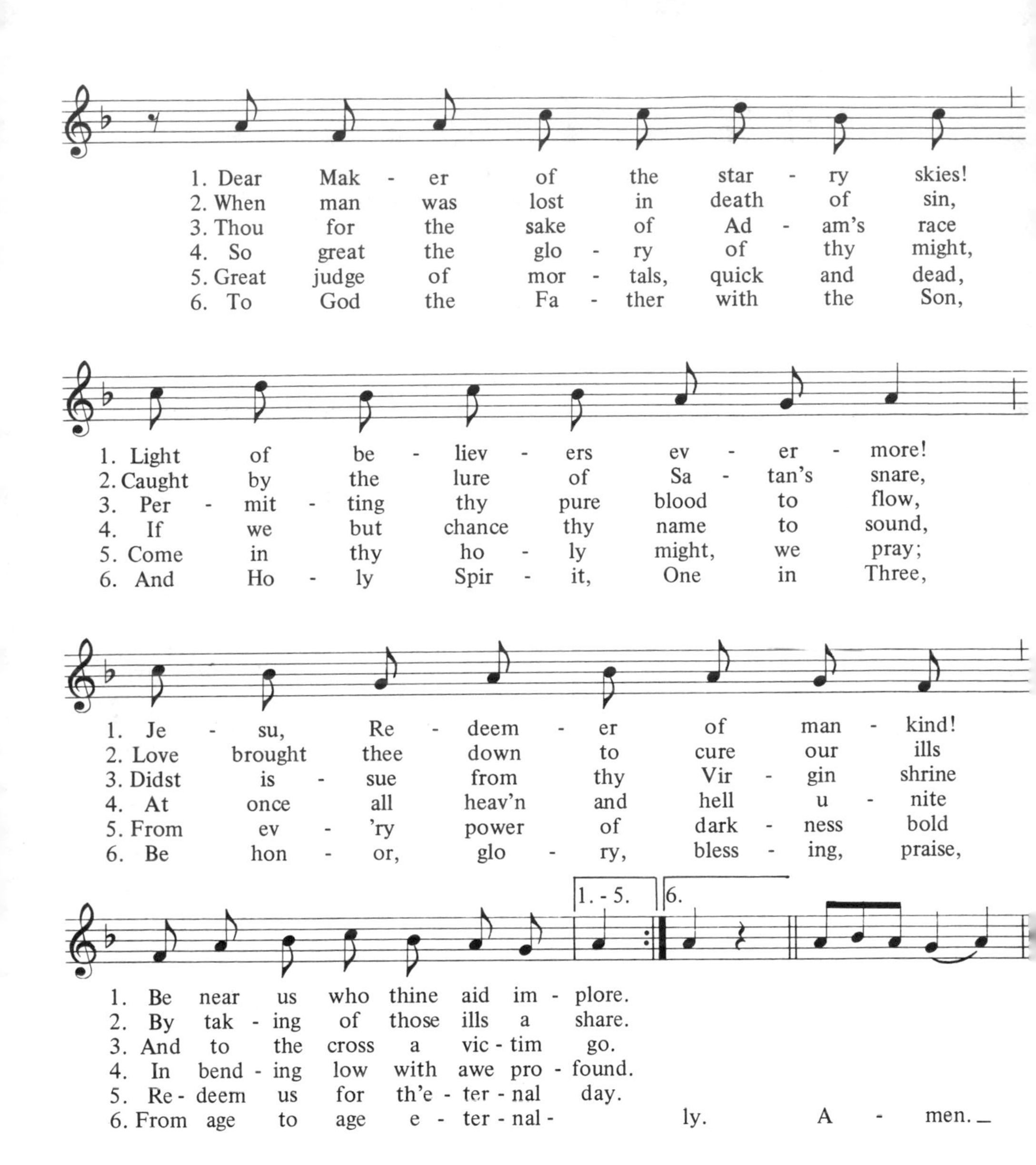
1. Dear Mak - er of the star - ry skies!
2. When man was lost in death of sin,
3. Thou for the sake of Ad - am's race
4. So great the glo - ry of thy might,
5. Great judge of mor - tals, quick and dead,
6. To God the Fa - ther with the Son,
1. Light of be - liev - ers ev - er - more!
2. Caught by the lure of Sa - tan's snare,
3. Per - mit - ting thy pure blood to flow,
4. If we but chance thy name to sound,
5. Come in thy ho - ly might, we pray;
6. And Ho - ly Spir - it, One in Three,
1. Je - su, Re - deem - er of man - kind!
2. Love brought thee down to cure our ills
3. Didst is - sue from thy Vir - gin shrine
4. At once all heav'n and hell u - nite
5. From ev - 'ry power of dark - ness bold
6. Be hon - or, glo - ry, bless - ing, praise,
1. - 5.
6.
1. Be near us who thine aid im - plore.
2. By tak - ing of those ills a share.
3. And to the cross a vic - tim go.
4. In bend - ing low with awe pro - found.
5. Re - deem us for th'e - ter - nal day.
6. From age to age e - ter - nal - ly. A - men.

Text: 7th Century, anon. Trans. E. Caswall, +1878, alt.
Tune: *Creator alme siderum,* Plainchant, Mode 4.

Dear Saint Joseph, Son of David

148

1. Dear Saint Jo - seph, son of Da - vid, Spouse of Mar - y__ un - de - filed,
2. Fa - ther of the Ho - ly Fam-'ly, Mod - el for the_ work - er's day,

1. You were cho - sen Fos - ter Fa - ther, Guard - ian of the Ho - ly Child.
2. Be our strength when ill and wea - ry, At death's hour_ be our stay.

1. O how blessed with spe - cial grac - es Was your hum - ble, ho - ly way;
2. As the Church - 's Saint Pro - tec - tor, Con - stant guard - ian at her side,

1. In - ter - cede for us in heav - en, Be our sup - pliant when we pray.
2. Be our light in doubt and dark - ness, Dear Saint Jo - seph, be our guide.

Text: T. Marier.
Tune: *Rex gloriae*, H. Smart, +1879.

149 Easter Glory Fills the Sky! Alleluia!

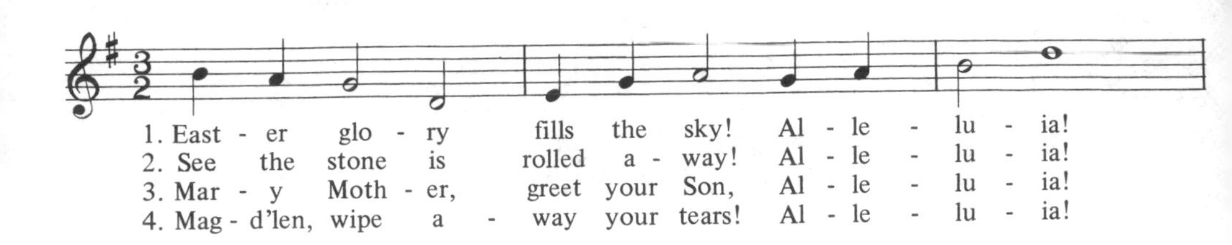
1. East - er glo - ry fills the sky! Al - le - lu - ia!
2. See the stone is rolled a - way! Al - le - lu - ia!
3. Mar - y Moth - er, greet your Son, Al - le - lu - ia!
4. Mag - d'len, wipe a - way your tears! Al - le - lu - ia!

1. Christ now lives no more to die! Al - le - lu - ia!
2. From the tomb where once he lay! Al - le - lu - ia!
3. Ra - diant from his tri - umph won! Al - le - lu - ia!
4. He has won who calms all fears! Al - le - lu - ia!

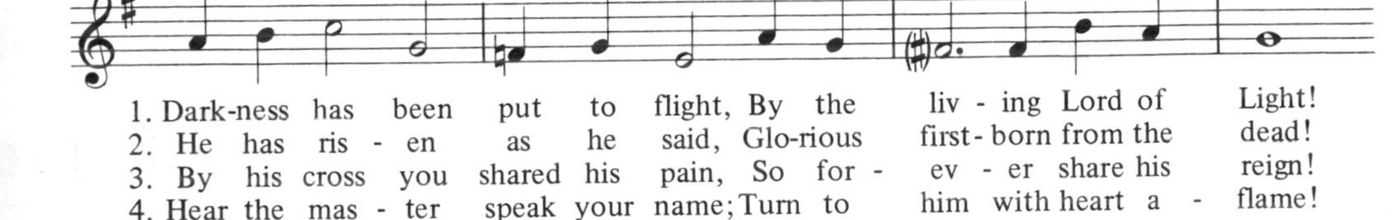
1. Dark-ness has been put to flight, By the liv - ing Lord of Light!
2. He has ris - en as he said, Glo-rious first- born from the dead!
3. By his cross you shared his pain, So for - ev - er share his reign!
4. Hear the mas - ter speak your name; Turn to him with heart a - flame!

1.-8. Al - le - lu - ia! Al - le - lu - ia! Al - le - lu - ia!

5. Shepherd, seek the sheep that strayed!
Come to contrite Peter's aid!
Strengthen him to be the rock;
Make him shepherd of your flock!

6. Seek not life within the tomb;
Christ stands in the upper room!
Risen glory he conceals,
Risen body he reveals!

7. Though we see his face no more,
He is with us as before!
Glory veiled, he is our priest,
His true flesh and blood our feast!

8. Christ, the victor over death,
Breathes on us the Spirit's breath!
Paradise is our reward,
Endless Easter with our Lord!

Ecce Panis Angelorum **150**

Sequence for Solemnity of Corpus Christi

1. Ec - ce pa - nis An - ge - ló - rum, Fa - ctus ci - bus vi - a - tó - rum:
2. In fi - gú - ris prae - si - gná - tur, Cum I - sá - ac im - mo - lá - tur,

Behold, the bread of angels has become the food of pilgrims;
It was symbolically prefigured when Isaac was brought as an offering,

1.

1. Ve - re pa - nis fi - li - ó - rum, Non mit - tén - dus__ cá - ni - bus.
2. A - gnus Pa - schae de - pu - tá - tur, Da - tur man - na__

Truly it is the bread of sons and not to be cast to dogs.
When a lamb was designated for the Pasch, when manna was given to the Fathers (Jews of old).

2.

2. pá-tri-bus. 3. Bo - ne Pa - stor, pa - nis ve - re, Je - su, no - stri mi - se -
4. Tu - que cun - cta scis et va - les, Qui nos pa - scis hic mor -

Good Shepherd and true bread, Jesus, have mercy on us;
You know all things and can do all things, you feed us in this life.

3. ré - re: Tu nos pa - sce, nos tu - é - re, Tu nos bo - na fac vi - dé - re
4. tá - les. Tu - os i - bi com-men - sá - les, Co - he - ré - des et so - dá - les,

Feed us, guard us, grant us to find happiness
Make us your guests there (in heaven), co-heirs and companions

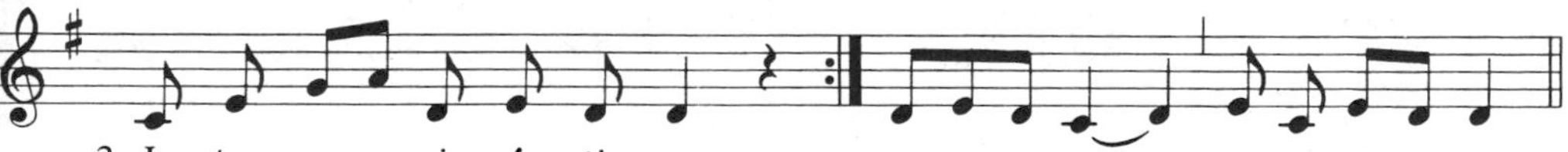

3. In ter - ra__ vi - vén - ti - um.
4. Fac san - ctó - rum cí - vi - um. A - men.__ Al - le - lú - ia.

In the land of the living.
Of the citizens of heaven.

Text: Verses from *Lauda Sion*, by St. Thomas Aquinas, +1274. Tr. anon.
Tune: *Lauda Sion*, Plainchant, Mode 7.

151 Ding, Dong! Merrily on High

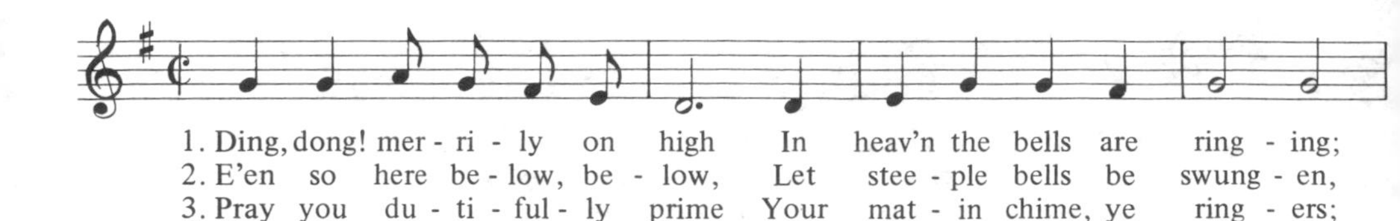
1. Ding, dong! mer - ri - ly on high In heav'n the bells are ring - ing;
2. E'en so here be - low, be - low, Let stee - ple bells be swung - en,
3. Pray you du - ti - ful - ly prime Your mat - in chime, ye ring - ers;

1. Ding, dong! ver - i - ly the sky Is riv'n with an - gels sing - ing.
2. And i - o, i - o, i - o, By priest and peo - ple sung - en.
3. May you beau - ti - ful - ly rime Your eve - time song, ye sing - ers.

REFRAIN

Gló - - - - - - - - -

- - - - ri - a, ho - san - na in ex - cél - sis!

Text: G. R. Woodward, +1934.
Tune: *Branle de l'official,* from T. Arbeau's "Orchésographie", 1588.

Faith of Our Fathers

152

1. Faith of our fa - thers! liv - ing still In spite of
2. Our fa - thers, chained in pri - sons dark, Were still in
3. Faith of our fa - thers! faith and prayer Shall win all
4. Faith of our fa - thers! We will love Both friend and

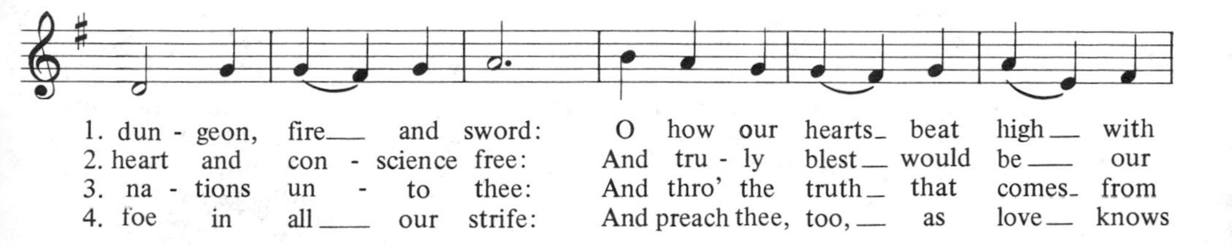
1. dun - geon, fire and sword: O how our hearts beat high with
2. heart and con - science free: And tru - ly blest would be our
3. na - tions un - to thee: And thro' the truth that comes from
4. foe in all our strife: And preach thee, too, as love knows

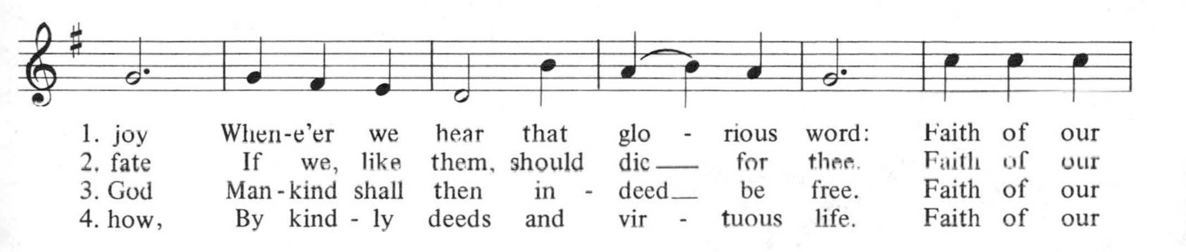
1. joy When-e'er we hear that glo - rious word: Faith of our
2. fate If we, like them, should dic for thee. Faith of our
3. God Man-kind shall then in - deed be free. Faith of our
4. how, By kind - ly deeds and vir - tuous life. Faith of our

1.-4. fa - thers, ho - ly faith! We will be true to thee till death.

Text: F.W. Faber, +1863.
Tune: *St. Catherine,* H. Hemy, +1888.

153 Father Almighty, Pour on Us Thy Blessing

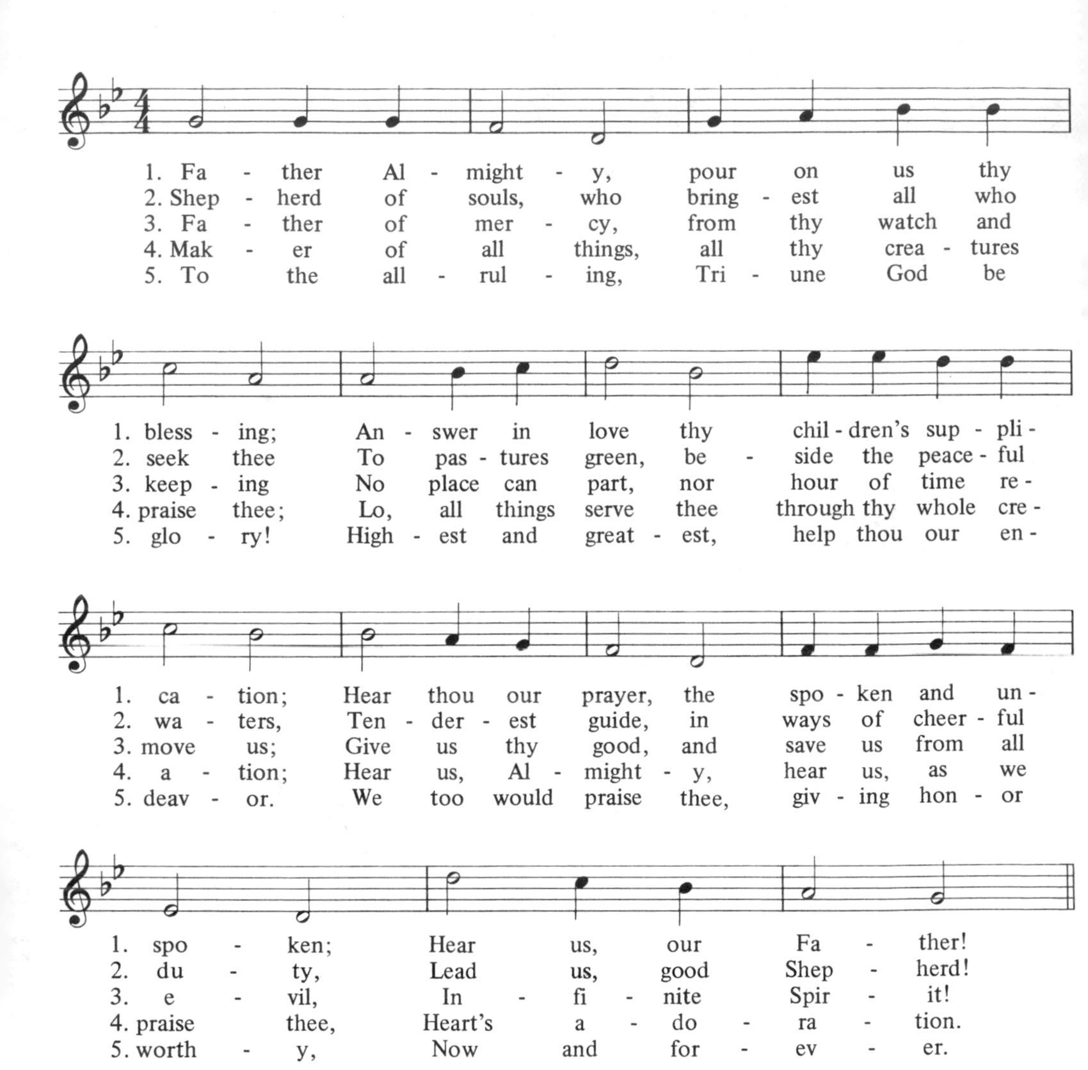
1. Fa - ther Al - might - y, pour on us thy
2. Shep - herd of souls, who bring - est all who
3. Fa - ther of mer - cy, from thy watch and
4. Mak - er of all things, all thy crea - tures
5. To the all - rul - ing, Tri - une God be
1. bless - ing; An - swer in love thy chil - dren's sup - pli -
2. seek thee To pas - tures green, be - side the peace - ful
3. keep - ing No place can part, nor hour of time re -
4. praise thee; Lo, all things serve thee through thy whole cre -
5. glo - ry! High - est and great - est, help thou our en -
1. ca - tion; Hear thou our prayer, the spo - ken and un -
2. wa - ters, Ten - der - est guide, in ways of cheer - ful
3. move us; Give us thy good, and save us from all
4. a - tion; Hear us, Al - might - y, hear us, as we
5. deav - or. We too would praise thee, giv - ing hon - or
1. spo - ken; Hear us, our Fa - ther!
2. du - ty, Lead us, good Shep - herd!
3. e - vil, In - fi - nite Spir - it!
4. praise thee, Heart's a - do - ra - tion.
5. worth - y, Now and for - ev - er.

Text: Verses 1-3, "Berwick Hymnal", 1886, alt. © 1956 in "Hymnal for Colleges and Schools", Yale University Press. Used with permission. Verses 4-5, Latin, 10th Century, anon. Trans. P. Dearmer, +1936, in "Father, most holy" from the "English Hymnal", Oxford University Press. Used with permission.

Tune: *Herzliebster Jesu,* J. Crüger, +1622.

Father, Lord of Earth and Heaven

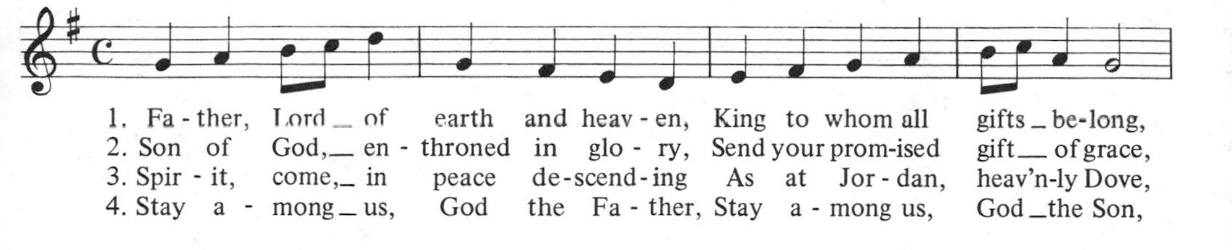

1. Fa - ther, Lord _ of earth and heav - en, King to whom all gifts _ be-long,
2. Son of God,_ en - throned in glo - ry, Send your prom-ised gift_ of grace,
3. Spir - it, come,_ in peace de-scend-ing As at Jor - dan, heav'n-ly Dove,
4. Stay a - mong _ us, God the Fa - ther, Stay a - mong us, God _the Son,

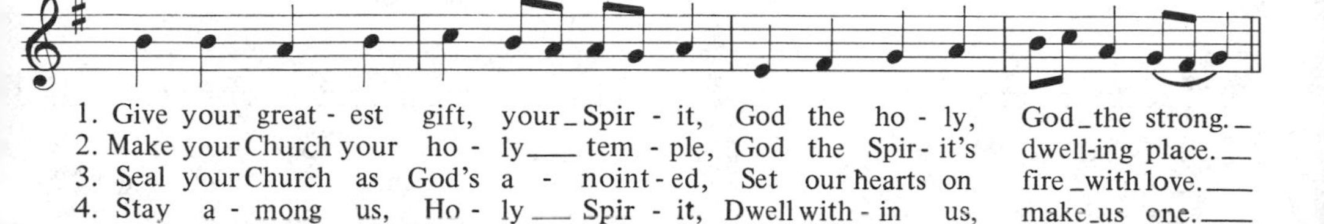

1. Give your great - est gift, your _ Spir - it, God the ho - ly, God _ the strong. _
2. Make your Church your ho - ly_ tem - ple, God the Spir - it's dwell-ing place. _
3. Seal your Church as God's a - noint - ed, Set our hearts on fire _ with love. _
4. Stay a - mong us, Ho - ly _ Spir - it, Dwell with - in us, make _us one. _

Tune: *Gott des Himmels und der Erden,* H. Albert, +1651.

155 Father of Mercy, God of Consolation

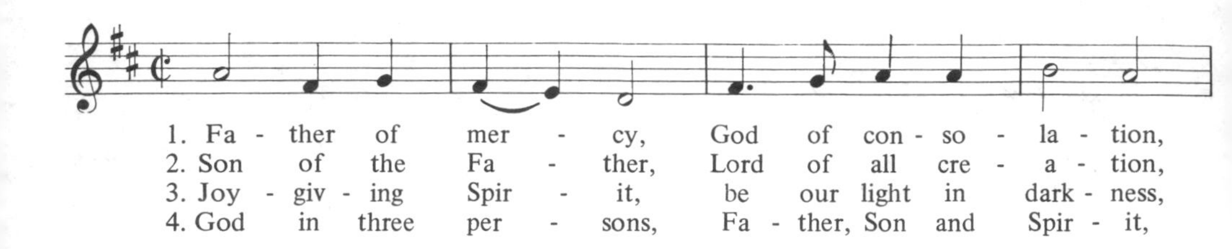
1. Fa - ther of mer - cy, God of con - so - la - tion,
2. Son of the Fa - ther, Lord of all cre - a - tion,
3. Joy - giv - ing Spir - it, be our light in dark - ness,
4. God in three per - sons, Fa - ther, Son and Spir - it,

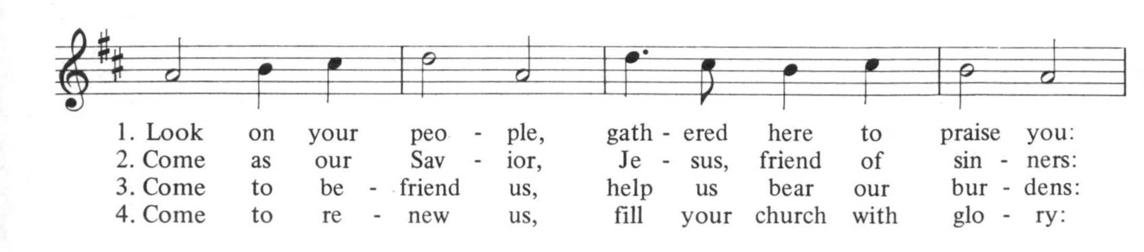
1. Look on your peo - ple, gath - ered here to praise you:
2. Come as our Sav - ior, Je - sus, friend of sin - ners:
3. Come to be - friend us, help us bear our bur - dens:
4. Come to re - new us, fill your church with glo - ry:

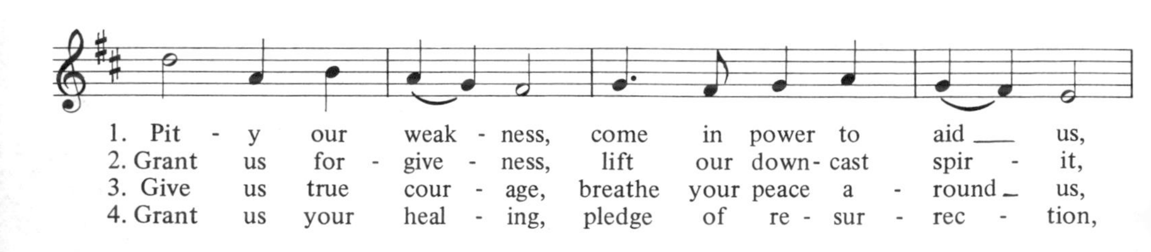
1. Pit - y our weak - ness, come in power to aid ___ us,
2. Grant us for - give - ness, lift our down - cast spir - it,
3. Give us true cour - age, breathe your peace a - round _ us,
4. Grant us your heal - ing, pledge of re - sur - rec - tion,

1. Source of all bless - ing.
2. Heal us and save ___ us.
3. Stay with us al - ways.
4. Fore - taste of heav - en.

Text: J. Quinn, S.J.,
Tune: *Christe sanctorum,* French melody, in "Antiphone", Paris, 1681.

Father, We Thank Thee

158

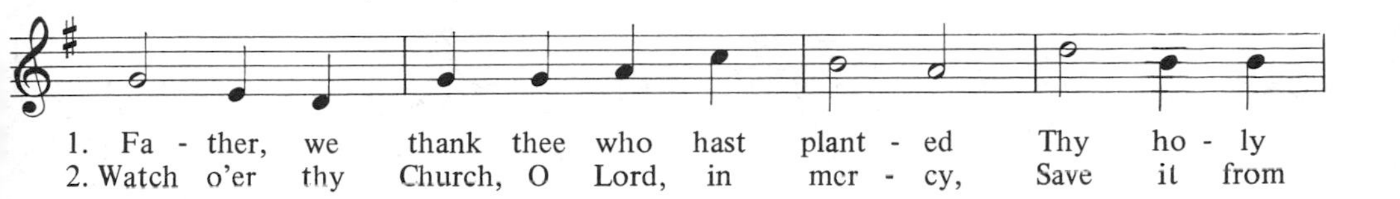
1. Fa - ther, we thank thee who hast plant - ed Thy ho - ly
2. Watch o'er thy Church, O Lord, in mer - cy, Save it from

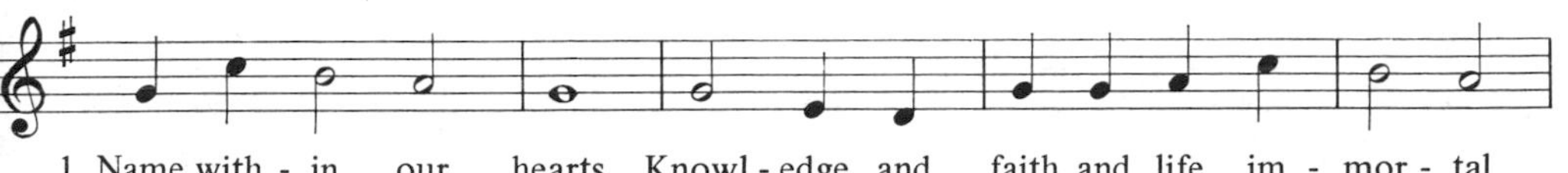
1. Name with - in our hearts. Knowl - edge and faith and life im - mor - tal,
2. e - vil, guard it still, Per - fect it in thy love, u - nite it,

1. Je - sus thy Son to us im - parts. Thou, Lord, didst make all for thy
2. Cleansed and con - formed un - to thy will. As grain, once scat - tered on the

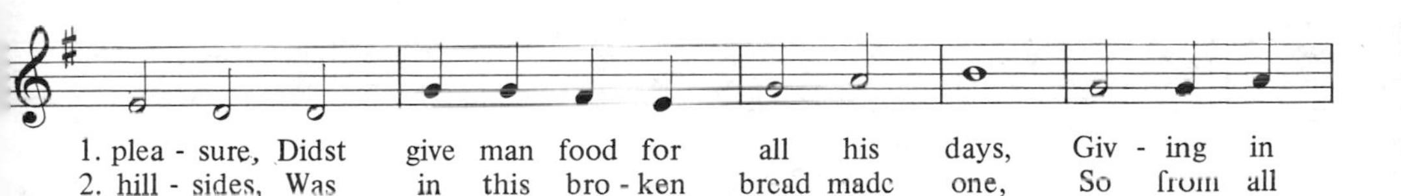
1. plea - sure, Didst give man food for all his days, Giv - ing in
2. hill - sides, Was in this bro - ken bread made one, So from all

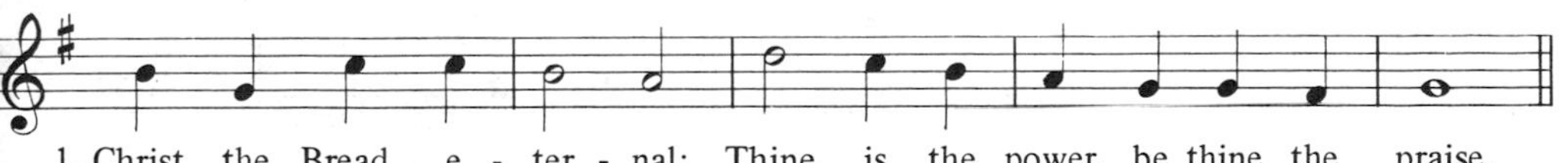
1. Christ the Bread e - ter - nal; Thine is the power, be thine the praise.
2. lands thy Church be gath - ered In - to thy king - dom by thy Son.

Text: From the *Didache*, 2nd Century. Trans. F. Bland Tucker.

Tune: *Rendez à Dieu*, L. Bourgeois, +1561.

157 For All the Saints

1. For all the saints, who from their la - bors
2. O blest com - mun - ion, fel - low - ship di -
3. But lo! there breaks a yet more glo - rious
4. From earth's wide bounds, from o - cean's far - thest
1. rest, Who thee by faith be -
2. vine! We fee - bly strug - gle,
3. day, The saints tri - umph - ant
4. coast, Through gates of pearl streams
1. fore the world con - fessed, Thy name, O
2. they in glo - ry shine; Yet all are
3. rise in bright ar - ray; The King of
4. in the count - less host, Sing - ing to
Je - sus, be for - ev - er blest.
one in thee, for all are thine.
Glo - ry pass - es on his way.
Fa - ther, Son and Ho - ly Ghost.
Al -
le - lu - ia, Al - le - lu - ia.

Text: W. How, +1897.
Tune: *Sine nomine,* R. Vaughan Williams, +1958. From the "English Hymnal", Oxford University Press. Used with permission.

For the Beauty of the Earth

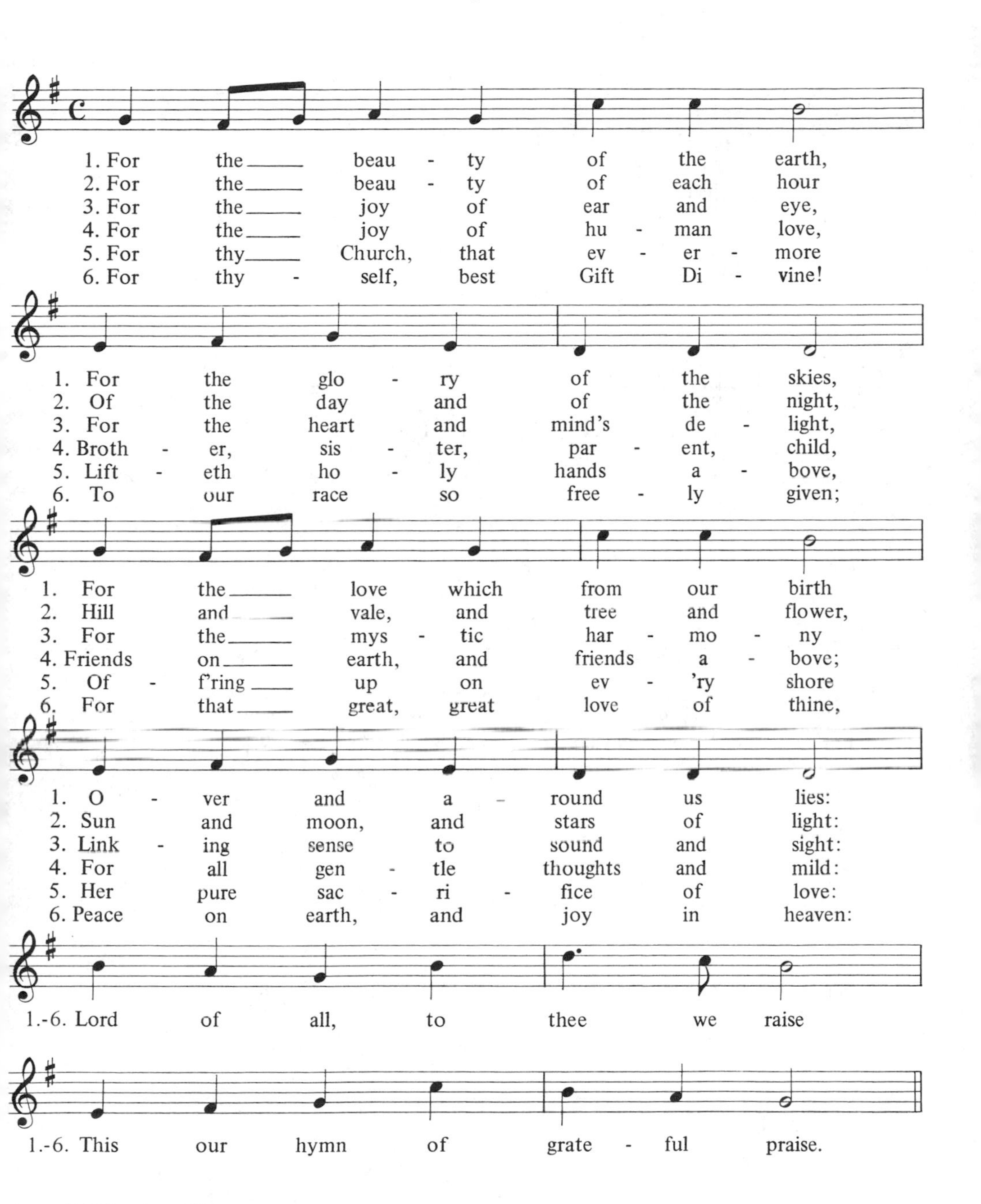
1. For the beau - ty of the earth,
2. For the beau - ty of each hour
3. For the joy of ear and eye,
4. For the joy of hu - man love,
5. For thy Church, that ev - er - more
6. For thy - self, best Gift Di - vine!
1. For the glo - ry of the skies,
2. Of the day and of the night,
3. For the heart and mind's de - light,
4. Broth - er, sis - ter, par - ent, child,
5. Lift - eth ho - ly hands a - bove,
6. To our race so free - ly given;
1. For the love which from our birth
2. Hill and vale, and tree and flower,
3. For the mys - tic har - mo - ny
4. Friends on earth, and friends a - bove;
5. Of - f'ring up on ev - 'ry shore
6. For that great, great love of thine,
1. O - ver and a - round us lies:
2. Sun and moon, and stars of light:
3. Link - ing sense to sound and sight:
4. For all gen - tle thoughts and mild:
5. Her pure sac - ri - fice of love:
6. Peace on earth, and joy in heaven:
1.-6. Lord of all, to thee we raise
1.-6. This our hymn of grate - ful praise.

Text: F.S. Pierpoint, +1917.
Tune: *Dix*, C. Kocher, +1872, W.H. Monic, +1889, alt.

159 For the Fruit of All Creation

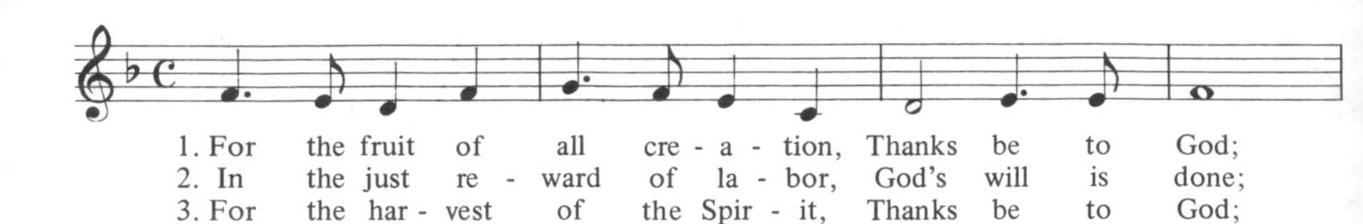
1. For the fruit of all cre - a - tion, Thanks be to God;
2. In the just re - ward of la - bor, God's will is done;
3. For the har - vest of the Spir - it, Thanks be to God;

1. For his gifts to ev - 'ry na - tion, Thanks be to God;
2. In the help we give our neigh - bor, God's will is done;
3. For the good we all in - her - it, Thanks be to God.

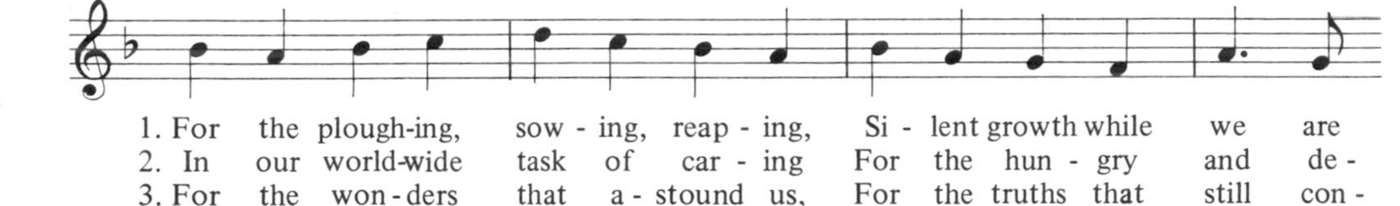
1. For the plough-ing, sow - ing, reap - ing, Si - lent growth while we are
2. In our world-wide task of car - ing For the hun - gry and de -
3. For the won - ders that a - stound us, For the truths that still con -

1. sleep - ing, Fu - ture needs in earth's safe keep - ing, Thanks be to God.
2. spair - ing, In the har - vests we are shar - ing, God's will is done.
3. found us, Most of all, that love has found us, Thanks be to God.

Text: F.P. Green.
Tune: *Ar hyd y nos,* Welsh Folk Melody.

Forth in the Peace of Christ We Go

1. Forth in the peace of Christ we go;
2. King of our hearts, Christ makes us kings;
3. Priests of the world, Christ sends us forth
4. Christ's are our lips, his word we speak;
5. We are the Church; Christ bids us show
1. Christ to the world with joy we bring;
2. King - ship with him his ser - vants gain;
3. The world of time to con - se - crate,
4. Proph - ets are we whose deeds pro - claim
5. That in his Church all na - tions find
1. Christ in our minds, Christ on our lips,
2. With Christ the Ser - vant - Lord of all
3. The world of sin by grace to heal,
4. Christ's truth in love that we may be
5. Their hearth and home where Christ re - stores
1. Christ in our hearts, the world's true King.
2. Christ's world we serve to share Christ's reign.
3. Christ's world in Christ to re - cre - ate.
4. Christ in the world to spread Christ's name.
5. True peace, true love, to all man - kind.

Tune: *Andernach,* anon.,1608.

Forth in Thy Name, O Lord

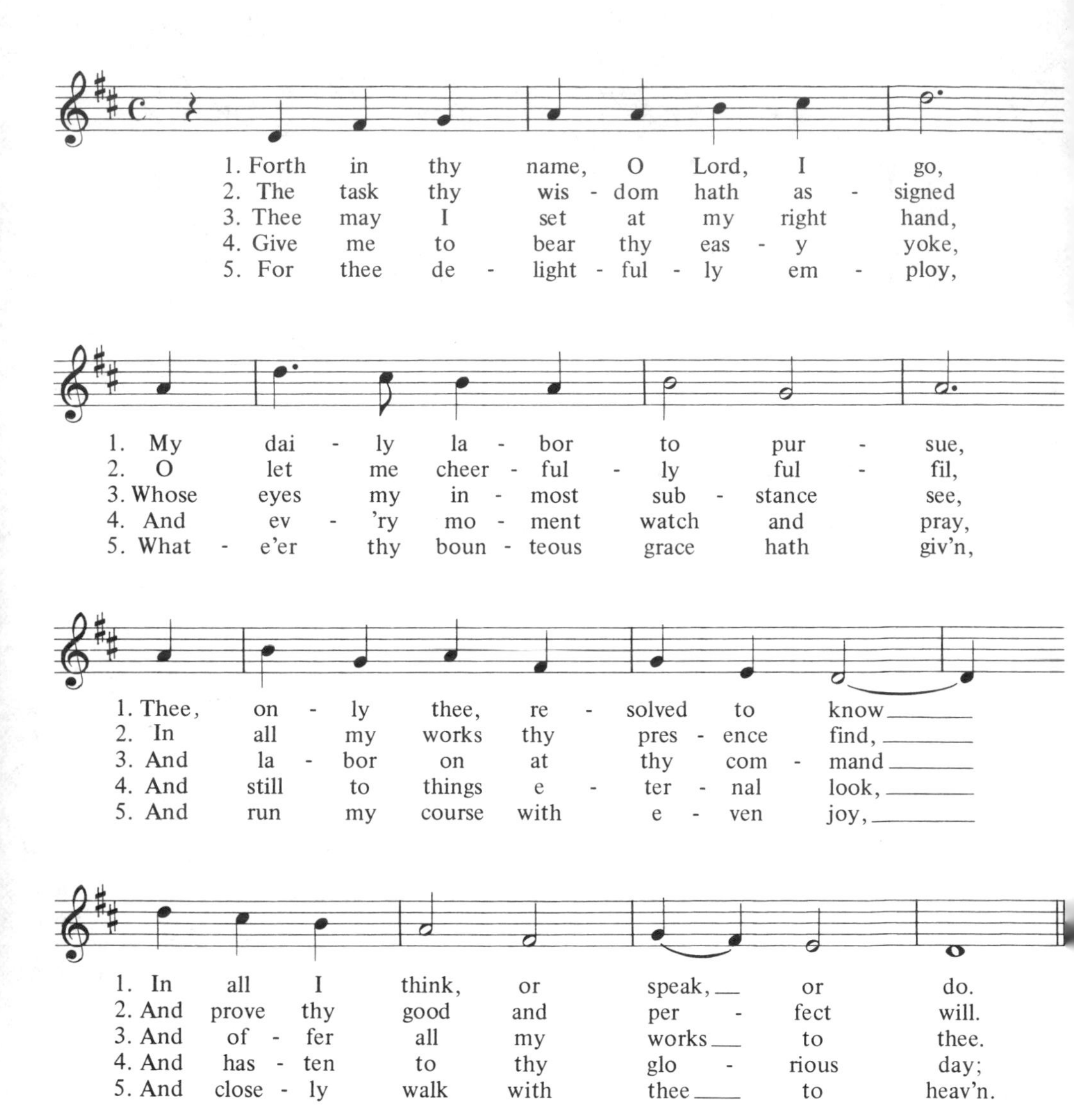
1. Forth in thy name, O Lord, I go,
2. The task thy wis - dom hath as - signed
3. Thee may I set at my right hand,
4. Give me to bear thy eas - y yoke,
5. For thee de - light - ful - ly em - ploy,
1. My dai - ly la - bor to pur - sue,
2. O let me cheer - ful - ly ful - fil,
3. Whose eyes my in - most sub - stance see,
4. And ev - 'ry mo - ment watch and pray,
5. What - e'er thy boun - teous grace hath giv'n,
1. Thee, on - ly thee, re - solved to know
2. In all my works thy pres - ence find,
3. And la - bor on at thy com - mand
4. And still to things e - ter - nal look,
5. And run my course with e - ven joy,
1. In all I think, or speak, or do.
2. And prove thy good and per - fect will.
3. And of - fer all my works to thee.
4. And has - ten to thy glo - rious day;
5. And close - ly walk with thee to heav'n.

Text: Charles Wesley, +1788.
Tune: *Andernach,* anon. 1608.

Give Thanks to God for He Is Good

Ps. 136

1. Give thanks to God for he is good; His mer-cy lives for - ev - er.
2. The Lord a - lone did won-drous things; His mer-cy lives for - ev - er.
3. He made the star - ry lights to rise; His mer-cy lives for - ev - er.
4. He res - cues us from ev - 'ry foe: His mer-cy lives for - ev - er.
1. His kind-ness from of old has stood; His love will keep us_ ev - er.
2. Now thank the might - y King of kings; His love will keep us_ ev - er.
3. His glo - ries shine in ra - diant skies; His love will keep us_ ev - er.
4. He feeds his crea-tures here be - low; His love will keep us_ ev - er.
1. The God of gods, the sov - 'reign Lord, O bless him
2. His wis - dom made the heav'ns to be; He spread the
3. Praise him whose moon a - dorns the night; His sun fills
4. Give thanks to God, the might - y King; Let all on
1. all with_ one ac - cord: His love is ev - er - last - ing.
2. earth a - bove the sea: His love is ev - er - last - ing.
3. all with_ morn - ing light: His love is ev - er - last - ing.
4. earth his_ prais - es sing: His love is ev - er - last - ing.

Text: Psalm 136 paraphrase, J. Dunn. © by author. Used with permission.
Tune: *Was Gott tut das ist wohlgetan,* Severus Gastorius, c. 1650.

God, Father, Praise and Glory

1. God, Fa - ther, praise and glo - ry, Thy chil - dren bring to thee; Good -
2. And thou, Lord Co - e - ter - nal, God's sole _ be - got - ten Son; O
3. O Ho - ly Ghost, Cre - a - tor, Thou gift _ of God most high; Life,
4. O Fa - ther, Son, and Spir - it, All crea - tures thee a - dore, The
1. will and peace to man - kind Shall now _ for - ev - er be.
2. Je - sus, King a - noint - ed Who hast _ re - demp - tion won,
3. love and sa - cred unc - tion Our weak - ness thou sup - ply.
4. Three in One u - nit - ed For now _ and ev - er - more.
1.-4. O most Ho - ly Trin - i - ty, Un - di - vid - ed _ Un - i - ty,
1.-4. Ho - ly God, Might - y God, God Im - mor - tal, be a - dored!

Text: Verses 1-3, anon. Trans. J. Rothensteiner, +1936,
Martin Hellriegel, +1981. Used with permission.
Verse 4, J. Dunn. © by author. Used with permission.
Tune: *Mainz*, anon.,1661.

Godhead Here in Hiding

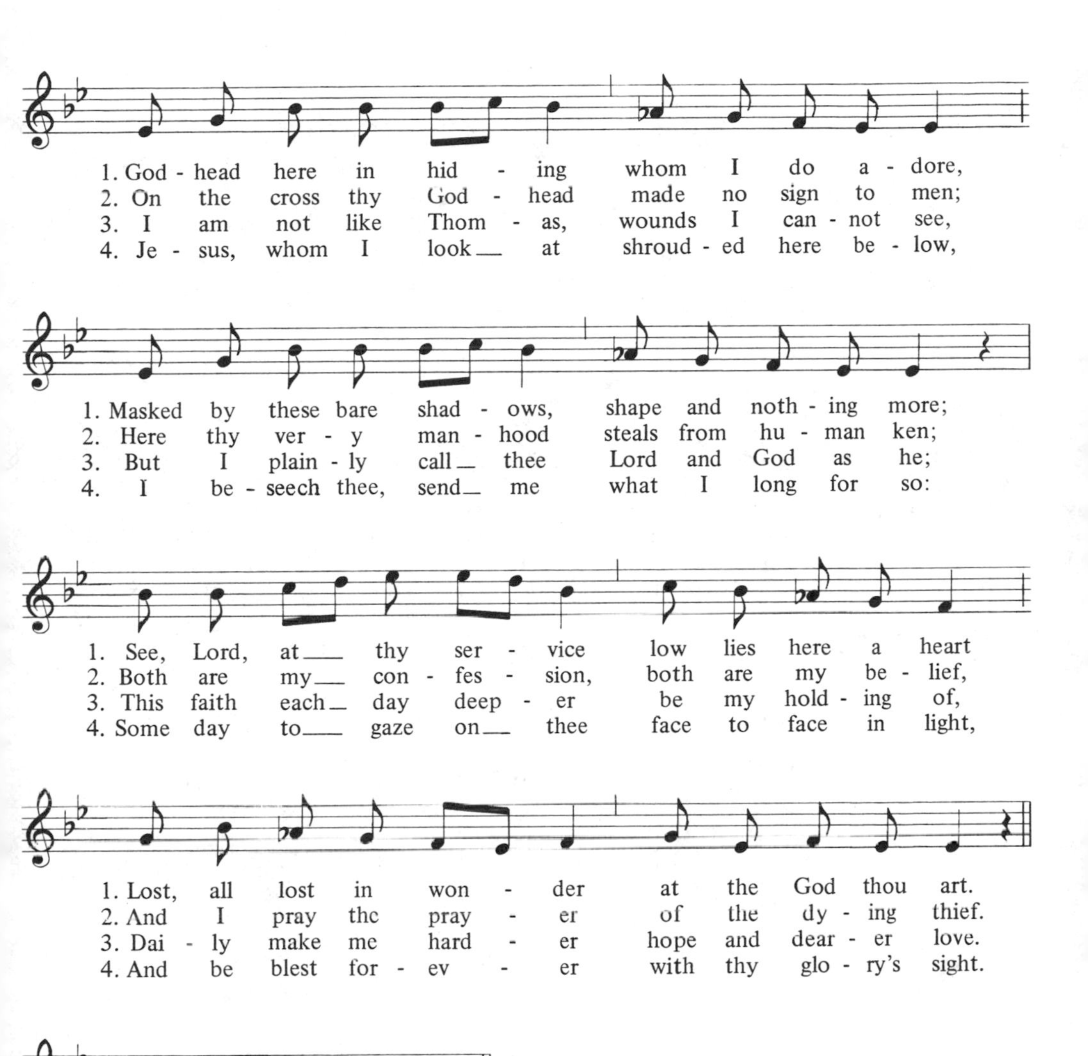
1. God - head here in hid - ing whom I do a - dore,
2. On the cross thy God - head made no sign to men;
3. I am not like Thom - as, wounds I can - not see,
4. Je - sus, whom I look at shroud - ed here be - low,
1. Masked by these bare shad - ows, shape and noth - ing more;
2. Here thy ver - y man - hood steals from hu - man ken;
3. But I plain - ly call thee Lord and God as he;
4. I be - seech thee, send me what I long for so:
1. See, Lord, at thy ser - vice low lies here a heart
2. Both are my con - fes - sion, both are my be - lief,
3. This faith each day deep - er be my hold - ing of,
4. Some day to gaze on thee face to face in light,
1. Lost, all lost in won - der at the God thou art.
2. And I pray the pray - er of the dy - ing thief.
3. Dai - ly make me hard - er hope and dear - er love.
4. And be blest for - ev - er with thy glo - ry's sight.
A - men.

Text: Ascribed to St. Thomas Aquinas, +1274. Trans. G.M. Hopkins, +1889, alt.
Tune: *Adoro te,* Plainchant, Mode 5.

165

God Is My Strong Salvation

Ps. 27

1. God is my strong sal - va - tion; What foe have I to fear? In
2. Though hosts en - camp a - round me, Firm in the fight I stand; What
3. From him thro' faith a - bid - ing Comes strength to per - se - vere; With
4. His might thy heart shall strength-en, His love thy joy in - crease; Mer -

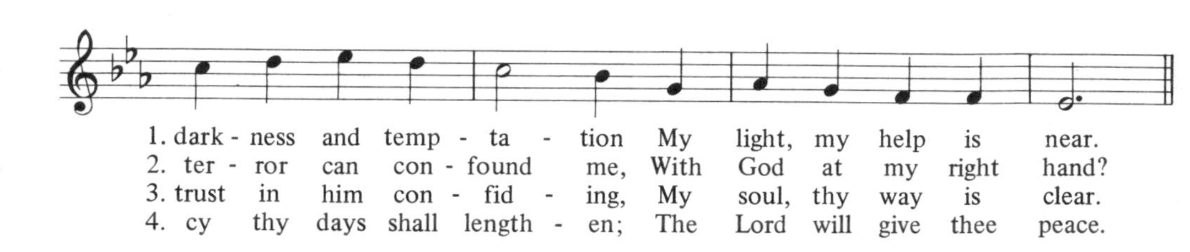
1. dark - ness and temp - ta - tion My light, my help is near.
2. ter - ror can con - found me, With God at my right hand?
3. trust in him con - fid - ing, My soul, thy way is clear.
4. cy thy days shall length - en; The Lord will give thee peace.

Text: Psalm 27 paraphrase, J. Montgomery, +1854, alt.
Tune: *Christus der ist mein Leben,* M. Vulpius, +1615.

God of Gods, We Sound His Praises

166

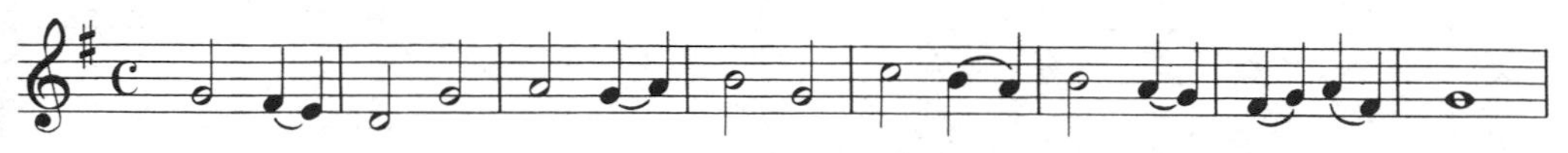

1. God of gods, we sound his praises, Highest heav'n its homage brings;
2. Christians in their hearts enthrone him, Tell his praises wide abroad;
3. Hail the Christ, the King of glory, He whose praise the angels cry,
4. Lord, we look for your returning, Teach us so to walk your ways,

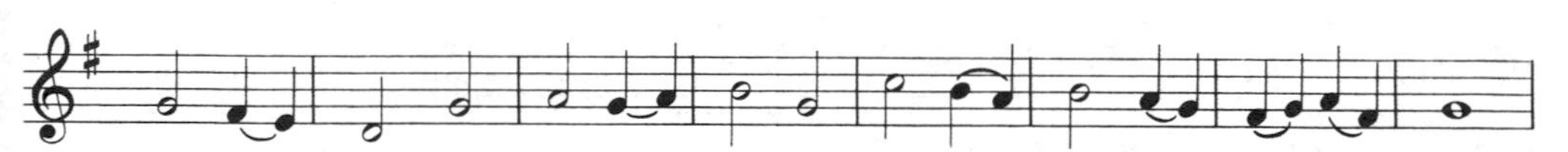

1. Earth and all creation raises Glory to the King of kings.
2. Prophets, priests, apostles own him, Martyrs' crown and saints' reward.
3. Born to share our human story, Love and labor, grieve and die.
4. Hearts and minds your will discerning, Lives alight with joy and praise.

1. Holy, holy, holy name him, Lord of all his hosts proclaim him,
2. Three in One his glory sharing, Earth and heav'n his praise declaring,
3. By his cross his work completed, Sinners ransomed, death defeated,
4. In your love and care enfold us, By your constancy uphold us,

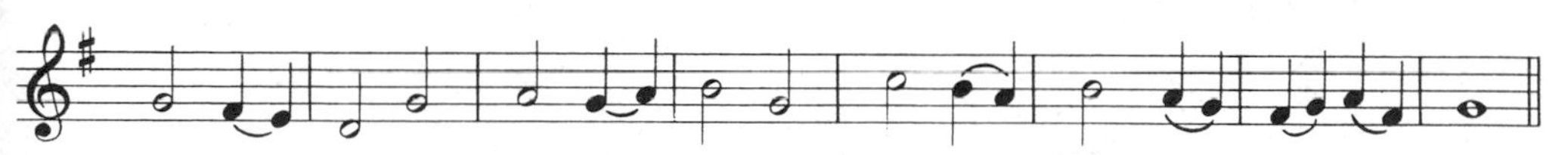

1. To the everlasting Father Ev'ry tongue in triumph sings.
2. Praise the high majestic Father, Praise the everlasting Lord.
3. In the glory of the Father Christ ascended reigns on high.
4. May your mercy, Lord and Father, Keep us now and all our days.

Text: *Te Deum,* ascribed to St. Nicetas, +415, Paraphrase by T. Dudley-Smith,

Tune: *In Babilone,* Dutch Melody, c.1710.

167

God of Our Fathers

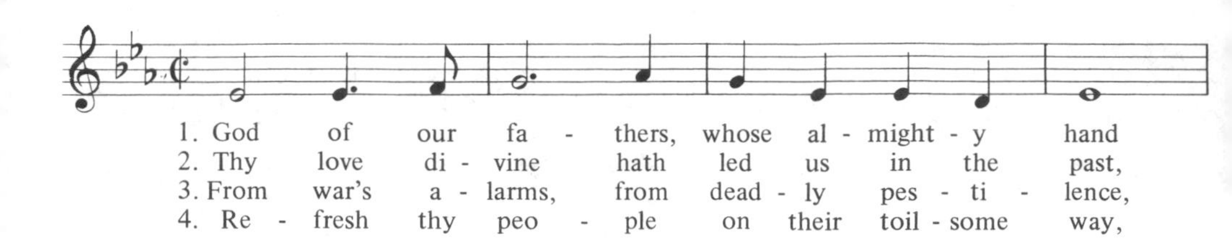
1. God of our fa - thers, whose al - might - y hand
2. Thy love di - vine hath led us in the past,
3. From war's a - larms, from dead - ly pes - ti - lence,
4. Re - fresh thy peo - ple on their toil - some way,

1. Leads forth in beau - ty all the star - ry band
2. In this free land by thee our lot is cast.
3. Be thy strong arm our ev - er sure de - fense;
4. Lead us from night to nev - er - end - ing day;

1. Of shin - ing worlds in splen - dor through the skies,
2. Be thou our rul - er, guar - dian, guide and stay,
3. Thy true re - li - gion in our hearts in - crease,
4. Fill all our lives with love and grace di - vine,

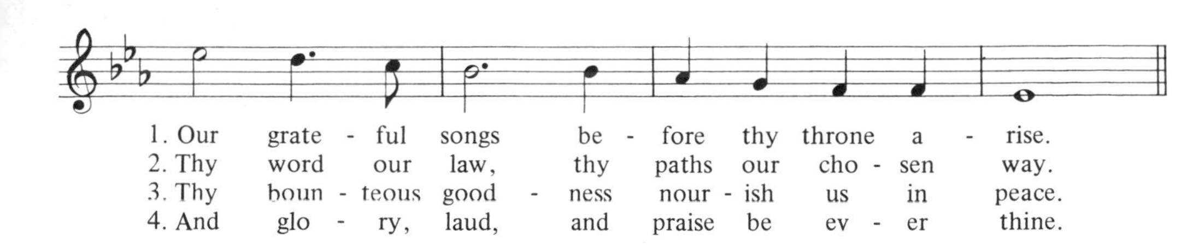
1. Our grate - ful songs be - fore thy throne a - rise.
2. Thy word our law, thy paths our cho - sen way.
3. Thy boun - teous good - ness nour - ish us in peace.
4. And glo - ry, laud, and praise be ev - er thine.

Text: D.C. Roberts, +1907.
Tune: *National Hymn,* G.W. Warren, +1902.

God of All Mercy, Lord Above

Ps. 51

1. God of all mer - cy, Lord ______ a - bove, Show your com -
2. Be - fore you I con - fess ______ my wrong, And pray you
3. God of all mer - cy, hear ______ my prayer, And keep me
4. Sal - va - tion's joy to me ______ re - store; From death now

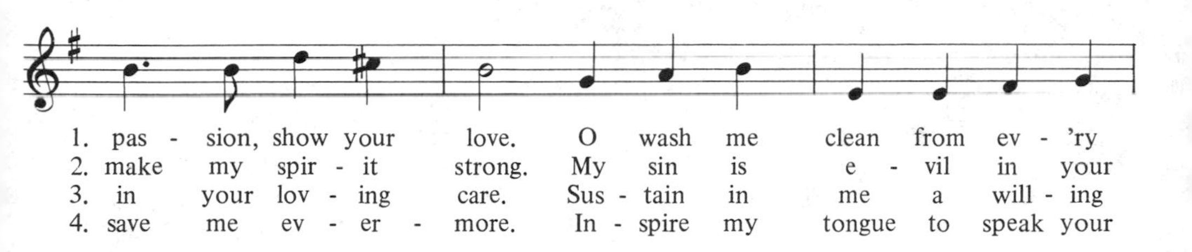
1. pas - sion, show your love. O wash me clean from ev - 'ry
2. make my spir - it strong. My sin is e - vil in your
3. in your lov - ing care. Sus - tain in me a will - ing
4. save me ev - er - more. In - spire my tongue to speak your

1. sin, And make my heart re - newed with - in.
2. sight; Be kind to judge my heart con - trite.
3. heart, And let your spir - it ne'er de - part.
4. praise, And sing your mer - cy all my days.

169

God of Mercy, God of Grace

Ps. 67

1. God of mer - cy, God of grace, Show the bright - ness
2. Let the peo - ple praise thee, Lord; Be by all that
3. Let the peo - ple praise thee, Lord; Earth shall then her
1. of thy face. Shine up - on us, Sav - ior, shine,
2. live a - dored. Let the na - tions shout and sing:
3. fruits af - ford. God to man his bless - ing give,
1. Fill thy Church with light di - vine, And thy sav - ing
2. Glo - ry to their Sav - ior King! At thy feet their
3. Man to God de - vot - ed live; All be - low, and
1. health ex - tend Un - to earth's re - mot - est end.
2. trib - ute pay And thy ho - ly will o - bey.
3. all a - bove, One in joy and light and love.

Text: Psalm 67 paraphrase, H.F. Lyte, +1847.
Tune: *Ratisbon,* J.G. Werner, +1822, ed. "Choralbuch", 1815.

Hail, Holy Queen

1. Hail, ho - ly Queen, en - throned a - bove,
2. Our life, our sweet - ness here be - low,
3. To thee we cry, poor heirs of Eve,
4. O gen - tle, lov - ing, ho - ly One,
1. O Ma - ri - a! Hail, Moth - er of mer - cy
2. O Ma - ri - a! Our hope in sor - row
3. O Ma - ri - a! To thee we sigh, we
4. O Ma - ri - a! The God of light be -
REFRAIN
1. and of love, O Ma - ri - a!
2. and in woe, O Ma - ri - a!
3. mourn, we grieve, O Ma - ri - a!
4. came your Son, O Ma - ri - a!
Tri - umph, all ye
1.-4. cher - u - bim, Sing with us, ye ser - a - phim;
1.-4. Heav'n and earth re - sound the hymn: Sal - ve,
1.-4. sal - ve, sal - ve Re - gi - na!

Text: Salve Regina paraphrase, anon.
Tune: *Salve Regina*, traditional.

171

Hail, O Holy Queen!
Salve Regina

Compline Anthem During Ordinary Time

Cantor(s)
All
Hail, O Ho - ly Queen! Hail, O Moth - er all mer - ci - ful, our life,
Sal - ve Re - gí - na, Ma - ter mi - se - ri - cór - di - ae: Vi - ta,

our sweet - ness, and our hope, we hail _ thee! To thee do we cry, poor
dul - cé - do, et spes no - stra, sal - ve. Ad te cla - má-mus, éx -

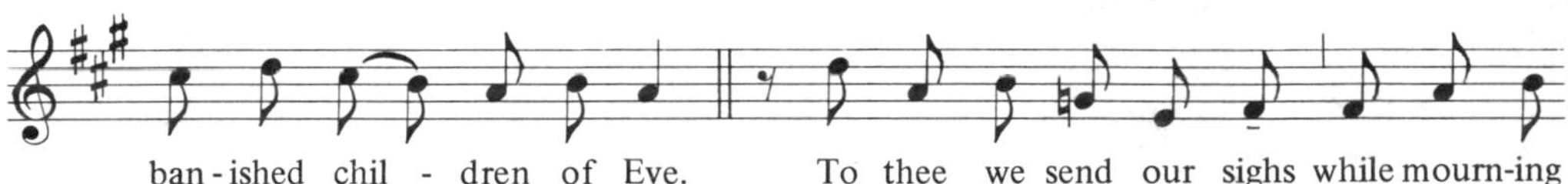
ban - ished chil - dren of Eve. To thee we send our sighs while mourn-ing
su - les, fí - li - i He - vae. Ad te su - spi - rá - mus, ge - mén - tes

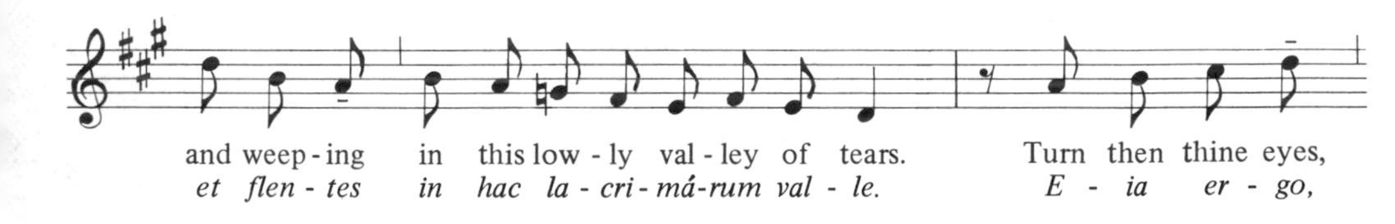
and weep - ing in this low - ly val - ley of tears. Turn then thine eyes,
et flen - tes in hac la - cri - má-rum val - le. E - ia er - go,

most gra-cious Ad - vo - cate, O turn thine eyes, so lov - ing and com -
Ad - vo - cá - ta no - stra, il - los tu - os mi - se - ri - cór - des

pas - sion - ate, up - on us sin - ners. And Je - su, the most bless -
ó - cu - los ad nos con - vér - te. Et Je - sum, be - ne - dí -

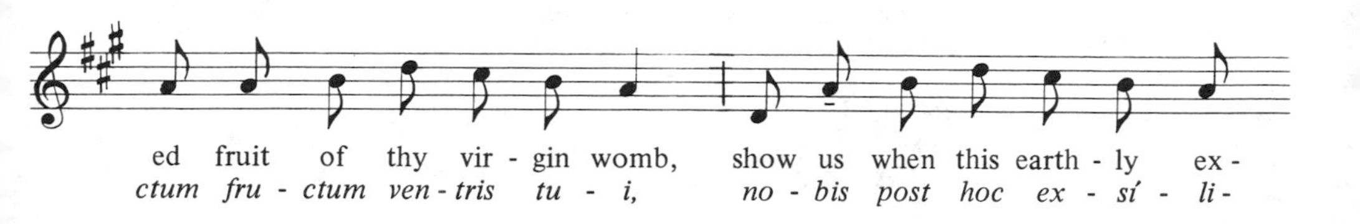
ed fruit of thy vir - gin womb, show us when this earth - ly ex -
ctum fru - ctum ven - tris tu - i, no - bis post hoc ex - sí - li -

ile is end - ed. O clem - ent. O lov - ing.
um os - tén - de. O cle - mens. O pi - a.

O most sweet, Vir - gin Mar - y.
O dul - cis, Vir - go Ma - rí - a.

℣. Pray for us, O holy Mother of God.
℟. That we may become worthy of the promises of Christ.

℣. Ora pro nobis Sancta Dei Génitrix.
℟. Ut digni efficiámur promissiónibus Christi.

Text: Hermann Contractus, +1054. English adaptation by T.M.

Tune: Plainchant, Mode 5.

172 Hail Mary, Queen of Heav'n
Ave Regina Caelorum

Compline Anthem During Lent

Cantor (s)
All

Hail Mar - y, Queen of Heav'n en - throned! Hail, by all the an - gels
A - ve Re - gí - na cae - ló - rum, A - ve Dó - mi - na An-

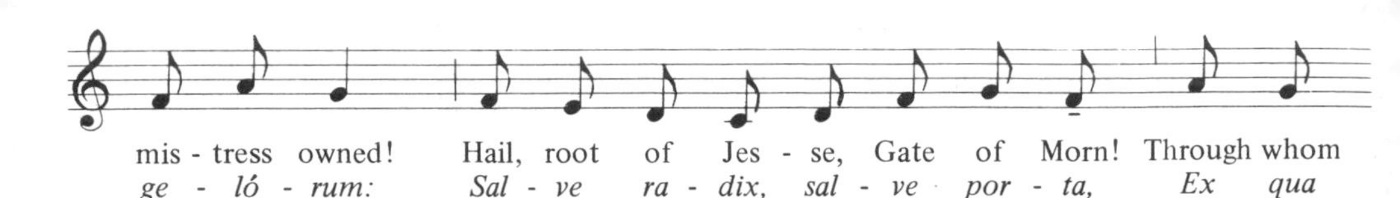

mis - tress owned! Hail, root of Jes - se, Gate of Morn! Through whom
ge - ló - rum: Sal - ve ra - dix, sal - ve por - ta, Ex qua

the world's true light was born! O glo - rious Vir - gin, joy to thee,
mun - do lux est or - ta: Gau - de, Vir - go glo - ri - ó - sa,

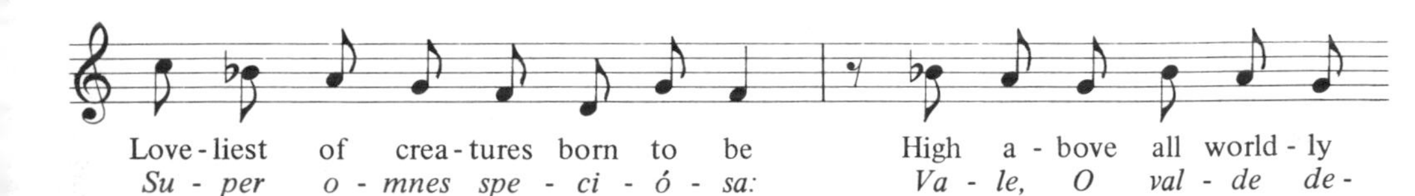

Love - liest of crea - tures born to be High a - bove all world - ly
Su - per o - mnes spe - ci - ó - sa: Va - le, O val - de de-

sta - tion, Bring to Je - sus our sup - pli - ca - tion.
có - ra, Et pro no - bis Chri - stum ex - ó - ra.

℣. Grant that I may be worthy to praise thee, O holy Virgin.
℟. Give me strength against thy enemies.

℣. Dignáre me laudáre te Virgo sacráta.
℟. Da mihi virtútem contra hostes tuos.

Text: 12th Century, anon. English adaptation by T.M. in "Pius X Hymnal",

Tune: Plainchant, Mode 6.

Hail, Redeemer, King Divine!

1. Hail, Re - deem - er, King di - vine! Priest and Lamb, the throne is thine, King whose reign shall nev - er cease, Prince of ev - er - last - ing peace.
2. Let thy sub - jects all pro - claim Hon - or to thy ho - ly name, Till in peace each na - tion rings With thy prais - es, King of kings.
3. King most ho - ly, King of truth, Guide the low - ly, guide the youth; Christ thou King of glo - ry bright, Be to us e - ter - nal Light.
4. Hymns of glo - ry, songs of praise Let the earth and heav - ens raise, To the King by all a - dored, Ho - ly, might - y, gra - cious Lord.
REFRAIN
1.-4. An - gels, saints and na - tions sing, "Praise be Je - sus Christ, our King; Lord of life, earth, sky and sea, King of all for - ev - er be."

Text: Verses 1-3, P. Brennan, C.S.S.R., +1952, alt.
Text published by kind permission of Search Press Ltd., London.
Verse 4, J. Dunn. ©by author. Used with permission.
Tune: *Salzburg*, J. Hintze, +1702.

174 Hail, O Once Despised Jesus!

First Tune
1. Hail, O once de - spis - ed Je - sus! Hail, our Gal - i -
2. Pas - chal Lamb, by God ap - point - ed, All our sins on
3. Je - sus, King of heav'n all glo - rious, There for - ev - er
4. Hail, O Lord of our sal - va - tion, Live with - in us
1. le - an King! Lord, who suf - fered to re - lease us,
2. you were laid. By al - mighty - y love a - noint - ed,
3. to a - bide; Hope of Chris - tians, Lord vic - to - rious,
4. all our days. Ran - somed souls from ev - 'ry na - tion,
1. Son of heav'n, to you we sing. Hail, O u - ni -
2. You have full a - tone - ment made. All your peo - ple
3. Seat - ed at your Fa - ther's side, There for sin - ners
4. Ren - der thanks and end - less praise. Lamb of God, our
1. ver - sal Sav - ior, Bear - er of our sin and shame! By your
2. are for - giv - en Through the vir - tue of your blood; O - pened
3. al - ways plead - ing, Set - ting trou - bled hearts to rest, Ev - er
4. Christ, we name you; Hear our grate - ful voi - ces cry. Prince of
1. mer - it we find fa - vor: Life is giv - en through your Name.
2. is the gate of heav - en, We shall live in peace with God.
3. for us in - ter - ced - ing, Till in glo - ry we are blessed.
4. life we now pro - claim you, God Al - might - y, Lord most High.

Text: J. Blakewell, +1757, M. Madan, +1760. Alterations © by J. Dunn.
Used with permission.
Tune: *Rex gloriae*, H. Smart, +1879.

Hail, O Once Despised Jesus! 175

Second Tune

1. Hail, O once de spis - ed Je - sus! Hail, our Gal - i -
2. Pas - chal Lamb, by God ap - point - ed, All our sins on
3. Je - sus, King of heav'n all glo - rious, There for - ev - er
4. Hail, O Lord of our sal - va - tion, Live with - in - us

1. le - an King! Lord, who suf - fered to re - lease us,
2. you were laid. By al - might - y love a - noint - ed,
3. to a - bide; Hope of Chris - tians, Lord vic - to - rious,
4. all our days. Ran - somed souls from ev - 'ry na - tion,

1. Son of heav'n, to you we sing. Hail, O u - ni -
2. You have full a - tone - ment made. All your peo - ple
3. Seat - ed at your Fa - ther's side, There for sin - ners
4. Ren - der thanks and end - less praise. Lamb of God, our

1. ver - sal Sav - ior, Bear - er of our sin and shame! By thy
2. are for - giv - en Through the vir - tue of your blood; O - pened
3. al - ways plead - ing, Set - ting trou - bled hearts to rest, Ev - er
4. Christ, we name you, Hear our grate - ful voi - ces cry. Prince of

1. mer - it we find fa - vor: Life is giv - en through your Name.
2. is the gate of heav - en, We shall live in peace with God.
3. for us in - ter - ced - ing, Till in glo - ry we are blessed.
4. life we now pro - claim you, God Al - might - y, Lord Most High.

Text: J. Blakewell, +1757, M. Madan, +1760. Alterations © by J. Dunn. Used with permission.
Tune: *In Babilone,* Dutch melody, c. 1760.

176 Hail the Day That Sees Him Rise

1. Hail the day that sees him_ rise, Al - le - lu - ia!
2. There the glo - rious tri - umph_ waits; Al - le - lu - ia!
3. See! he lifts his hands a - bove; Al - le - lu - ia!
4. Lord, tho' part - ed from our_ sight, Al - le - lu - ia!

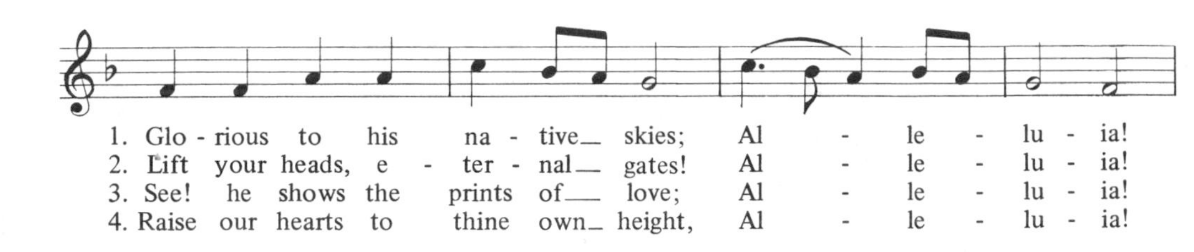
1. Glo - rious to his na - tive_ skies; Al - le - lu - ia!
2. Lift your heads, e - ter - nal_ gates! Al - le - lu - ia!
3. See! he shows the prints of_ love; Al - le - lu - ia!
4. Raise our hearts to thine own_ height, Al - le - lu - ia!

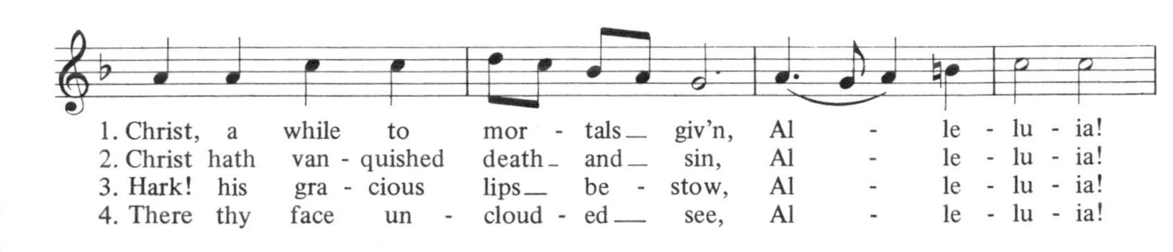
1. Christ, a while to mor - tals_ giv'n, Al - le - lu - ia!
2. Christ hath van - quished death_ and_ sin, Al - le - lu - ia!
3. Hark! his gra - cious lips_ be - stow, Al - le - lu - ia!
4. There thy face un - cloud - ed_ see, Al - le - lu - ia!

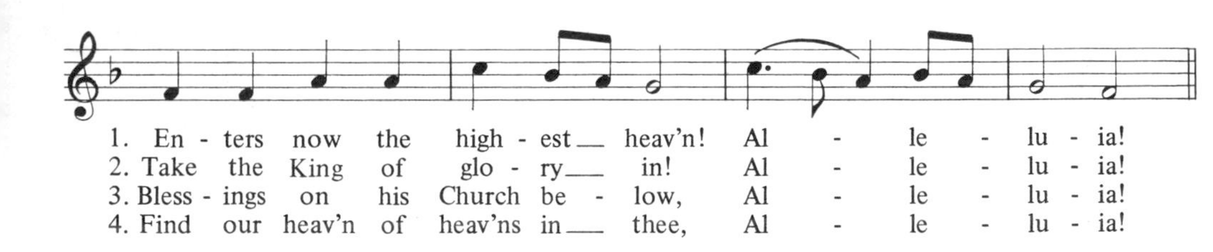
1. En - ters now the high - est_ heav'n! Al - le - lu - ia!
2. Take the King of glo - ry_ in! Al - le - lu - ia!
3. Bless - ings on his Church be - low, Al - le - lu - ia!
4. Find our heav'n of heav'ns in_ thee, Al - le - lu - ia!

Text: C. Wesley, +1788, alt.
Tune: *Llanfair*, R. Williams, +1821.

Hail the Sign, the Cross of Jesus **177**

1. Hail the Sign, the Cross of Je - sus, Hail ex - alt - ed tree,
2. Source of strength to Chris - tian peo - ple, Loft - y tree so dear,
3. Source of mar - tyrs, stead - fast cour - age, Tree which all re - vere,
4. Sign that Je - sus loves his peo - ple, Tree on which he died,
1. Roy - al Stan - dard of the Mon - arch, Lord, who set us free.
2. Grant - ing hope and in - spir - a - tion, Faith to per - se - vere:
3. Ref - uge, hope, to saints and sin - ners, Sav - ing Sign, so clear:
4. Pas - chal joy to all im - part - ing, New life to pro - vide:
REFRAIN
1.-4. Hail the Cross! True Sign of glo - ry, Tell - ing all sal -
1.-4. va - tion's sto - ry, No - ble tree di - vine!

178

Hail, This Festival Day!

Blessed Virgin Mary

REFRAIN

All
Hail, this fes - ti - val day! Blest day to be hal-lowed for - ev - er When

Fine
we in___ Mar - y's praise Our joy - ful___ an - them raise.

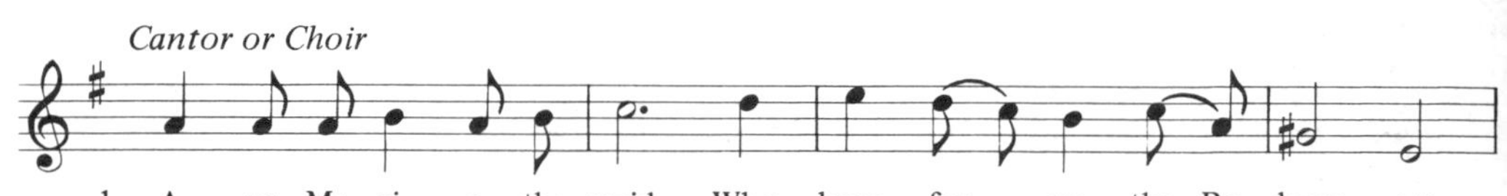
Cantor or Choir
1. A - ve Ma - ri - a, the maid Who bore for___ us the Re - deem - er;
3. Star of the o - cean most fair, O lead us to Christ, our___ broth - er;

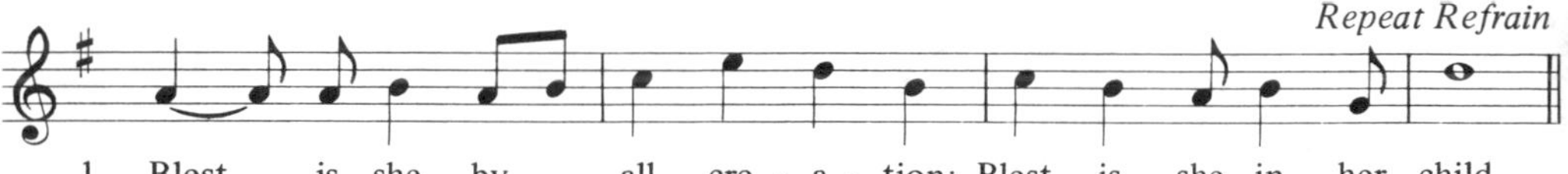
Repeat Refrain
1. Blest___ is she by___ all cre - a - tion; Blest is she in her child.
3. Pray God de-fend us,___ ev - er guide us, Show us his lov - ing care.

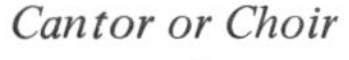
Cantor or Choir

3 3
2. A - ve Ma - ri - a, the Vir - gin Moth - er, Pray for us sin - ners.
4. Sing out her prais - es, ye choirs of an - gels, Sing all ye peo - ples.

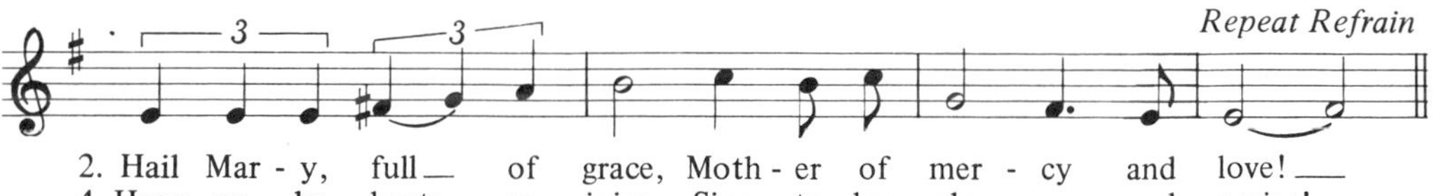
3 3
Repeat Refrain
2. Hail Mar - y, full___ of grace, Moth - er of mer - cy and love!___
4. Heav - en - ly hosts___ re - joice; Sing to her glo - ry and praise!___

Text: J. Dunn. © by author. Used with permission.
Tune: *Salve feste dies,* R. Vaughan Williams, +1958. © 1906 "The English Hymnal", Oxford University Press, London. Used with permission.

Hail, This Festival Day!

Christ the King

REFRAIN

All
Hail, this fes - ti - val day! Blest day to be hal-lowed for - ev - er When

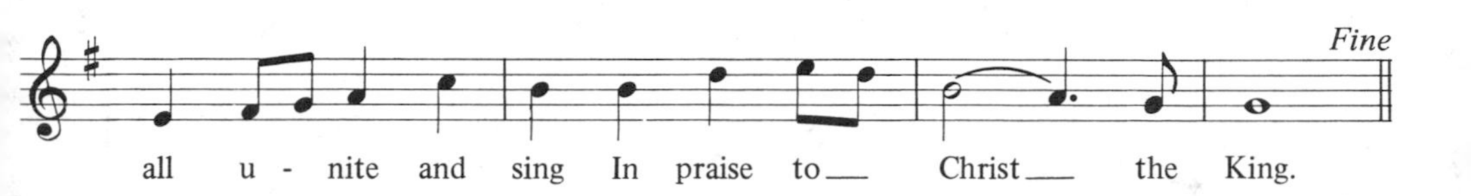
Fine
all u - nite and sing In praise to___ Christ___ the King.

Cantor or Choir
1. Sing a new song to the Lord, Ac - claim him with joy, all you na - tions!
3. Sing to the Lord in his might Who fills the___ earth and the o - cean.

Repeat Refrain
1. Sing to the Lord and___ bless his name;___ Give him___ glo - ry and praise.
3. Sing to the Lord of___ all cre - a - tion, Wor - ship the mak - er of all.

Cantor or Choir
3
3
2. All the ends of the earth have seen his truth, his sal - va - tion.
4. He will reign o - ver all the earth in peace and with jus - tice.

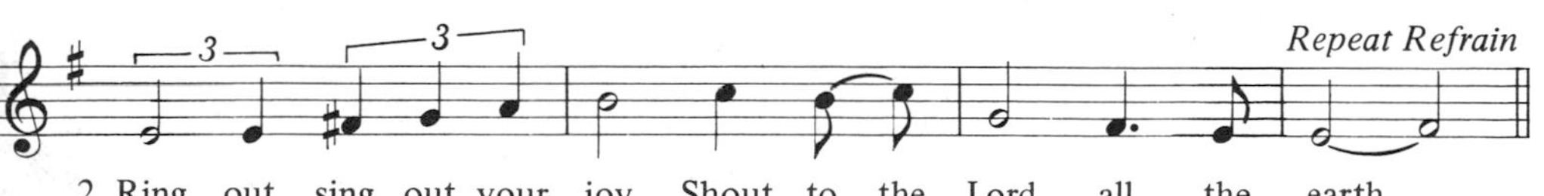
3
3
Repeat Refrain
2. Ring out, sing out your joy, Shout to the Lord, all the earth.___
4. Let the heav - ens be glad; Let the___ na - tions re - joice.___

180 Holy God, We Praise Thy Name

Te Deum

1. Ho - ly God, we praise thy name! Lord of
2. Hark! the loud ce - les - tial hymn An - gel
3. Lo! the Bless - ed Twelve pro - claim To the
4. Ho - ly Fa - ther, Ho - ly Son, Ho - ly
1. all, we bow be - fore thee. All on
2. choirs a - bove are rais - ing, Cher - u -
3. Fa - ther hymns of glo - ry; Proph - ets
4. Spir - it, Three we name thee; While in
1. earth thy scep - tre claim; All in heav'n a -
2. bim and ser - a - phim In un - ceas - ing
3. sing in loud ac - claim; Mar - tyrs tell the
4. es - sence on - ly One, Un - di - vid - ed
1. bove a - dore thee. In - fi - nite thy vast do -
2. cho - rus prais - ing, Fill the heav'ns with sweet ac -
3. won - drous sto - ry; And from morn to set of
4. God we claim thee; And a - dor - ing bow to
1. main, Ev - er - last - ing is thy reign.
2. cord: Ho - ly, Ho - ly, Ho - ly Lord.
3. sun, Through the Church they sing as one.
4. thee, While we own the mys - ter - y.

Text: *Te Deum,* ascribed to St. Nicetas, +415. Paraphrase C. Walworth, +1900, alt.
Tune: *Te Deum,* Vienna, c. 1774.

Hail to the Lord's Anointed

Ps. 72

1. Hail to the Lord's A - noint - ed, Great Da - vid's roy - al Son!
2. He comes with sol - ace speed - y To those who suf - fer wrong;
3. He shall come down like show - ers Up - on the fruit - ful earth;
4. Kings shall fall down be - fore him, And gold and in - cense bring;
5. O'er ev - 'ry foe vic - to - rious, He on his throne shall rest;
1. Hail, in the time ap - point - ed, His reign on earth be - gun!
2. To help the poor and need - y, And bid the weak be strong;
3. And love, joy, hope, like flow - ers, Spring in his path to birth;
4. All na - tions shall a - dore him, His praise all peo - ple sing;
5. From age to age more glo - rious, All bless - ing and all blest;
1. He comes to break op - pres - sion, To set the cap - tive free,
2. To give them songs for sing - ing, Their dark - ness turn to light,
3. Be - fore him on the moun - tains Shall peace, the her - ald, go;
4. To him shall pray'r un - ceas - ing Of thank - ful praise as - cend;
5. The tide of time shall nev - er His cov - e - nant re - move;
1. To take a - way trans - gres - sion, And rule in eq - ui - ty.
2. Whose souls, con-demned and dy - ing, Were pre - cious in his sight.
3. And right - eous - ness, in foun - tains, From hill to val - ley flow.
4. His king - dom still in - creas - ing, A king - dom with - out end.
5. His name shall stand for - ev - er; That name to us is Love.

Text: Psalm 72 paraphrase, J. Montgomery, +1854, alt.
Tune: *Jesus Christ unser Herre,* B. Gesius, +1613.

182 Hark! the Herald Angels Sing

1. Hark! the her - ald an - gels sing, Glo - ry to the
2. Christ, by high - est heav'n a - dored, Christ, the ev - er -
3. Mild he lays his glo - ry by, Born that man no
4. What good news the an - gels bring, What glad ti - dings
1. new - born King! Peace on earth and mer - cy mild,
2. last - ing Lord, Late in time be - hold him come,
3. more may die, Born to raise the heirs of earth,
4. of our King! Christ the Lord is born to - day,
1. God and sin - ners rec - on - ciled! Joy - ful, all ye
2. Off - spring of the Vir - gin's womb. Veiled in flesh the
3. Born to give them sec - ond birth. Ris'n with heal - ing
4. Christ who takes our sins a - way! He who rules both
1. na - tions, rise, Join the tri - umph of the skies;
2. God - head see; Hail th'In - car - nate De - i - ty,
3. in his wings, Light and life to all he brings.
4. heav'n and earth Hath in Beth - le - hem his birth;
1. With th'an - gel - ic host pro - claim, "Christ is born in
2. Pleased as man with man to dwell, Je - sus our Em -
3. Hail, the Sun of Right - eous - ness! Hail, the heav'n - born
4. With th'an - gel - ic host pro - claim, "Christ is born in
1. Beth - le - hem!"
2. man - u - el!
3. Prince of Peace!
4. Beth - le - hem!"
Hark! the her - ald an - gels sing,

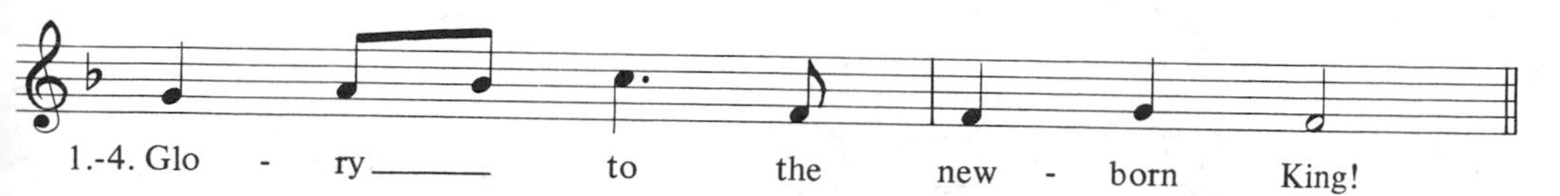
1.-4. Glo - ry to the new - born King!

Text: Verses 1-3, C. Wesley, +1788.
Verse 4, W. Hammond, +1783.
Tune: *Festgesang,* F. Mendelssohn, +1847.

Hark! a Herald Voice Is Sounding 183

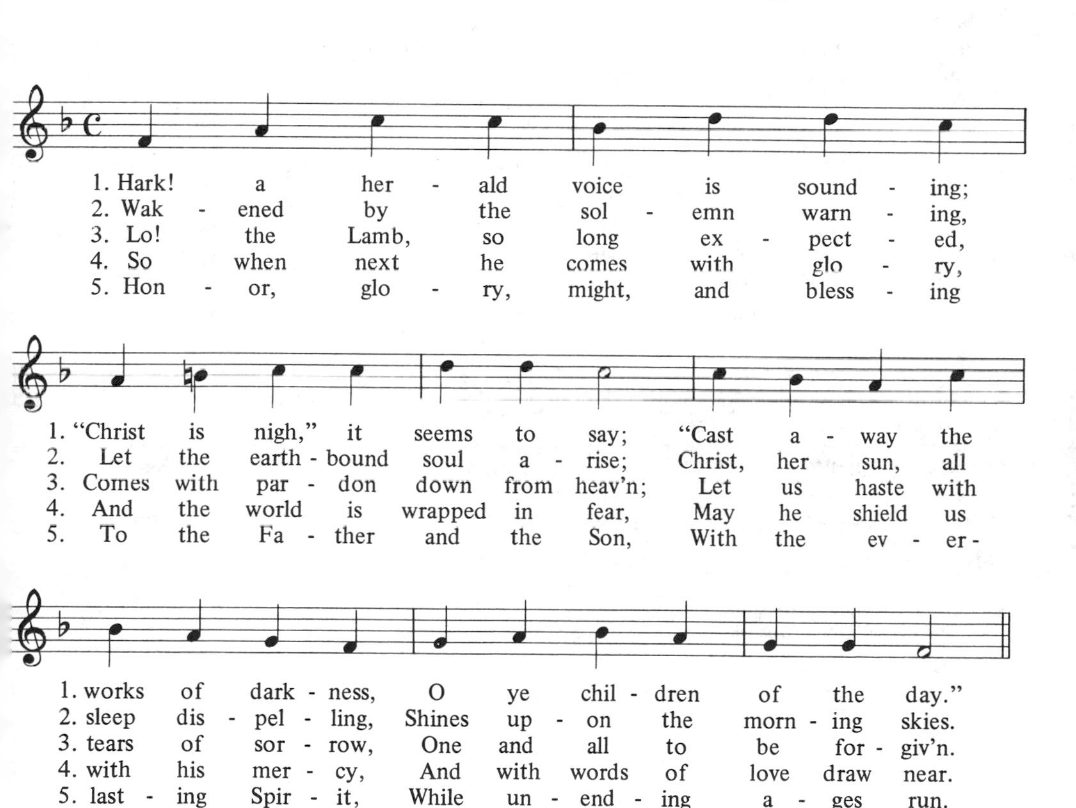
1. Hark! a her - ald voice is sound - ing;
2. Wak - ened by the sol - emn warn - ing,
3. Lo! the Lamb, so long ex - pect - ed,
4. So when next he comes with glo - ry,
5. Hon - or, glo - ry, might, and bless - ing
1. "Christ is nigh," it seems to say; "Cast a - way the
2. Let the earth - bound soul a - rise; Christ, her sun, all
3. Comes with par - don down from heav'n; Let us haste with
4. And the world is wrapped in fear, May he shield us
5. To the Fa - ther and the Son, With the ev - er -
1. works of dark - ness, O ye chil - dren of the day."
2. sleep dis - pel - ling, Shines up - on the morn - ing skies.
3. tears of sor - row, One and all to be for - giv'n.
4. with his mer - cy, And with words of love draw near.
5. last - ing Spir - it, While un - end - ing a - ges run.

Text: Latin, 6th Century. Trans. E. Caswall, +1878, alt.
Tune: *Merton,* W.H. Monk, +1889.

184 High in the Heav'ns, Eternal God

Ps. 36

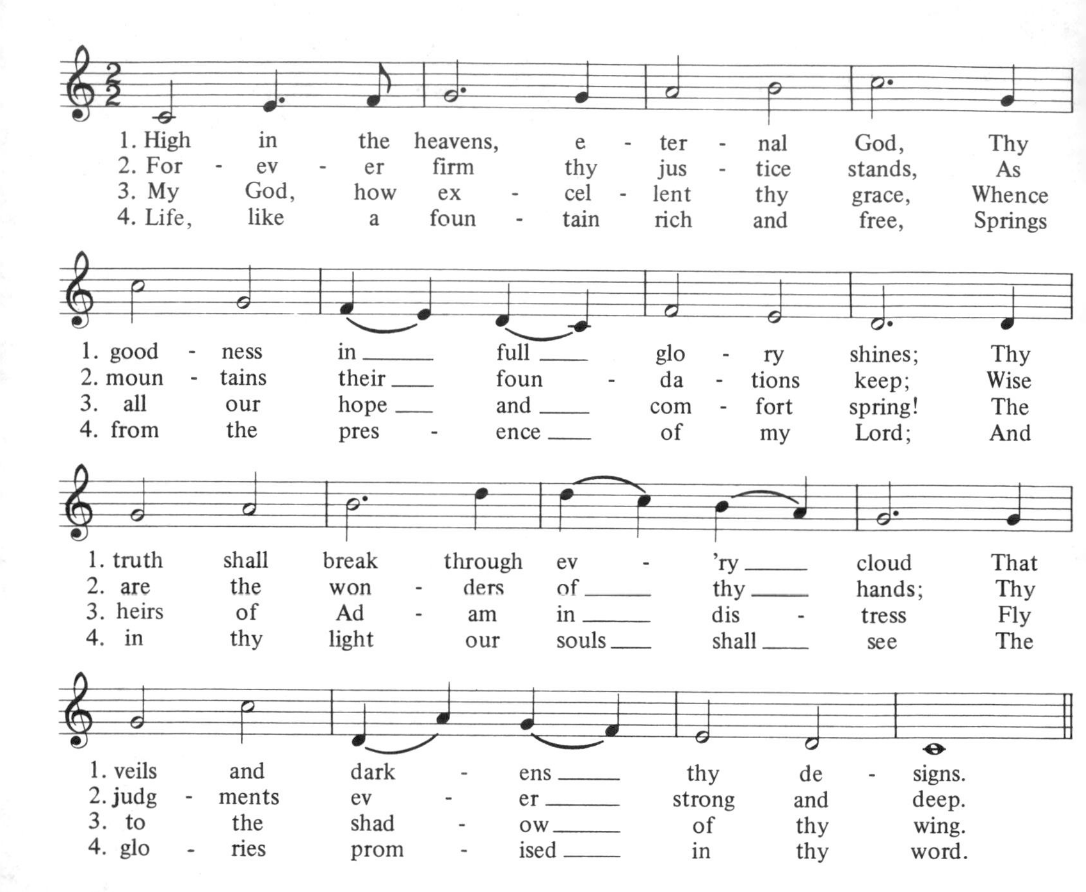
1. High in the heavens, e - ter - nal God, Thy
2. For - ev - er firm thy jus - tice stands, As
3. My God, how ex - cel - lent thy grace, Whence
4. Life, like a foun - tain rich and free, Springs
1. good - ness in full glo - ry shines; Thy
2. moun - tains their foun - da - tions keep; Wise
3. all our hope and com - fort spring! The
4. from the pres - ence of my Lord; And
1. truth shall break through ev - 'ry cloud That
2. are the won - ders of thy hands; Thy
3. heirs of Ad - am in dis - tress Fly
4. in thy light our souls shall see The
1. veils and dark - ens thy de - signs.
2. judg - ments ev - er strong and deep.
3. to the shad - ow of thy wing.
4. glo - ries prom - ised in thy word.

Text: Psalm 36 paraphrase, I. Watts, +1748, alt.
Tune: *Truro*, T. Williams, "Psalmodica Evangelica", 1789.

Holy, Holy, Holy!

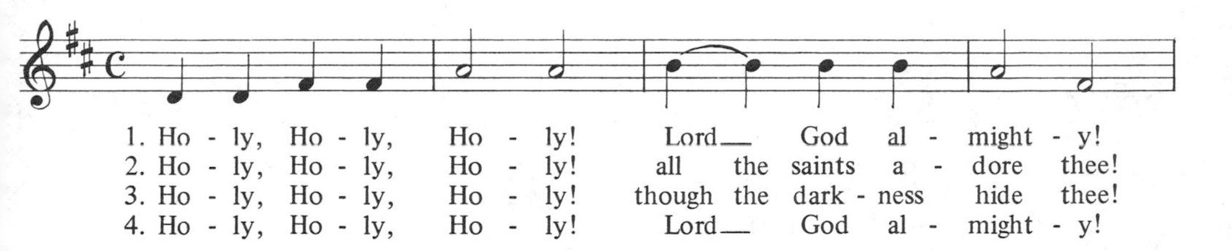
1. Ho - ly, Ho - ly, Ho - ly! Lord God al - might - y!
2. Ho - ly, Ho - ly, Ho - ly! all the saints a - dore thee!
3. Ho - ly, Ho - ly, Ho - ly! though the dark - ness hide thee!
4. Ho - ly, Ho - ly, Ho - ly! Lord God al - might - y!

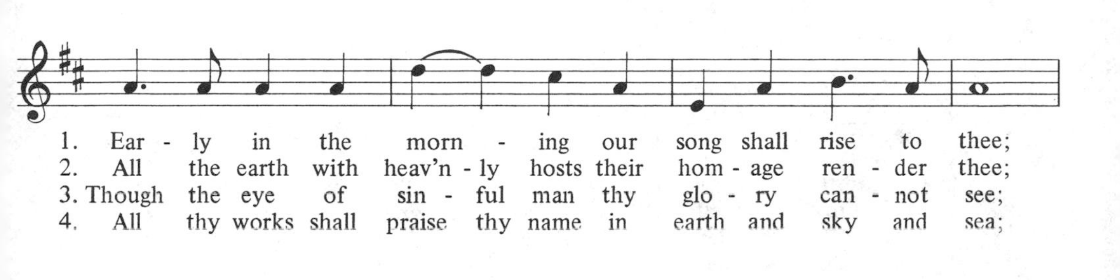
1. Ear - ly in the morn - ing our song shall rise to thee;
2. All the earth with heav'n - ly hosts their hom - age ren - der thee;
3. Though the eye of sin - ful man thy glo - ry can - not see;
4. All thy works shall praise thy name in earth and sky and sea;

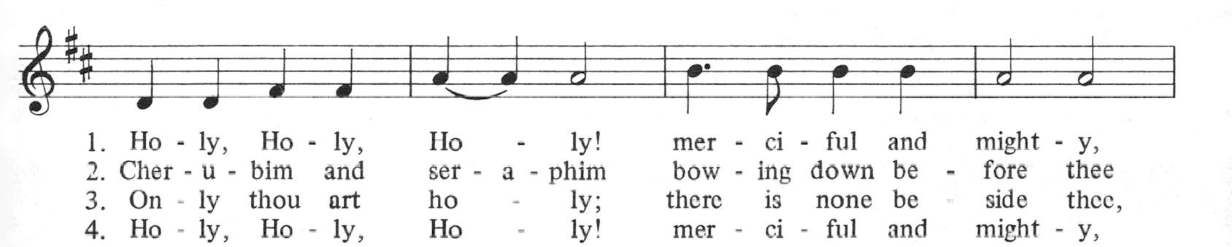
1. Ho - ly, Ho - ly, Ho - ly! mer - ci - ful and might - y,
2. Cher - u - bim and ser - a - phim bow - ing down be - fore thee
3. On - ly thou art ho - ly; there is none be - side thee,
4. Ho - ly, Ho - ly, Ho - ly! mer - ci - ful and might - y,

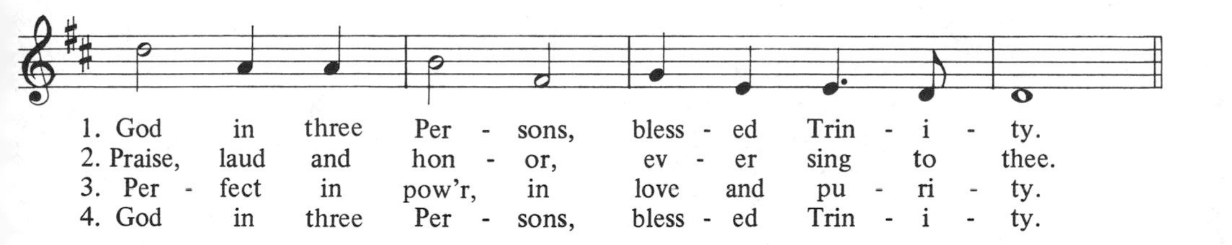
1. God in three Per - sons, bless - ed Trin - i - ty.
2. Praise, laud and hon - or, ev - er sing to thee.
3. Per - fect in pow'r, in love and pu - ri - ty.
4. God in three Per - sons, bless - ed Trin - i - ty.

Text: R. Heber, +1826, alt.
Tune: *Nicaea*, J.B. Dykes, +1876.

186 How Good a Thing It Is

Ps. 133

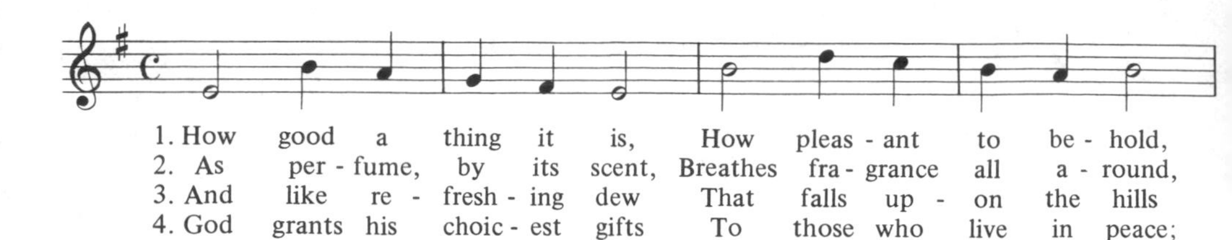
1. How good a thing it is, How pleas - ant to be - hold,
2. As per - fume, by its scent, Breathes fra - grance all a - round,
3. And like re - fresh - ing dew That falls up - on the hills
4. God grants his choic - est gifts To those who live in peace;

1. When breth - ren learn to live at one, The law of love up - hold.
2. So life it - self will sweet - er be, Where u - ni - ty is found.
3. True u - nion sheds its gen - tle grace, And deep - er love in - stills.
4. To them his bless - ings shall a - bound And ev - er - more in - crease.

Text: Psalm 133 paraphrase, J.E. Seddon.

Tune: *Aylesbury*, J. Chetham, +1746, in "Psalms", 1718.

Holy Spirit, Come and Shine

187

Sequence for Pentecost

1. Ho - ly Spir - it, come and shine On our souls with rays
2. Come, O Fa - ther of the poor, Ev - er boun-teous of
1. di - vine, Is - suing from thy ra - diance bright.
2. thy store, Come, our heart's un - fail - ing light.
3. Come, Con - sol - er, kind - est, best, Come, our bos - om's
4. Rest in la - bor, cool - ness sweet, Tem - per - ing the
3. dear - est guest, Sweet re - fresh - ment, sweet re - pose.
4. burn - ing heat, Tru - est com - fort of our woes.
5. Light im - mor - tal, light di - vine! Vis - it thou these
6. If thou take thy grace a - way, Noth - ing pure in
5. hearts of thine, And our in - most be - ing fill.
6. man will stay; All his good is turned to ill.

Continued

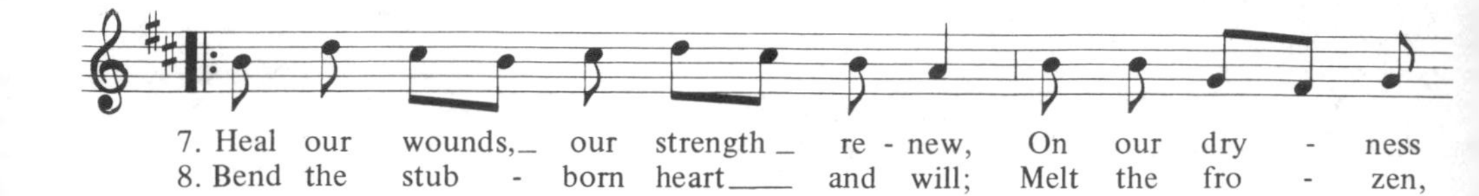
7. Heal our wounds, our strength re - new, On our dry - ness
8. Bend the stub - born heart and will; Melt the fro - zen,

7. pour thy dew; Wash the stains of guilt a - way.
8. warm the chill; Guide the steps that go a - stray.

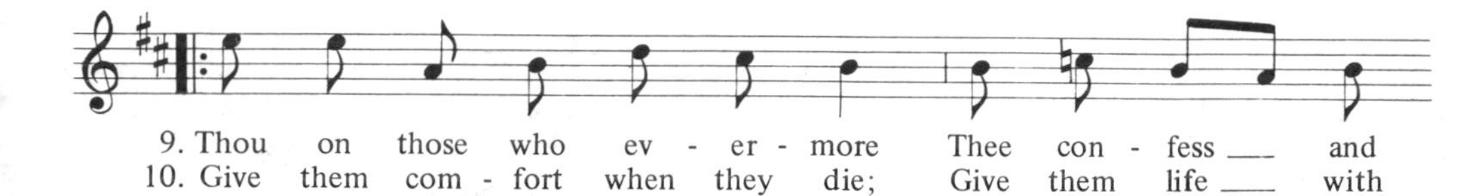
9. Thou on those who ev - er - more Thee con - fess and
10. Give them com - fort when they die; Give them life with

9. thee a - dore, In the sev'n - fold gifts de - scend.
10. thee on high; Give them joys which nev - er end.

A - men. Al - le - lu - ia.

Text: Ascribed to Innocent III, +1216.
Verses 1-4, J.A. Aylward, +1872.
Verses 5-10, from Roman Missal.

Tune: *Veni, Sancte Spiritus,* Plainchant, Mode 1.

Holy Spirit, Ever Dwelling

188

1. Ho - ly_ Spir - it, ev - er_ dwell - ing In the_ ho - liest_
2. Ho - ly_ Spir - it, ev - er_ liv - ing As the_ Chur - ch's_
3. Ho - ly_ Spir - it, ev - er_ work - ing Thro' the_ Chur - ch's_
4. Glo - ry_ be to God the_ Fa - ther; Glo - ry_ be to_
1. realms_ of_ light; Ho - ly_ Spir - it,_ ev - er_ shin - ing
2. own_ true_ life; Ho - ly_ Spir - it,_ ev - er_ striv - ing
3. min - is - try, Quick - 'ning,_strength-'ning,_ and ab - solv - ing,
4. God_ the_ Son, Dy - ing,_ ris - en, as - cend - ing_ for us,
1. O'er the_ world with_ ra - diance_ bright; Ho - ly_ Spir - it,
2. Thro' her_ in a_ cease - less_ strife; Ho - ly_ Spir - it,
3. Set - ting_ cap - tive_ sin - ners_ free; Ho - ly_ Spir - it,
4. Who the_ heav'n - ly_ realm_ has_ won; Glo - ry_ to the
1. ev - er rais - ing Sons of_ earth to thrones on_ high;_
2. ev - er form - ing In the_ Church the mind of_ Christ;_
3. ev - er bind - ing Age to_ age and soul to_ soul_
4. Ho - ly Spir - it; To one_ God in per - sons_ three;_
1. Liv - ing_prom - ise of the_ Fa - ther Thee we_praise and_ mag - ni - fy.
2. Thee we_praise with end - less_wor - ship For thy_ fruit and_ gifts_ un - priced.
3. In a_ fel - low - ship un - end - ing, Thee we_ wor - ship_ and_ ex - tol.
4. Glo - ry_both in earth and_heav - en, Glo - ry,_ end - less_ glo - ry_ be.

Text: T. Rees, +1939.
Tune: *In Babilone,* Dutch Melody, c. 1710.

189

I Clasp unto My Heart This Day

Lorica of Saint Patrick

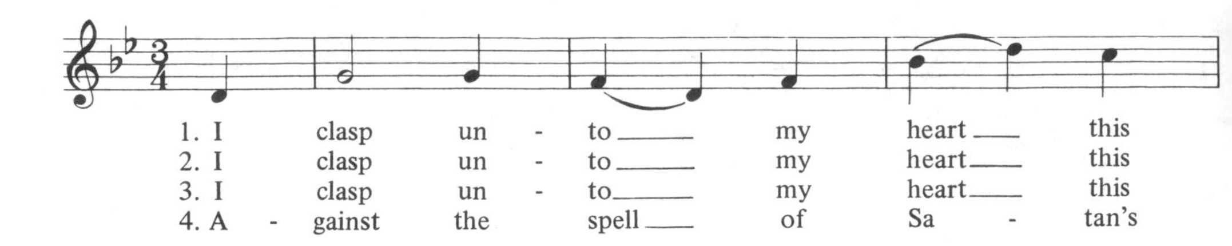
1. I clasp un - to my heart this
2. I clasp un - to my heart this
3. I clasp un - to my heart this
4. A - gainst the spell of Sa - tan's

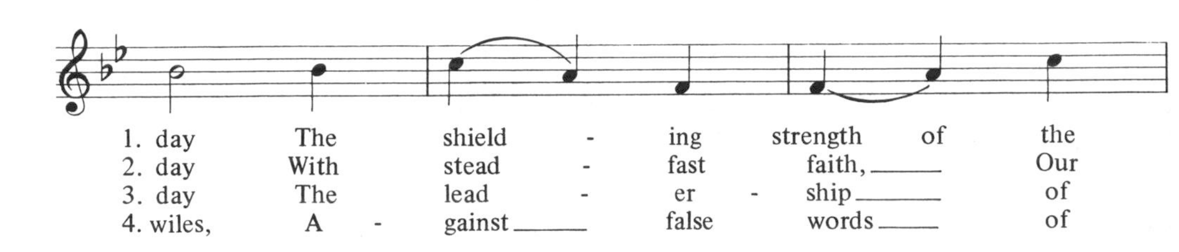
1. day The shield - ing strength of the
2. day With stead - fast faith, Our
3. day The lead - er - ship of
4. wiles, A - gainst false words of

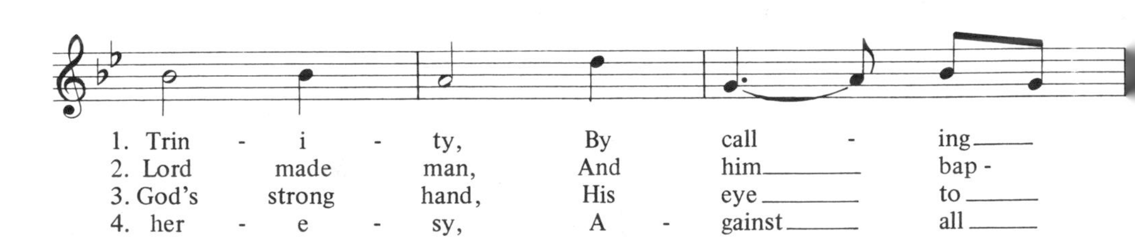
1. Trin - i - ty, By call - ing
2. Lord made man, And him bap -
3. God's strong hand, His eye to
4. her - e - sy, A - gainst all

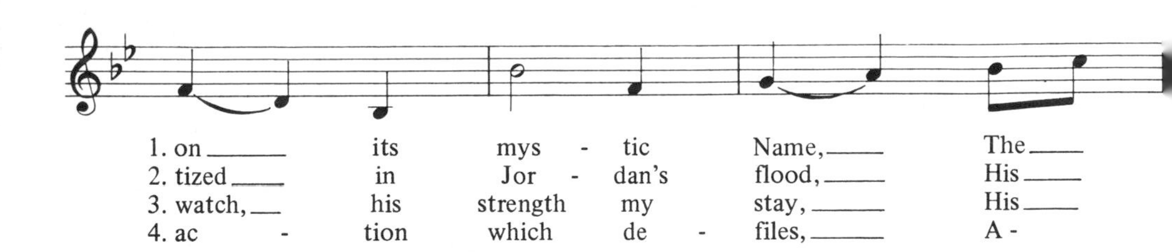
1. on its mys - tic Name, The
2. tized in Jor - dan's flood, His
3. watch, his strength my stay, His
4. ac - tion which de - files, A -

1. Three in One, the One in Three; Through
2. Cross of death, sal - va - tion's plan; His
3. ears to hear and un - der - stand: The
4. gainst the heart's i - dol - a - try, A -
1. whom all na - ture was cre - a - ted, E -
2. ris - ing from the en - clos - ing tomb, His
3. truths God wills that I should teach, His
4. gainst all pride of earth - ly state, A -
1. ter - nal Fa - ther, Spir - it, Word. I
2. bright as - cent to heav - en's way, His
3. guid - ance sure, his shield - ing arm, The
4. gainst hell's pain and bond - age stern, A -
1. praise thee, God of my sal - va - tion, Sal -
2. com - ing on the day of doom, I
3. word of God which I should preach, The
4. gainst that end - less fier - y fate, Pro -
1. va - tion won by Christ the Lord.
2. clasp un - to my heart this day.
3. an - gels guard - ing me from harm.
4. tect me, Christ, till thy re - turn.

Text: St. Patrick, 5th Century. Trans. E.C. Currie, +1967, alt.
Tune: *St. Patrick's Breastplate,* Gaelic.

190 I Come with Joy to Meet the Lord

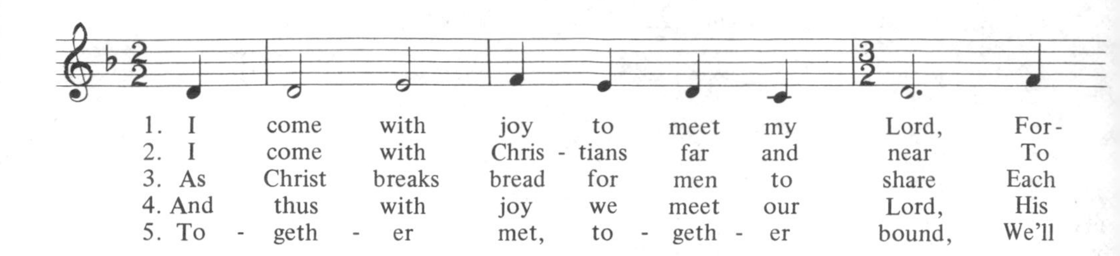
1. I come with joy to meet my Lord, For-
2. I come with Chris - tians far and near To
3. As Christ breaks bread for men to share Each
4. And thus with joy we meet our Lord, His
5. To - geth - er met, to - geth - er bound, We'll

1. giv - en, loved and free, In awe and won - der
2. find, as all are fed, Man's true com - mu - ni -
3. proud di - vi - sion ends. That love that made us
4. pres - ence, al - ways near, Is in such friend - ship
5. go our dif - f'rent ways, And as his peo - ple

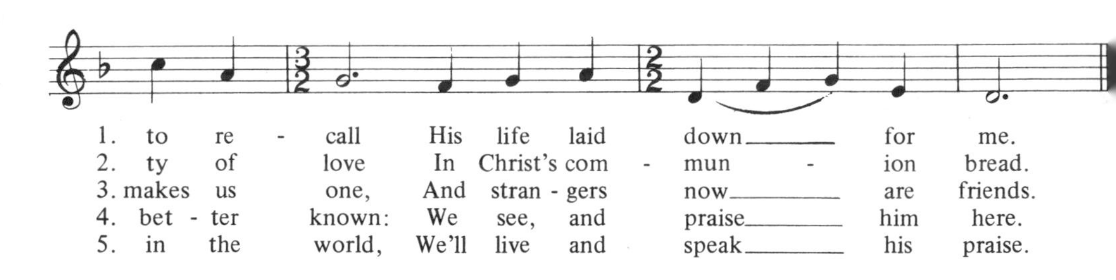
1. to re - call His life laid down for me.
2. ty of love In Christ's com - mun - ion bread.
3. makes us one, And stran - gers now are friends.
4. bet - ter known: We see, and praise him here.
5. in the world, We'll live and speak his praise.

Text: B.A. Wren.
Tune: *Freuen wir uns all in ein,* M. Weisse, +1534, alt.

If Thou but Trust in God to Guide Thee

1. If thou but trust in God to guide thee,
2. Who pours on thee his grace and bless - ing?
3. On - ly be still and wait his lei - sure
4. Sing, pray and keep his way un - swerv - ing;
1. And hope in him thro' all thy ways, He'll
2. Who but the Lord, the God of love. Who
3. In cheer - ful hope, with heart con - tent To
4. In all thy la - bor faith - ful be And
1. give thee strength what - e'er be - tide thee And bear thee
2. shields thee from thy fears op - press - ing? 'Tis he, the
3. take what - e'er thy Fa - ther's plea - sure And all dis -
4. trust his word; tho' un - de - serv - ing, Thou yet shall
1. thro' the e - vil days; Who trusts in God's un -
2. God of hosts a - bove. He heed - eth all thy
3. cern - ing love have sent; Nor doubt our in - most
4. find it true for thee; God nev - er will for -
1. chang - ing love Builds on the rock that nought can move.
2. anx - ious prayers, With all in need his mer - cy shares.
3. wants are known To him who chose us for his own.
4. sake in need The soul that trusts in him in - deed.

Text: G. Neumark, +1681. Trans. C. Winkworth, +1878, alt.
Tune: *Wen nur den lieben Gott,* G. Neumark, +1681.

192 I Heard the Voice of Jesus Say

1. I heard the voice of Je - sus say, "Come un - to me_ and_ rest;
2. I heard the voice of Je - sus say, "Be - hold, I free - ly__ give
3. I heard the voice of Je - sus say, "I am this dark_ world's_ light;

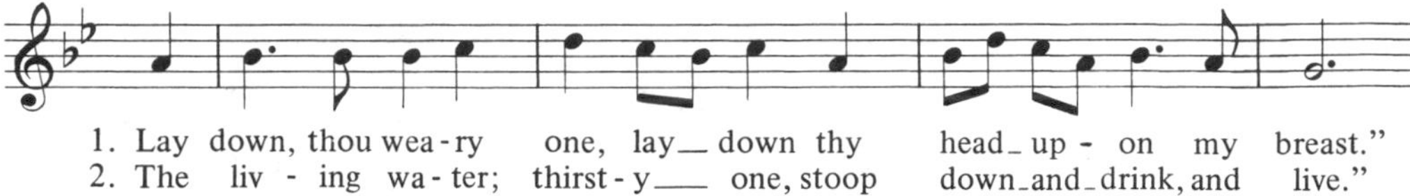

1. Lay down, thou wea - ry one, lay__ down thy head_ up - on my breast."
2. The liv - ing wa - ter; thirst - y__ one, stoop down_and_drink, and live."
3. Look un - to me, thy morn shall_ rise, and all__ thy_ day be bright."

1. I came to Je - sus as I was, so wea - ry, worn and sad;
2. I came to Je - sus and I drank of that life - giv - ing stream;
3. I looked to Je - sus and I found in him my star, my sun;

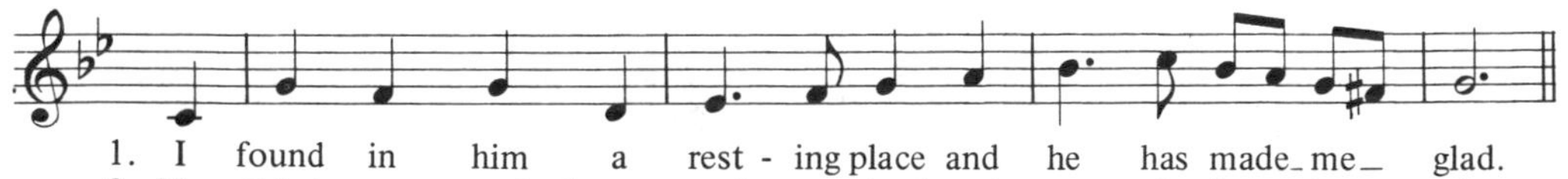

1. I found in him a rest - ing place and he has made_me_ glad.
2. My thirst was quenched, my soul re-vived, and now I live_ in__ him.
3. And in that light of life I'll walk till trav'l - ing days_ are_ done.

Text: H. Bonar, +1889.
Tune: *Tregaron,* P. James, © 1941 by H.W. Gray Co., Inc.

Immaculate Mary **193**

Lourdes Hymn

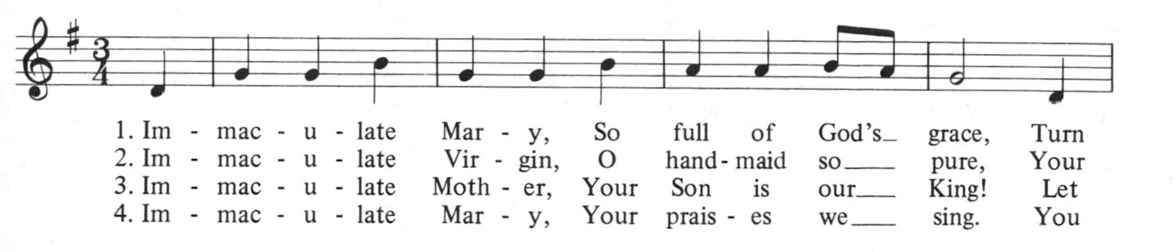

1. Im - mac - u - late Mar - y, So full of God's_ grace, Turn
2. Im - mac - u - late Vir - gin, O hand-maid so___ pure, Your
3. Im - mac - u - late Moth - er, Your Son is our___ King! Let
4. Im - mac - u - late Mar - y, Your prais - es we___ sing. You

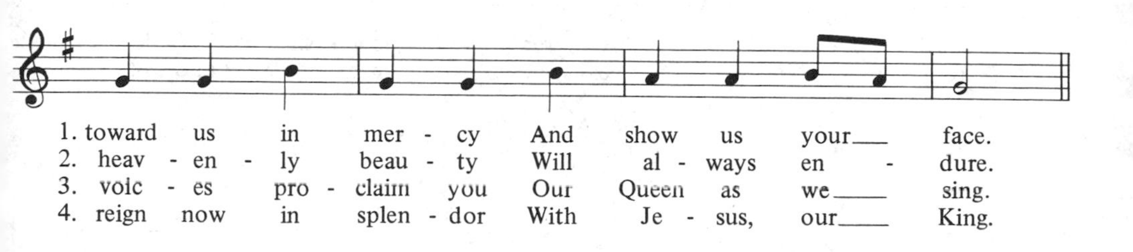

1. toward us in mer - cy And show us your___ face.
2. heav - en - ly beau - ty Will al - ways en - dure.
3. voic - es pro - claim you Our Queen as we___ sing.
4. reign now in splen - dor With Je - sus, our___ King.

REFRAIN

1.-4. A - ve, A - ve, A - ve Ma - ri -

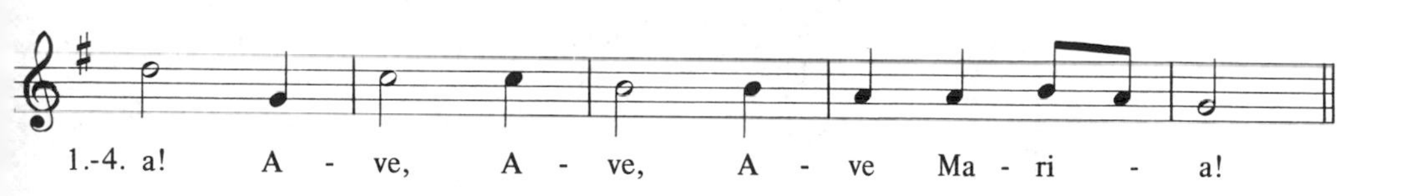

1.-4. a! A - ve, A - ve, A - ve Ma - ri - a!

Text: Traditional. Trans. C.A. Peloquin, alt. © 1963 in "Cantus Populi", by Summy-Birchard Music division of Birch Tree Group Ltd. Used with permission.
Tune: *Lourdes Hymn*, traditional.

194 In Christ There Is No East or West

1. In Christ there is no East or West, In him no
2. Join hands, then, all who hold the faith, What - e'er your

1. South or North, But one great fel - low - ship of love Through-
2. race may be! Who serves my Fa - ther cheer - ful - ly Is

1. out the whole wide earth. In him shall true hearts
2. sure - ly friend to me. In Christ now meet both

1. ev - 'ry - where Their high com - mun - ion find; His ser - vice
2. East and West, In him meet South and North, All Christ - ly

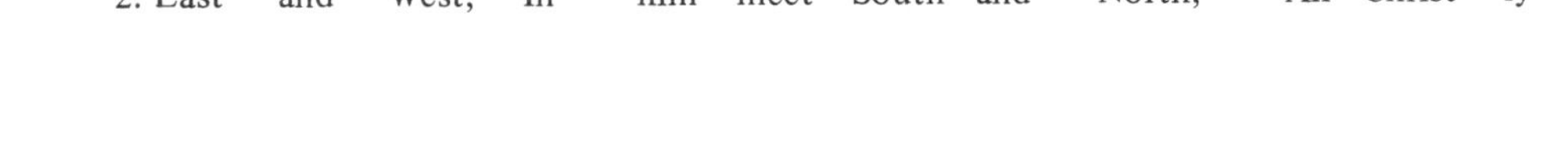

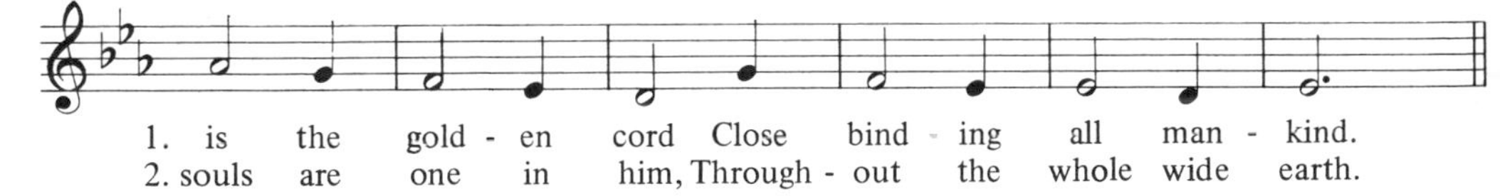
1. is the gold - en cord Close bind - ing all man - kind.
2. souls are one in him, Through - out the whole wide earth.

Text: J. Oxenham, +1941, alt. From "Bees in Amber". Used with permission.
Tune: *Old 81st*, Day's "Psalms", 1562.

In Dulci Jubilo

195

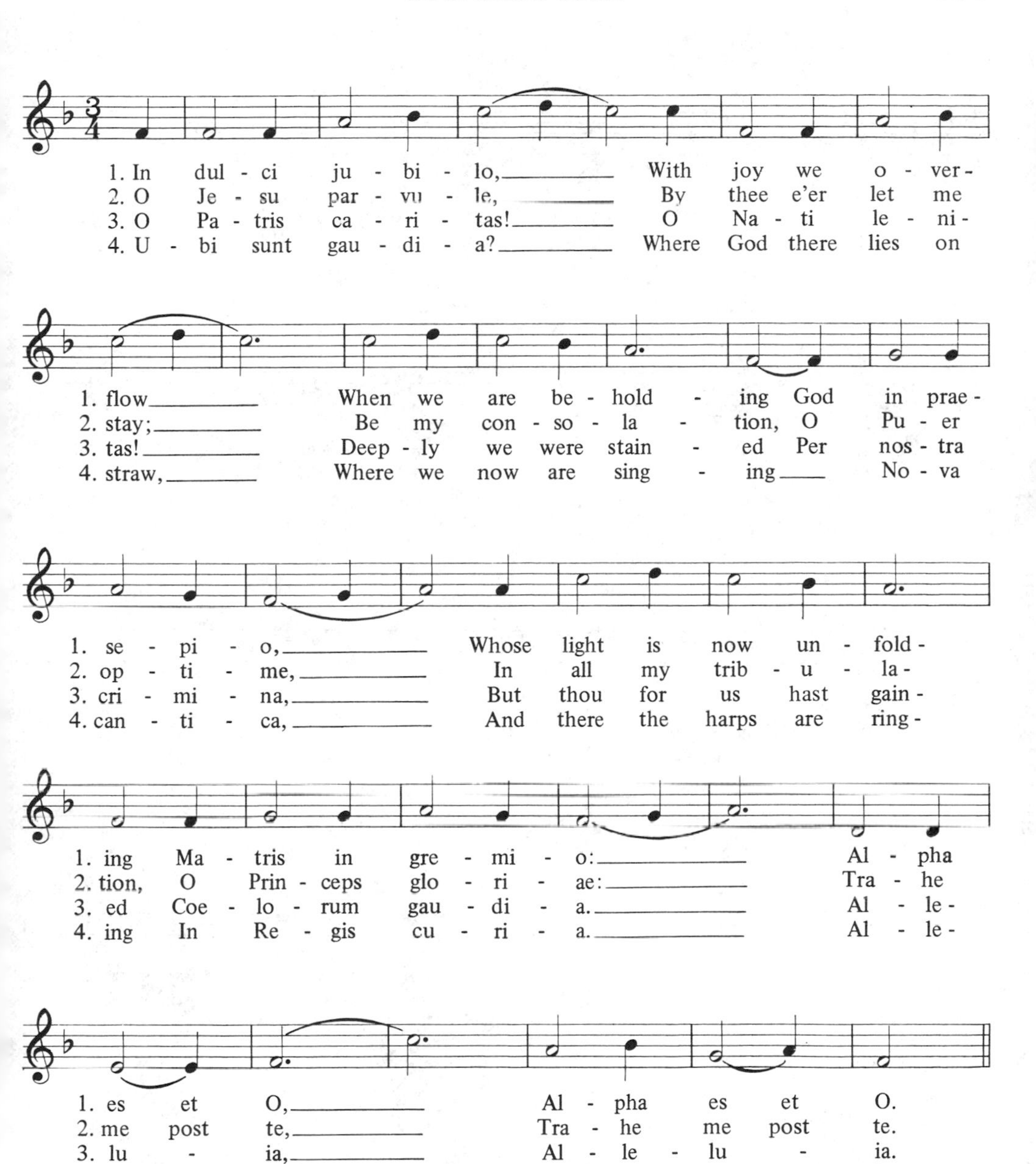
1. In dul - ci ju - bi - lo, With joy we o - ver -
2. O Je - su par - vu - le, By thee e'er let me
3. O Pa - tris ca - ri - tas! O Na - ti le - ni -
4. U - bi sunt gau - di - a? Where God there lies on
1. flow When we are be - hold - ing God in prae -
2. stay; Be my con - so - la - tion, O Pu - er
3. tas! Deep - ly we were stain - ed Per nos - tra
4. straw, Where we now are sing - ing No - va
1. se - pi - o, Whose light is now un - fold -
2. op - ti - me, In all my trib - u - la -
3. cri - mi - na, But thou for us hast gain -
4. can - ti - ca, And there the harps are ring -
1. ing Ma - tris in gre - mi - o: Al - pha
2. tion, O Prin - ceps glo - ri - ae: Tra - he
3. ed Coe - lo - rum gau - di - a. Al - le -
4. ing In Re - gis cu - ri - a. Al - le -
1. es et O, Al - pha es et O.
2. me post te, Tra - he me post te.
3. lu - ia, Al - le - lu - ia.
4. lu - ia, Al - le - lu - ia.

Text: German, 14th Century. Verses 1, 2, and 4, trans. A. Bachofen, O.S.B.
Verse 3, trans. R.L. Pearsall, +1856.

Tune: *In dulci jubilo,* 14th Century.

196 In His Temple Now Behold Him

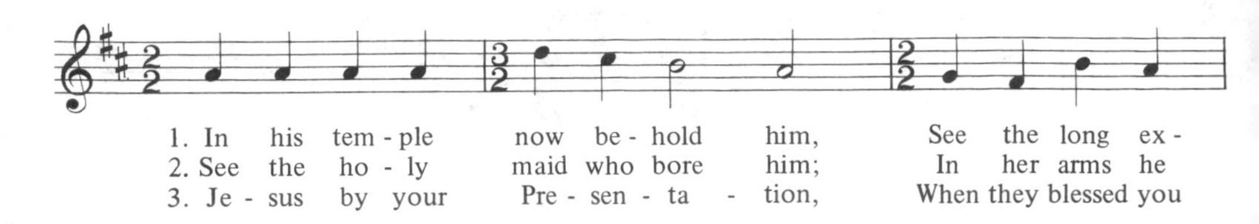
1. In his tem - ple now be - hold him, See the long ex -
2. See the ho - ly maid who bore him; In her arms he
3. Je - sus by your Pre - sen - ta - tion, When they blessed you

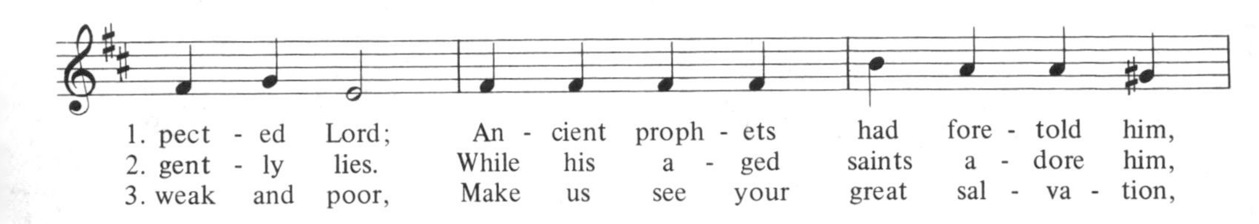
1. pect - ed Lord; An - cient proph - ets had fore - told him,
2. gent - ly lies. While his a - ged saints a - dore him,
3. weak and poor, Make us see your great sal - va - tion,

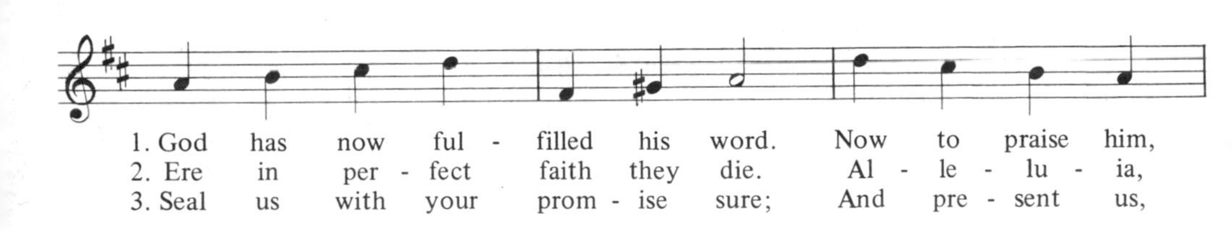
1. God has now ful - filled his word. Now to praise him,
2. Ere in per - fect faith they die. Al - le - lu - ia,
3. Seal us with your prom - ise sure; And pre - sent us,

1. his re - deem - ed Shall break forth with one ac - cord.
2. Al - le - lu - ia! Lo, th'in - car - nate God most high!
3. In your glo - ry, To your Fa - ther, cleansed and pure.

Text: H.J. Pye, +1903, alt.
Tune: *Lauda anima,* J. Goss, +1880.

I Sing the Mighty Power of God

197

1. I sing the__ might - y power of God That made__ the moun-tains
2. I sing the__ good - ness of the Lord That filled__ the earth with
3. There's not a__ plant or flower be - low But makes__ his glo - ries
4. From heav'n he__ sends his beams of love To those__ on earth be -
1. rise, That spread the__ flow - ing seas a - broad And
2. food; He formed the__ crea - tures with his word And
3. known; And clouds a - rise and tem - pests blow By
4. neath; 'Tis in his__ world I stand or move And
1. built__ the loft - y skies. I__ sing the wis - dom
2. then__ pro - nounced them good. Lord,__ how your won - ders
3. or - der from his throne; While__ all that bor - rows
4. 'tis__ his air I breathe. His__ hand is my per -
1. that or - dained The__ sun to rule the day; The
2. are dis - played Where - e'er I turn my eye, If
3. life from__ him, Is__ ev - er in his care, And
4. pet - ual__ guard, He__ keeps me with his eye; How
1. moon - light__ glows at his com-mand And all__ the stars o - bey.
2. I sur - vey the ground I tread Or gaze__ up - on the sky!
3. ev - 'ry - where that we can be, our God,__ is pres - ent there.
4. can I__ then for - get the Lord Who is__ for - ev - er nigh?

Text: I. Watts, +1748, alt.
Tune: *Ellacombe,* "Würtemburg Gesangbuch", 1784.

198 Jesu, Joy and Treasure

1. Je - su, Joy and Treas - ure, Sol - ace pass - ing meas - ure,
2. Hence all fear and sad - ness, Come, sweet Lord of glad - ness,
3. Je - su, meek and low - ly, Sav - ior, pure and ho - ly,
4. Je - su, my sal - va - tion, Hear my sup - pli - ca - tion;
1. Gra - cious gift to me! Ban - ish earth - ly glo - ry,
2. Je - su, Mas - ter mine; Who do tru - ly serve thee
3. Now __ we come to thee! Prince of life and pow - er,
4. Je - su, en - ter in. They who love the Fa - ther
1. Nought to me its sto - ry, Yearn - ing, Lord, for thee.
2. Must by faith de - serve thee, Joy - ous bear thy sign.
3. Our sal - va - tion's tow - er, On __ the cross we see.
4. Though the storms may gath - er, Still __ have peace with - in.
1. Thine I am, O Spot - less Lamb, In thine arms I'd
2. Scorn and hate may be man's fate; Lit - tle worth in
3. Slain to take our sins a - way; Bless - ed Lamb, on
4. Yea, what - e'er I here must bear, Joy is mine be -
1. ev - er __ hide me; Earth holds nought be - side __ thee.
2. them I __ meas - ure: Je - su, Joy and Treas - ure!
3. Cal - v'ry's __ moun - tain, Hum - bly at thy feet we pray.
4. yond all __ meas - ure, Je - su, Joy and Treas - ure!

Text: Verses 1, 2, J. Franck, +1677. Trans. C.S. Terry, +1936.
Verses 3, 4, anon.
Tune: *Jesu meine Freude,* J. Crüger, +1662.

Jesu, Joy of Man's Desiring

8
A
1. Je - su, joy of man's de - sir - ing,
2. Through the way where hope is guid - ing,
6
1. Ho - ly wis - dom, love ___ most ___ bright,
2. Hark, what peace - ful mu - sic rings
B
1. Drawn by thee, our souls as - pir - ing
2. Where the flocks in thee con - fid - ing
7
C
1. Soar to un - cre - a - ted light.
2. Drink of joy from death - less springs!
Word of
Theirs is
2
1. God, our flesh ___ that fash - ion'd
2. beau - ty's fair - est pleas - ure,
With the
Theirs is
2
D
1. fire of life ___ im - pas - sion'd,
2. wis - dom's ho - liest treas - ure.
Striv - ing
Thou dost
1. still to truth un - known,
2. ev - er lead thine own
Soar - ing,
In the
1. 11
2. 11
1. dy - ing, round ___ thy throne.
2. love of joys ___ un - known.

Text: M. Jahn, +1682. Trans. anon.
Tune: *Werde munter mein Gemüthe*, J. Schop, +1664.

Jesus, Bread in Mercy Broken

1. Je - sus, bread in mer - cy bro - ken, Sa - cred
2. Prince of life, sal - va - tion's tow - er, By your
3. Pas - chal Lamb! Your of - f'ring fin - ished, Once for
4. Life - im - part - ing heav'n - ly man - na, Strick - en

1. wine in love out-poured, For the words which you have spo - ken,
2. bod - y souls are healed; Prince of peace, O Lord of pow - er,
3. all, when you were slain, In its full - ness un - di - min - ished
4. rock, with stream - ing side, Heav'n and earth with loud ho - san - na

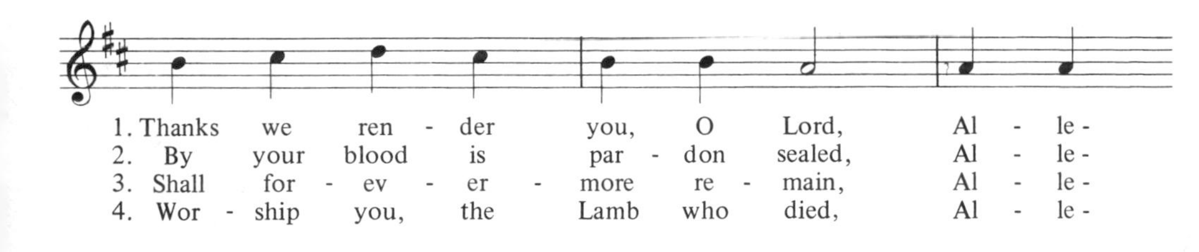
1. Thanks we ren - der you, O Lord, Al - le -
2. By your blood is par - don sealed, Al - le -
3. Shall for - ev - er - more re - main, Al - le -
4. Wor - ship you, the Lamb who died, Al - le -

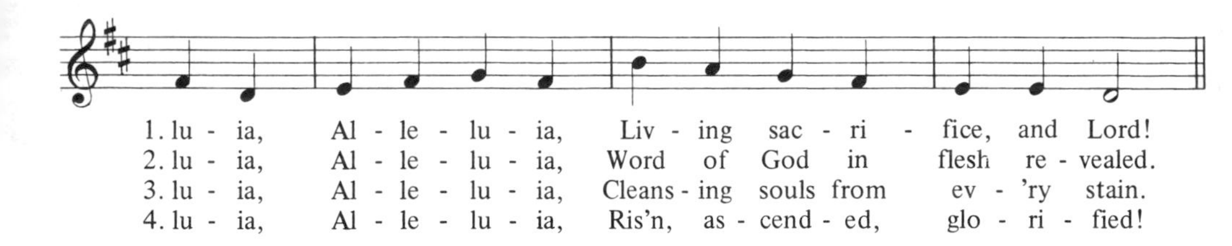
1. lu - ia, Al - le - lu - ia, Liv - ing sac - ri - fice, and Lord!
2. lu - ia, Al - le - lu - ia, Word of God in flesh re - vealed.
3. lu - ia, Al - le - lu - ia, Cleans - ing souls from ev - 'ry stain.
4. lu - ia, Al - le - lu - ia, Ris'n, as - cend - ed, glo - ri - fied!

Text: Verse 1, J. Dunn.
Verses 2-4, G.H. Bourne, +1925, alt.
Tune: *St. Thomas Old*, J.F. Wade, +1786, in "Cantus Diversi", 1751.

Jesus Christ Is Ris'n Today

201

1. Je - sus Christ is ris'n to - day,
2. Hymns of praise then let us sing,
3. But the pains which he en - dured,
4. Sing we to our God a - bove,
Al - le - lu - ia!
1. Our tri - umph - ant ho - ly day,
2. Un - to Christ, our heav'n - ly King,
3. Our sal - va - tion have pro - cured;
4. Praise e - ter - nal as his love;
Al - le - lu - ia!
1. Raise your joys and tri - umphs high,
2. Who en - dured the cross and grave,
3. Now a - bove the heav'ns he's King,
4. Praise him, all ye heav'n - ly host,
Al - le - lu - ia!
1. Sing, ye heav'ns, and earth re - ply,
2. Sin - ners to re - deem and save,
3. Where the an - gels ev - er sing,
4. Fa - ther, Son and Ho - ly Ghost,
1.-4. Al - - le - lu - ia!

Text: Verses 1-3, Latin, 14th Century. Trans. from "Lyra Davidica", 1708, alt.
Verse 4, C. Wesley, +1788.
Tune: *Lyra Davidica,* 1708.

202

Joyful, Joyful, We Adore Thee

First Tune
1. Joy - ful, joy - ful, we a - dore _ thee, God of glo - ry,
2. All thy works with joy sur - round _ thee, Earth and heav'n re -
3. Thou art giv - ing and for - giv - ing, Ev - er bless - ing,
4. Mor - tals, join the might - y cho - rus, Which the morn - ing
1. Lord of _ love; Hearts un - fold like flowers be - fore _ thee,
2. flect thy _ rays; Stars and an - gels sing a - round _ thee,
3. ev - er _ blest, Well - spring of the joy of liv - ing,
4. stars be - gan; Fa - ther - love is reign - ing o'er _ us,
1. Prais - ing thee, their sun a - bove. Melt the clouds _ of sin and
2. Cen - ter of un - bro - ken _ praise. Field and for - est, vale and
3. O - cean depth of hap - py _ rest! Thou our Fa - ther, Christ our
4. Broth - er - love binds man to _ man. Ev - er sing - ing, march we
1. sad - ness, Drive the dark of doubt a - way; Giv - er of _ im -
2. moun - tain, Bloom - ing mead - ow, flash - ing sea, Chant - ing bird _ and
3. Broth - er, All who live in love are thine; Teach us how _ to
4. on - ward, Vic - tors in the midst of strife. Joy - ful mu - sic
1. mor - tal glad - ness, Fill us _ with _ the _ light of _ day.
2. flow - ing foun - tain, Call us _ to _ re - joice in _ thee.
3. love each oth - er, Lift us _ to _ the _ joy di - vine.
4. lifts us sun - ward In the _ tri - umph _ song of _ life.

Text: H. van Dyke, +1933.
Tune: *Austria*, F.J. Haydn, +1809.

Joyful, Joyful, We Adore Thee

Second Tune
1. Joy - ful, joy - ful, we a - dore thee, God of glo - ry, Lord of love;
2. All thy works with joy sur-round thee, Earth and heav'n re - flect thy rays;
3. Thou art giv - ing and for - giv - ing, Ev - er bless-ing, ev - er blest,
4. Mor - tals, join the might - y cho - rus, Which the morn-ing stars be - gan;
1. Hearts un - fold like flowers be - fore thee, Prais - ing thee, their
2. Stars and an - gels sing a - round thee, Cen - ter of un -
3. Well - spring of the joy of liv - ing, O - cean depth of
4. Fa - ther - love is reign - ing o'er us, Broth - er - love binds
1. sun a - bove. Melt the clouds of sin and sad - ness,
2. bro - ken praise. Field and for - est, vale and moun - tain,
3. hap - py rest! Thou our Fa - ther, Christ our Broth - er,
4. man to man. Ev - er sing - ing, march we on - ward,
1. Drive the dark of doubt a - way; Giv - er of im -
2. Bloom - ing mead - ow, flash - ing sea, Chant - ing bird and
3. All who live in love are thine; Teach us how to
4. Vic - tors in the midst of strife. Joy - ful mu - sic
1. mor - tal glad - ness, Fill us with the light of day.
2. flow - ing foun - tain, Call us to re - joice in thee.
3. love each oth - er, Lift us to the joy di - vine.
4. lifts us sun - ward In the tri - umph song of life.

Text: H. van Dyke, +1933.
Tune: *Hymn to Joy,* L. van Beethoven, +1827.

204 Jesus, Name of Wondrous Love

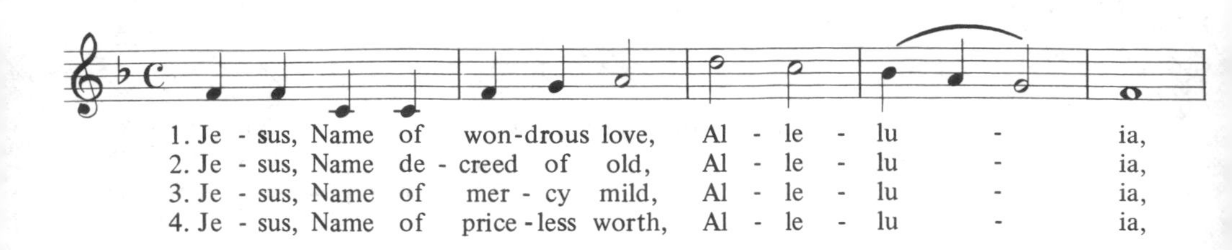
1. Je - sus, Name of won-drous love, Al - le - lu - ia,
2. Je - sus, Name de - creed of old, Al - le - lu - ia,
3. Je - sus, Name of mer - cy mild, Al - le - lu - ia,
4. Je - sus, Name of price - less worth, Al - le - lu - ia,

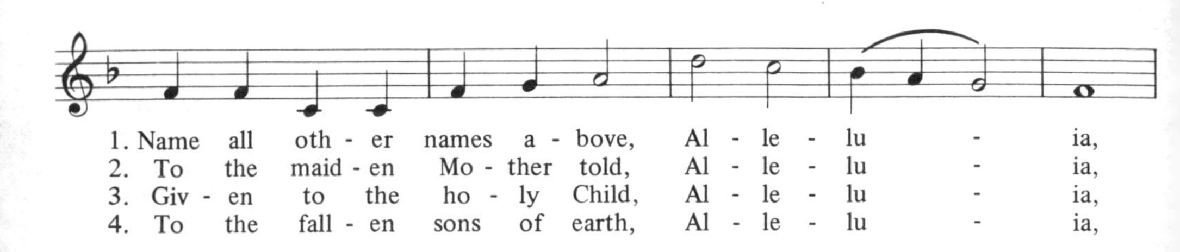
1. Name all oth - er names a - bove, Al - le - lu - ia,
2. To the maid - en Mo - ther told, Al - le - lu - ia,
3. Giv - en to the ho - ly Child, Al - le - lu - ia,
4. To the fall - en sons of earth, Al - le - lu - ia,

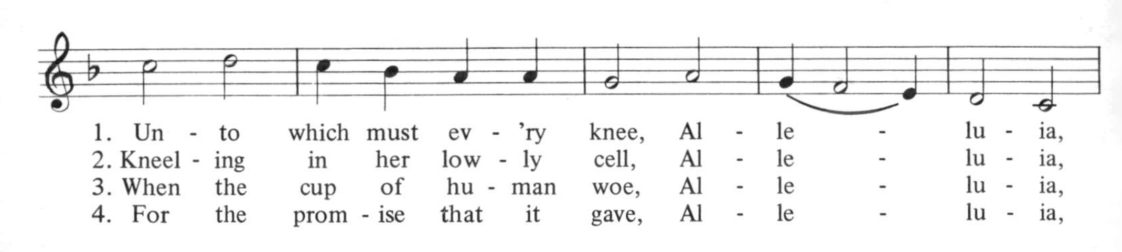
1. Un - to which must ev - 'ry knee, Al - le - lu - ia,
2. Kneel - ing in her low - ly cell, Al - le - lu - ia,
3. When the cup of hu - man woe, Al - le - lu - ia,
4. For the prom - ise that it gave, Al - le - lu - ia,

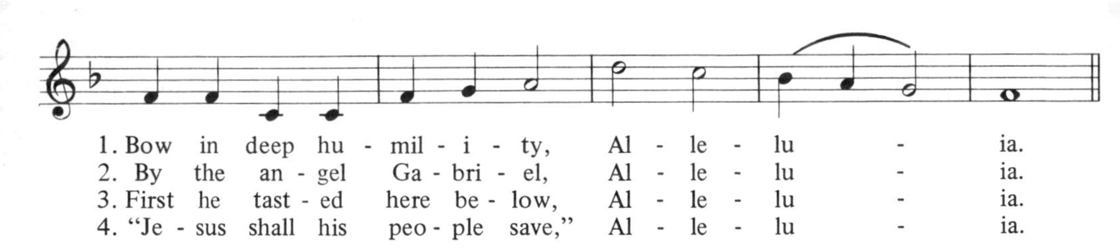
1. Bow in deep hu - mil - i - ty, Al - le - lu - ia.
2. By the an - gel Ga - bri - el, Al - le - lu - ia.
3. First he tast - ed here be - low, Al - le - lu - ia.
4. "Je - sus shall his peo - ple save," Al - le - lu - ia.

Text: W.W. How, +1897, alt.
Tune: *Gaudeamus pariter,* J. Horn, +1547.

Joy to the World

Ps. 98

1. Joy to the world! the Lord is come; Let
2. Joy to the world! the Sav - ior reigns; Let
3. He rules the world with truth and grace And
4. His name shall be the Prince of Peace, The
5. "Glo - ry to God," the sound - ing skies With
1. earth re - ceive her King; Let ev - 'ry
2. earth her songs em - ploy; While fields and
3. makes the na - tions prove The glo - ries
4. ev - er - last - ing Lord, The Won - der -
5. joy their an - thems ring: "Peace to the
1. heart pre - pare him room, And
2. floods, rocks, hills and plains Re -
3. of his right - eous - ness, And
4. ful, the Coun - sel - lor, The
5. earth, good - will to all," From
1. heav'n and na - ture sing, And heav'n and na - ture
2. peat the sound - ing joy, Re - peat the sound - ing
3. won - ders of his love, And won - ders of his
4. God by all a - dored, The God by all a -
5. heav'n's e - ter - nal King, From heav'n's e - ter - nal
1. sing, And heav'n, and heav'n, and na - ture sing.
2. joy, Re - peat, re - peat the sound - ing joy.
3. love, And won ders, won - ders of his love.
4. dored, The God, the God by all a - dored.
5. King, From heav'n's, from heav'n's e - ter - nal King.

Text: Verses 1-3, Psalm 98 paraphrase, I. Watts, +1748, alt.
Verse 4, J. Morison, +1798.
Verse 5, E.H. Sears, +1876, alt.
Tune: *Antioch,* G.F. Handel, +1759. Adapted L. Mason, +1872.

206 Let All the World in Ev'ry Corner Sing

Let all the world in ev - 'ry_ cor- ner sing, My God and King!
The heav'ns are not too high, His praise may thith - er fly; The
earth is not too low, His prais - es_ there may grow. Let all the
world in ev - 'ry_ cor - ner sing, My God and King!
The Church with psalms must shout, No door can keep them out; But
a - bove all, the heart Must bear the_ long - est part. Let all the
world in ev - 'ry_ cor - ner sing, My God and King!

Text: G. Herbert, +1633.
Tune: *Augustine,* E. Routley.

Lift High the Cross

REFRAIN
Lift high the Cross, the love of Christ pro - claim Till
Fine
all the world a - dore his sa - cred Name.
1. Let ev - 'ry race and ev - 'ry lan - guage
2. From far - thest re - gions let them hom - age
3. Set up thy throne that earth's de - spair may
4. For thy blest Cross which doth for all a -
*5. Come, breth - ren, fol - low where our Sav - ior
*6. Led on their way by this tri - um - phant
*7. Saved by this Cross where - on their Lord was
*8. O Lord, once lift - ed on the glo - rious
1. tell Of him who saves our
2. bring And on his Cross a -
3. cease Be - neath the shad - ow
4. tone, Cre - a - tion's prais - es
*5. trod, Our King vic - to - rious,
*6. sign, The hosts of God in
*7. slain, The heirs of Ad - am
*8. tree, As thou hast prom - ised,
Repeat Refrain
1. souls from death and hell.
2. dore their Sav - ior King.
3. of its heal - ing peace.
4. rise be - fore thy throne.
*5. Christ, the Son of God.
*6. con - qu'ring ranks com - bine.
*7. their lost home re - gain.
*8. draw us un - to thee.

*Lenten verses.

Text: G.W. Kitchin, +1912 and M.R. Newbolt, +1956, alt.
Tune: *Crucifer,* S.H. Nicholson, +1947.

208

Let All Things Now Living

1. Let all things now liv - ing A song of thanks -
2. Be - side us to guide us, Our God with us
3. We praise thee, O God, our Re - deem - er, Cre -
4. His law he en - forc - es, The stars in their

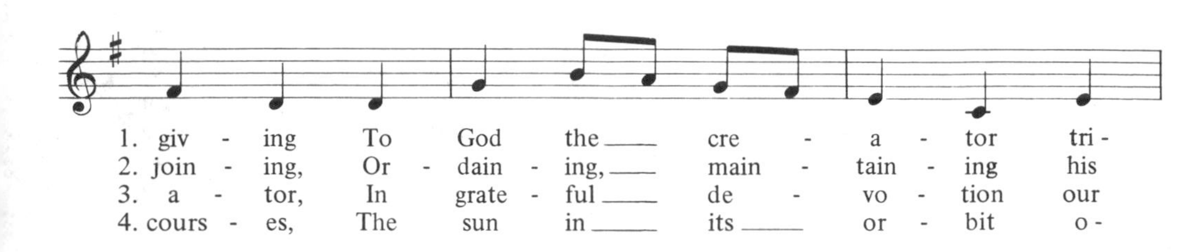
1. giv - ing To God the cre - a - tor tri -
2. join - ing, Or - dain - ing, main - tain - ing his
3. a - tor, In grate - ful de - vo - tion our
4. cours - es, The sun in its or - bit o -

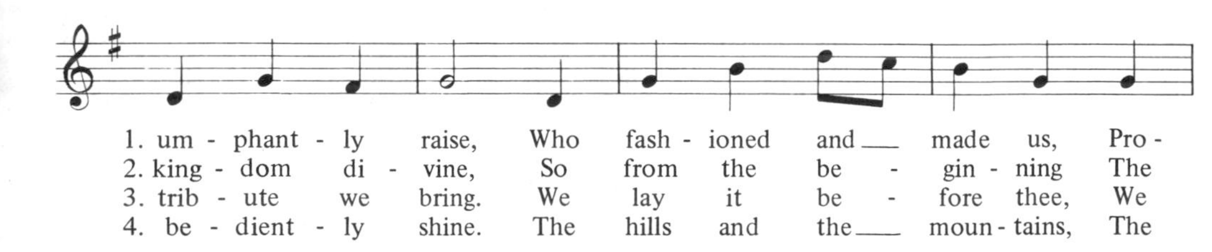
1. um - phant - ly raise, Who fash - ioned and made us, Pro -
2. king - dom di - vine, So from the be - gin - ning The
3. trib - ute we bring. We lay it be - fore thee, We
4. be - dient - ly shine. The hills and the moun - tains, The

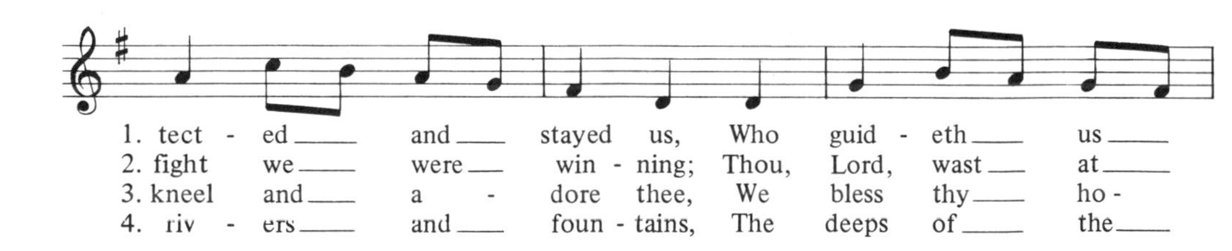
1. tect - ed and stayed us, Who guid - eth us
2. fight we were win - ning; Thou, Lord, wast at
3. kneel and a - dore thee, We bless thy ho -
4. riv - ers and foun - tains, The deeps of the

1. on to the end of our days. His ban - ners are
2. our side, all glo - ry be thine. We all do ex -
3. ly name, glad prais - es we sing. With voic - es u -
4. o - cean pro - claim him di - vine. We too should be
1. o'er us, His light goes be - fore us, A
2. tol thee, Our lead - er tri - um - phant, And
3. nit - ed Our prais - es we of - fer, And
4. voic - ing Our love and re - joic - ing; With
1. pil - lar of fire shin - ing forth in the night, Till
2. pray that thou still our de - fend - er wilt be. Let
3. glad - ly our songs of true wor - ship we raise. Thy
4. glad ad - o - ra - tion a song let us raise, Till
1. shad - ows have van - ished And dark - ness is ban - ished, As
2. thy con - gre - ga - tion Es - cape trib - u - la - tion; Thy
3. grace now con - fess - ing, We pray for thy bless - ing; To
4. all things now liv - ing U - nite in thanks - giv - ing To
1. for - ward we trav - el from light in - to light.
2. name be praised al - ways; O Lord, make us free.
3. thee, great Re - deem - er, for - ev - er be praise.
4. God in the high - est, ho - san - na and praise.

Text: Verses 1, 4, J. Cowley.
Verse 2, anon.
Verse 3, J.C. Cory, +1963.

Tune: *Ashgrove,* Welsh Folk Tune.

209 Let All Mortal Flesh Keep Silence

1. Let all mor - tal flesh keep si - lence
2. King of kings yet born of Mar - y,
3. Rank on rank the host of heav - en
4. At his feet the six - winged ser - aph,
1. And in awe and won - der stand;
2. As of old on earth he stood,
3. Spreads its van - guard on the way,
4. Cher - u - bim with sleep - less eye,
1. Pon - der noth - ing earth - ly mind - ed,
2. Lord of Lords in hu - man ves - ture,
3. As the Light of light de - scend - eth
4. Veil their fac - es to the Pres - ence,
1. For with bless - ing in his hand
2. In the bod - y and the blood,
3. From the realms of end - less day,
4. As with cease - less voice they cry,
1. Christ, our God, to earth de - scend - eth,
2. He will give to all the faith - ful
3. That the pow'rs of hell may van - ish
4. "Al - le - lu - ia, al - le - lu - ia,
1. Our full hom - age to de - mand.
2. His own self for heav'n - ly food.
3. As the dark - ness clears a - way.
4. Al - le - lu - ia, Lord Most High!"

Text: Cherubic Hymn from the Liturgy of St. James, paraphrase G. Moultrie, +1885.
Tune: *Picardy*, 17th Century French Carol.

Let the Whole Creation Cry

Ps. 148

1. Let the whole cre - a - tion cry, Al - le -
2. Praise him, all ye hosts a - bove, Al - le -
3. Men and wom - en, young and old, Al - le -
4. From the north to south - ern pole, Al - le -
1. lu - ia! Glo - ry to the Lord on high;
2. lu - ia! Ev - er bright and fair in love;
3. lu - ia! Raise the an - them man - i - fold;
4. lu - ia! Let the might - y cho - rus roll;
1. Al - le - lu - ia! Heav'n and earth, a -
2. Al - le - lu - ia! Sun and moon, up -
3. Al - le - lu - ia! Join with chil - dren's
4. Al - le - lu - ia! Ho - ly, ho - ly,
1. wake and sing: Al - le - lu - ia!
2. lift your voice, Al - le - lu - ia!
3. song - ful praise, Al - le - lu - ia!
4. ho - ly Lord, Al - le - lu - ia!
1. God is our e - ter - nal King! Al - le - lu - ia!
2. Night and stars, in God re - joice! Al - le - lu - ia!
3. Wor - ship God thro' length of days. Al - le - lu - ia!
4. Heav'n - ly King, by all a - dored! Al - le - lu - ia!

Text: Psalm 148 paraphrase, S.A. Brooke, +1916, alt.
Tune: *Llanfair,* R. Williams, +1821.

211 Lift up Your Heads, Ye Mighty Gates

1. Lift up your heads, ye might - y gates:
2. O blest the land, the cit - y blest,
3. Fling wide the por - tals of your heart;
4. Re - deem - er, come! we o - pen wide
1. Be - hold the King of glo - ry waits!
2. Where Christ, the Rul - er, is con - fessed!
3. Make it a tem - ple, set a - part
4. Our hearts to thee; here, Lord, a - bide.
1. The King of kings is draw - ing near;
2. O hap - py hearts and hap - py homes
3. From earth - ly use, for heav'n's em - ploy,
4. Let us thy in - ner pres - ence feel,
1. The Sav - ior of the world is here.
2. To whom this King of tri - umph comes!
3. A - dorned with prayer and love and joy.
4. Thy grace and love in us re - veal,

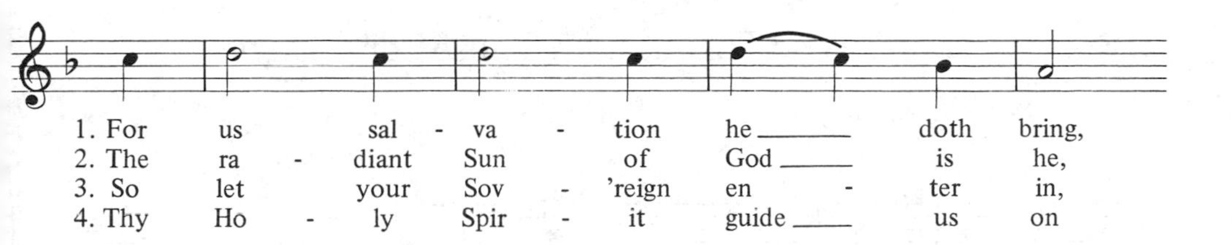
1. For us sal - va - tion he ___ doth bring,
2. The ra - diant Sun of God ___ is he,
3. So let your Sov - 'reign en - ter in,
4. Thy Ho - ly Spir - it guide ___ us on

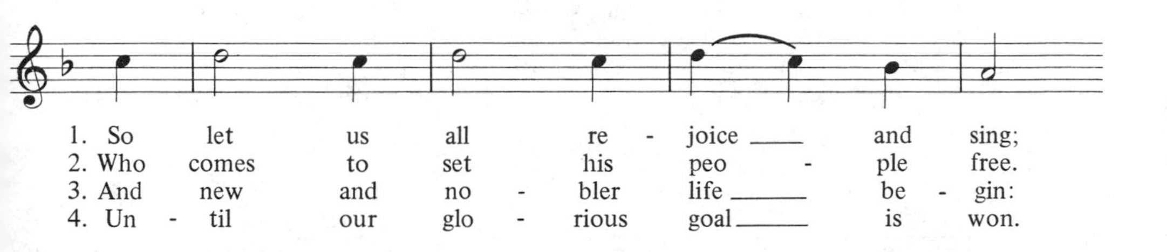
1. So let us all re - joice ___ and sing;
2. Who comes to set his peo - ple free.
3. And new and no - bler life ___ be - gin:
4. Un - til our glo - rious goal ___ is won.

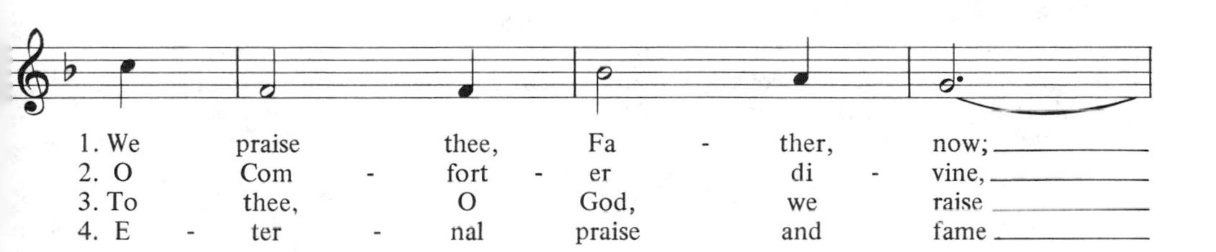
1. We praise thee, Fa - ther, now; ___
2. O Com - fort - er di - vine, ___
3. To thee, O God, we raise ___
4. E - ter - nal praise and fame ___

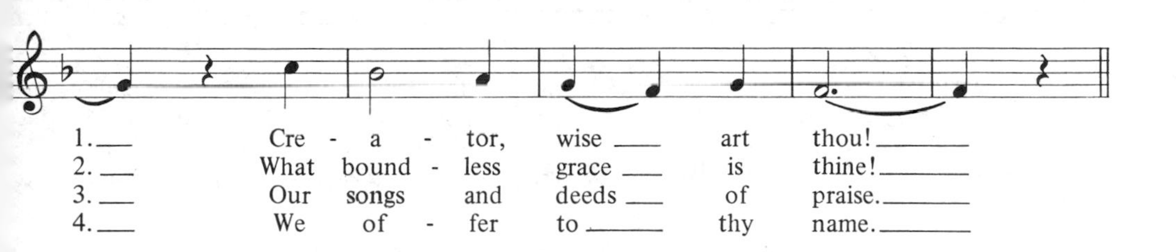
1. ___ Cre - a - tor, wise ___ art thou! ___
2. ___ What bound - less grace ___ is thine! ___
3. ___ Our songs and deeds ___ of praise. ___
4. ___ We of - fer to ___ thy name. ___

Text: G. Weissel, +1635. Trans. C. Winkworth, +1878, alt.
Tune: *Macht hoch die Tür,* "Geistreiches Gesang-Buch", 1704.

212 Lord, Who Throughout These Forty Days

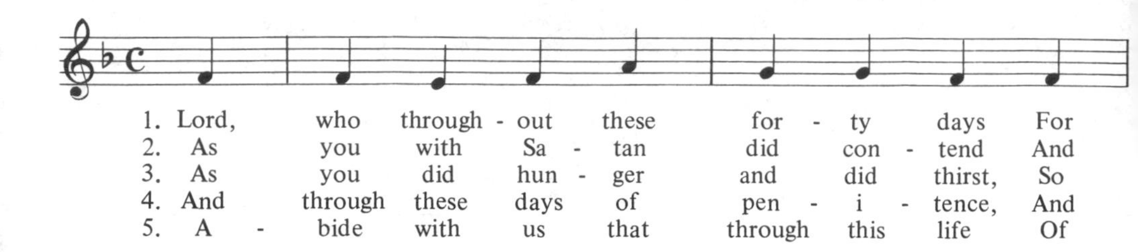
1. Lord, who through - out these for - ty days For
2. As you with Sa - tan did con - tend And
3. As you did hun - ger and did thirst, So
4. And through these days of pen - i - tence, And
5. A - bide with us that through this life Of

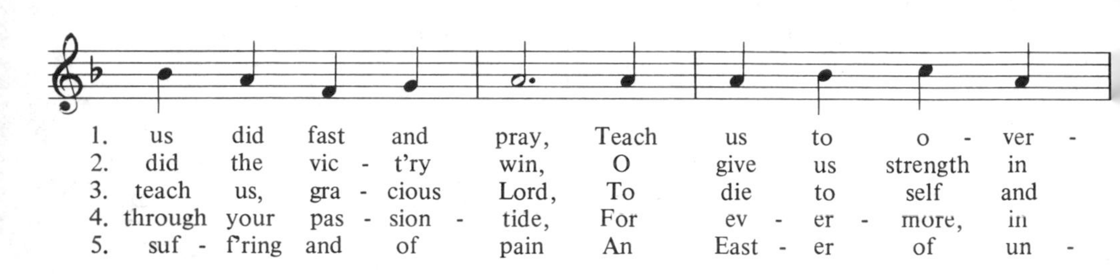
1. us did fast and pray, Teach us to o - ver -
2. did the vic - t'ry win, O give us strength in
3. teach us, gra - cious Lord, To die to self and
4. through your pas - sion - tide, For ev - er - more, in
5. suf - f'ring and of pain An East - er of un -

1. come our sins And close by you to stay.
2. you to fight, In you to con - quer sin.
3. so to live By your most ho - ly word.
4. life and death, O Lord, with us a - bide.
5. end - ing joy We may at last at - tain.

Text: C. F. Hernaman, +1898, alt.
Tune: *St. Flavian,* from "Day's Psalter", 1562.

Lord Jesus, as We Turn from Sin **213**

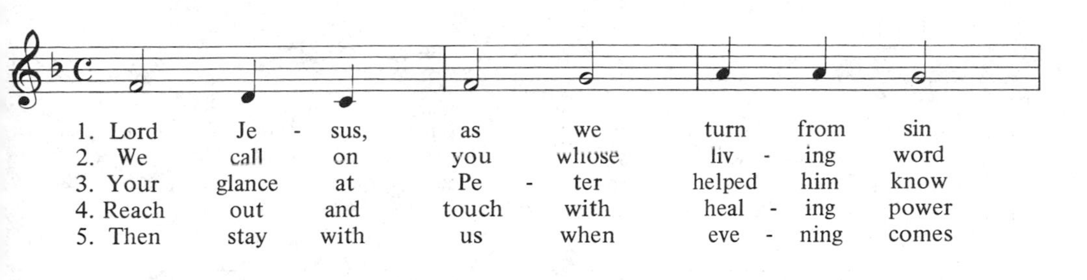
1. Lord Je - sus, as we turn from sin
2. We call on you whose liv - ing word
3. Your glance at Pe - ter helped him know
4. Reach out and touch with heal - ing power
5. Then stay with us when eve - ning comes

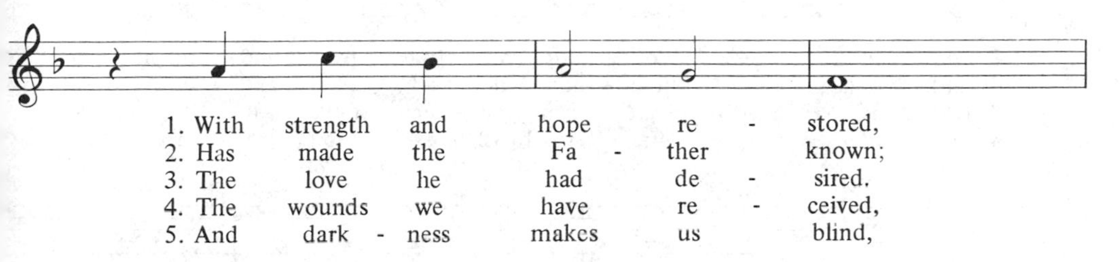
1. With strength and hope re - stored,
2. Has made the Fa - ther known;
3. The love he had de - sired.
4. The wounds we have re - ceived,
5. And dark - ness makes us blind,

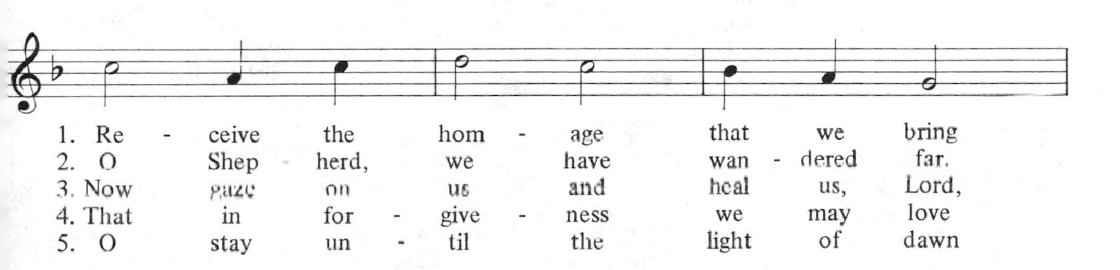
1. Re - ceive the hom - age that we bring
2. O Shep - herd, we have wan - dered far.
3. Now gaze on us and heal us, Lord,
4. That in for - give - ness we may love
5. O stay un - til the light of dawn

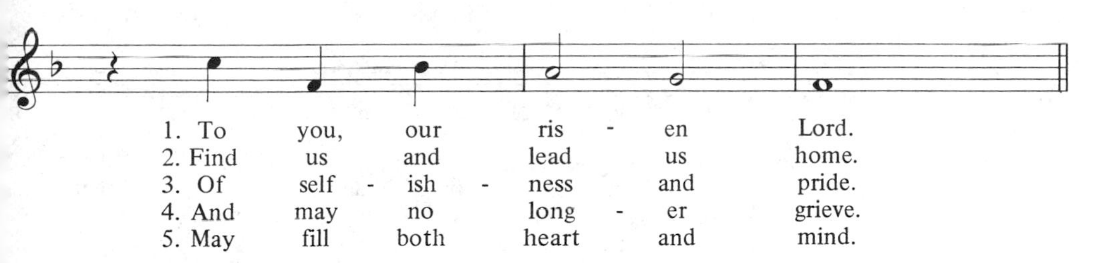
1. To you, our ris - en Lord.
2. Find us and lead us home.
3. Of self - ish - ness and pride.
4. And may no long - er grieve.
5. May fill both heart and mind.

Text: R. Wright, © International Committee on English in the Liturgy.
Used with permission.
Tune: *Nun danket all und bringet Ehr,* J. Crüger, +1662.

214 Lord of Nations, God Eternal

First Tune
1. Lord of na - tions, God E - ter - nal, Lift we songs of
2. Make our na - tion strong in jus - tice, That the peo - ple
3. Turn our eyes to things e - ter - nal, Let us learn the
4. Fill our hearts with hope and cour - age, Let us sing the
1. praise to thee, For our na - tion strong and might - y;
2. still shall know Free - dom from all fear and dan - ger
3. truth a - new That man nev - er finds sal - va - tion
4. songs of peace, As in broth - er - hood we la - bor
1. May thy bless - ings ev - er be On our land, a land of
2. From with - in, from out - ward foe. O re - new us in true
3. By the things that he can do. Teach us that we are but
4. That true jus - tice may in - crease. Give us hearts that know com -
1. beau - ty, Land of free - dom, land we love; Fields and val - leys,
2. va - lor, That like found - ers of this land We may stand for
3. pil - grims As our fa - thers were be - fore; That we jour - ney
4. pas - sion, Help - ing oth - ers on their way; Till all men shall
1. plains and moun - tains, Spread - ing 'neath blue skies a - bove.
2. right and hon - or, Seek - ing guid - ance by your hand.
3. here a sea - son, Trav - 'ling to an un - known shore.
4. live in free - dom, And ac - cept your sov - 'reign sway.

Text: H.G. Lanier, +1978. Copyright © 1975 by The Hymn Society of America, Wittenberg University, Springfield, OH 45501. Used by permission.
Tune: *Austria,* F.J. Haydn, +1809.

Lord of Nations, God Eternal

Second Tune

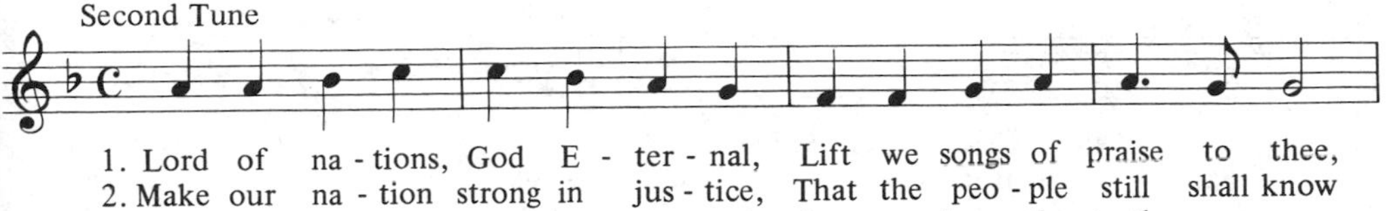

1. Lord of na - tions, God E - ter - nal, Lift we songs of praise to thee,
2. Make our na - tion strong in jus - tice, That the peo - ple still shall know
3. Turn our eyes to things e - ter - nal, Let us learn the truth a - new
4. Fill our hearts with hope and cour - age, Let us sing the songs of peace,

1. For our na - tion strong and might - y; May thy bless - ings ev - er be
2. Free - dom from all fear and dan - ger From with - in, from out - ward foe.
3. That man nev - er finds sal - va - tion By the things that he can do.
4. As in broth - er - hood we la - bor That true jus - tice may in - crease.

1. On our land, a land of_ beau - ty, Land of_ free - dom, land we love;
2. O re - new us in true_ val - or, That like_ found - ers of this land
3. Teach us that we are but_ pil - grims As our_ fa - thers were be - fore;
4. Give us hearts that know com - pas - sion, Help - ing_ oth - ers on their way;

1. Fields_ and val - leys, plains and moun - tains, Spread ing 'neath blue skies a - bove.
2. We__ may stand for right and hon - or, Seek - ing guid - ance by your hand.
3. That_ we jour - ney here a sea - son, Trav - 'ling to an un - known shore.
4. Till_ all men shall live in free - dom, And ac - cept your sov - 'reign sway.

Text: H.G. Lanier, +1978, in "New Hymns for America".
Tune: *Hymn to Joy,* L. van Beethoven, +1827.

Lord, Thou Hast Searched Me

Ps. 139

1. Lord, thou hast searched me and sure - ly know
2. My words from thee I can - not hide;
3. Where can I go a - part from thee,
4. If I the wings of morn - ing take
5. If deep - est dark - ness cov - er me,
1. Wher - e'er I rest, wher - e'er I go;
2. I feel thy power on ev - 'ry side;
3. Or whith - er from thy pres - ence flee?
4. And far a - way my dwell - ing make,
5. The dark - ness hid - eth not from thee;
1. Thou know - est all that I have planned,
2. O won - drous knowl - edge, awe - some might,
3. In heaven? It is thy dwell - ing fair;
4. The hand that lead - eth me is thine,
5. To thee both night and day are bright;
1. And all my ways are in thy hand.
2. Un - fath - omed depth, un - meas - ured height!
3. In death's a - bode? Lo, thou art there.
4. And my sup - port thy power di - vine.
5. The dark - ness shin - eth as the light.

Text: Psalm 139 paraphrase, from "Psalter Hymnal", 1959, alt.
Tune: *The King's Majesty*, G. George, © 1941 by H.W. Gray Co., Inc.

Lord, Who at Your First Eucharist Did Pray

217

1. Lord, who at your first eu - cha - rist did pray That all your Church might
2. For all your Church, O Lord, we in - ter - cede; In you our lack of
3. So, Lord, at length when sac - ra - ments shall cease, May we be one with

1. be for - ev - er one, Grant us at ev - 'ry eu - cha - rist to say
2. char - i - ty will cease; Draw us the near - er each to each, we plead,
3. all your Church a - bove, One with your saints in one un - end - ing peace,

1. With long - ing heart and soul, "Your will be done." O may we all one
2. By draw - ing all to you, O Prince of Peace; Thus may we all one
3. One with your saints in one un - bound - ed love; More bless - ed still, in

1. bread, one bod - y be, Through this blest sac - ra - ment of u - ni - ty.
2. bread, one bod - y be, Through this blest sac - ra - ment of u - ni - ty.
3. peace and love to be One with the Trin - i - ty in U - ni - ty.

Text: William H. Turton, +1938, alt.
Tune: *Song 1 (Var.)*, Orlando Gibbons, +1625.

218 Lord, Who Hast Made Us for Thine Own

Ps. 148

1. Lord, who hast made us for thine own, Hear
2. Waves roll - ing in on ev - 'ry shore Pause
3. Earth, ev - er thro' the pow'r di - vine, Seed -
4. Burn, lamps of night with con - stant flame, Shine
1. as we sing be - fore thy throne. Al - le -
2. at his foot - fall and a - dore. Al - le -
3. time and har - vest shall be thine. Al - le -
4. to the hon - or of his name. Al - le -
1. lu - ia, Al - le - lu - ia. Ac -
2. lu - ia, Al - le - lu - ia. Ye
3. lu - ia, Al - le - lu - ia. Sweet
4. lu - ia, Al - le - lu - ia. Thou
1. cept thy chil - dren's rev - 'rent praise For
2. tor - rents rush - ing from the hills Bless
3. flowers that per - fume all the air, Thank
4. sun, whom all the lands o - bey, Re -
1. all thy won - drous works and ways. Al - le -
2. him whose hand your foun - tains fills. Al - le -
3. him that he hath made you fair. Al - le -
4. new his praise from day to day. Al - le -
1.-4. lu - ia, Al - le - lu - ia, Al - le -
1.-4. lu - ia, Al - le - lu - ia, Al - le - lu - ia.

Text: Psalm 148 paraphrase, R.F. Gray.
Tune: *Vigiles et sancti,* "Cologne Gesangbuch", 1623.

Loving Mother of Our Savior
Alma Redemptoris Mater

219

Compline Anthem During Lent

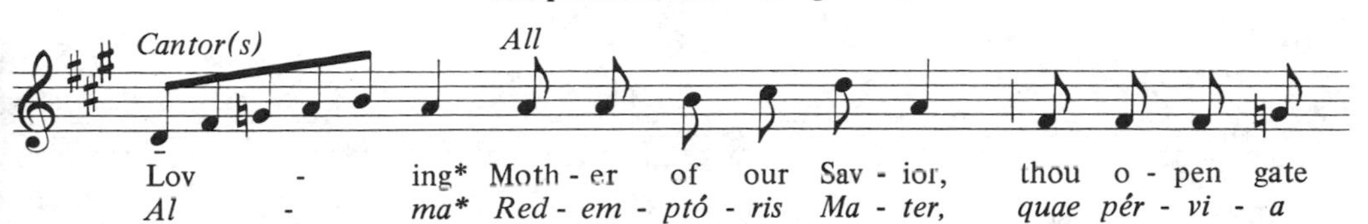

Cantor(s)
All

Lov - ing* Moth - er of our Sav - ior, thou o - pen gate
Al - ma Red - em - ptó - ris Ma - ter, quae pér - vi - a*

lead - ing us to heav - en, and Star of the Sea, help thy fall - en peo -
cae - li por - ta ma - nes, Et stel - la ma - ris, suc - cúr - re ca - dén -

ple, help all those who seek to rise a - gain. Maid - en who didst give birth,
ti súr - ge - re qui cu - rat pó - pu - lo: Tu quae ge - nu - í - sti,

all na - ture won - der - ing, to thy ho - ly Lord Cre - a - tor:__
na - tú - ra mi - rán - te, tu - um san - ctum Ge - ni - tó - rem:__

Vir - gin be - fore and vir - gin al - ways who re - ceived from Ga-briel's mouth
Vir - go pri - us ac po - sté - ri - us, Ga - bri - é - lis ab o - re

this mes - sage from heav - en, take pit - y on__ us poor sin - ners.
su - mens il - lud A - ve, pec - ca - tó - rum__ mi - se - ré - re.

℣. The angel of the Lord declared unto Mary.
℟. And she conceived of the Holy Ghost.

℣. Angelus Dómini nuntiávit Maríae.
℟. Et concépit de Spíritu Sancto.

Text: Ascribed to H. Contractus, +1054. English adaptation by T.M.

Tune: Plainchant, Mode 5.

Mary, Queen of Heav'n
Regina Caeli, Laetare

Compline Anthem During Eastertide

Cantor(s)
All
Mar - y, Queen of Heav'n, be joy - ful, Al - le - lu - ia.
Re - gí - na cae - li, lae - tá - re, Al - le - lú - ia:

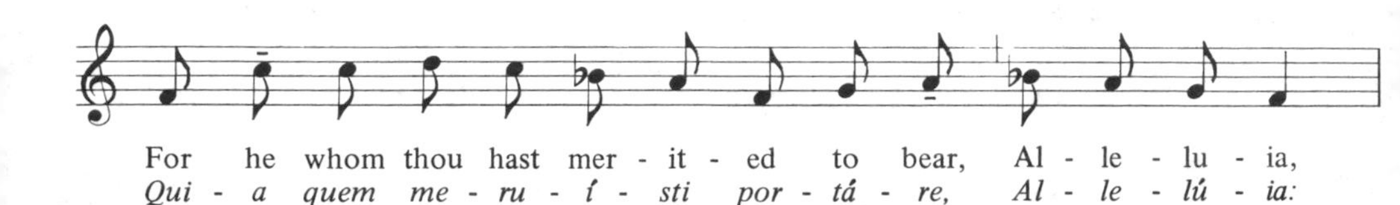
For he whom thou hast mer - it - ed to bear, Al - le - lu - ia,
Qui - a quem me - ru - í - sti por - tá - re, Al - le - lú - ia:

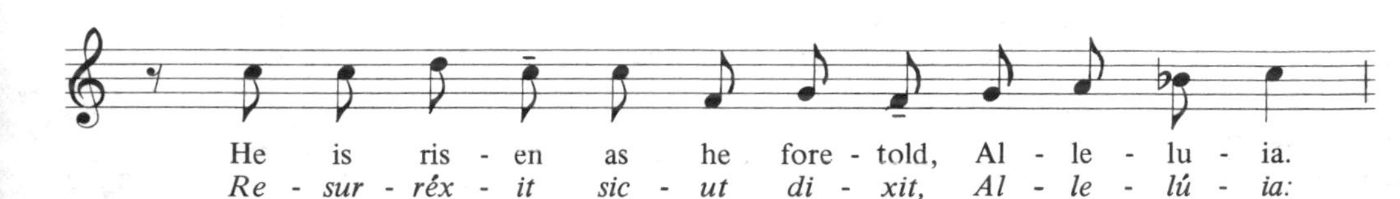
He is ris - en as he fore - told, Al - le - lu - ia.
Re - sur - réx - it sic - ut di - xit, Al - le - lú - ia:

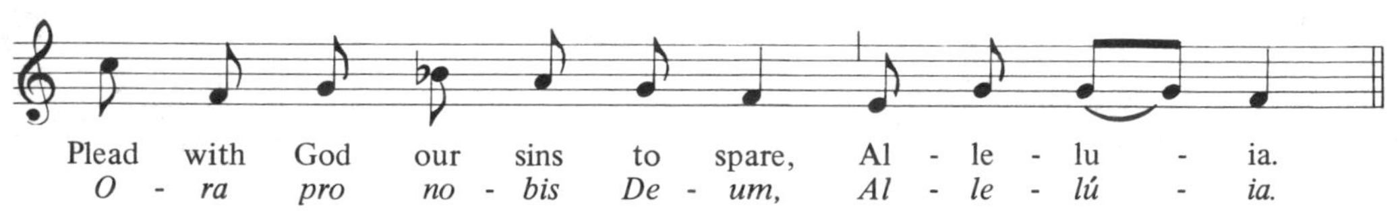
Plead with God our sins to spare, Al - le - lu - ia.
O - ra pro no - bis De - um, Al - le - lú - ia.

℣. Rejoice and be glad, O Virgin Mary, Alleluia.
℟. For the Lord is truly arisen, Alleluia.

℣. Gaude et laetáre Virgo María, Allelúia.
℟. Quia surréxit Dóminus vere, Allelúia.

Text: 14th Century, anon. English text adaptation by T.M. in "Pius X Hymnal",
Tune: Plainchant, Mode 6.

Mary the Dawn **221**

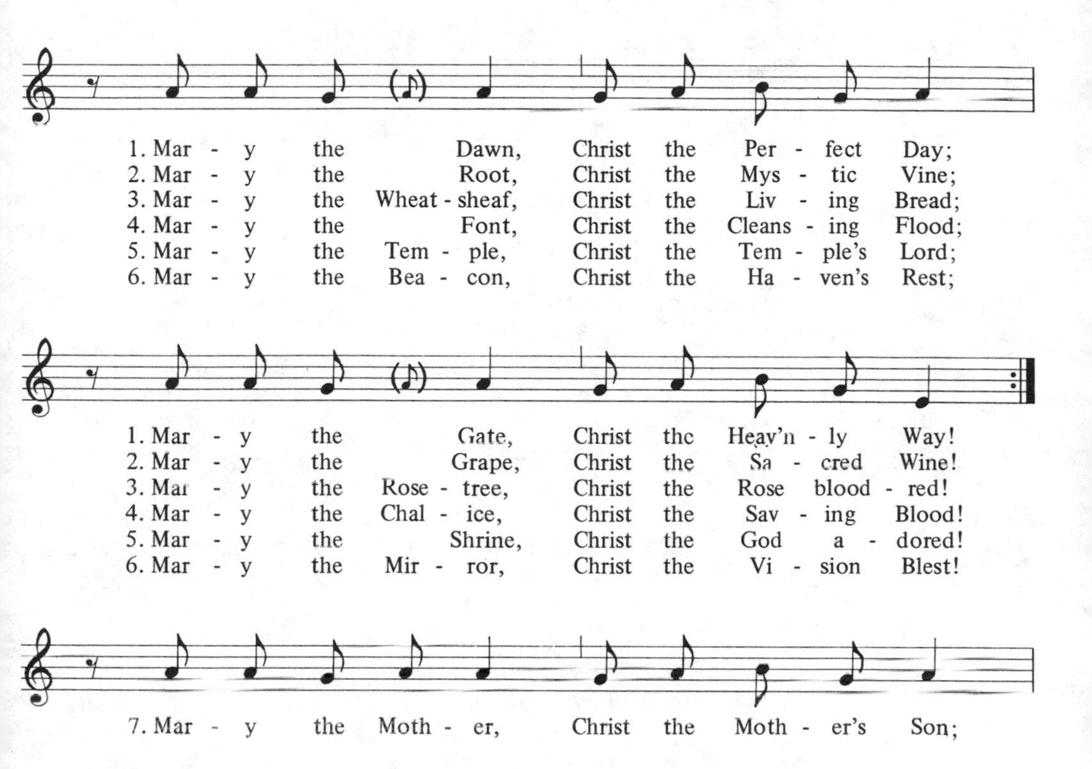
1. Mar - y the Dawn, Christ the Per - fect Day;
2. Mar - y the Root, Christ the Mys - tic Vine;
3. Mar - y the Wheat - sheaf, Christ the Liv - ing Bread;
4. Mar - y the Font, Christ the Cleans - ing Flood;
5. Mar - y the Tem - ple, Christ the Tem - ple's Lord;
6. Mar - y the Bea - con, Christ the Ha - ven's Rest;
1. Mar - y the Gate, Christ the Heav'n - ly Way!
2. Mar - y the Grape, Christ the Sa - cred Wine!
3. Mar - y the Rose - tree, Christ the Rose blood - red!
4. Mar - y the Chal - ice, Christ the Sav - ing Blood!
5. Mar - y the Shrine, Christ the God a - dored!
6. Mar - y the Mir - ror, Christ the Vi - sion Blest!
7. Mar - y the Moth - er, Christ the Moth - er's Son;

7. Both ev - er blest while end - less a - ges_ run. A - men._

Text: Anon.
Tune: Adapted to Psalm Tone, Mode 4 by P. Cross.

222

My Country, Tis of Thee

America

1. My coun - try, 'tis of thee, Sweet land of
2. My na - tive coun - try, thee, Land of the
3. Let mu - sic swell the breeze, And ring from
4. Our fa - thers' God, to thee, Au - thor of
1. lib - er - ty, Of thee I sing; Land where my
2. no - ble free, Thy name I love; I love thy
3. all the trees, Sweet free - dom's song; Let mor - tal
4. lib - er - ty, To thee we sing; Long may our
1. fa - thers died, Land of the Pil - grims' pride,
2. rocks and rills, Thy woods and tem - pled hills;
3. tongues a - wake; Let all that breathe par - take;
4. land be bright With free - dom's ho - ly light;
1. From ev - 'ry moun - tain - side Let free - dom ring.
2. My heart with rap - ture thrills Like that a - bove.
3. Let rocks their si - lence break; The sound pro - long.
4. Pro - tect us by thy might, Great God, our King.

Text: S.F. Smith, +1895.
Tune: *America,* English, 18th Century. Adapted in "Thesaurus Musicus", c. 1741.

My God, Accept My Heart This Day

223

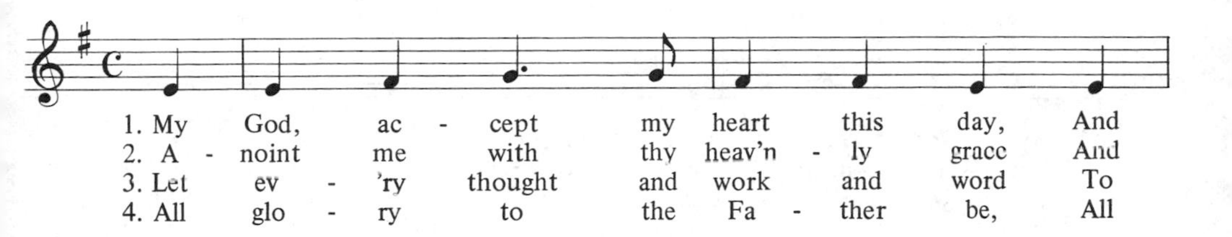
1. My God, ac - cept my heart this day, And
2. A - noint me with thy heav'n - ly grace And
3. Let ev - 'ry thought and work and word To
4. All glo - ry to the Fa - ther be, All

1. make it whol - ly thine, That I from thee no
2. seal me for thine own; That I may see thy
3. thee be ev - er giv'n; Then life shall be thy
4. glo - ry to the Son, All glo - ry, Ho - ly

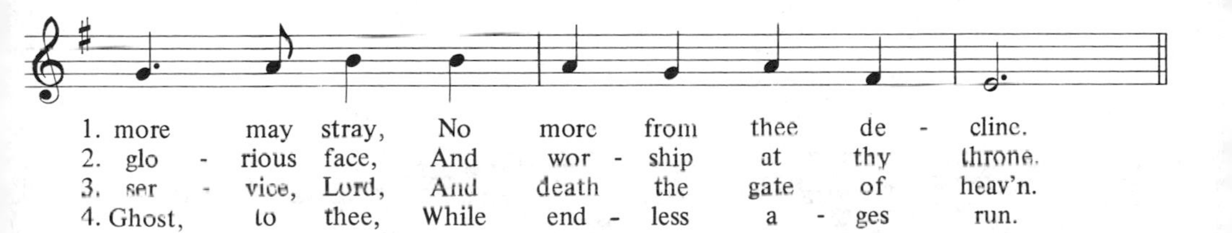
1. more may stray, No more from thee de - cline.
2. glo - rious face, And wor - ship at thy throne.
3. ser - vice, Lord, And death the gate of heav'n.
4. Ghost, to thee, While end - less a - ges run.

Text: M. Bridges, +1894.
Tune: *Cheshire*, 16th Century, anon.

224 My God, How Wonderful You Are

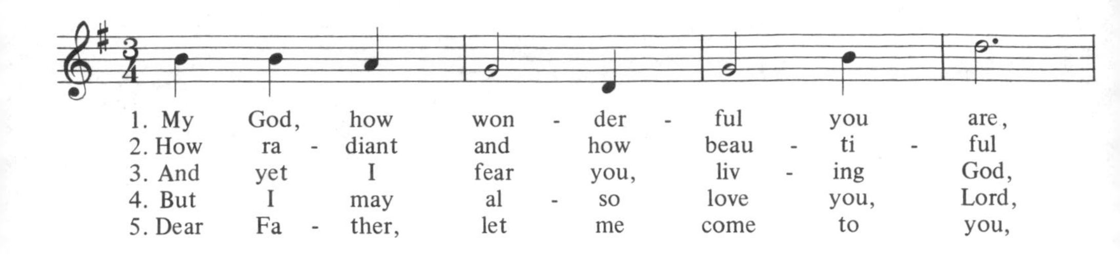
1. My God, how won - der - ful you are,
2. How ra - diant and how beau - ti - ful
3. And yet I fear you, liv - ing God,
4. But I may al - so love you, Lord,
5. Dear Fa - ther, let me come to you,

1. In maj - es - ty so bright, How beau - ti - ful your
2. Your pres - ence, Lord, must be, Your end - less wis - dom,
3. With deep - est, anx - ious fears, And wor - ship you with
4. For good - ness you im - part, And you have stooped to
5. Your pres - ence let me see, That I may live with -

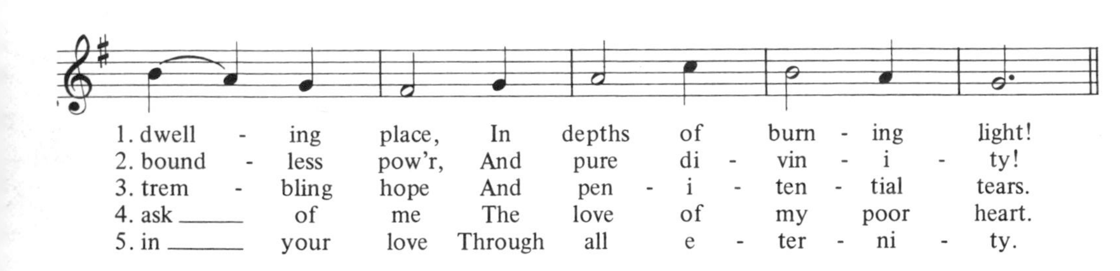
1. dwell - ing place, In depths of burn - ing light!
2. bound - less pow'r, And pure di - vin - i - ty!
3. trem - bling hope And pen - i - ten - tial tears.
4. ask ___ of me The love of my poor heart.
5. in ___ your love Through all e - ter - ni - ty.

Text: F.W. Faber, +1863. Adapted by A.G. Petti in
"New Catholic Hymnal", © 1971 by Faber Music Limited.
Tune: *Gerontius,* J.B. Dykes, +1876, var.

My God, My God, O Hear My Plea

Ps. 22

1. My God, my God, O hear my plea, O why have you
2. All those who see me scoff at me. They shake their heads
3. Un - num-bered foes would do me wrong; They press a - bout
4. While on my dy - ing form they gaze, My cour - age fails;

1. a - ban - doned me? I pray to you in
2. and sneer at me: "He prays his God will
3. me harsh and strong. With cru - el hate and
4. my strength de - cays. My shame and sor - row

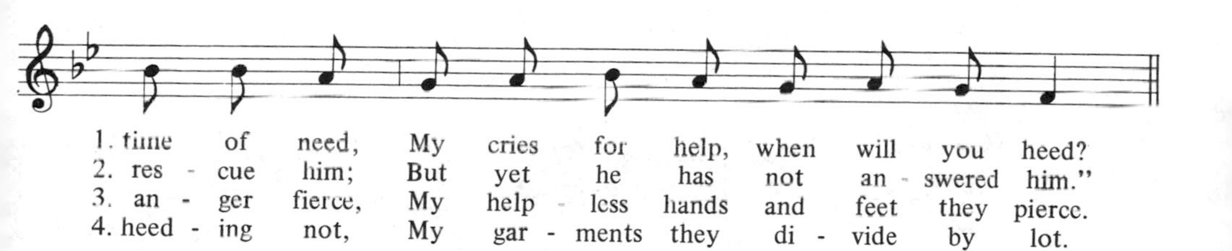
1. time of need, My cries for help, when will you heed?
2. res - cue him; But yet he has not an - swered him."
3. an - ger fierce, My help - less hands and feet they pierce.
4. heed - ing not, My gar - ments they di - vide by lot.

5. O God, now hasten to my side;
Your face from me, oh do not hide.
From death and suffering set me free;
I live if you will answer me.

6. I always will declare your fame
To brethren gathered in your name:
"Give glory to the Lord always,
All you, his people, give him praise."

Text: Psalm 22 paraphrase, J. Dunn. © by author. Used with permission.
Tune: *Aurora caelum,* Plainchant, Mode 8.

Now Fades All Earthly Splendor

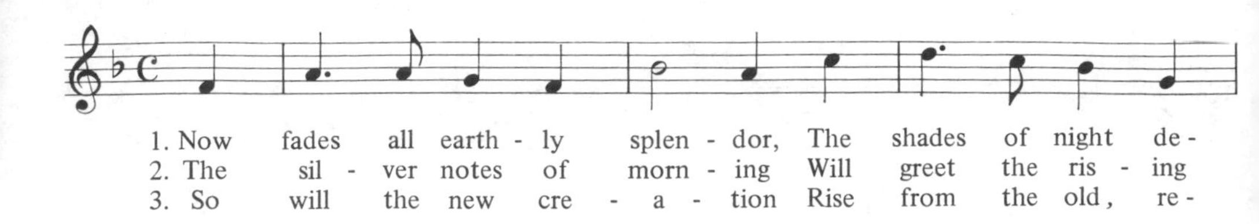
1. Now fades all earth - ly splen - dor, The shades of night de -
2. The sil - ver notes of morn - ing Will greet the ris - ing
3. So will the new cre - a - tion Rise from the old, re -

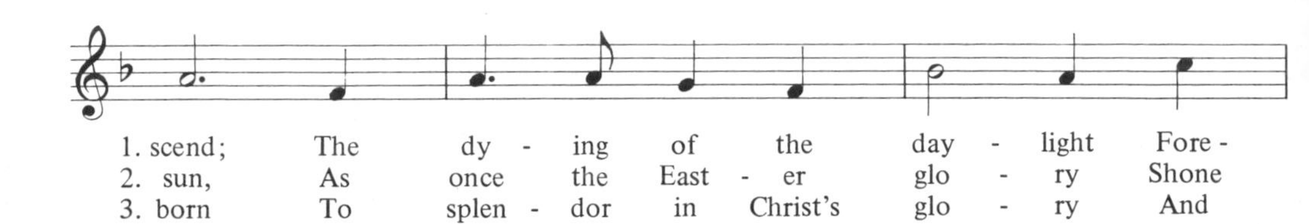
1. scend; The dy - ing of the day - light Fore -
2. sun, As once the East - er glo - ry Shone
3. born To splen - dor in Christ's glo - ry And

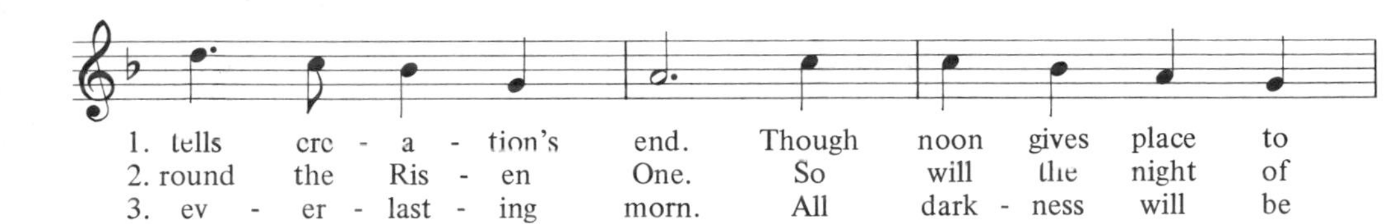
1. tells cre - a - tion's end. Though noon gives place to
2. round the Ris - en One. So will the night of
3. ev - er - last - ing morn. All dark - ness will be

1. sun - set, Yet dark gives place to light: The
2. dy - ing Give place to heav - en's day, And
3. end - ed As faith gives place to sight Of

1. prom - ise of to - mor - row With dawn's new hope is bright.
2. hope of heav - en's vi - sion Will light our pil - grim way.
3. Fa - ther, Son and Spir - it, One God in heav - en's light.

Text: J. Quinn, S.J.
Tune: *Cantique,* "Cantiques Gothiques", 1648.

Now, His Years of Life Perfected

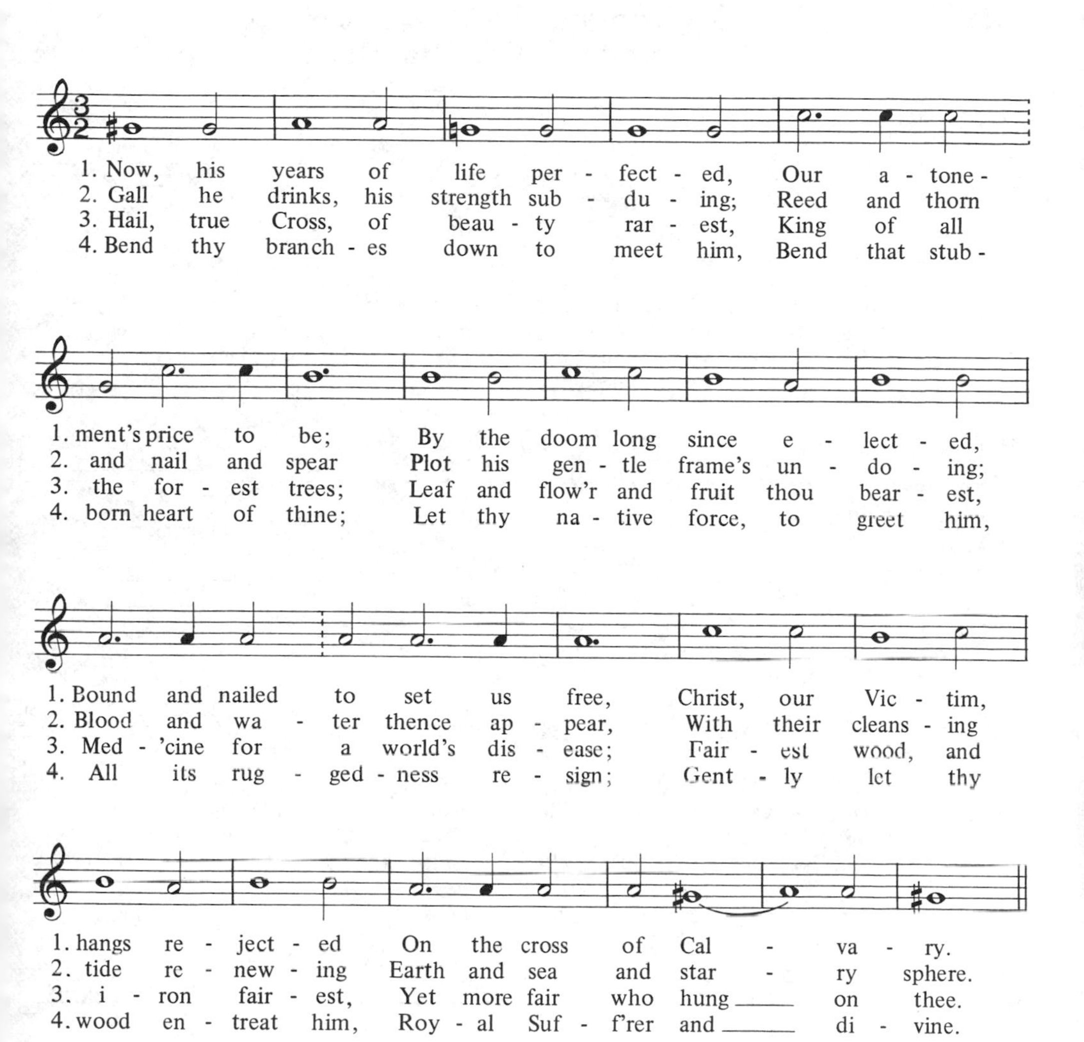
1. Now, his years of life per - fect - ed, Our a - tone -
2. Gall he drinks, his strength sub - du - ing; Reed and thorn
3. Hail, true Cross, of beau - ty rar - est, King of all
4. Bend thy branch - es down to meet him, Bend that stub -
1. ment's price to be; By the doom long since e - lect - ed,
2. and nail and spear Plot his gen - tle frame's un - do - ing;
3. the for - est trees; Leaf and flow'r and fruit thou bear - est,
4. born heart of thine; Let thy na - tive force, to greet him,
1. Bound and nailed to set us free, Christ, our Vic - tim,
2. Blood and wa - ter thence ap - pear, With their cleans - ing
3. Med - 'cine for a world's dis - ease; Fair - est wood, and
4. All its rug - ged - ness re - sign; Gent - ly let thy
1. hangs re - ject - ed On the cross of Cal - va - ry.
2. tide re - new - ing Earth and sea and star - ry sphere.
3. i - ron fair - est, Yet more fair who hung on thee.
4. wood en - treat him, Roy - al Suf - f'rer and di - vine.

Text: Venantius Fortunatus, +609. Trans. R. Knox, +1957.
Tune: Ascribed to G.P. da Palestrina, +1594.

BENEDICTION SERVICE (English)

228

Now My Tongue, the Myst'ry Telling
Therefore, We Before Him Bending

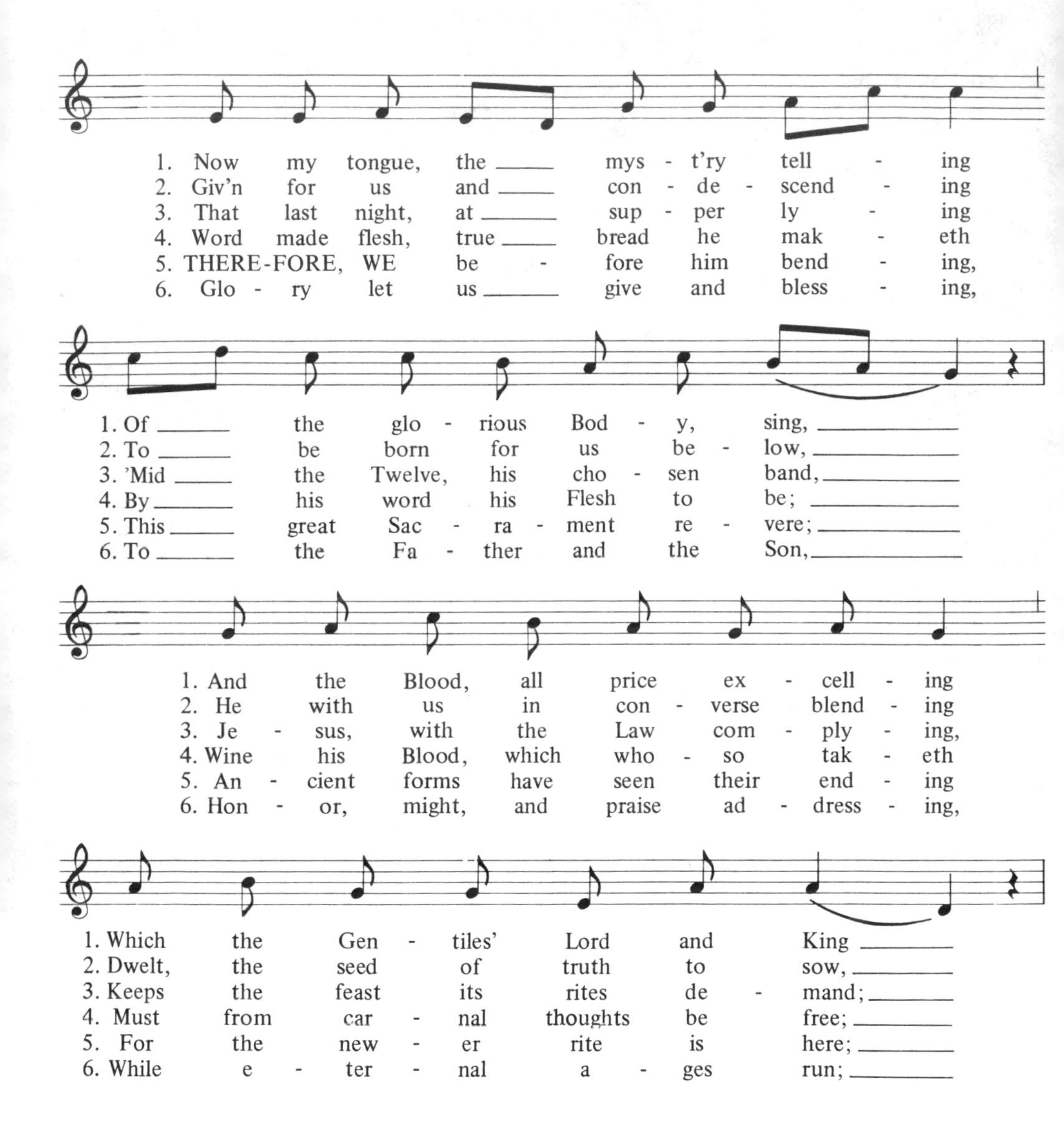
1. Now my tongue, the mys - t'ry tell - ing
2. Giv'n for us and con - de - scend - ing
3. That last night, at sup - per ly - ing
4. Word made flesh, true bread he mak - eth
5. THERE-FORE, WE be - fore him bend - ing,
6. Glo - ry let us give and bless - ing,
1. Of the glo - rious Bod - y, sing,
2. To be born for us be - low,
3. 'Mid the Twelve, his cho - sen band,
4. By his word his Flesh to be;
5. This great Sac - ra - ment re - vere;
6. To the Fa - ther and the Son,
1. And the Blood, all price ex - cell - ing
2. He with us in con - verse blend - ing
3. Je - sus, with the Law com - ply - ing,
4. Wine his Blood, which who - so tak - eth
5. An - cient forms have seen their end - ing
6. Hon - or, might, and praise ad - dress - ing,
1. Which the Gen - tiles' Lord and King
2. Dwelt, the seed of truth to sow,
3. Keeps the feast its rites de - mand;
4. Must from car - nal thoughts be free;
5. For the new - er rite is here;
6. While e - ter - nal a - ges run;

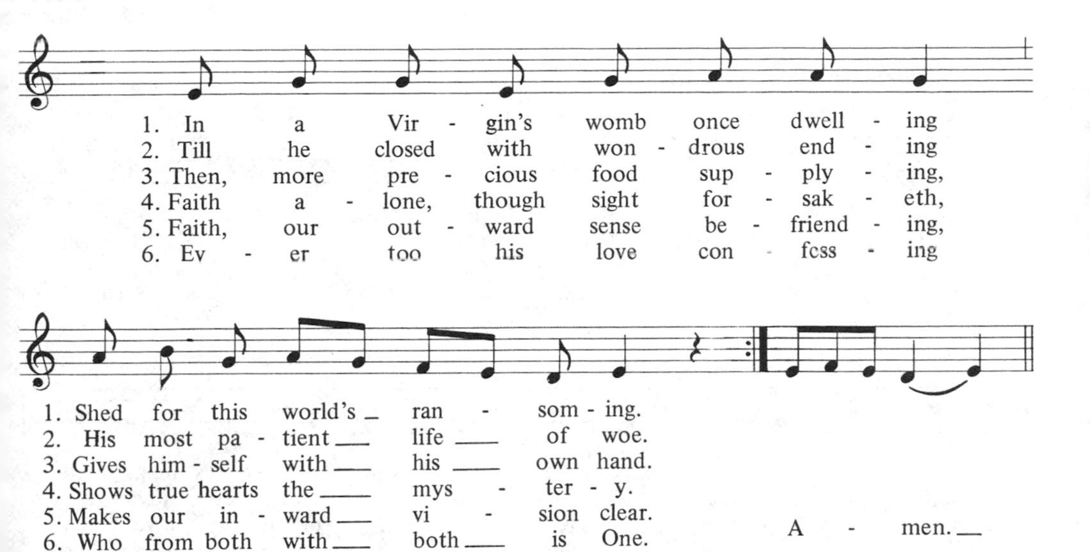
1. In a Vir - gin's womb once dwell - ing
2. Till he closed with won - drous end - ing
3. Then, more pre - cious food sup - ply - ing,
4. Faith a - lone, though sight for - sak - eth,
5. Faith, our out - ward sense be - friend - ing,
6. Ev - er too his love con - fess - ing
1. Shed for this world's ran - som - ing.
2. His most pa - tient life of woe.
3. Gives him - self with his own hand.
4. Shows true hearts the mys - ter - y.
5. Makes our in - ward vi - sion clear.
6. Who from both with both is One.
A - men.

Text: St. Thomas Aquinas, +1274. Trans. anon.
Tune: *Pange lingua sacramentum.* Plainchant, Mode 3.

Versicle - Response - Oration for Benediction **229**

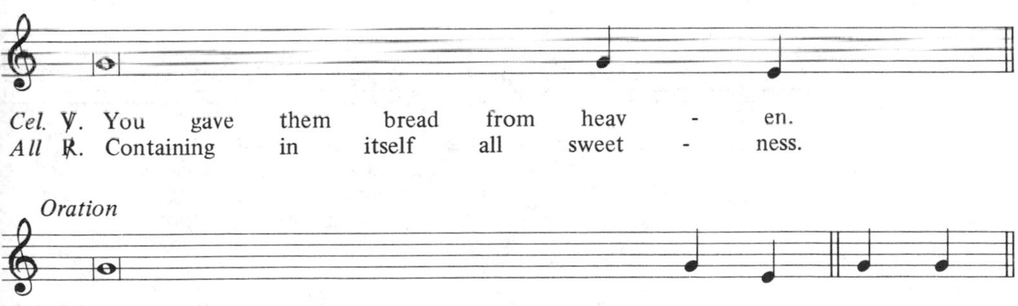
Cel. ℣. You gave them bread from heav - en.
All ℟. Containing in itself all sweet - ness.
Oration
Cel. Let us pray.

O God, who in this wonderful sacrament has left us a memorial of your passion, grant that we may so venerate the sacred mysteries of your body and blood that we may ever feel within ourselves the effects of your redemption. You who live and reign for ever and ______ ev - er. *All* A - men.

230 Now Thank We All Our God

First Tune
1. Now thank we all our God With
2. O may this boun - teous God Through
3. Lord God, we wor - ship thee! In
4. All praise and thanks to God, The
1. heart, and hands and voic - es, Who won - drous things hath
2. all our life be near us, With ev - er joy - ful
3. loud and hap - py cho - rus, We praise thy love and
4. Fa - ther, now be giv - en, The Son and him who
1. done, In whom his world re - joic - es; Who
2. hearts And bless - ed peace to cheer us, And
3. power Whose good - ness reign - eth o'er us. To
4. reigns With them in high - est heav - en. The
1. from our moth - ers' arms Hath blessed us on our way With
2. keep us in his grace, And guide us when per - plexed, And
3. heav'n our song shall soar, For - ev - er it shall be Re -
4. one e - ter - nal God, Whom earth and heav'n a - dore, For
1. count - less gifts of love, And still is ours to - day.
2. free us from all ills In this world and the next.
3. sound - ing o'er and o'er: Lord God, we wor - ship thee.
4. thus it was, is now, And shall be ev - er - more.

Text: Verses 1, 2 and 4, M. Rinckart, +1649. Trans. C. Winkworth, +1878.
Verse 3, J. Franck, +1677, alt.
Tune: *Nun danket,* J. Crüger, +1662.

Now Thank We All Our God

Second Tune
1. Now thank we all our God With
2. O may this boun - teous God Through
3. Lord God, we wor - ship thee! In
4. All praise and thanks to God, The
1. heart, and hands and voic - es, Who won - drous things hath
2. all our life be near us, With ev - er joy - ful
3. loud and hap - py cho - rus, We praise thy love and
4. Fa - ther, now be giv - en, The Son and him who
1. done, In whom his world re - joic - es; Who
2. hearts And bless - ed peace to cheer us, And
3. power Whose good - ness reign - eth o'er us. To
4. reigns With them in high - est heav - en. The
1. from our moth - ers' arms Hath blessed_ us on our way With
2. keep us in his grace, And guide_ us when per - plexed, And
3. heav'n our song shall soar, For - ev - er it shall be Re -
4. one e - ter - nal God, Whom earth_ and heav'n a - dore, For
1. count - less gifts of love, And still is ours to - day.
2. free us from all ills In this world and the next.
3. sound - ing o'er and o'er: Lord God, we wor - ship thee.
4. thus it was, is now, And shall be ev - er - more.

Text: Verses 1, 2 and 4, M. Rinckart, +1649. Trans. C. Winkworth, +1878.
Verse 3, J. Franck, +1677, alt.
Tune: *Nun danket,* J. Crüger, +1662.

O Beautiful for Spacious Skies

America the Beautiful

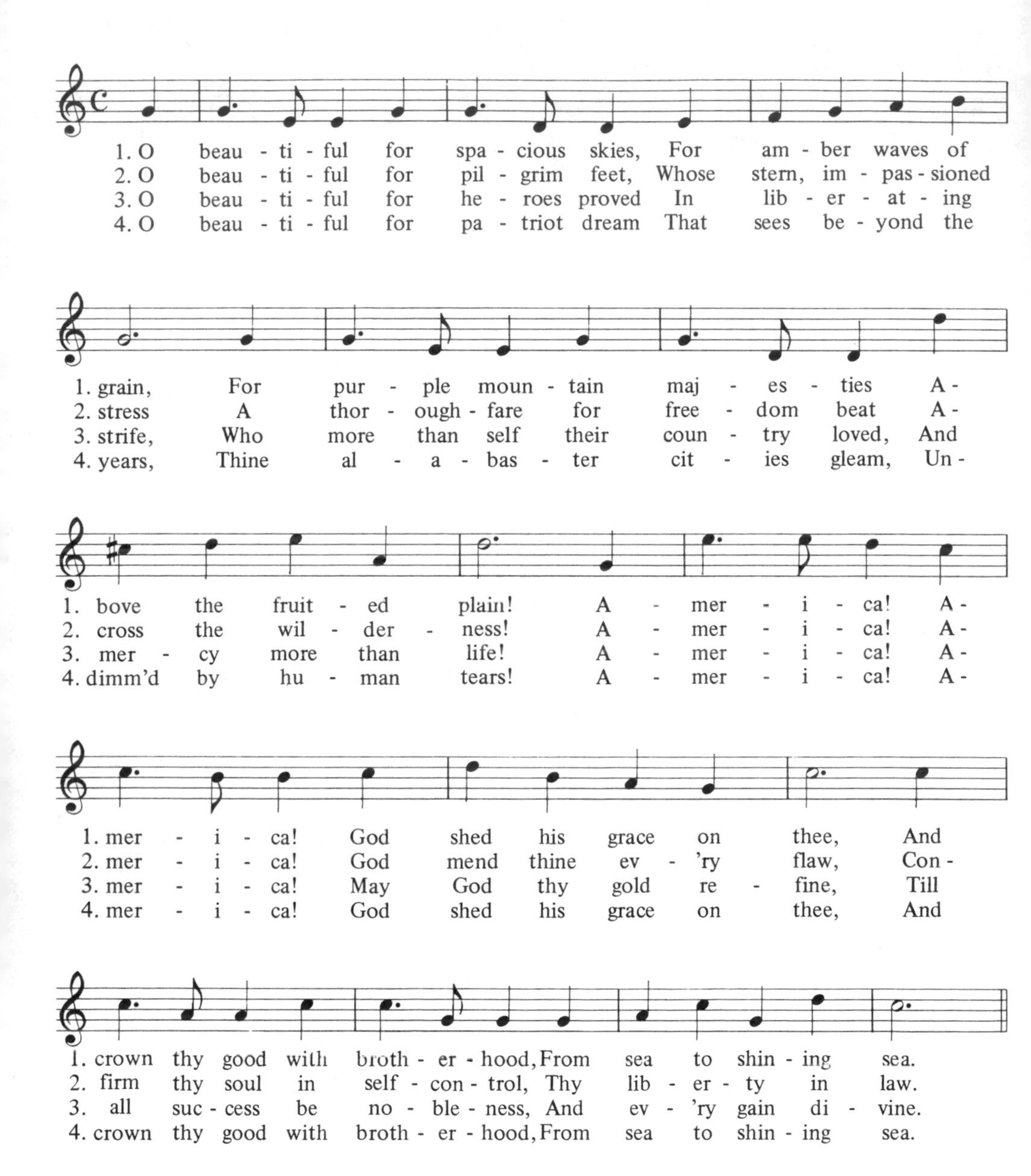
1. O beau - ti - ful for spa - cious skies, For am - ber waves of
2. O beau - ti - ful for pil - grim feet, Whose stern, im - pas - sioned
3. O beau - ti - ful for he - roes proved In lib - er - at - ing
4. O beau - ti - ful for pa - triot dream That sees be - yond the
1. grain, For pur - ple moun - tain maj - es - ties A -
2. stress A thor - ough - fare for free - dom beat A -
3. strife, Who more than self their coun - try loved, And
4. years, Thine al - a - bas - ter cit - ies gleam, Un -
1. bove the fruit - ed plain! A - mer - i - ca! A -
2. cross the wil - der - ness! A - mer - i - ca! A -
3. mer - cy more than life! A - mer - i - ca! A -
4. dimm'd by hu - man tears! A - mer - i - ca! A -
1. mer - i - ca! God shed his grace on thee, And
2. mer - i - ca! God mend thine ev - 'ry flaw, Con -
3. mer - i - ca! May God thy gold re - fine, Till
4. mer - i - ca! God shed his grace on thee, And
1. crown thy good with broth - er - hood, From sea to shin - ing sea.
2. firm thy soul in self - con - trol, Thy lib - er - ty in law.
3. all suc - cess be no - ble - ness, And ev - 'ry gain di - vine.
4. crown thy good with broth - er - hood, From sea to shin - ing sea.

Text: K.L. Bates, +1929.
Tune: *Materna,* S. Ward, +1903.

O Be Glad, My Soul, Rejoice

233

Magnificat

REFRAIN
1.-4. O be glad, my soul, re - joice In the
1.-4. great - ness of the Lord. O my spir - it,
1.-4. leap for joy In my Sav - ior and my God.
1. He has dealt so gra - cious - ly, Looked on
2. Blest for - ev - er shall I be From this
3. Ev - er mer - ci - ful is he, Ev - er -
4. Glo - ry to th'In - car - nate Word, Fa - ther,
1. me so ten - der - ly; How sub - lime what
2. day, e - ter - nal - ly; This his spo - ken
3. more so shall it be; These the deeds his
4. Son and Spir - it, Lord. While un - end - ing
Repeat REFRAIN
1. he has done, He the Lord, the Might - y One!
2. word has done, He the Lord, the Might - y One!
3. arm has done, He the Lord, the Might - y One!
4. a - ges run, Praise the Lord, the Might - y One!

Text: Verses 1-3, Magnificat, Luke 1:46-51 paraphrase, St. Joseph's Abbey, 1967, alt. Used with permission. Verse 4, J. Dunn, © by author. Used with permission.
Tune: *Freu dich sehr,* Genevan Psalter, 1551.

O Be Joyful in the Lord

Ps. 100

1. O be joy - ful in the Lord! Sing be - fore him,
2. Know ye that the Lord is King! All his works his
3. En - ter now his ho - ly gate; Let our bur - dened
4. For the Lord, our God, is kind, And his love shall
1. all the earth! Praise him with a glad ac - cord And with lives of
2. wis - dom prove! By his might the heav - ens ring; In his love we
3. hearts be still; In the sa - cred si - lence wait, As we seek to
4. con - stant be; In his will our peace we find; In his ser - vice,
1. no - blest worth. Sons of ev - 'ry land, Hum - bly
2. live and move. By him we are made, So we
3. know his will. Let our lives ex - press Our a -
4. lib - er - ty. Yea, his law is sure; In his
1. now be - fore him stand! Raise your voice
2. trust him un - a - fraid. Stand - ing fast
3. bun - dant thank - ful - ness; All our days,
4. light we walk se - cure; Ev - er - more,
1. and re - joice In the boun - ty of his hand.
2. to the last, By his hand our lives are stayed.
3. all our ways, Shall our Fa - ther's love con - fess.
4. as of yore, Shall his change - less truth en - dure.

Text: Psalm 100 paraphrase, Curtis Beach. From "Pilgrim Hymnal".
Tune: *Finlay,* H. Friedell, +1958.

O Come, All Ye Faithful

235

1. O come, all ye faith - ful, Joy - ful and tri - umph - ant, O
2. Sing, choirs of an - gels, Sing with ex - ul - ta - tion,
3. See how the shep - herds Sum-moned to his cra - dle,
4. Child, for us sin - ners, Poor and in the man - ger,
5. Yea, Lord, we greet thee, Born this hap - py morn - ing;
1. come ye, O come ye to Beth - le - hem;
2. Sing, all ye cit - i - zens of heav'n a - bove:
3. Leav - ing their flocks, draw nigh to gaze;
4. We would em - brace thee with love and awe;
5. Je - sus, to thee be glo - ry giv'n;
1. Come and be - hold him, Born the King of an - gels;
2. Glo - ry to God In the high - est.
3. We there will al - so turn our joy - ful foot - steps.
4. Who would not love thee, Lov - ing us so dear - ly?
5. Word of the Fa - ther, Now in flesh ap - pear - ing.
REFRAIN
1.-5. O come, let us a - dore him, O come, let us a - dore him, O
1.-5. come, let us a - dore him, Christ, the Lord.

Text: Attributed to J.F. Wade, +1786. Trans. F. Oakeley, +1880, and others.
Tune: *Adeste fideles,* attributed to J.F. Wade, +1786, in "Cantus Diversi", 1751.

236 O Come, O Come Emmanuel

1. O come, O come, Em - man - u - el, And ran - som
2. O come, thou Wis - dom from on high, Who or - d'rest
3. O come, A - don - ai, Lord of might, Who to thy
4. O come, thou Rod of Jes - se's stem, From ev - 'ry
5. O come, thou Key of Da - vid, come, And o - pen
6. O come, thou Day - spring from on high, And cheer us
7. O come, De - sire of na - tions, bind In one the
1. cap - tive Is - ra - el, That mourns in lone - ly
2. all things might - i - ly; To us the path of
3. tribes on Si - nai's height In an - cient times did
4. foe de - liv - er them That trust thy might - y
5. wide our heav'n - ly home; Make safe the way that
6. by thy draw - ing nigh; Dis - perse the gloom - y
7. hearts of all man - kind; Bid thou our sad di -
1. ex - ile here Un - til the Son of God ap - pear.
2. knowl - edge show And teach us in her ways to go.
3. give the law, In cloud and maj - es - ty and awe.
4. power to save, And give them vic - t'ry o'er the grave.
5. leads on high, And close the path to mis - er - y.
6. clouds of night, And death's dark shad - ow put to flight.
7. vi - sions cease, And be thy - self our King of Peace.
1.-7. Re - joice! Re - joice! Em - man - u -
1.-7. el Shall come to thee, O Is - ra - el.

Text: "Psalteriolum Cantionum Catholicarum", Cologne, 1710. Trans. J.M. Neale, +1866.
Tune: *Veni Emmanuel,* Plainchant, Mode 1.

O for a Thousand Tongues to Sing

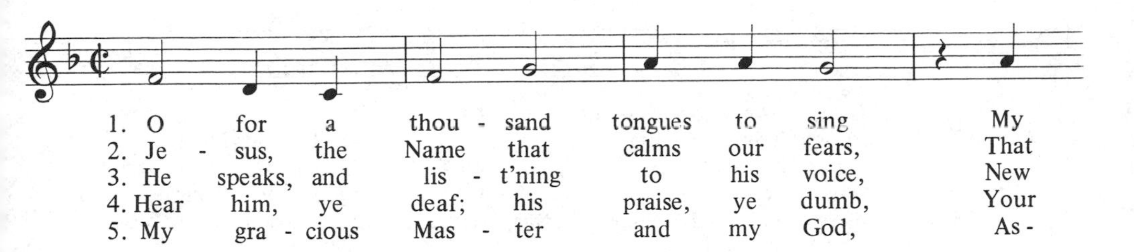
1. O for a thou - sand tongues to sing My
2. Je - sus, the Name that calms our fears, That
3. He speaks, and lis - t'ning to his voice, New
4. Hear him, ye deaf; his praise, ye dumb, Your
5. My gra - cious Mas - ter and my God, As -

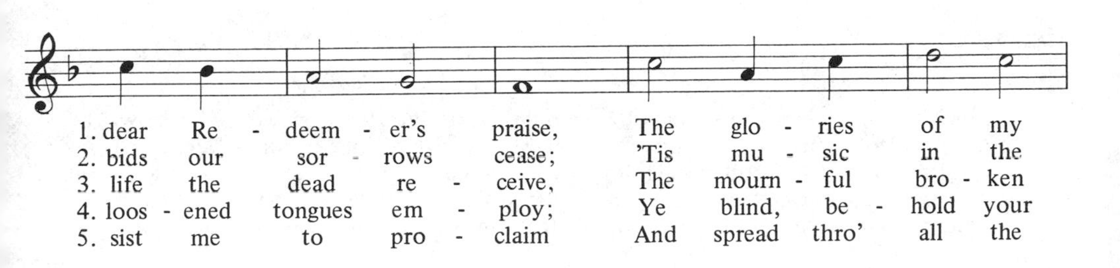
1. dear Re - deem - er's praise, The glo - ries of my
2. bids our sor - rows cease; 'Tis mu - sic in the
3. life the dead re - ceive, The mourn - ful bro - ken
4. loos - ened tongues em - ploy; Ye blind, be - hold your
5. sist me to pro - claim And spread thro' all the

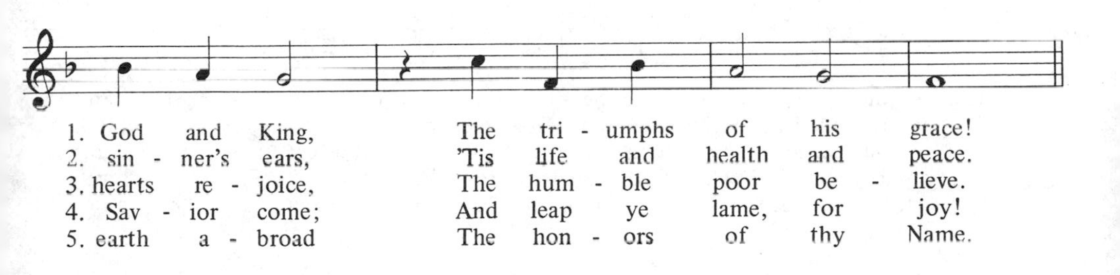
1. God and King, The tri - umphs of his grace!
2. sin - ner's ears, 'Tis life and health and peace.
3. hearts re - joice, The hum - ble poor be - lieve.
4. Sav - ior come; And leap ye lame, for joy!
5. earth a - broad The hon - ors of thy Name.

Text: C. Wesley, +1788. alt.
Tune: *Nun danket all und bringet Ehr,* J. Crüger, +1662.

238 O God, from Whom Mankind Derives Its Name

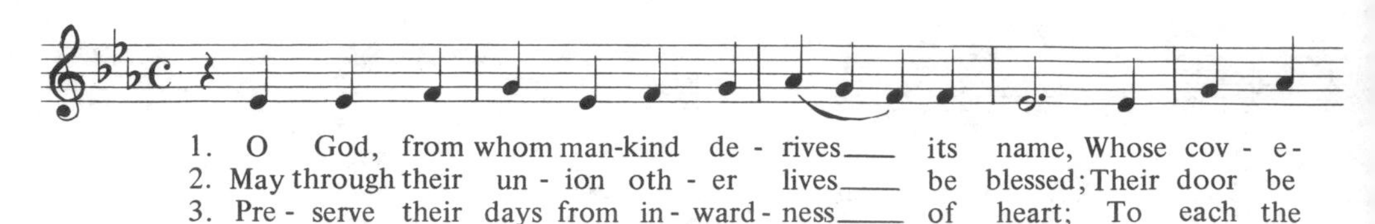

1. O God, from whom man-kind de - rives ___ its name, Whose cov - e-
2. May through their un - ion oth - er lives ___ be blessed; Their door be
3. Pre - serve their days from in - ward - ness ___ of heart; To each the
4. From stage to stage on life's un - fold - ing way Bring to their
5. Lord, bless us all to whom this day ___ brings joy, Let no e-

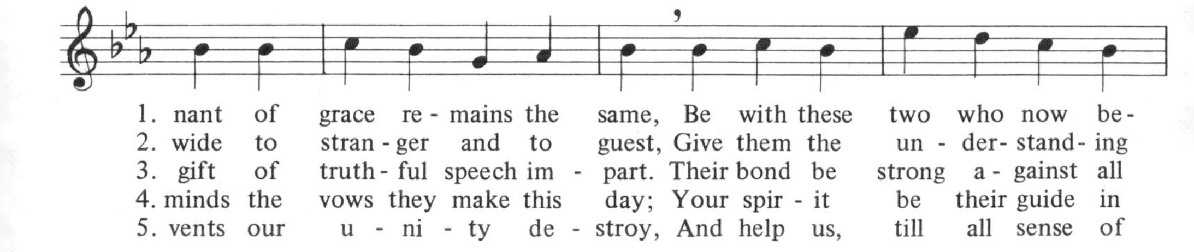

1. nant of grace re - mains the same, Be with these two who now be-
2. wide to stran - ger and to guest, Give them the un - der- stand - ing
3. gift of truth - ful speech im - part. Their bond be strong a - gainst all
4. minds the vows they make this day; Your spir - it be their guide in
5. vents our u - ni - ty de - stroy, And help us, till all sense of

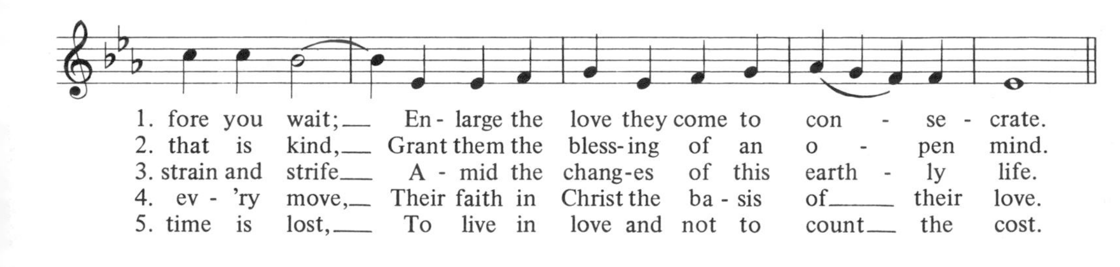

1. fore you wait; ___ En - large the love they come to con - se - crate.
2. that is kind, ___ Grant them the bless-ing of an o - pen mind.
3. strain and strife ___ A - mid the chang-es of this earth - ly life.
4. ev - 'ry move, ___ Their faith in Christ the ba - sis of ___ their love.
5. time is lost, ___ To live in love and not to count ___ the cost.

Text: F.H. Kaan. In "The Hymn Book", © 1971. Used with permission of Galaxy Music Corp., New York.
Tune: *Christi munera,* freely adapted from plainchant by T. Marier.

O God in Heaven

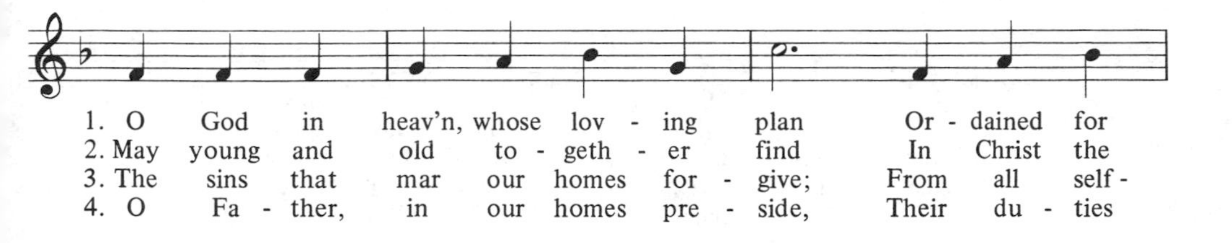
1. O God in heav'n, whose lov - ing plan Or - dained for
2. May young and old to - geth - er find In Christ the
3. The sins that mar our homes for - give; From all self -
4. O Fa - ther, in our homes pre - side, Their du - ties

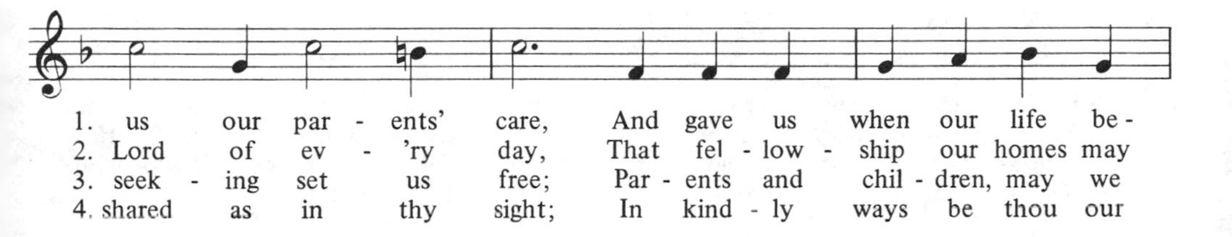
1. us our par - ents' care, And gave us when our life be -
2. Lord of ev - 'ry day, That fel - low - ship our homes may
3. seek - ing set us free; Par - ents and chil - dren, may we
4. shared as in thy sight; In kind - ly ways be thou our

1. gan The shel - ter of a home to share: Our Fa - ther, on the
2. bind In joy and sor - row, work and play. Our Fa - ther, on the
3. live In glad o - be - di - ence to thee. Our Fa - ther, on the
4. guide; On mirth and trou - ble shed thy light. Our Fa - ther, bless the

1. homes we love Send down thy bless - ing from a - bove.
2. homes we love Send down thy bless - ing from a - bove.
3. homes we love Send down thy bless - ing from a - bove.
4. homes we love And make them like thy home a - bove.

Text: H. Martin, +1964.
Tune: *Angel's Song,* O. Gibbons, +1625.

240 O God of Light

1. O God of light, the dawn - ing day
2. Your bless - ings, Fa - ther, nev - er fail:
3. Make us the ser - vants of your peace,
4. To Fa - ther, Son and Spir - it blest,
1. Gives us new prom - ise of your love. Each fresh
2. Your Son who is our dai - ly Bread, The Ho -
3. Re - new our strength, re - move all fear; Be with
4. One on - ly God, we hum - bly pray: Show us
1. be - gin - ning is your gift, Like gen - tle
2. ly Spir - it of your love, By whom each
3. us, Lord, through - out this day, For all is
4. the splen - dor of your light, In death, the
1.-3.
4.
1. dew from heav'n a - bove.
2. day your sons are led.
3. joy if you are near.
4. dawn of per - fect day. A - men.

Text: J. Quinn, S.J.
Tune: *Te Lucis ante terminum,* Plainchant, Mode 8.

O God, Our Help in Ages Past **241**

Ps. 90

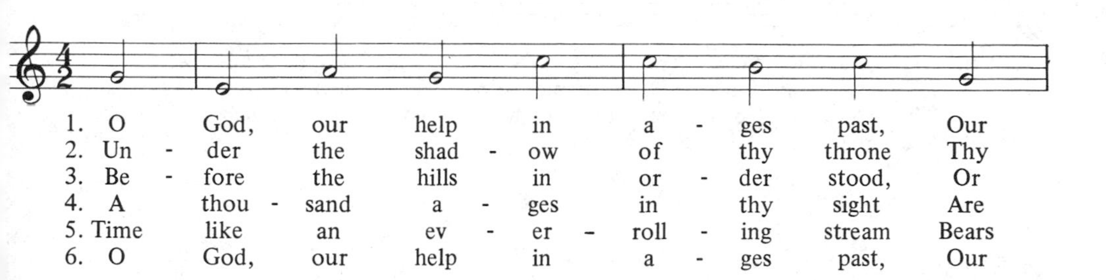
1. O God, our help in a - ges past, Our
2. Un - der the shad - ow of thy throne Thy
3. Be - fore the hills in or - der stood, Or
4. A thou - sand a - ges in thy sight Are
5. Time like an ev - er - roll - ing stream Bears
6. O God, our help in a - ges past, Our

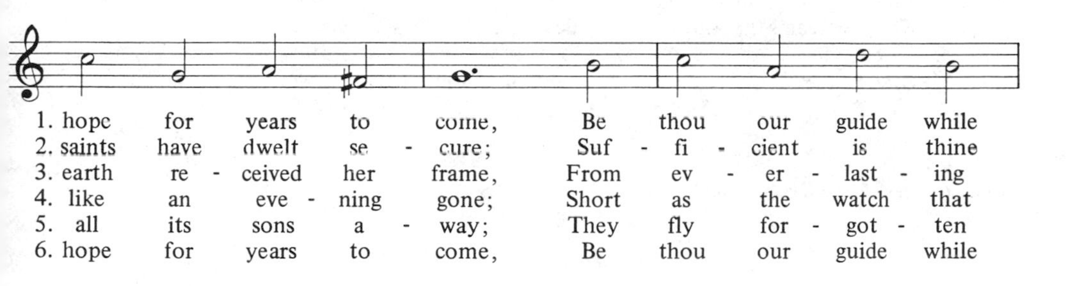
1. hope for years to come, Be thou our guide while
2. saints have dwelt se - cure; Suf - fi - cient is thine
3. earth re - ceived her frame, From ev - er - last - ing
4. like an eve - ning gone; Short as the watch that
5. all its sons a - way; They fly for - got - ten
6. hope for years to come, Be thou our guide while

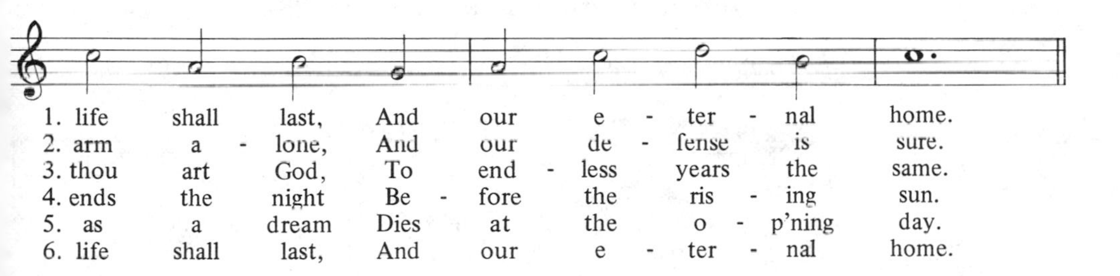
1. life shall last, And our e - ter - nal home.
2. arm a - lone, And our de - fense is sure.
3. thou art God, To end - less years the same.
4. ends the night Be - fore the ris - ing sun.
5. as a dream Dies at the o - p'ning day.
6. life shall last, And our e - ter - nal home.

Text: Psalm 90 paraphrase, I. Watts, +1748, alt.
Tune: *St. Anne,* W. Croft, +1727.

242 O God, Unseen, Yet Ever Near

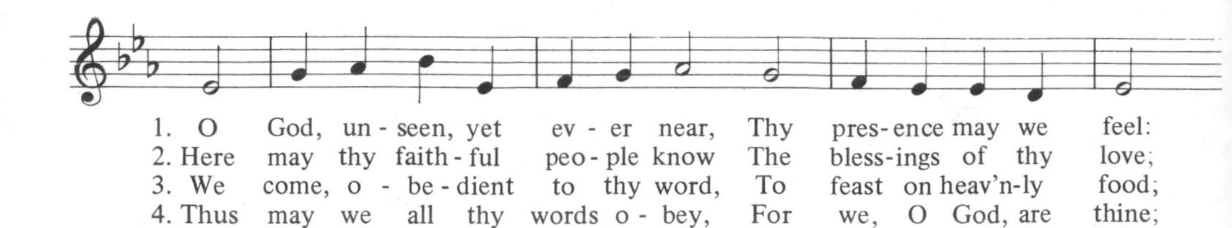
1. O God, un - seen, yet ev - er near, Thy pres- ence may we feel:
2. Here may thy faith - ful peo - ple know The bless-ings of thy love;
3. We come, o - be - dient to thy word, To feast on heav'n-ly food;
4. Thus may we all thy words o - bey, For we, O God, are thine;

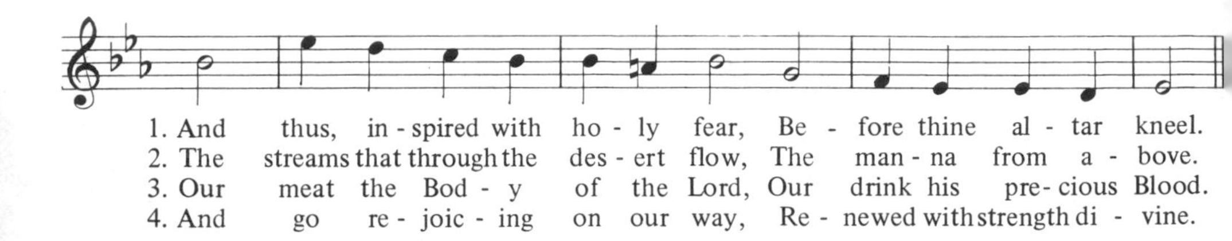
1. And thus, in - spired with ho - ly fear, Be - fore thine al - tar kneel.
2. The streams that through the des - ert flow, The man - na from a - bove.
3. Our meat the Bod - y of the Lord, Our drink his pre- cious Blood.
4. And go re - joic - ing on our way, Re - newed with strength di - vine.

Text: E. Osler, +1863.
Tune: *Dundee,* "Scottish Psalter", 1615.

243 O How Glorious, Full of Wonder

Ps. 8

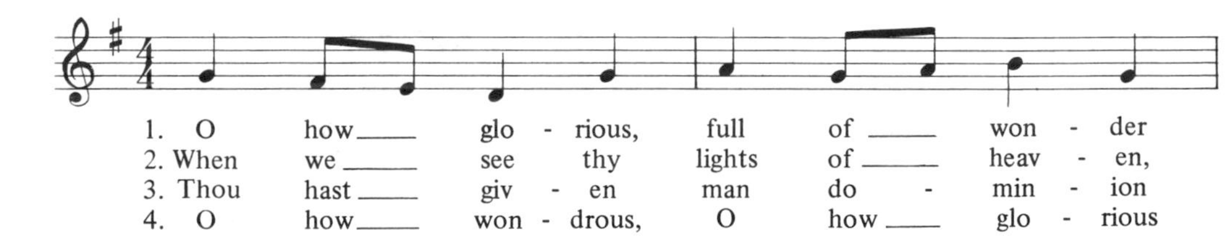
1. O how glo - rious, full of won - der
2. When we see thy lights of heav - en,
3. Thou hast giv - en man do - min - ion
4. O how won - drous, O how glo - rious

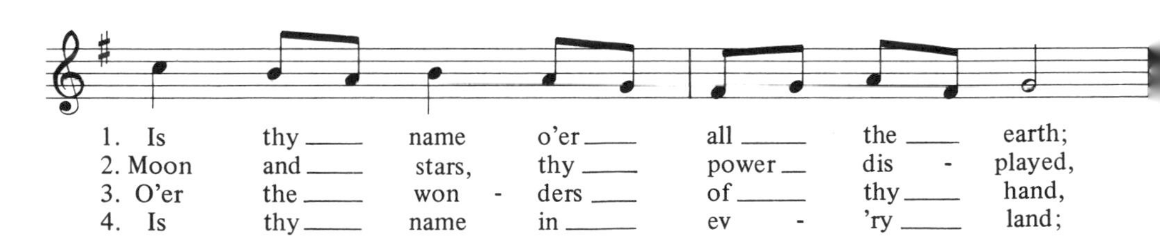
1. Is thy name o'er all the earth;
2. Moon and stars, thy power dis - played,
3. O'er the won - ders of thy hand,
4. Is thy name in ev - 'ry land;

1. Thou who wrought cre - a - tion's splen - dor,
2. What is man that thou shouldst love him,
3. Made him fly with ea - gle pin - ion,
4. Thou whose pur - pose moves be - fore us
1. Bring - ing suns and stars to birth!
2. Crea - ture that thy hand hath made?
3. Mas - ter o - ver sea and land.
4. Toward the goal that thou hast planned!
1. Rapt in rev - 'rence we a - dore thee,
2. Child of earth yet full of yearn - ing,
3. Soar - ing spire and ru - ined cit - y,
4. 'Tis thy will our hearts are seek - ing,
1. Mar - v'ling at thy mys - tic ways.
2. Mix - ture strange of good and ill,
3. These our hopes and fail - ures show.
4. Con - scious of our hu - man need.
1. Hum - bly now we bow be - fore thee,
2. From thy ways so of - ten turn - ing,
3. Teach us more of hu - man pit - y,
4. Spir - it in our spir - it speak - ing,
1. Lift - ing up our hearts in praise.
2. Yet thy love doth seek him still.
3. That we in thine im - age grow.
4. Make us sons of God in - deed!

Text: Psalm 8 paraphrase, Curtis Beach. Words reprinted with permission of the United Church Press from "Pilgrim Hymnal", © 1958, by the Pilgrim Press.
Tune: *In Babilone*, Dutch Melody, c. 1710.

O Gracious Light

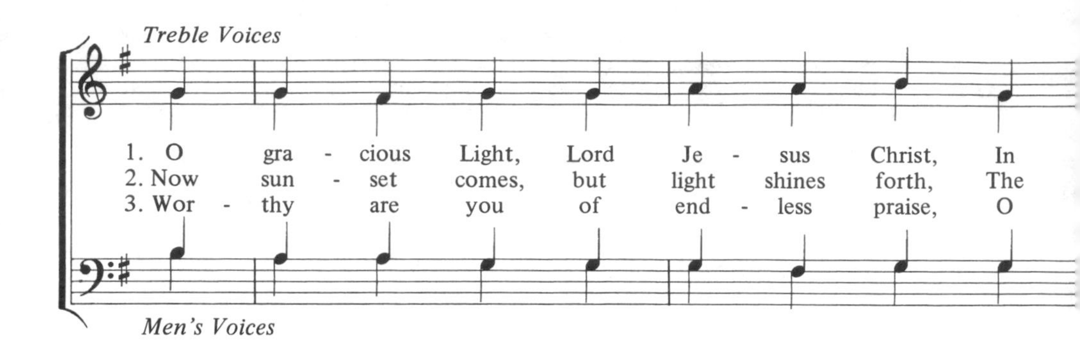
Treble Voices
1. O gra - cious Light, Lord Je - sus Christ, In
2. Now sun - set comes, but light shines forth, The
3. Wor - thy are you of end - less praise, O
Men's Voices

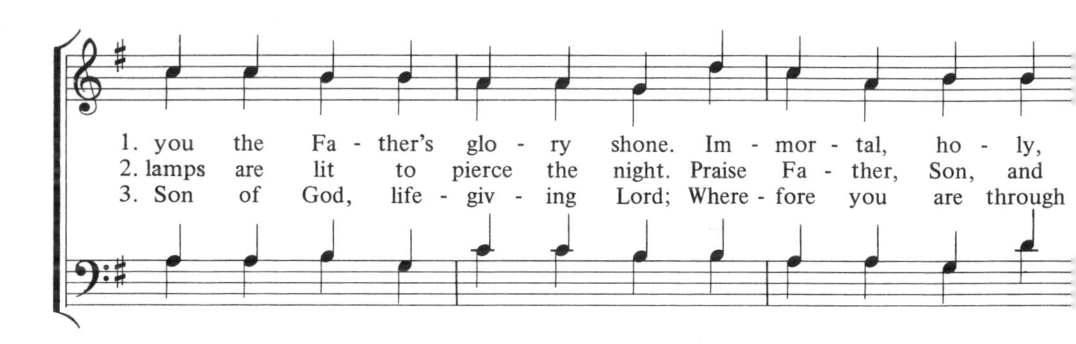
1. you the Fa - ther's glo - ry shone. Im - mor - tal, ho - ly,
2. lamps are lit to pierce the night. Praise Fa - ther, Son, and
3. Son of God, life - giv - ing Lord; Where - fore you are through

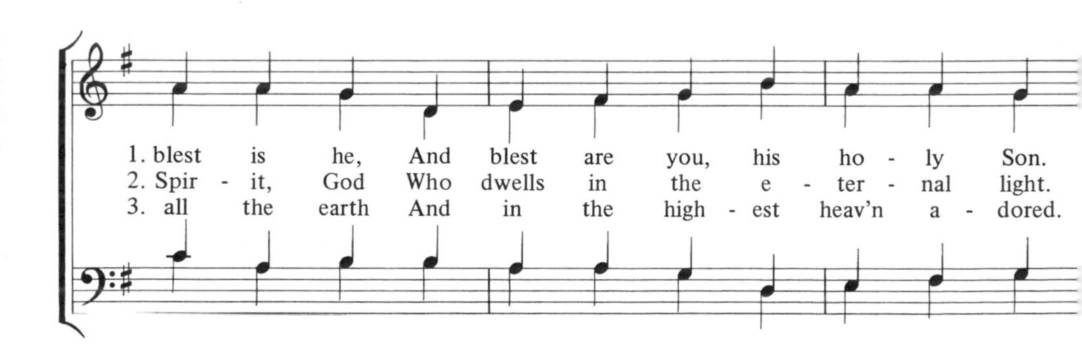
1. blest is he, And blest are you, his ho - ly Son.
2. Spir - it, God Who dwells in the e - ter - nal light.
3. all the earth And in the high - est heav'n a - dored.

Text: *Phos hilaron,* ancient Greek hymn. Trans. by F. Bland Tucker.

Tune: *Tallis' Canon,* T. Tallis, +1585.

O Holy Spirit, Enter In

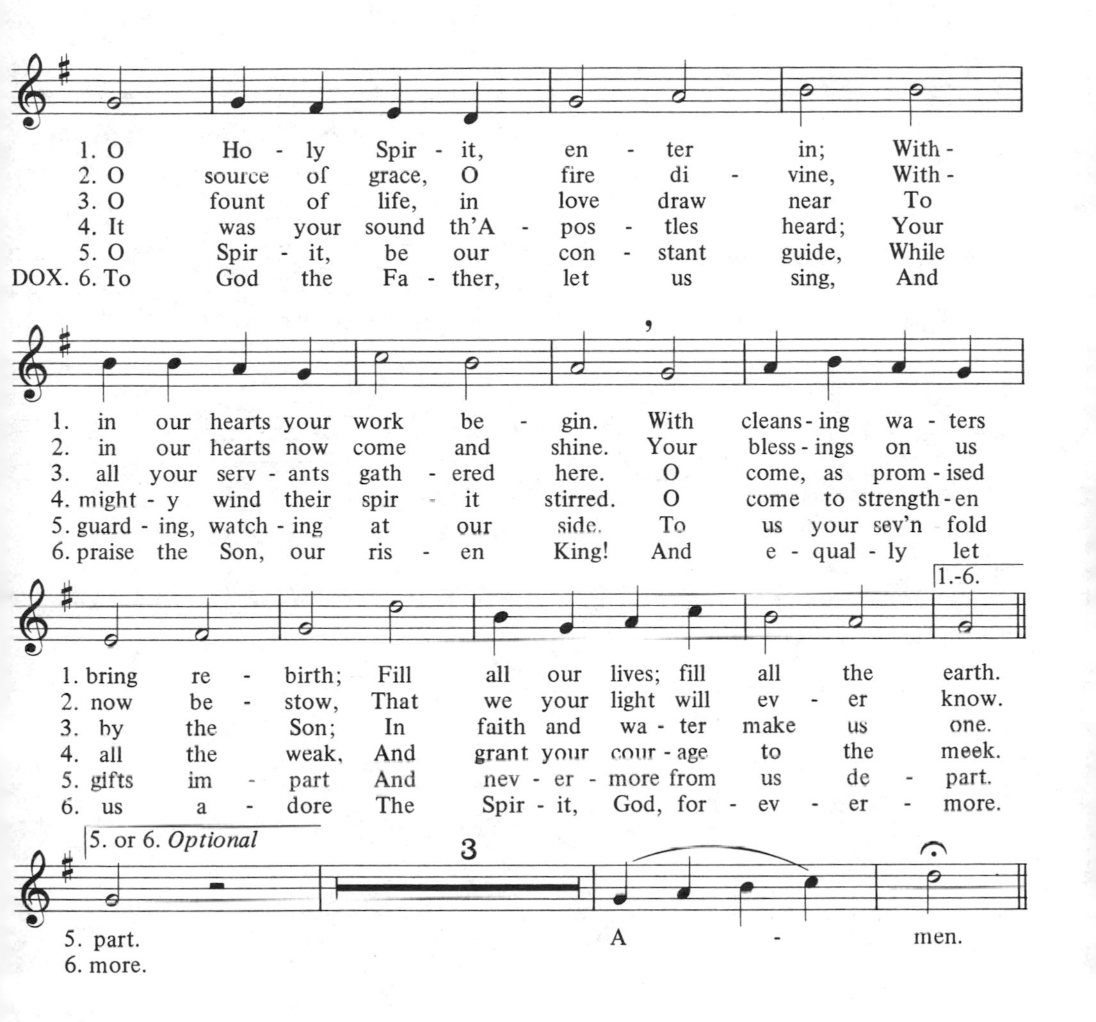
1. O Ho - ly Spir - it, en - ter in; With -
2. O source of grace, O fire di - vine, With -
3. O fount of life, in love draw near To
4. It was your sound th'A - pos - tles heard; Your
5. O Spir - it, be our con - stant guide, While
DOX. 6. To God the Fa - ther, let us sing, And
1. in our hearts your work be - gin. With cleans - ing wa - ters
2. in our hearts now come and shine. Your bless - ings on us
3. all your serv - ants gath - ered here. O come, as prom - ised
4. might - y wind their spir - it stirred. O come to strength - en
5. guard - ing, watch - ing at our side. To us your sev'n fold
6. praise the Son, our ris - en King! And e - qual - ly let
1.-6.
1. bring re - birth; Fill all our lives; fill all the earth.
2. now be - stow, That we your light will ev - er know.
3. by the Son; In faith and wa - ter make us one.
4. all the weak, And grant your cour - age to the meek.
5. gifts im - part And nev - er - more from us de - part.
6. us a - dore The Spir - it, God, for - ev - er - more.
5. or 6. Optional
3
5. part.
6. more.
A - men.

Text: J. Dunn. © by author. Used with permission.
Tune: *Old Hundredth*, Genevan Psalter, 1551.

246 O Lamb of God, All Holy

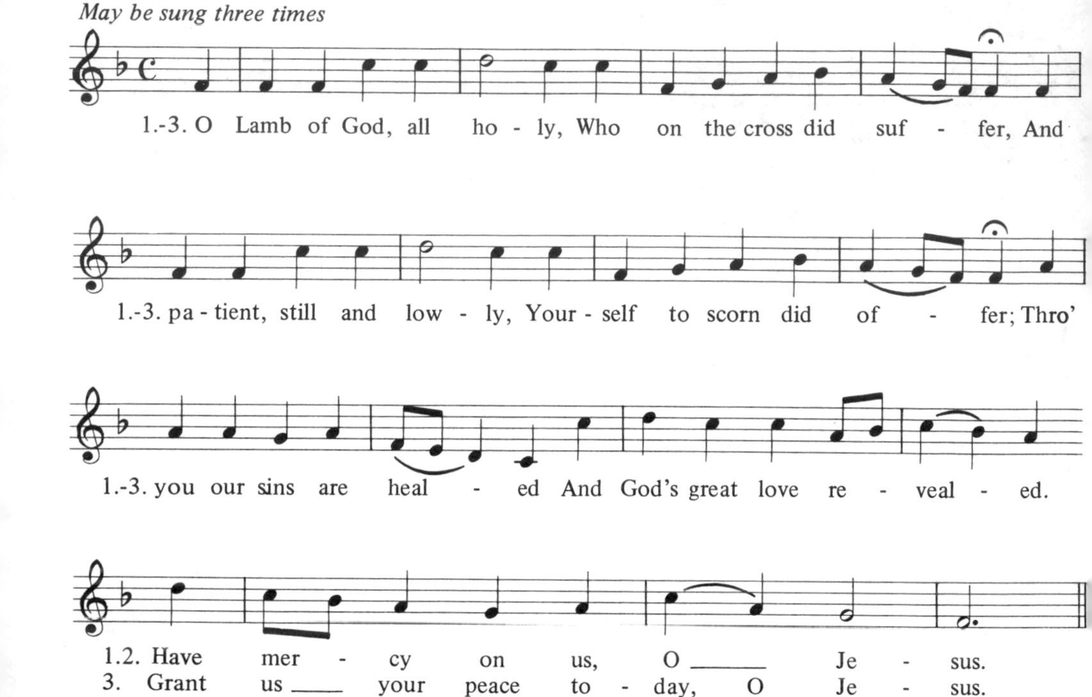
May be sung three times
1.-3. O Lamb of God, all ho - ly, Who on the cross did suf - fer, And
1.-3. pa - tient, still and low - ly, Your - self to scorn did of - fer; Thro'
1.-3. you our sins are heal - ed And God's great love re - veal - ed.
1.2. Have mer - cy on us, O ___ Je - sus.
3. Grant us ___ your peace to - day, O Je - sus.

Text: N. Decius, +c. 1546. Trans. A.T. Russell, +1874, alt.
Tune: *O Lamm Gottes unschuldig,* N. Decius, +c. 1546.

O Jesus, in Thy Heart Divine 247

1. O Je - sus, in thy heart di - vine
2. For this thy sa - cred heart was pierced
3. Thee, Sav - ior, love a - lone con - strained
4. To God the Fa - ther, and the Son
1. May that same love for - ev - er glow;
2. And both with blood and wa - ter ran
3. To make our mor - tal flesh thine own;
4. All praise and pow'r and glo - ry be,
1. For - ev - er mer - cy to man - kind
2. To cleanse us from the stains of guilt
3. To us a sec - ond Ad - am came
4. With thee, O Ho - ly Com - fort - er,
1. - 3.
4.
1. From that ex - haust - less foun - tain flow.
2. And be the hope and strength of man.
3. For the first Ad - am to a - tone.
4. Hence-forth through all e - ter - ni - ty. A - men.

Text: Anon.
Tune: *Jesu dulcis memoria,* Plainchant, Mode 1.

248 O Sacred Head Surrounded

1. O Sa - cred Head sur - round - ed By crown of pierc - ing
2. I see thy strength and vig - or All fad - ing in the
3. In this, thy bit - ter Pas - sion, Good Shep - herd, think of
4. Here would I stand be - side thee; Lord, bid me not de -
1. thorn! O bleed - ing Head, so wound - ed, Re -
2. strife, And death with cru - el rig - or Be -
3. me, With thy most sweet com - pas - sion, Un -
4. part! From thee I will not sev - er, Though
1. viled and put to scorn! Death's pal - lid hue comes
2. reav - ing thee of life; O ag - o - ny and
3. worth - y though I be: Be - neath thy Cross a -
4. breaks thy lov - ing heart. When bit - ter pain shall
1. o'er thee, The glow of life de - cays, Yet an - gel hosts a -
2. dy - ing! O love to sin - ners free! Je - sus, all grace sup -
3. bid - ing For - ev - er would I rest, In thy dear love con -
4. hold thee In ag - o - ny op - pressed, O then will I en -
1. dore thee, And trem - ble as they gaze.
2. ply - ing, O turn thy face on me.
3. fid - ing, And with thy pres - ence blest.
4. fold thee With - in my lov - ing breast.

Text: Verses 1-3, St. Bernard of Clairvaux, +1153. Trans. H.W. Baker, +1877.
Verse 4, German anon. Trans. I. Atkins.
Tune: *Passion Chorale,* H.L. Hassler, +1612.

O Little Town of Bethlehem

1. O lit - tle town of Beth - le - hem, How still we see thee
2. For Christ is born of Mar - y, And gath - ered all a -
3. How si - lent - ly, how si - lent - ly, The won - drous gift is
4. O ho - ly Child of Beth - le - hem! De - scend to us we
1. lie! A - bove thy deep and dream - less sleep, The
2. bove, While mor - tals sleep, the an - gels keep Their
3. giv'n! So God im - parts to hu - man hearts The
4. pray! Cast out our sin and en - ter in, Be
1. si - lent stars go by; Yet in thy dark streets
2. watch of won - drous love. O morn - ing stars, to -
3. bless - ings of his heav'n. No ear may hear his
4. born in us to - day. We hear the Christ - mas
1. shin - eth The ev - er - last - ing Light; The
2. geth - er Pro - claim the ho - ly birth! And
3. com - ing, But in this world of sin, Where
4. an - gels The great glad ti - dings tell; O
1. hopes and fears of all the years Are met in thee to - night.
2. prais - es sing to God the King, And peace to all on earth.
3. meek souls will re - ceive him, still The dear Christ en - ters in.
4. come to us, a - bide with us, Our Lord Em - man - u - el!

Text: P. Brooks, +1893, alt.
Tune: *Forest Green,* traditional English melody, adapted and arr. R. Vaughan Williams, +1958. From the "English Hymnal," Oxford University Press. Used with permission.

250 O Lord, Incline Thine Ear

REFRAIN *Fine*

O Lord, in- cline thine ear and show thy mer-cy, for we have sinned_a-gainst_ thee.

1. O most might - y King,__ all man - kind's Re - deem - er,
2. Right hand of the God - head, key - stone of the cor - ner,
3. All of our trans - gres - sions free - ly now con - fess - ing,

1. See our eyes lift - ed un - to thee im - plor - ing:
2. Way of sal - va - tion, en - trance gate of heav - en,
3. Our hearts we o - pen, e'en the hid - den plac - es:

Repeat REFRAIN

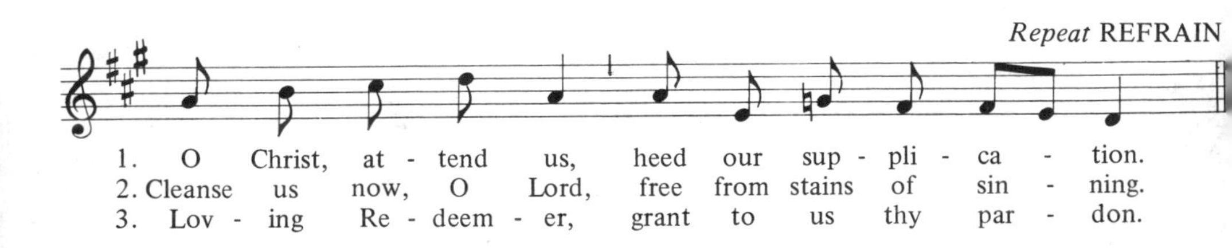

1. O Christ, at - tend us, heed our sup - pli - ca - tion.
2. Cleanse us now, O Lord, free from stains of sin - ning.
3. Lov - ing Re - deem - er, grant to us thy par - don.

Text: *Attende Domine.* Trans. E.C. Currie, +1967, alt.
Tune: *Attende Domine,* Plainchant, Mode 5.

O Lord, Make Haste to Hear My Cry

Ps. 141

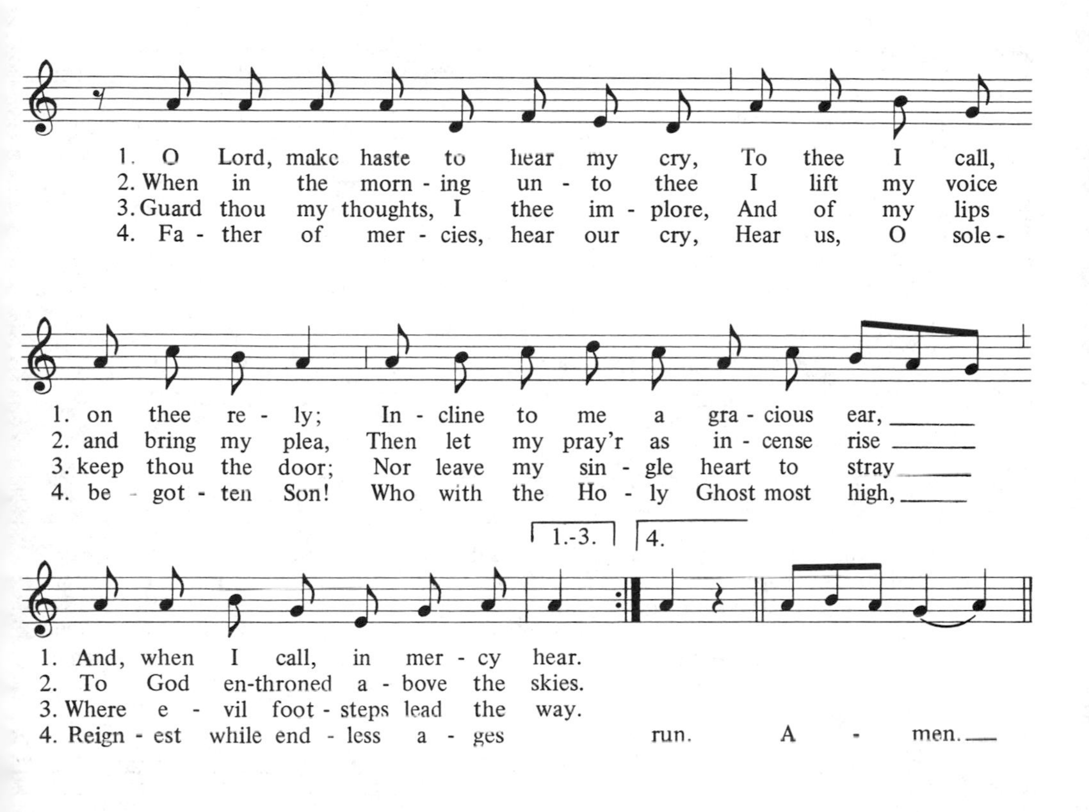
1. O Lord, make haste to hear my cry, To thee I call,
2. When in the morn - ing un - to thee I lift my voice
3. Guard thou my thoughts, I thee im - plore, And of my lips
4. Fa - ther of mer - cies, hear our cry, Hear us, O sole -
1. on thee re - ly; In - cline to me a gra - cious ear,
2. and bring my plea, Then let my pray'r as in - cense rise
3. keep thou the door; Nor leave my sin - gle heart to stray
4. be - got - ten Son! Who with the Ho - ly Ghost most high,
1.-3.
4.
1. And, when I call, in mer - cy hear.
2. To God en-throned a - bove the skies.
3. Where e - vil foot - steps lead the way.
4. Reign - est while end - less a - ges run. A - men.

Text: Verses 1-3, Psalm 141 paraphrase. "Psalter Hymnal", 1959 alt. vs. 4 anon.
Tune: *Jesu dulcis memoria,* Plainchant, Mode 1.

252

O Lord, You Are My God and King

Ps. 145

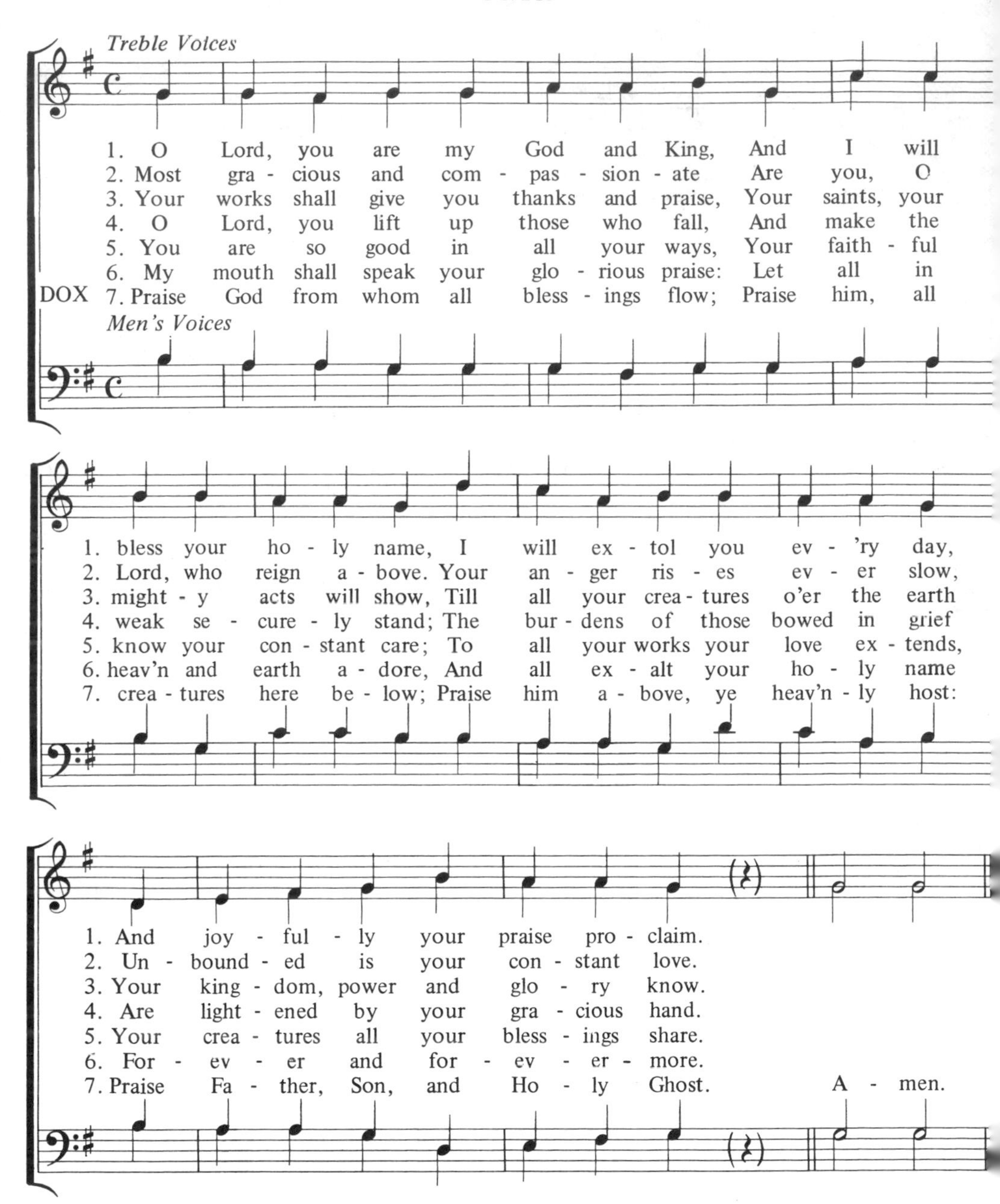
Treble Voices
1. O Lord, you are my God and King, And I will
2. Most gra - cious and com - pas - sion - ate Are you, O
3. Your works shall give you thanks and praise, Your saints, your
4. O Lord, you lift up those who fall, And make the
5. You are so good in all your ways, Your faith - ful
6. My mouth shall speak your glo - rious praise: Let all in
DOX 7. Praise God from whom all bless - ings flow; Praise him, all
Men's Voices
1. bless your ho - ly name, I will ex - tol you ev - 'ry day,
2. Lord, who reign a - bove. Your an - ger ris - es ev - er slow,
3. might - y acts will show, Till all your crea - tures o'er the earth
4. weak se - cure - ly stand; The bur - dens of those bowed in grief
5. know your con - stant care; To all your works your love ex - tends,
6. heav'n and earth a - dore, And all ex - alt your ho - ly name
7. crea - tures here be - low; Praise him a - bove, ye heav'n - ly host:
1. And joy - ful - ly your praise pro - claim.
2. Un - bound - ed is your con - stant love.
3. Your king - dom, power and glo - ry know.
4. Are light - ened by your gra - cious hand.
5. Your crea - tures all your bless - ings share.
6. For - ev - er and for - ev - er - more.
7. Praise Fa - ther, Son, and Ho - ly Ghost. A - men.

Text: Psalm 145 paraphrase, J. Dunn. © by author. Used with permission.
Doxology, T. Ken, +1711.
Tune: *Tallis' Canon*, T. Tallis, +1585.

O Lord, You Are My God

253

Ps. 63

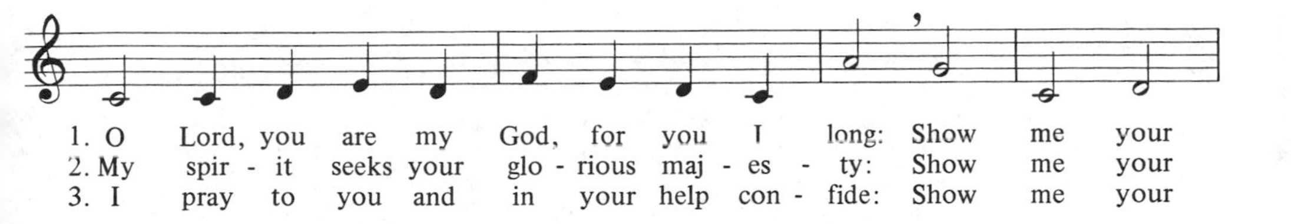
1. O Lord, you are my God, for you I long: Show me your
2. My spir - it seeks your glo - rious maj - es - ty: Show me your
3. I pray to you and in your help con - fide: Show me your

1. face. Your life with - in me makes my spir - it strong: Lord
2. face. Your con - stant love gives more than life to me: Lord
3. face. You feed my soul and I am sat - is - fied: Lord

1. of all grace. For you I thirst like des - erts parched and
2. of all grace. Thus will I bless your name through all my
3. of all grace. O keep me in the shel - ter of your

1. dried. With - in your care my soul is sat - is - fied.
2. days; And lift my hands to you in thank - ful praise.
3. throne; To you I cling, my joy, my God a - lone.

254 O Love of God, How Strong and True

1. O love of God, how strong and true, E-
2. O heav'n - ly love, how pre - cious still In
3. O wide em - brac - ing, won - drous love! We
4. We read thee best in him who came To
5. We read thy pow'r to bless and save, E'en
6. O love of God, our shield and stay Through
1. ter - nal, and yet ev - er new, Un-
2. days of wear - i - ness and ill, In
3. read thee in the sky a - bove; We
4. bear for us the cross of shame; Sent
5. in the dark - ness of the grave; Still
6. all the per - ils of our way; E-
1. com - pre - hend - ed and un - bought, Be-
2. night of pain and help - less - ness, To
3. read thee in the earth be - low, In
4. by the Fa - ther from on high, Our
5. more in re - sur - rec - tion light We
6. ter - nal love, in thee we rest, For-
1. yond all knowl - edge and all thought.
2. heal, to com - fort, and to bless.
3. seas that swell and streams that flow.
4. life to live, our death to die.
5. read the full - ness of thy might.
6. ev - er safe, for - ev - er blest.

Text: H. Bonar, +1889.
Tune: *Wareham*, W. Knapp, +1768.

O My Soul, Bless God the Father

255

Ps. 103

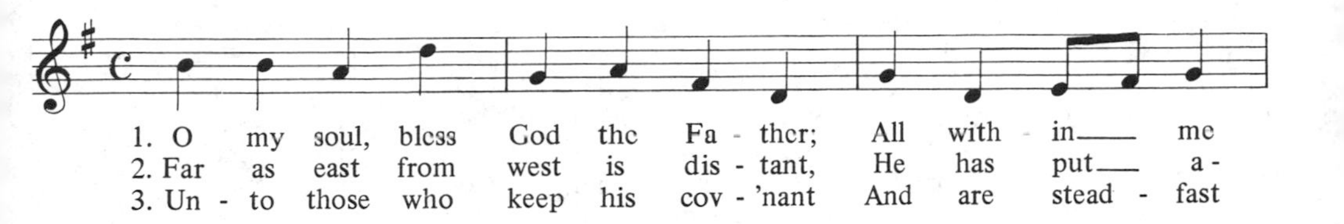
1. O my soul, bless God the Fa - ther; All with - in__ me
2. Far as east from west is dis - tant, He has put__ a -
3. Un - to those who keep his cov - 'nant And are stead - fast

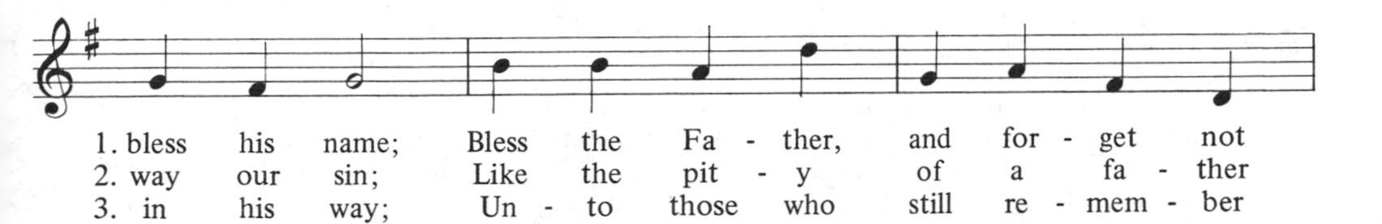
1. bless his name; Bless the Fa - ther, and for - get not
2. way our sin; Like the pit - y of a fa - ther
3. in his way; Un - to those who still re - mem - ber

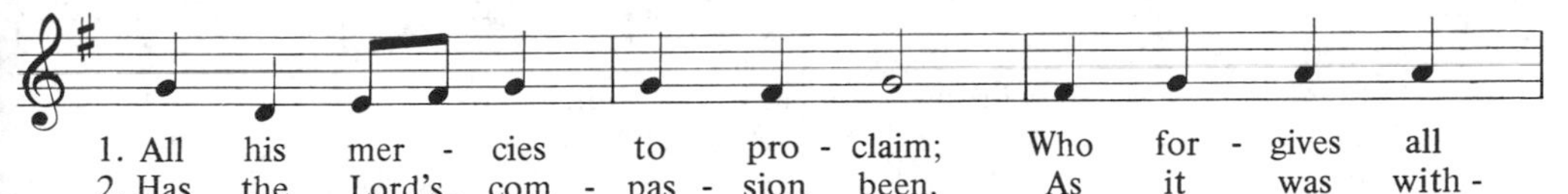
1. All his mer - cies to pro - claim; Who for - gives all
2. Has the Lord's_ com - pas - sion been. As it was with -
3. His com - mand - ments to o - bey. Bless the Fa - ther,

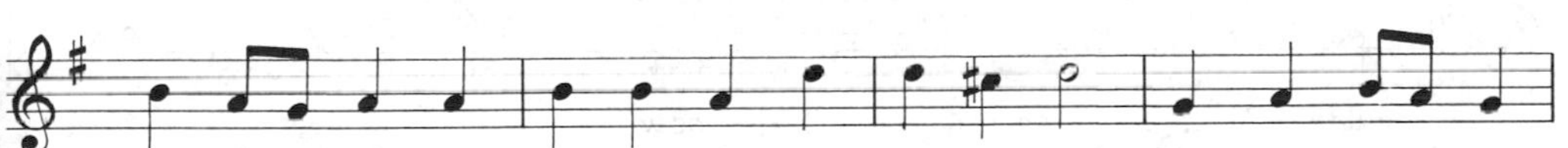
1. your trans - gres - sions, All of your dis - eas - es heals; Who re - deems_you
2. out be - gin - ning, So it lasts with - out an end; To their chil - dren's
3. all his__ crea - tures, Ev - er un - der his con-trol; All through-out_ his

1. from de - struc - tion, Who with you_ so__ kind - ly deals.
2. chil - dren ev - er Shall his right - eous - ness ex - tend;
3. vast do - min - ion Bless the Fa - ther,_ O my soul.

Text: Psalm 103 paraphrase, United Presbyterian "Book of Psalms", 1871, alt.
Tune: *Sunrise*, "Trier Gesangbuch", 1695.

256 O Morning Star, How Fair and Bright

1. O Morn - ing Star, how fair and bright, Come
2. Thou heav'n - ly bright - ness, light di - vine! O
3. As King di - vine and God most high, He
4. Re - joice, ye heav'ns, O earth re - ply; With
1. shine on us in truth and light, Up -
2. deep with - in our hearts now shine, Be
3. chose to cast a lov - ing eye Up -
4. praise, ye sin - ners, fill the sky For
1. lift - ing hearts and voic - es; O
2. ev - er in us dwell - ing! Fill
3. on his earth - ly crea - tures; The
4. Je - sus' in - car - na - tion. The
1. guid - ing star with pow'r be - nign, Re -
2. us with joy and strength to be Thy
3. whole cre - a - tion's Head and Lord, By
4. sav - ing faith in us he wrought And
1. veal to us God's Son di - vine, In
2. mem - bers ev - er joined to thee In
3. high - est ser - a - phim a - dored, As -
4. un - to us sal - va - tion brought, Made

1. him the world re - joic - es.
2. love be - yond all tell - ing.
3. sumed our ver - y na - ture.
4. us his cho - sen na - tion.
1. Ho - ly! Ho - ly! Lord all glo - rious,
2. Ho - ly! Ho - ly! Lord all glo - rious,
3. A - men, A - men! Al - le - lu - ia!
4. A - men, A - men! Al - le - lu - ia!
1. King vic - to - rious, Rich in bless -
2. King vic - to - rious, Rich in bless -
3. Al - le - lu - ia! Praise bc giv -
4. Al - le - lu - ia! Praise be giv -
1. ing, Rule and might o'er all pos - sess - ing.
2. ing, Rule and might o'er all pos - sess - ing.
3. en Ev - cr - more by earth and heav - en.
4. en Ev - er - more by earth and heav - en.

Text: P. Nicolai, +1608. Verses 1-2, trans. C. Winkworth, +1878, alt.
Verses 3-4, trans. W. Mercer, +1873, alt.
Tune: *Wie schön leuchtet der Morgenstern*, P. Nicolai, +1608.

257 O Perfect Love

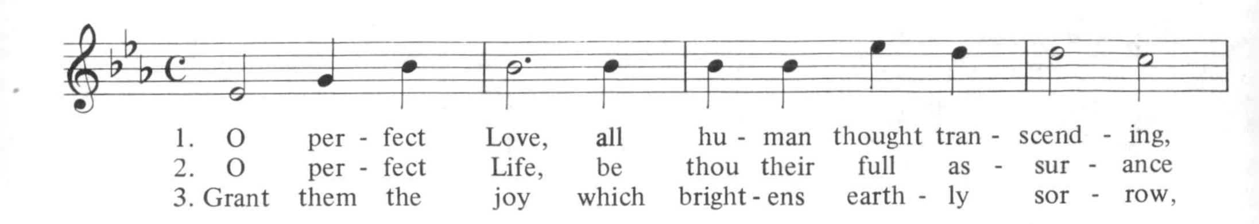
1. O per - fect Love, all hu - man thought tran - scend - ing,
2. O per - fect Life, be thou their full as - sur - ance
3. Grant them the joy which bright - ens earth - ly sor - row,

1. Low - ly we kneel in prayer be - fore thy throne,
2. Of ten - der char - i - ty and stead - fast faith,
3. Grant them the peace which calms all earth - ly strife,

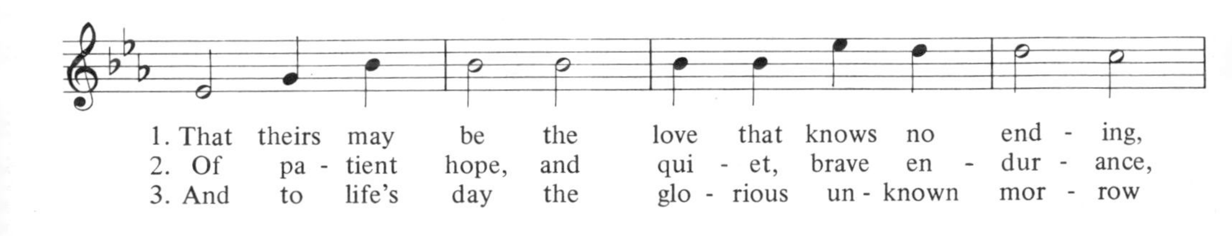
1. That theirs may be the love that knows no end - ing,
2. Of pa - tient hope, and qui - et, brave en - dur - ance,
3. And to life's day the glo - rious un - known mor - row

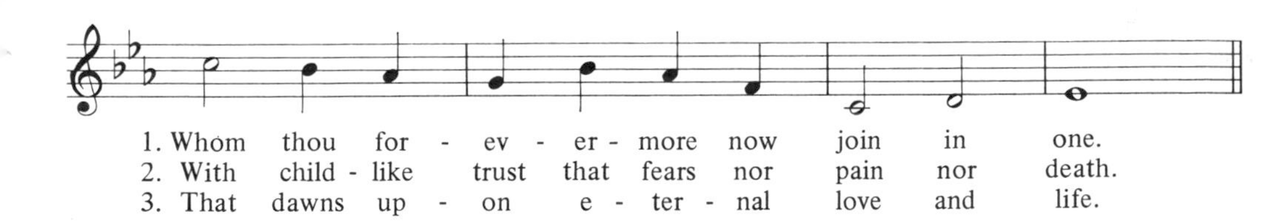
1. Whom thou for - ev - er - more now join in one.
2. With child - like trust that fears nor pain nor death.
3. That dawns up - on e - ter - nal love and life.

Text: D.F. Gurney, +1932.
Tune: *Sandringham*, J. Barnby, +1896.

O Praise Our Great and Gracious Lord

258

Ps. 78

1. O praise our great and_ gra-cious Lord And call up-on_ his_ name;
2. He gave the shad-owing_cloud by day, The mov-ing fire_ by_ night;
3. We, too, have man-na_ from a-bove, The bread that came_ from_ heav'n;
4. O let us prize this_ bless-ed food, And trust our heav'n-ly_ guide;

1. To strains of joy tune_ ev-'ry chord, His might-y acts_ pro-claim;
2. To guide his Is-rael_ on their way, He made their dark-ness_ light;
3. To us the same kind_ hand of love Hath liv-ing wa-ters_ giv'n.
4. So shall we find death's_ fear-ful flood Se-rene as Jor-dan's_ tide,

1. Tell how_ he led_ his cho-sen race To Ca-naan's prom-ised_ land;
2. And have_ not we_ a sure re-treat, A Sav-ior ev-er_ nigh,
3. A rock_ we have_ from whence the spring In rich a-bun-dance_ flows;
4. And safe-ly reach_ that hap-py shore, The land of peace and_ rest,

1. Tell how his cov-e-nant of grace Un-changed shall ev-er_ stand.
2. The same clear light to guide our feet, The day-spring from on_ high?
3. That rock is Christ, our priest, our king, Who life and health be-stows.
4. Where an-gels wor-ship and a-dore In God's own pres-ence_ blest.

Text: Psalm 78 paraphrase, H. Auber, +1862.
Tune: *Rockport,* T.T. Noble, +1953.

259 O Praise Ye the Lord

Ps. 150

1. O praise ye the Lord! Praise him in the height;
2. O praise ye the Lord! Praise him up - on earth,
3. O praise ye the Lord! All things that give sound;
4. O praise ye the Lord! Thanks - giv - ing and song
1. Re - joice in his word, Ye an - gels of light;
2. In tune - ful ac - cord, Ye lands of new birth;
3. Each ju - bi - lant chord Re - ech - o a - round;
4. To him be out - poured All a - ges a - long:
1. Ye heav - ens a - dore him, By whom ye were made,
2. Praise him who hath brought you His grace from a - bove,
3. Loud or - gans, his glo - ry Forth tell in deep tone,
4. For love in cre - a - tion, For heav - en re - stored,
1. And wor - ship be - fore him, In bright - ness ar - rayed.
2. Praise him who hath taught you To sing of his love.
3. And, sweet harp, the stor - ry Of what he hath done.
4. For grace of sal - va - tion, O praise ye the Lord!

Text: Psalm 150 paraphrase, H.W. Baker, +1877, alt.
Tune: *Laudate Dominum*, C.H.H. Parry, +1918.

O Saving Victim
O Salutaris Hostia

First Tune
1. O sav - ing Vic - tim, op'n - ing wide
2. All praise and thanks to thee as - cend
1. O sa - lu - tá - ris Hó - sti - a
2. U - ni - tri - nó - que Dó - mi - no
1. The gate of heav'n to us be - low,
2. For - ev - er - more, blest One in Three;
1. Quae cae - li pan - dis ó - sti - um,
2. Sit sem - pi - tér - na gló - ri - a,
1. Our foes press on from ev - 'ry side,
2. O grant us life that will not end,
1. Bel - la prae - munt ho - stí - li - a,
2. Qui vi - tam si - ne tér - mi - no
1. 2.
1. Thine aid sup - ply, thy strength be - stow.
2. In our true na - tive land with thee. A - men.
1. Da ro - bur, fer au - xí - li - um.
2. No - bis do - net in pá - tri - a. A - men.

Text: Verses from *Verbum supernum,* St. Thomas Aquinas, +1274. Trans. E. Caswall, +1878, alt.
Tune: *Creator alme siderum,* Plainchant, Mode 4.

261 O Saving Victim
O Salutaris Hostia

Second Tune
1. O sav - ing Vic - tim, op'n - ing wide
2. All praise and thanks to thee as - cend
1. O sa - lu - tá - ris Hó - sti - a
2. U - ni - tri - nó - que Dó - mi - no

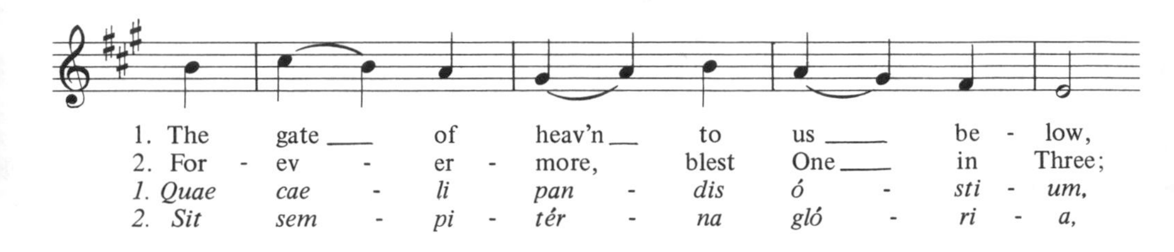
1. The gate of heav'n to us be - low,
2. For - ev - er - more, blest One in Three;
1. Quae cae - li pan - dis ó - sti - um,
2. Sit sem - pi - tér - na gló - ri - a,

1. Our foes press on from ev - 'ry side,
2. O grant us life that will not end,
1. Bel - la prae - munt ho - stí - li - a,
2. Qui vi - tam si - ne tér - mi - no

1. Thine aid sup - ply, thy strength be - stow.
2. In our true na - tive land with thee.
1. Da ro - bur, fer au - xí - li - um.
2. No - bis do - net in pá - tri - a.

A - men.

Text: Verses from *Verbum supernum*, St. Thomas Aquinas, +1274. Trans. E. Caswall, +1878, alt.
Tune: *Wareham*, W. Knapp, +1768.

O Splendor of Eternal Light

Evening Hymn

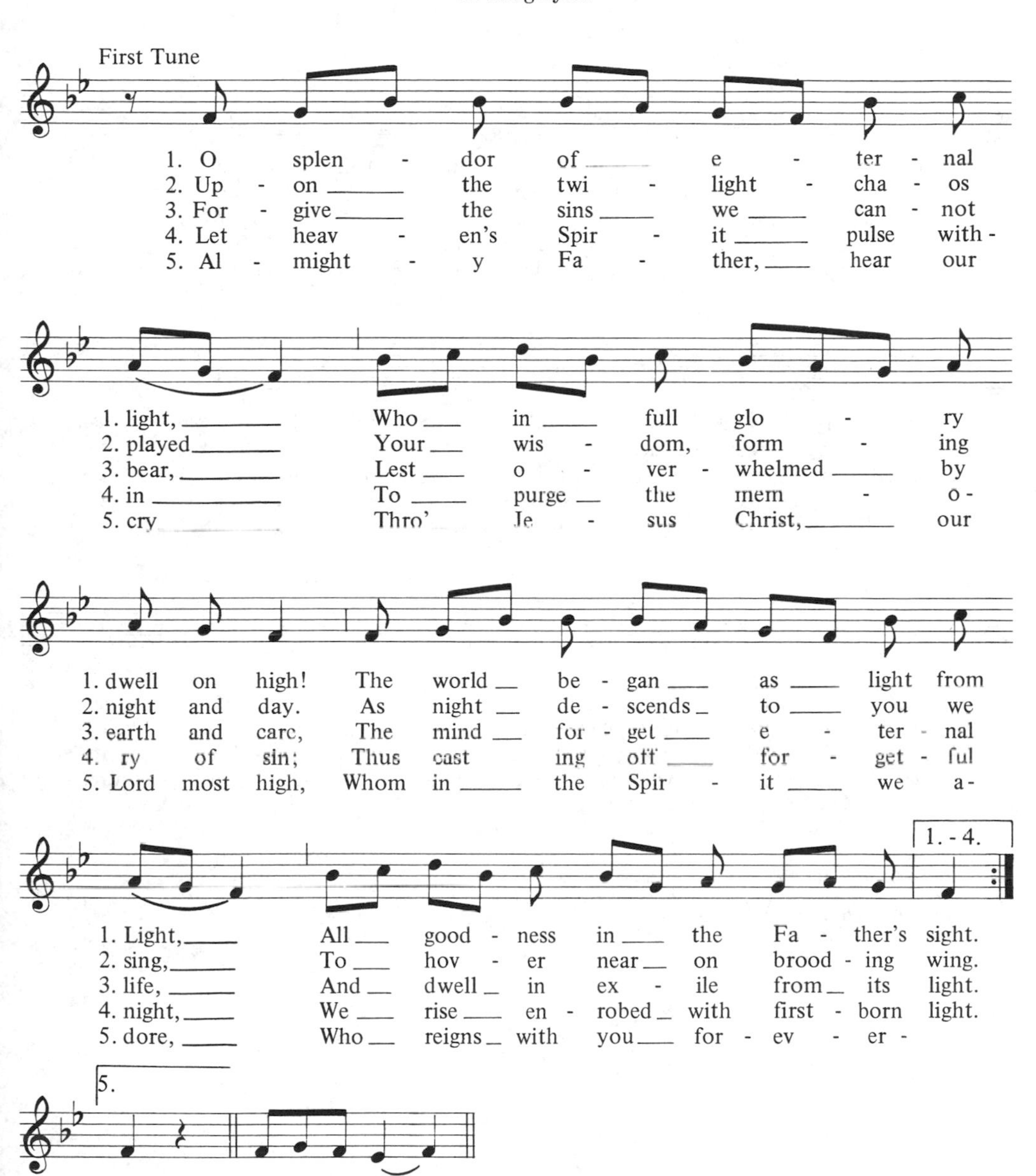
First Tune
1. O splen - dor of e - ter - nal
2. Up - on the twi - light - cha - os
3. For - give the sins we can - not
4. Let heav - en's Spir - it pulse with -
5. Al - might - y Fa - ther, hear our
1. light, Who in full glo - ry
2. played Your wis - dom, form - ing
3. bear, Lest o - ver - whelmed by
4. in To purge the mem - o -
5. cry Thro' Je - sus Christ, our
1. dwell on high! The world be - gan as light from
2. night and day. As night de - scends to you we
3. earth and care, The mind for - get e - ter - nal
4. ry of sin; Thus cast ing off for - get - ful
5. Lord most high, Whom in the Spir - it we a -
1. - 4.
1. Light, All good - ness in the Fa - ther's sight.
2. sing, To hov - er near on brood - ing wing.
3. life, And dwell in ex - ile from its light.
4. night, We rise en - robed with first - born light.
5. dore, Who reigns with you for - ev - er -
5.
more. A - men.

Text: *Lucis Creator optime.* Trans. Br. P. Quenon, OCSO,
in "Morning Praise and Evensong",
Tune: *Lucis Creator optime,* Plainchant, Mode 8.

263 O Splendor of Eternal Light

Evening Hymn

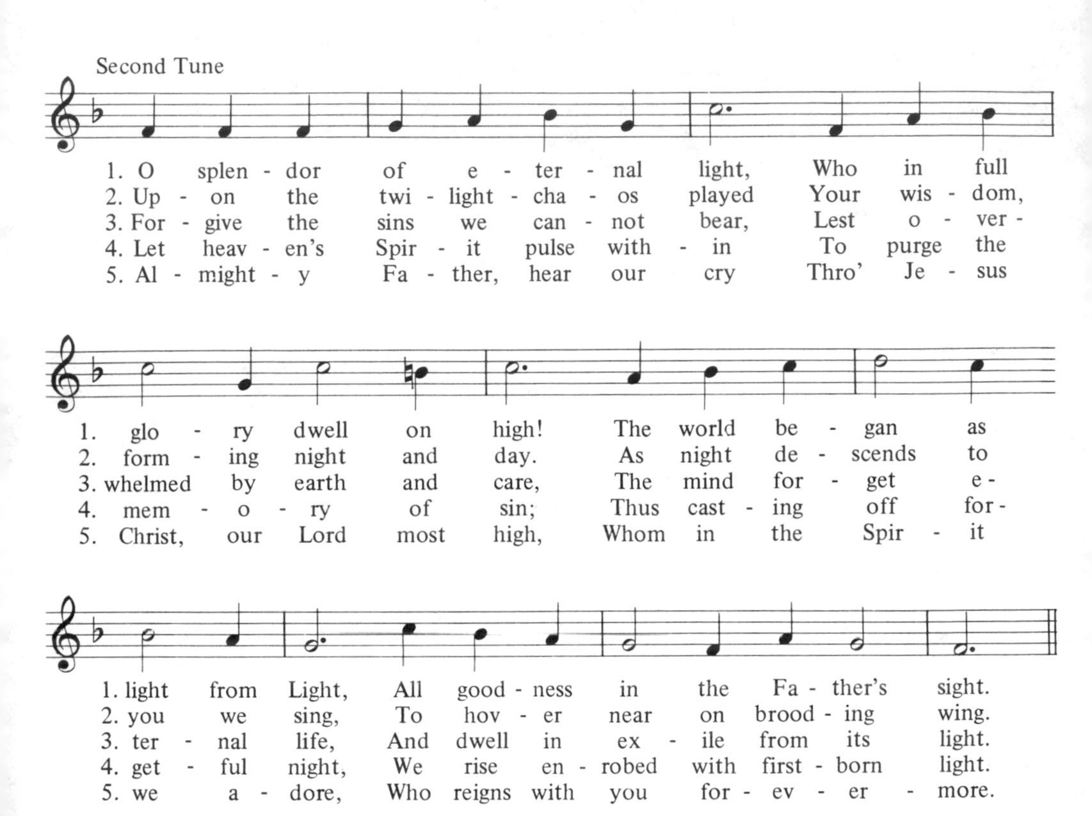
Second Tune
1. O splen - dor of e - ter - nal light, Who in full
2. Up - on the twi - light - cha - os played Your wis - dom,
3. For - give the sins we can - not bear, Lest o - ver -
4. Let heav - en's Spir - it pulse with - in To purge the
5. Al - might - y Fa - ther, hear our cry Thro' Je - sus
1. glo - ry dwell on high! The world be - gan as
2. form - ing night and day. As night de - scends to
3. whelmed by earth and care, The mind for - get e -
4. mem - o - ry of sin; Thus cast - ing off for -
5. Christ, our Lord most high, Whom in the Spir - it
1. light from Light, All good - ness in the Fa - ther's sight.
2. you we sing, To hov - er near on brood - ing wing.
3. ter - nal life, And dwell in ex - ile from its light.
4. get - ful night, We rise en - robed with first - born light.
5. we a - dore, Who reigns with you for - ev - er - more.

Text: *Lucis Creator optime.* Trans. Br. P. Quenon, OCSO,
in "Morning Praise and Evensong", © 1973 Fides/Claretian Publishing Co.,
Notre Dame, Ind. Used with permission.
Tune: *Angel's Song,* O. Gibbons, +1625.

O Sun of Justice, Fill Our Hearts

Morning Hymn

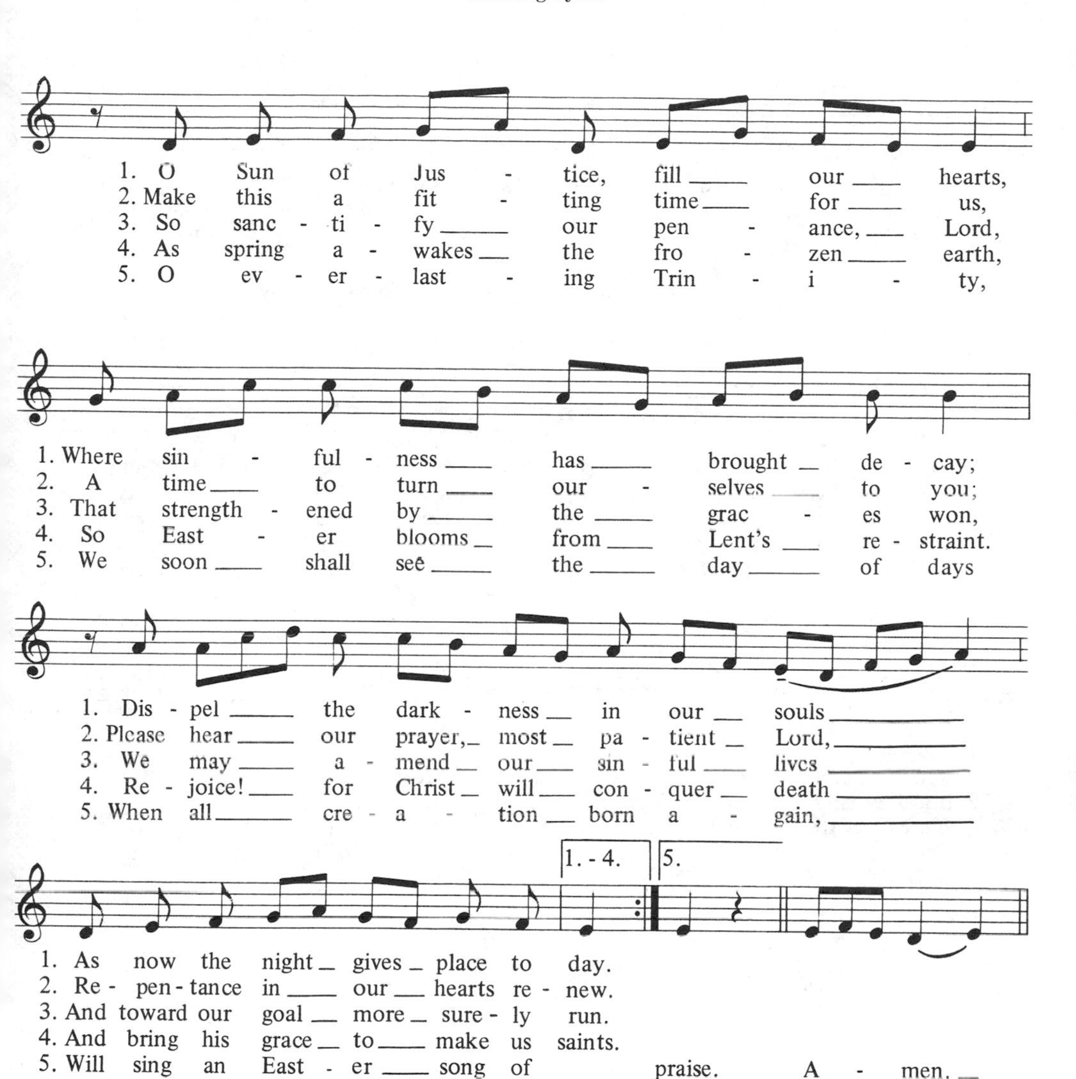
1. O Sun of Jus - tice, fill our hearts,
2. Make this a fit - ting time for us,
3. So sanc - ti - fy our pen - ance, Lord,
4. As spring a - wakes the fro - zen earth,
5. O ev - er - last - ing Trin - i - ty,
1. Where sin - ful - ness has brought de - cay;
2. A time to turn our - selves to you;
3. That strength - ened by the grac - es won,
4. So East - er blooms from Lent's re - straint.
5. We soon shall see the day of days
1. Dis - pel the dark - ness in our souls
2. Please hear our prayer, most pa - tient Lord,
3. We may a - mend our sin - ful lives
4. Re - joice! for Christ will con - quer death
5. When all cre - a - tion born a - gain,
1. - 4.
5.
1. As now the night gives place to day.
2. Re - pen - tance in our hearts re - new.
3. And toward our goal more sure - ly run.
4. And bring his grace to make us saints.
5. Will sing an East - er song of praise. A - men.

Text: *Jam Christe sol justitiae,* Office Hymn. Trans. M. Quinn, O.P., in "Morning Praise and Evensong", © 1973 Fides/Claretian Publishing Co., Notre Dame, Ind. Used with permission.
Tune: *A solis ortus cardine,* Plainchant, Mode 3.

265 O Taste and See That God Is Good

Ps. 34

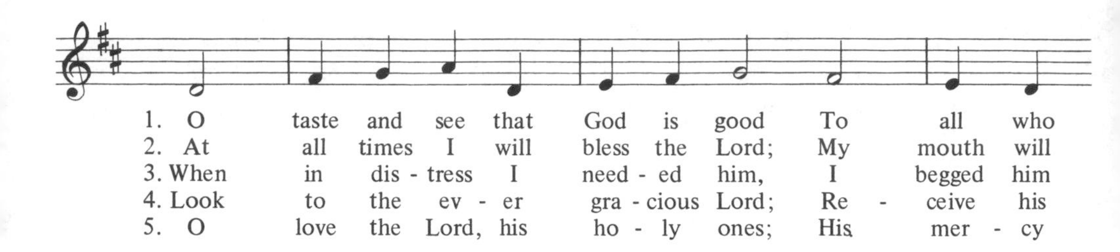
1. O taste and see that God is good To all who
2. At all times I will bless the Lord; My mouth will
3. When in dis - tress I need - ed him, I begged him
4. Look to the ev - er gra - cious Lord; Re - ceive his
5. O love the Lord, his ho - ly ones; His mer - cy

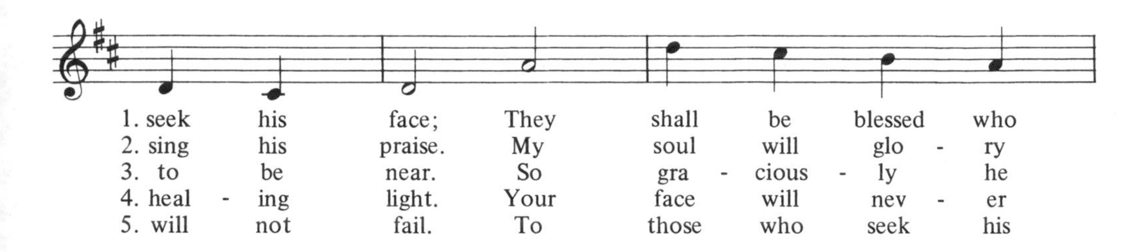
1. seek his face; They shall be blessed who
2. sing his praise. My soul will glo - ry
3. to be near. So gra - cious - ly he
4. heal - ing light. Your face will nev - er
5. will not fail. To those who seek his

1. trust in him, Con - fid - ing in his grace.
2. in my God; How good are all his ways.
3. heard my plea, And freed me from my fear.
4. blush with shame, But shine so ra - diant bright.
5. ho - ly grace, All good - ness shall pre - vail.

Text: Psalm 34 paraphrase, J. Dunn.
Tune: *Dundee,* "Scottish Psalter", 1615.

O Thou, the Heav'ns' Eternal King

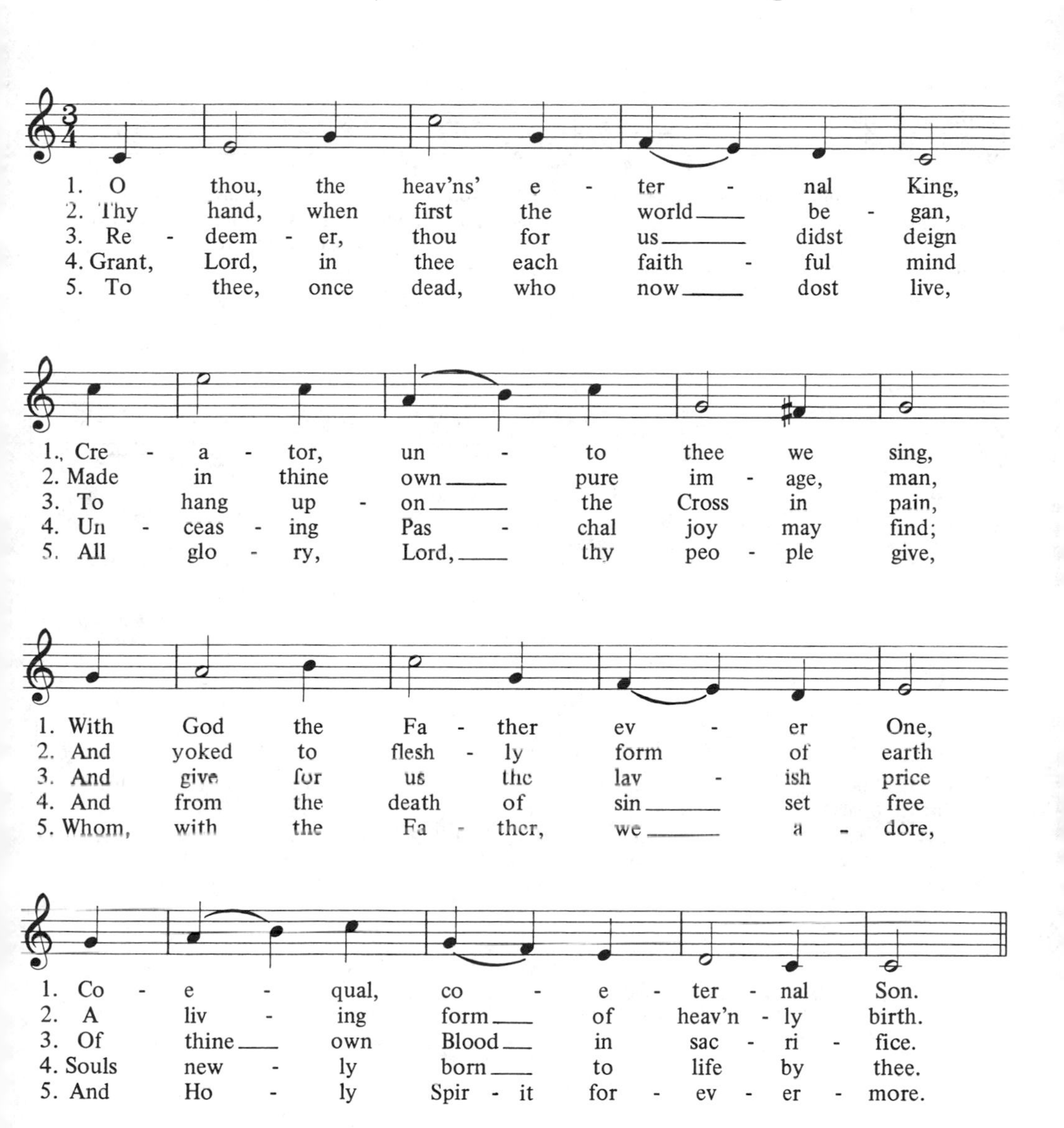
1. O thou, the heav'ns' e - ter - nal King,
2. Thy hand, when first the world be - gan,
3. Re - deem - er, thou for us didst deign
4. Grant, Lord, in thee each faith - ful mind
5. To thee, once dead, who now dost live,
1. Cre - a - tor, un - to thee we sing,
2. Made in thine own pure im - age, man,
3. To hang up - on the Cross in pain,
4. Un - ceas - ing Pas - chal joy may find;
5. All glo - ry, Lord, thy peo - ple give,
1. With God the Fa - ther ev - er One,
2. And yoked to flesh - ly form of earth
3. And give for us the lav - ish price
4. And from the death of sin set free
5. Whom, with the Fa - ther, we a - dore,
1. Co - e - qual, co - e - ter - nal Son.
2. A liv - ing form of heav'n - ly birth.
3. Of thine own Blood in sac - ri - fice.
4. Souls new - ly born to life by thee.
5. And Ho - ly Spir - it for - ev - er - more.

Text: Ambrosian, 6th Century. Trans. anon., 1573.
Tune: *Deus tuorum militum*, Grenoble Church Melody.

267 O Wondrous Sight, O Vision Fair

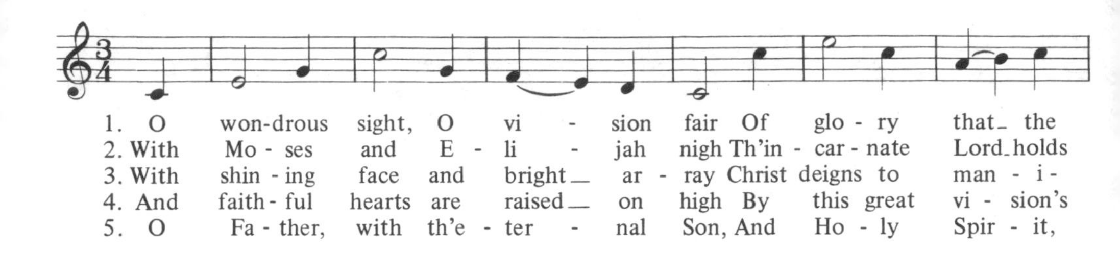
1. O won-drous sight, O vi - sion fair Of glo - ry that_ the
2. With Mo - ses and E - li - jah nigh Th'in - car - nate Lord_holds
3. With shin - ing face and bright_ ar - ray Christ deigns to man - i -
4. And faith - ful hearts are raised_ on high By this great vi - sion's
5. O Fa - ther, with th'e - ter - nal Son, And Ho - ly Spir - it,

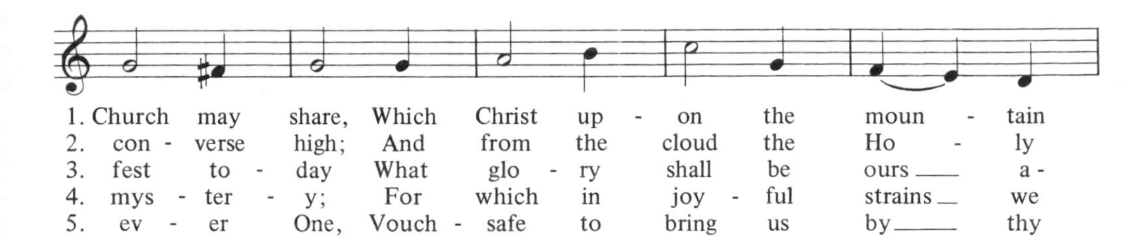
1. Church may share, Which Christ up - on the moun - tain
2. con - verse high; And from the cloud the Ho - ly
3. fest to - day What glo - ry shall be ours ___ a -
4. mys - ter - y; For which in joy - ful strains_ we
5. ev - er One, Vouch - safe to bring us by___ thy

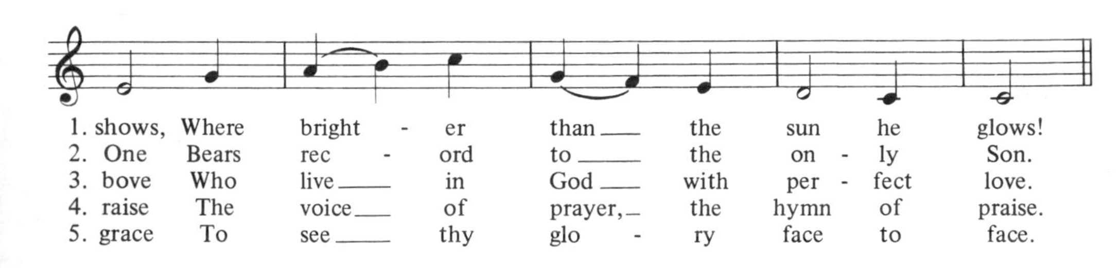
1. shows, Where bright - er than___ the sun he glows!
2. One Bears rec - ord to___ the on - ly Son.
3. bove Who live___ in God___ with per - fect love.
4. raise The voice___ of prayer,_ the hymn of praise.
5. grace To see___ thy glo - ry face to face.

Text: Latin hymn, 15th Century. Trans. J.M. Neale, +1866, alt.
Tune: *Deus tuorum militum*, Grenoble Church Melody.

O Worship the King

Ps. 104

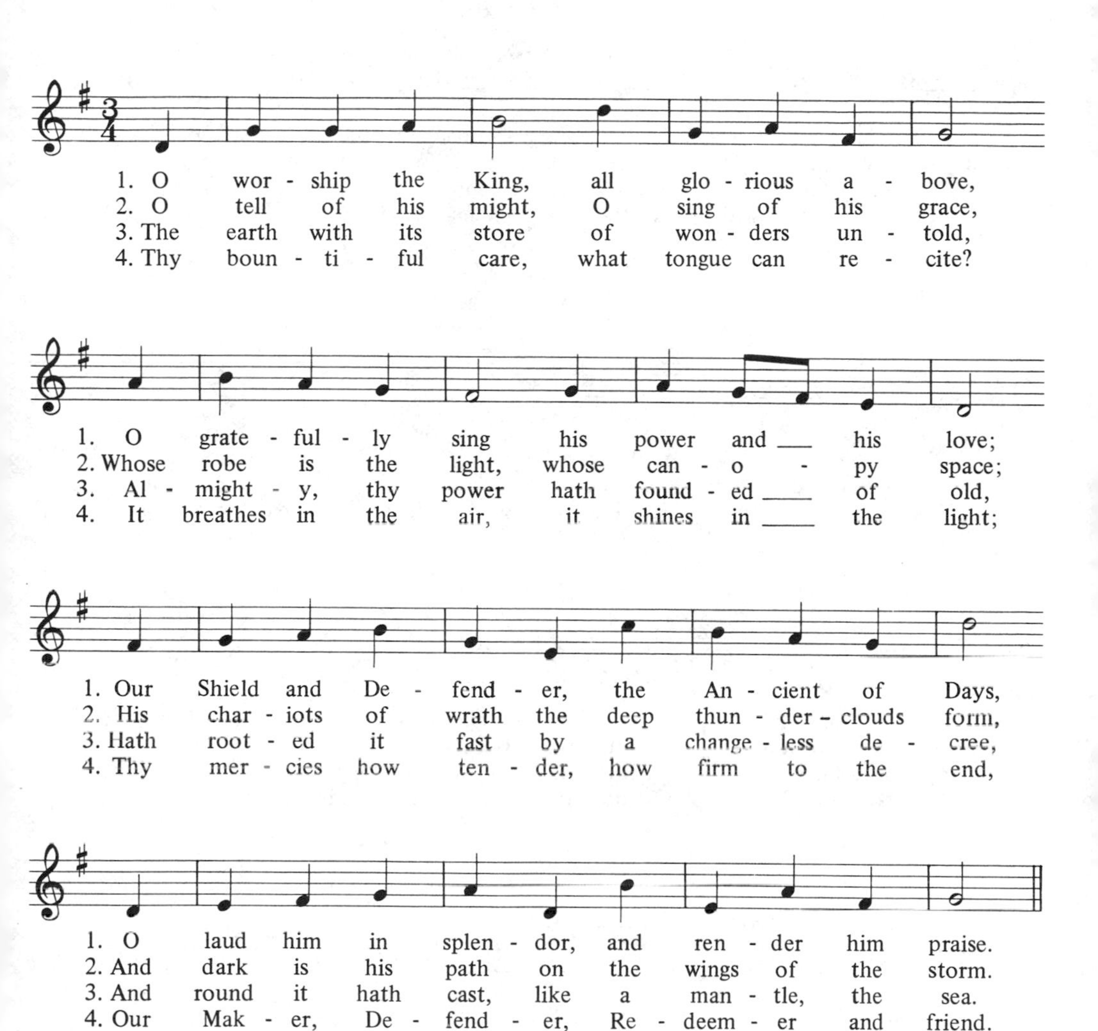
1. O wor - ship the King, all glo - rious a - bove,
2. O tell of his might, O sing of his grace,
3. The earth with its store of won - ders un - told,
4. Thy boun - ti - ful care, what tongue can re - cite?
1. O grate - ful - ly sing his power and his love;
2. Whose robe is the light, whose can - o - py space;
3. Al - might - y, thy power hath found - ed of old,
4. It breathes in the air, it shines in the light;
1. Our Shield and De - fend - er, the An - cient of Days,
2. His char - iots of wrath the deep thun - der – clouds form,
3. Hath root - ed it fast by a change - less de - cree,
4. Thy mer - cies how ten - der, how firm to the end,
1. O laud him in splen - dor, and ren - der him praise.
2. And dark is his path on the wings of the storm.
3. And round it hath cast, like a man - tle, the sea.
4. Our Mak - er, De - fend - er, Re - deem - er and friend.

Text: Psalm 104 paraphrase, R. Grant, +1838, alt.
Tune: *Hanover,* attributed to W. Croft, +1727.

269 Of the Father's Love Begotten

1. Of the Fa - ther's love be - got - ten, Ere the worlds be-gan_ to be,
2. O that birth for - ev - er bless - ed, When the Vir - gin, full_ of grace,
3. O ye heights of heav'n a - dore_ him; An - gel hosts, his prais - es sing,
4. Christ, to thee with God the Fa - ther, And, O Ho - ly Ghost,_to thee,

1. He is Al - pha and O - me - ga, He the source, the
2. By the Ho - ly Ghost con - ceiv - ing, Bore the Sav - ior
3. Pow - ers, do - min - ions, bow be - fore him, And ex - tol our
4. Hymn and chant and high thanks - giv - ing, And un - wea - ried

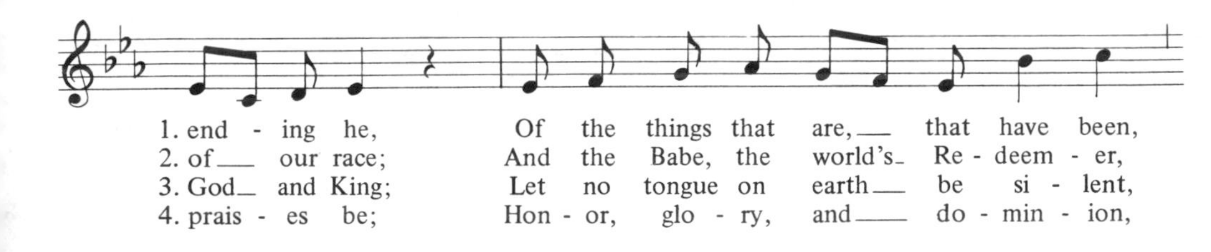

1. end - ing he, Of the things that are,_ that have been,
2. of_ our race; And the Babe, the world's_ Re - deem - er,
3. God_ and King; Let no tongue on earth_ be si - lent,
4. prais - es be; Hon - or, glo - ry, and_ do - min - ion,

1. And_ that fu - ture years_ shall_ see,
2. First_ re - veal'd_ his sa - cred_ face,
3. Ev - 'ry voice_ in con - cert_ ring,
4. And_ e - ter - nal vic - to - ry,

Ev - er - more and ev - er - more!_

Text: Prudentius, +413. Trans. J.M. Neale, +1866, and H.W. Baker, +1877.
Tune: *Divinum mysterium,* Medieval Chant Melody, Mode 5.

Once in Royal David's City

270

1. Once in roy - al Da - vid's city Stood a low - ly
2. He came down to earth from heav - en, Who is God and
3. And, thro' all his won - drous child-hood, He would hon - or
4. For he is our child - hood's mod - el; Day by day like
5. And our eyes at last shall see him, Thro' his own re -
1. cat - tle shed, Where a moth - er laid her ba - by
2. Lord of all, And his shel - ter was a sta - ble,
3. and o - bey, Love, and watch the low - ly maid - en
4. us he grew; He was lit - tle, weak, and help - less,
5. deem - ing love; For that child so dear and gen - tle
1. In a man - ger for his bed: Mar - y was that
2. And his cra - dle was a stall; With the poor, and
3. In whose gen - tle arms he lay: Chris - tian chil - dren
4. Tears and smiles like us he knew; And he feel - eth
5. Is our Lord in heav'n a - bove; And he leads his
1. moth - er mild, Je - sus Christ her lit - tle child.
2. mean, and low - ly, Lived on earth our Sav - ior ho - ly.
3. all must be Mild, o - be - dient, good as he.
4. for our sad - ness, And he shar - eth in our glad - ness.
5. chil - dren on To the place where he is gone.

Text: C.F. Alexander, +1895, alt.
Tune: *Irby*, H.J. Gauntlett, +1876.

271 On Jordan's Bank

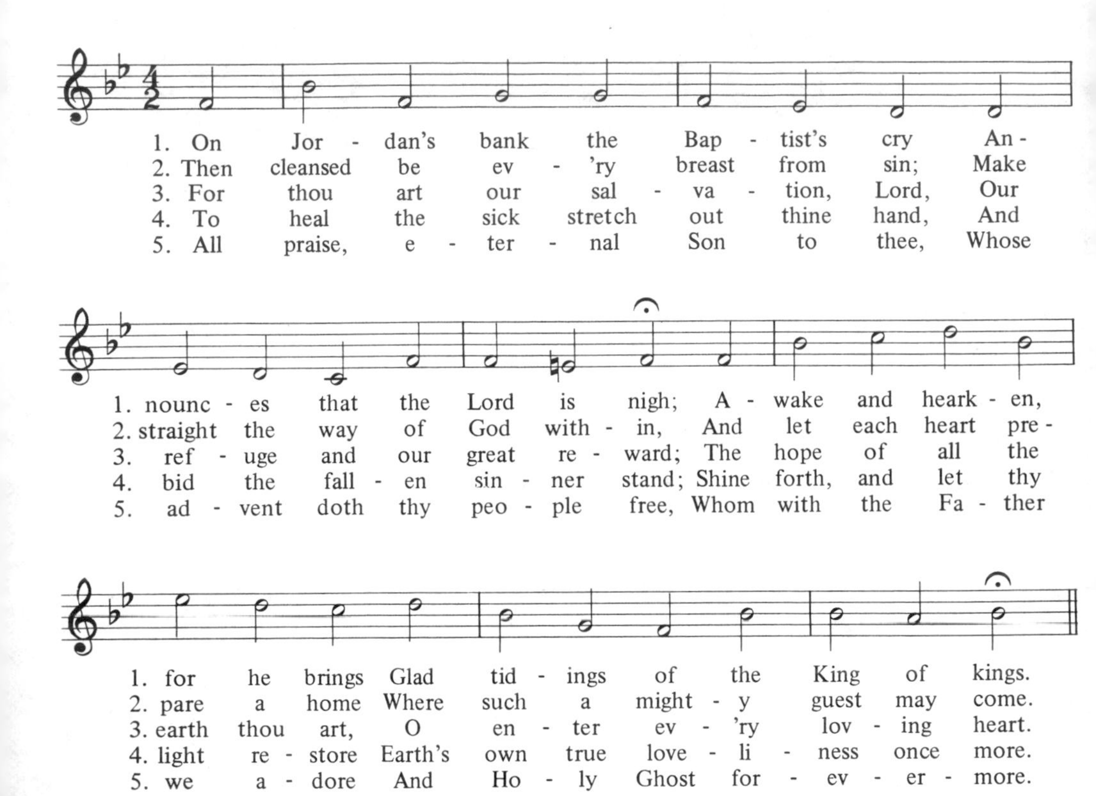

1. On Jor - dan's bank the Bap - tist's cry An -
2. Then cleansed be ev - 'ry breast from sin; Make
3. For thou art our sal - va - tion, Lord, Our
4. To heal the sick stretch out thine hand, And
5. All praise, e - ter - nal Son to thee, Whose
1. nounc - es that the Lord is nigh; A - wake and heark - en,
2. straight the way of God with - in, And let each heart pre -
3. ref - uge and our great re - ward; The hope of all the
4. bid the fall - en sin - ner stand; Shine forth, and let thy
5. ad - vent doth thy peo - ple free, Whom with the Fa - ther
1. for he brings Glad tid - ings of the King of kings.
2. pare a home Where such a might - y guest may come.
3. earth thou art, O en - ter ev - 'ry lov - ing heart.
4. light re - store Earth's own true love - li - ness once more.
5. we a - dore And Ho - ly Ghost for - ev - er - more.

Text: C. Coffin, +1749. Trans. J. Chandler, +1876, alt.
Tune: *Winchester New*, "Musicalisches Handbuch" (adapted), Hamburg, 1690.

On This Day

1. On this day earth shall ring With the song
2. His the doom, ours the mirth; When he came
3. God's bright star, o'er his head, Wise men three
4. On this day an - gels sing; With their song
1. chil - dren sing To the Lord, Christ our King,
2. down to earth, Beth - le - hem saw his birth;
3. to him led, Kneel they low by his bed,
4. earth shall ring, Prais - ing Christ, heav - en's King,
1. Born on earth to save us, Him the Fa - ther
2. Ox and ass be - side him, From the cold would
3. Lay their gifts be - fore him, Praise him and a -
4. Born on earth to save us, Peace and love he
1. gave us.
2. hide him.
3. dore him.
4. gave us.
Id - e - o - o - o, Id - e - o - o - o,
Id - e - o glo - ri - a in ex - cel - sis De - o!

Text: From *Piae Cantiones*, 1582, adapted J.M. Joseph, +1929.
Tune: *Personent hodie*, also from *Piae Cantiones.*

273 Only-Begotten, Word of God Eternal

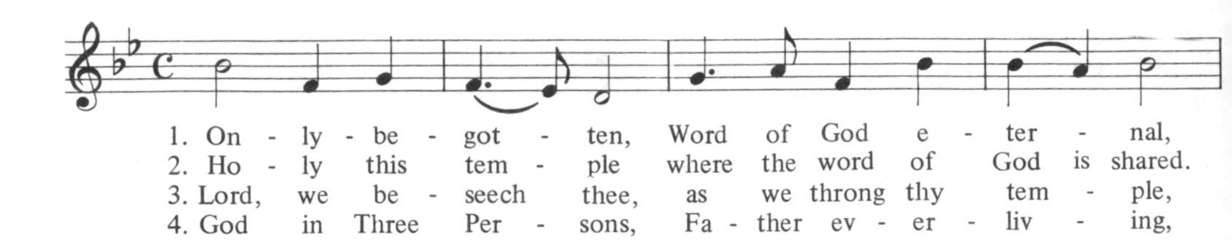

1. On - ly - be - got - ten, Word of God e - ter - nal,
2. Ho - ly this tem - ple where the word of God is shared.
3. Lord, we be - seech thee, as we throng thy tem - ple,
4. God in Three Per - sons, Fa - ther ev - er - liv - ing,

1. Lord of cre - a - tion, mer - ci - ful and might - y,
2. This is none oth - er than the gate of heav - en,
3. By thy past bless - ings, by thy pres - ent boun - ty,
4. Son co - e - ter - nal, ev - er bless - ed Spir - it,

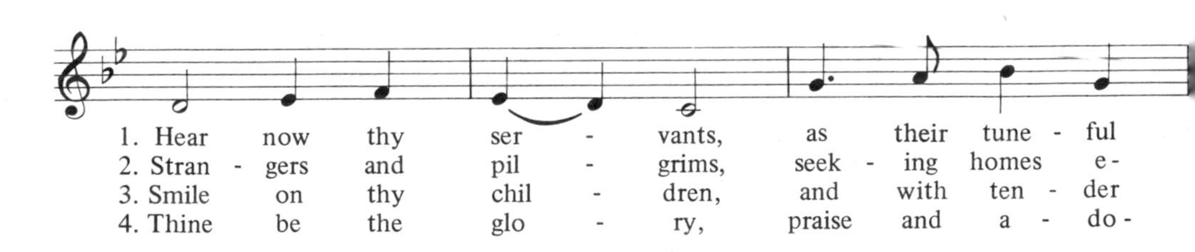

1. Hear now thy ser - vants, as their tune - ful
2. Stran - gers and pil - grims, seek - ing homes e -
3. Smile on thy chil - dren, and with ten - der
4. Thine be the glo - ry, praise and a - do -

1. voic - es Rise to thy pres - ence.
2. ter - nal, Pass through its por - tals.
3. mer - cy Hear now our plead - ings.
4. ra - tion, Now and for - ev - er.

Text: 9th Century Office Hymn, anon. Trans. M.J. Blacker, +1888, alt.
Tune: *Coelites plaudant,* Rouen Melody, 17th Century.

Our Father, We Have Wandered

1. Our_ Fa - ther, we have wan - dered And hid - den_ from your face;
2. And_ now at length dis - cern - ing The e - vil__ that we do,
3. O__ Lord of all the liv - ing, Both ban - ished_ and re - stored,

1. In__ fool - ish - ness have squan - dered Your leg - a - cy of grace.
2. Be - hold us, Lord, re - turn - ing With hope and_trust - to you.
3. Com - pas - sion - ate, for - giv - ing And ev - er - car - ing Lord,

1. But now, in ex - ile dwell - ing, We rise with fear and shame,
2. In haste you come to meet us And home re - joic - ing bring,
3. Grant now that our trans - gress - ing, Our faith - less - ness may cease.

1. As dis - tant but com - pel - ling, We hear you call our name.
2. In glad - ness there to greet us With calf and robe and ring.
3. Stretch out your hand in bless - ing, In par - don and in peace.

Text: K. Nichols, 1977.
Tune: *Munich*, "Meiningen Gesangbuch", 1693.

275 BENEDICTION SERVICE (Latin)

Pange Lingua-Tantum Ergo Sacramentum

1. Pan - ge lin - gua glo - ri - ó - si Cór - po - ris my-sté - ri - um,
San - gui - nís - que pre - ti - ó - si, Quem in mun - di pré - ti - um
1.-5.
6.
Fru-ctus ven-tris ge-ne-ró-si Rex ef-fú-dit gén - ti - um. o. A - men.

2. Nobis datus, nobis natus Ex intácta Vírgine,
   Et in mundo conversátus, Sparso verbi sémine,
   Sui moras incolátus Miro clausit órdine.

3. In suprémae nocte coenae Recúmbens cum frátribus,
   Observáta lege plene Cibis in legálibus,
   Cibum turbae duodénae Se dat suis mánibus.

4. Verbum caro, panem verum Verbo carnem éfficit:
   Fitque Sanguis Christi merum, Et si sensus déficit,
   Ad firmándum cor sincérum Sola fides súfficit.

5. TANTUM ERGO Sacraméntum Venerémur cérnui:
   Et antíquum documéntum Novo cédat ritui:
   Praestet fides suppleméntum Sénsuum deféctui.

6. Genitóri, Genitóque Laus et jubilátio,
   Salus, honor, virtus quoque Sit et benedíctio:
   Procedénti ab utróque Compar sit laudátio. Amen.

Text: St. Thomas Aquinas, +1274.
Tune: *Pange lingua,* Plainchant, Mode 3.

276 Versicle - Response - Oration for Benediction

℣. Panem de caelo praestitísti eis. *Cel.* Orémus.
℟. Omne delectaméntum in se habéntem. *All* A - men.

For translation, see "Now, My Tongue, the Myst'ry Telling".

Out of the Depths, to You, O Lord, We Cry

Ps. 130

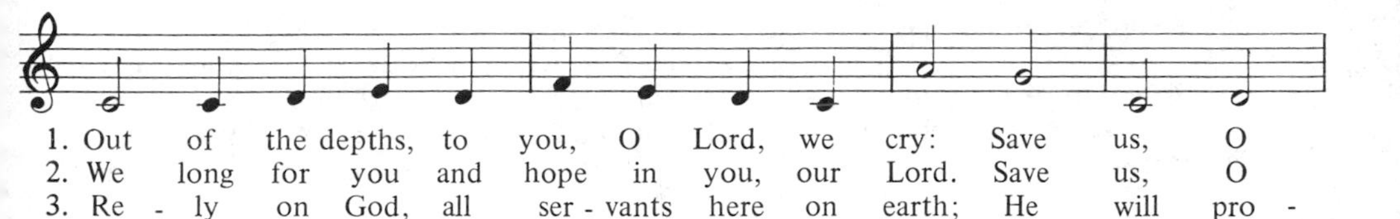
1. Out of the depths, to you, O Lord, we cry: Save us, O
2. We long for you and hope in you, our Lord. Save us, O
3. Re - ly on God, all ser - vants here on earth; He will pro -

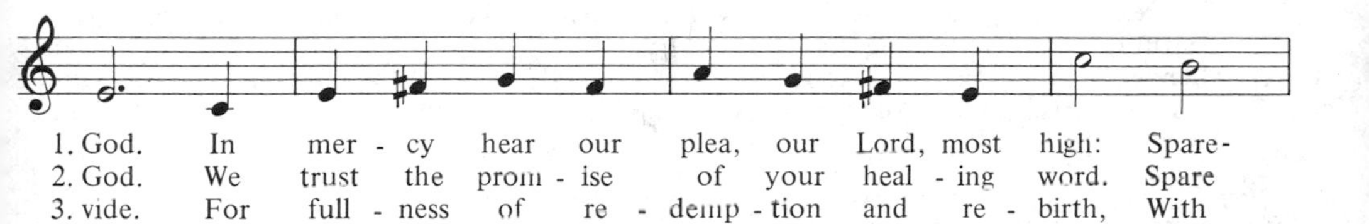
1. God. In mer - cy hear our plea, our Lord, most high: Spare-
2. God. We trust the prom - ise of your heal - ing word. Spare
3. vide. For full - ness of re - demp - tion and re - birth, With

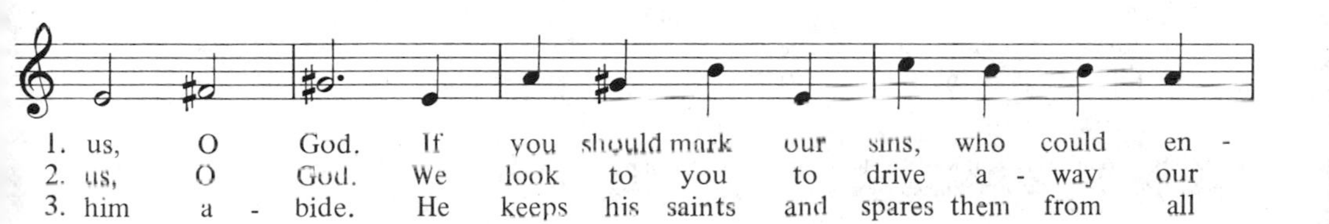
1. us, O God. If you should mark our sins, who could en -
2. us, O God. We look to you to drive a - way our
3. him a - bide. He keeps his saints and spares them from all

1. dure? But with your grace is mer - cy ev - er sure.
2. night, As watch - men look and wait for morn - ing light.
3. harm. Sal - va - tion comes through his al - might - y arm.

Text: Psalm 130 paraphrase, J. Dunn.
Tune: *Alberta,* W.H. Harris, +1973.

278 Praise and Thanksgiving Be to God

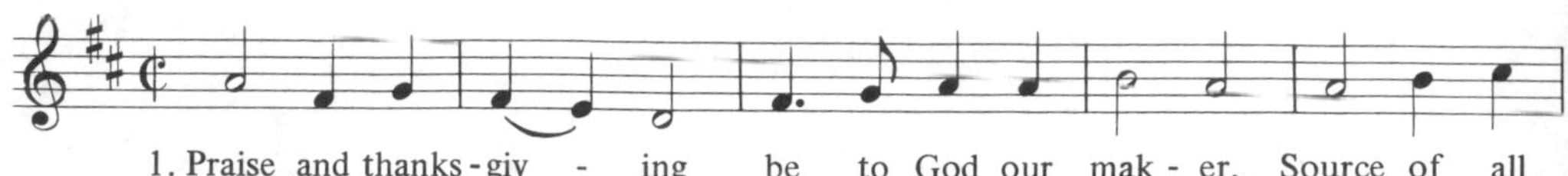

1. Praise and thanks - giv - ing be to God our mak - er, Source of all
2. Not our own ho - li - ness, nor that we have striv - en Brings us the
3. Come, Ho - ly Spir - it, come in vis - i - ta - tion; You are the
4. E - ter - nal Word, still by the Fa - ther spo - ken, Speak to us
5. Praise to the Fa - ther, Son, and Ho - ly Spir - it: One Lord, one

1. bless - ing, prod - i - gal Cre - a - tor. Bap - tize and make your own
2. peace which you, O Christ, have giv - en. Bap - tize and set a - part;
3. truth, our hope and our sal - va - tion. Bap - tize with joy and pow'r;
4. now in this bap - tis - mal to - ken; Pro - claim a - new to us
5. faith, one source of ev - 'ry mer - it. Here now re - new your Church

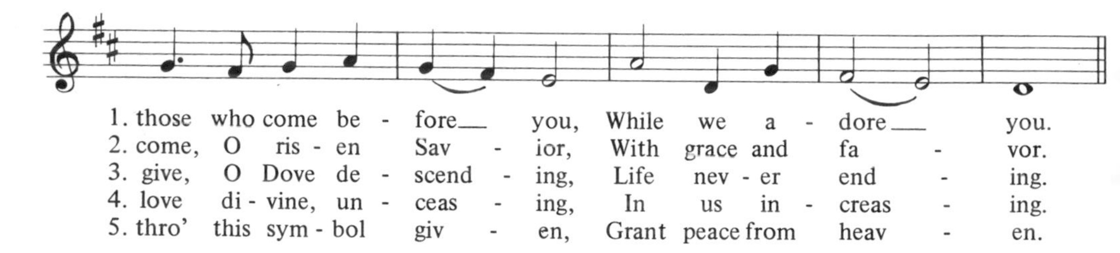
1. those who come be - fore you, While we a - dore you.
2. come, O ris - en Sav - ior, With grace and fa - vor.
3. give, O Dove de - scend - ing, Life nev - er end - ing.
4. love di - vine, un - ceas - ing, In us in - creas - ing.
5. thro' this sym - bol giv - en, Grant peace from heav - en.

Text: H.F. Yardley and F.J. Whitely, alt.
Tune: *Christe sanctorum,* French melody in "Antiphoner", Paris, 1681.

279 Praise, My Soul, the King of Heaven

Ps. 103

1. Praise, my soul, the King of heav - en; To his feet thy tri - bute bring;
2. Praise him for his grace and fa - vor To our fa - thers in dis - tress;
3. As a fa - ther tends and spares us, He so well our na - ture knows;
4. An - gels help us to a - dore him, Ye be - hold him face to face;

1. Ran-somed, healed, re - stored, for-giv - en, Ev - er - more his prais - es sing;
2. Praise him still the same as ev - er, Slow to an - ger, swift to bless;
3. In his hand he gent - ly bears us, Res - cues us from all our foes;
4. Sun and moon, bow down be-fore him, Dwel - lers all in time and space;

1. Al - le - lu - ia! Al - le - lu - ia! Praise the ev - er - last - ing King.
2. Al - le - lu - ia! Al - le - lu - ia! Glo - rious in his faith - ful - ness.
3. Al - le - lu - ia! Al - le - lu - ia! Wide - ly yet his mer - cy flows.
4. Al - le - lu - ia! Al - le - lu - ia! Praise with us the God of grace.

Text: Psalm 103 paraphrase, H.F. Lyte, +1847, alt.
Tune: *Lauda anima,* J. Goss, +1880.

Praise the Lord, His Glories Show **280**

Ps. 150

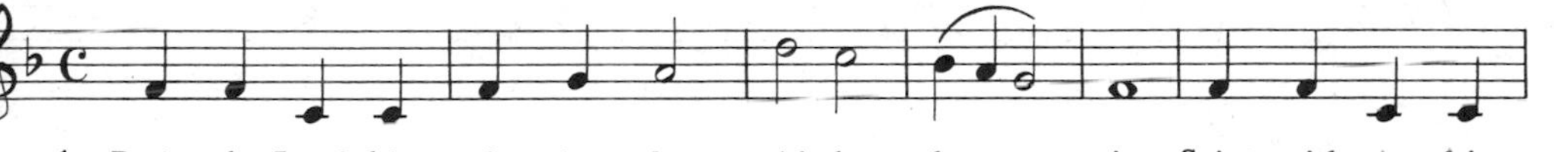

1. Praise the Lord, his glo - ries show, Al - le - lu - ia. Saints with - in his
2. Earth to heav'n and heav'n to earth, Al - le - lu - ia. Tell his won - ders,
3. Praise the Lord, his mer - cies trace, Al - le - lu - ia. Praise his prov - i -
4. Strings and voic - es, hearts up - raise Al - le - lu - ia. In cre - a - tion's

1. courts be - low, Al - le - lu - ia. An - gels 'round his throne a - bove, Al -
2. sing his worth, Al - le - lu - ia. Age to age and shore to shore, Al -
3. dence and grace, Al - le - lu - ia. All that he for us hath done, Al -
4. song - ful praise, Al - le - lu - ia. All that breathe, your Lord a - dore, Al -

1. le - lu - ia. All that see and share his love, Al - le - lu - ia.
2. le - lu - ia. Praise him, praise him ev - er - more! Al - le - lu - ia.
3. le - lu - ia. All he sends us through his Son, Al - le - lu - ia.
4. le - lu - ia. Praise him, praise him ev - er - more! Al - le - lu - ia.

Text: Psalm 150 paraphrase, H.F. Lyte, +1847, alt.
Tune: *Gaudeamus pariter,* J. Horn, +1547.

281 Praise the Lord Who Reigns Above

Ps. 150

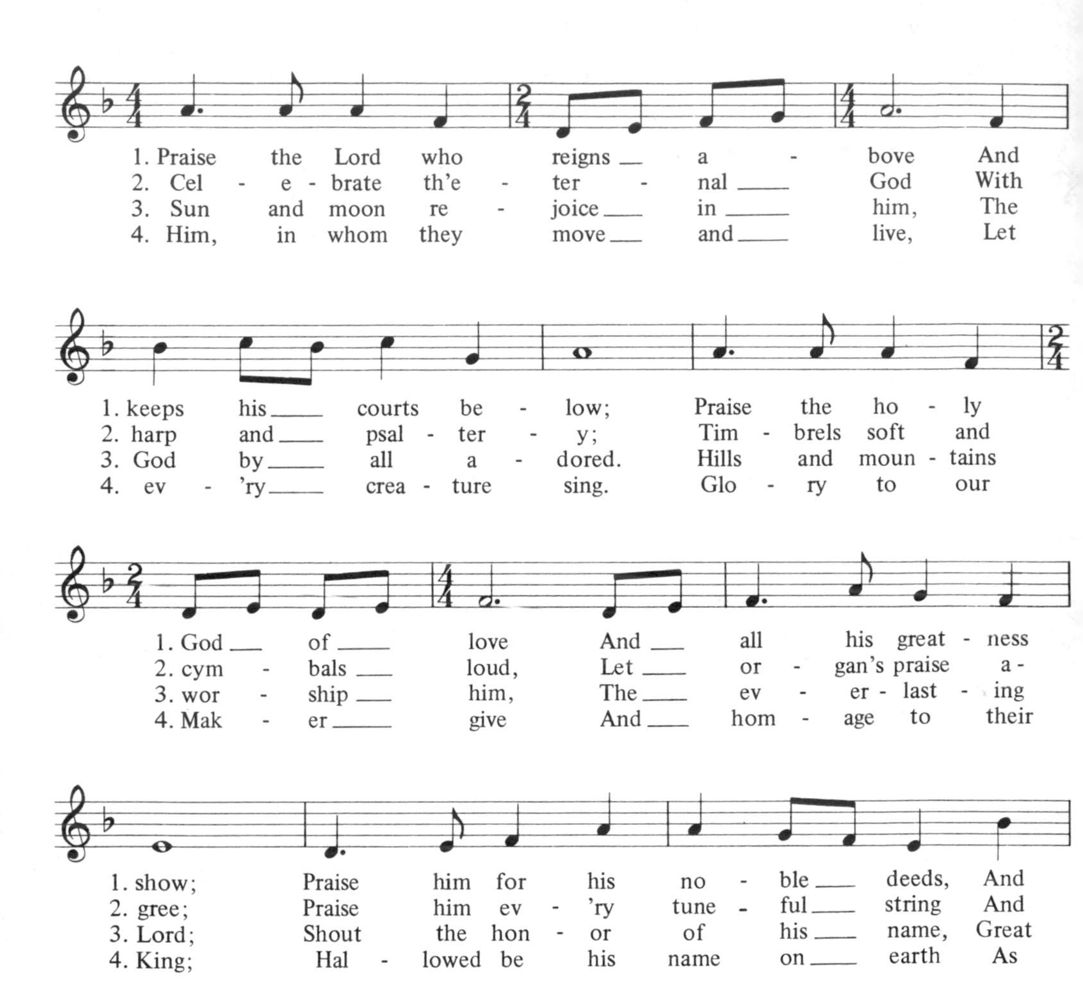
1. Praise the Lord who reigns a - bove And
2. Cel - e - brate th'e - ter - nal God With
3. Sun and moon re - joice in him, The
4. Him, in whom they move and live, Let
1. keeps his courts be - low; Praise the ho - ly
2. harp and psal - ter - y; Tim - brels soft and
3. God by all a - dored. Hills and moun - tains
4. ev - 'ry crea - ture sing. Glo - ry to our
1. God of love And all his great - ness
2. cym - bals loud, Let or - gan's praise a -
3. wor - ship him, The ev - er - last - ing
4. Mak - er give And hom - age to their
1. show; Praise him for his no - ble deeds, And
2. gree; Praise him ev - 'ry tune - ful string And
3. Lord; Shout the hon - or of his name, Great
4. King; Hal - lowed be his name on earth As

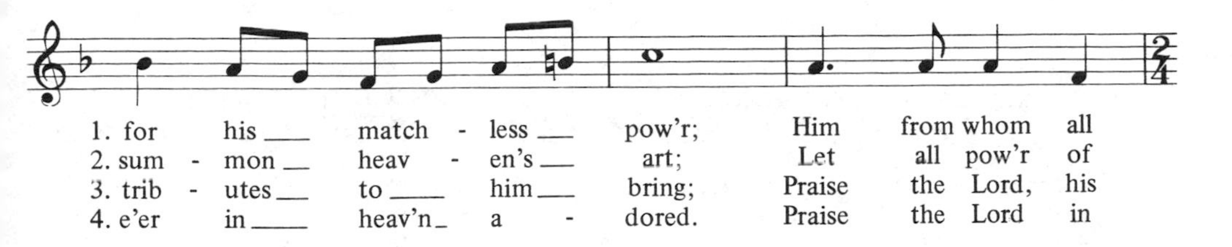
1. for his match - less pow'r; Him from whom all
2. sum - mon heav - en's art; Let all pow'r of
3. trib - utes to him bring; Praise the Lord, his
4. e'er in heav'n a - dored. Praise the Lord in

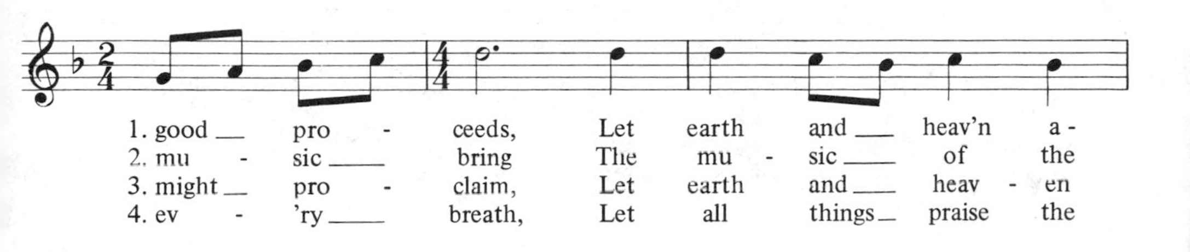
1. good pro - ceeds, Let earth and heav'n a -
2. mu - sic bring The mu - sic of the
3. might pro - claim, Let earth and heav - en
4. ev - 'ry breath, Let all things praise the

1. dore, Let earth and heav'n a - dore.
2. heart, The mu - sic of the heart.
3. ring, Let earth and heav - en ring.
4. Lord, Let all things praise the Lord.

Text: Verses 1, 2, and 4, Psalm 150 paraphrase, C. Wesley, +1788, alt.
Verse 3, Psalm 148, J. Dunn. © by author. Used with permission.
Tune: *Laudes,* T. Marier.

282 Praise the Lord, Ye Heav'ns Adore Him

Ps. 148

1. Praise the Lord, ye heav'ns a - dore him;
2. Praise the Lord, for he is glo - rious;
3. Praise the Lord, his might con fess - ing;
4. Wor - ship, hon - or, glo - ry, bless - ing,
1. Praise him, an - gels, in the height;
2. Nev - er shall his prom - ise fail;
3. Laud him ev - er; bless his name.
4. Lord, we of - fer to thy name;
1. Sun and moon, re - joice be - fore him,
2. God hath made his saints vic - to - rious;
3. An - gels, saints, his throne ad - dress - ing,
4. Young and old thy praise ex - press - ing,
1. Praise him all ye stars of light.
2. Sin and death shall not pre - vail.
3. Wor - ship him, his pow'r pro - claim.
4. Join their Sav - ior to pro - claim.

1. Praise the Lord, for he hath spo - ken,
2. Praise the God of our sal - va - tion,
3. Praise the Lord of all cre - a - tion,
4. As the saints in heav'n a - dore thee,

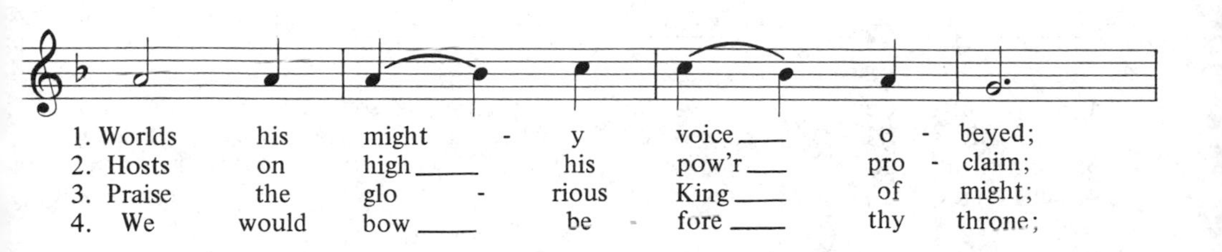
1. Worlds his might - y voice o - beyed;
2. Hosts on high his pow'r pro - claim;
3. Praise the glo - rious King of might;
4. We would bow be - fore thy throne;

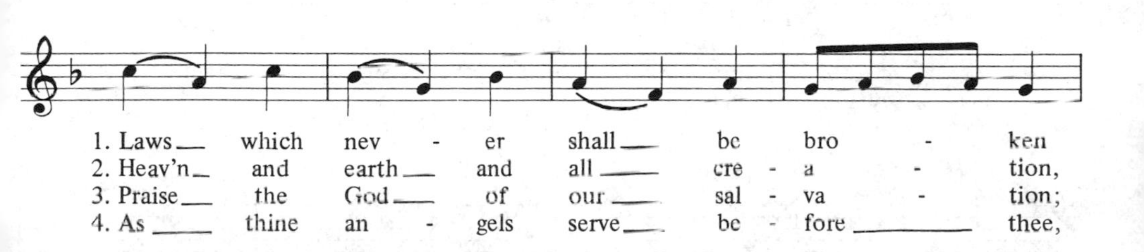
1. Laws which nev - er shall be bro - ken
2. Heav'n and earth and all cre - a - tion,
3. Praise the God of our sal - va - tion;
4. As thine an - gels serve be - fore thee,

1. For their guid - ance he hath made.
2. Laud and mag - ni - fy his name.
3. Praise him, praise him in the height.
4. So on earth thy will be done.

Text: Verses 1, 2, Psalm 148 paraphrase, Foundling Hospital Collection, c. 1801.
Verse 3, J. Dunn.
Verse 4, E. Osler, +1863.
Tune: *Hyfrydol,* R.H. Prichard, +1887.

283 Praise to the Lord

First Tune
1. Praise to the Lord, the Al - might - y, the
2. Praise to the Lord, who o'er all things so
3. Praise to the Lord, who doth pros - per thy
4. Praise to the Lord! O let all that is
1. King of cre - a - tion! O my soul, praise him, for
2. won - drous - ly reign - eth, Who, as on wings of an
3. work and de - fend thee; Sure - ly his good - ness and
4. in me a - dore him! All that hath life and breath,
1. he is thy health and sal - va - tion!
2 ea - gle, up - lift - eth, sus - tain - eth.
3. mer - cy here dai - ly at - tend thee.
4. come now with prais - es be - fore him!
1. All you who hear, Now to his al - tar draw
2. Hast thou not seen How thy de - sires all have
3. Pon - der a - new What the Al - might - y can
4. He is thy light; Soul, keep it al - ways in
1. near, Join - ing in glad ad - o - ra - tion.
2. been Grant - ed in what he or - dain - eth?
3. do, If with his love he be - friend thee.
4. sight; Glad - ly for - ev - er a - dore him.

Text: J. Neander, +1680. Trans. C. Winkworth, +1878.
Tune: *Lobe den Herrn,* "Stralsund Gesangbuch", 1665.

Praise to the Lord

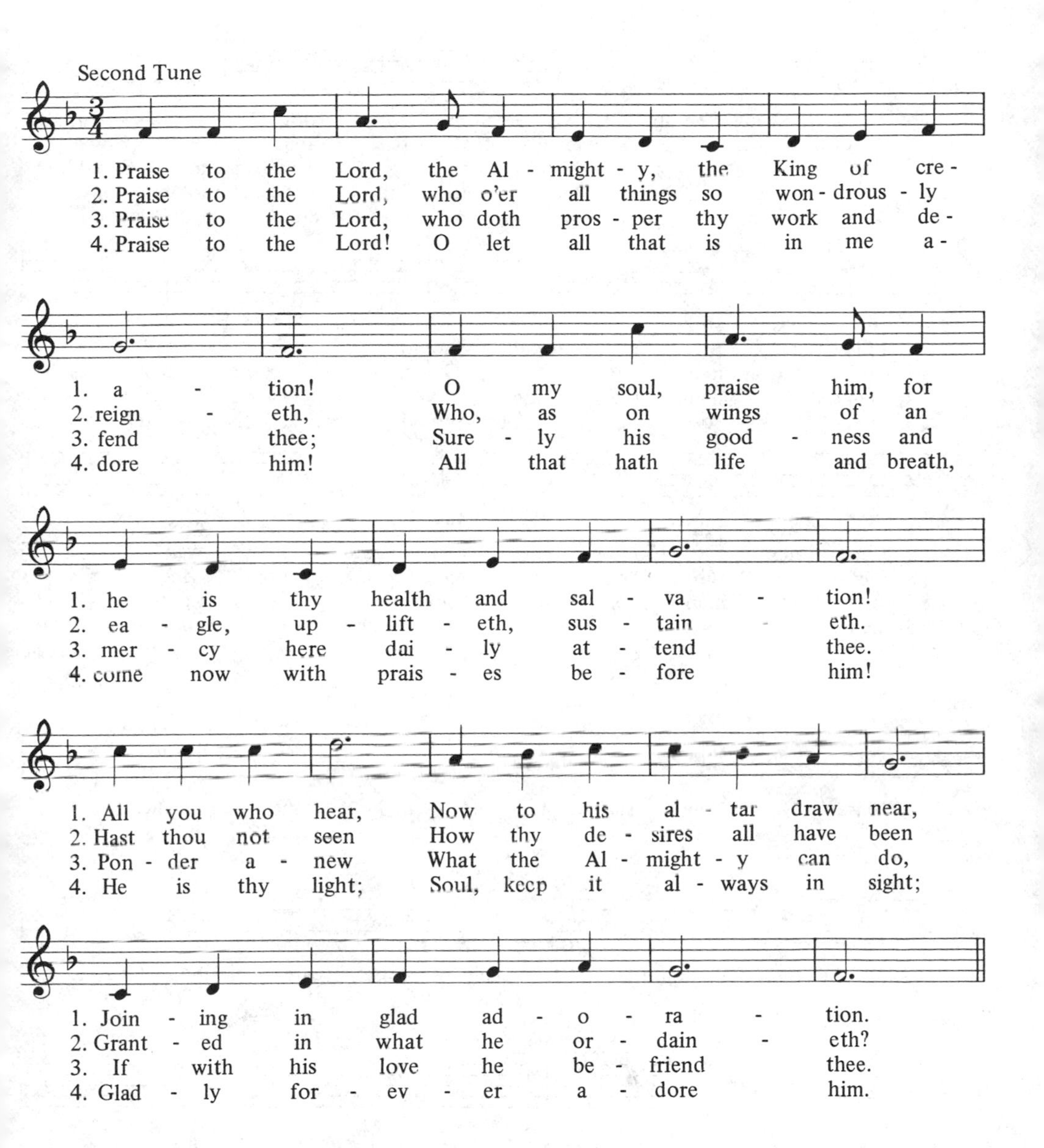
Second Tune
1. Praise to the Lord, the Al - might - y, the King of cre - a - tion! O my soul, praise him, for he is thy health and sal - va - tion! All you who hear, Now to his al - tar draw near, Join - ing in glad ad - o - ra - tion.
2. Praise to the Lord, who o'er all things so won - drous - ly reign - eth, Who, as on wings of an ea - gle, up - lift - eth, sus - tain - eth. Hast thou not seen How thy de - sires all have been Grant - ed in what he or - dain - eth?
3. Praise to the Lord, who doth pros - per thy work and de - fend thee; Sure - ly his good - ness and mer - cy here dai - ly at - tend thee. Pon - der a - new What the Al - might - y can do, If with his love he be - friend thee.
4. Praise to the Lord! O let all that is in me a - dore him! All that hath life and breath, come now with prais - es be - fore him! He is thy light; Soul, keep it al - ways in sight; Glad - ly for - ev - er a - dore him.

Text: J. Neander, +1680. Trans. C. Winkworth, +1878.
Tune: *Lobe den Herrn*, "Stralsund Gesangbuch", 1665.

285 Praise to the Holiest

1. O lov - ing wis - dom of our God! When
2. O wis - est love! that flesh and blood, Which
3. And that a high - er gift than grace Should
4. O gen - 'rous love! that he who smote In
5. And in the gar - den se - cret - ly, And
1. all was sin and shame, A sec - ond Ad - am
2. did in Ad - am fail, Should strive a - fresh a -
3. flesh and blood re - fine, God's pres - ence and his
4. man for man the foe, The dou - ble ag - o -
5. on the Cross on high, Should teach his breth - ren
1. to the fight And to the res - cue came!
2. gainst their foe, Should strive and should pre - vail!
3. ver - y self, And es - sence all di - vine!
4. ny in man For man should un - der - go!
5. and in - spire To suf - fer and to die!
REFRAIN
1.-5. Praise to the Ho - li - est in the height, And
1.-5. in the depth be praise: In all his

1.-5. words most won - der - ful, Most sure in all his ways.

Text: J.H. Newman, +1890.
Tune: *McGrath,* J.J. McGrath, +1967. From "Pius X Hymnal",

Rejoice, My Soul, and Bless the Lord 286

Ps. 103

1. Re - joice, my soul, and bless the Lord Cre - a - tor,
2. The Lord is good and full of kind com - pas - sion,
3. His love is like a fa - ther's to his chil - dren
4. We are so frail like flow'rs that grow in beau - ty,
5. High in the heav'ns his throne is fixed for - ev - er.
1. And all with - in me bless his ho - ly name;
2. Most slow to an - ger, rich in stead - fast love.
3. So ten - der, kind to those who trust his name.
4. Like ten - der grass that soon will dis - ap - pear;
5. His king - dom rules o'er all from pole to pole;
1. O bless our God, for - get not all his mer - cies,
2. His grace is sure to all that hum - bly seek him,
3. He sure - ly knows our weak - ness and our na - ture;
4. But ev - er more the love of God is change - less,
5. O bless the Lord through all his wide do - min - ion
1. His sav - ing grace and heal - ing love pro - claim.
2. As bound - less as the high - est heav'ns a - bove.
3. He knows we are dust; he knows our mor - tal frame.
4. Still shown to those who look to him in fear.
5. And bless his ho - ly name, re - joice, my soul.

Text: Psalm 103 paraphrase, anon., "Psalter Hymnal", 1959, alt.
Tune: *Northbrook*, R.S. Thatcher, +1957. From "The Clarendon Hymn Book", Oxford University Press. Used with permission.

Rejoice, Rejoice, Believers

1. Re - joice, re - joice, be - liev - ers, And let your lights ap - pear;
2. The watch - ers on the moun - tain Pro - claim the Bride-groom near;
3. The saints who here in pa - tience Their cross and suf - f'ring bore,
4. Our hope and ex - pec - ta - tion, O Je - sus, now ap - pear;

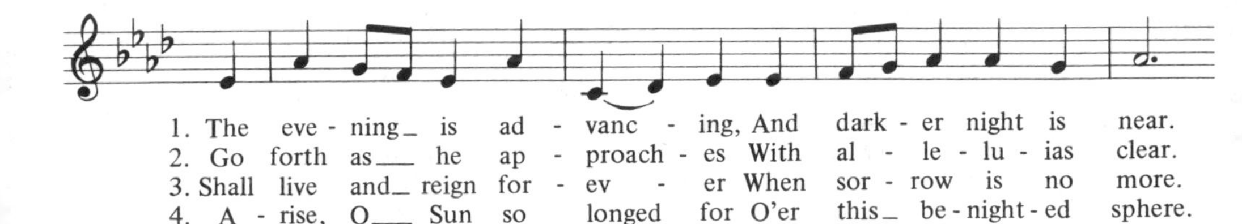

1. The eve - ning is ad - vanc - ing, And dark - er night is near.
2. Go forth as he ap - proach - es With al - le - lu - ias clear.
3. Shall live and reign for - ev - er When sor - row is no more.
4. A - rise, O Sun so longed for O'er this be - night - ed sphere.

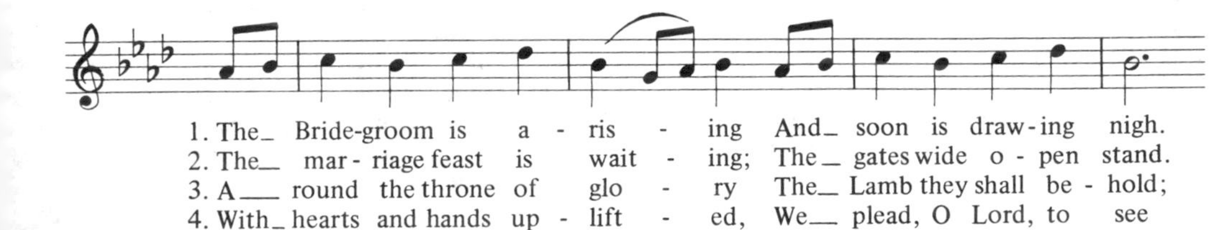

1. The Bride-groom is a - ris - ing And soon is draw - ing nigh.
2. The mar - riage feast is wait - ing; The gates wide o - pen stand.
3. A - round the throne of glo - ry The Lamb they shall be - hold;
4. With hearts and hands up - lift - ed, We plead, O Lord, to see

1. Be read - y, all ye faith - ful, At mid - night comes the cry.
2. A - rise, O heirs of glo - ry; The Bride-groom is at hand.
3. In tri - umph cast be - fore him Their di - a - dems of gold.
4. The day of earth's re - demp - tion That sets your peo - ple free!

Text: L. Laurentii, +1722. Trans. S.B. Findlater, +1907, alt.
Tune: *Ellacombe,* "Würtemburg Gesangbuch", 1784.

Rejoice, All Peoples, in the Lord

288

Ps. 33

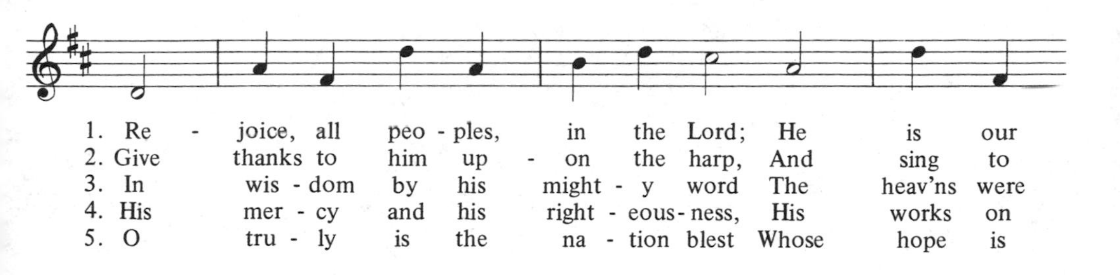
1. Re - joice, all peo - ples, in the Lord; He is our
2. Give thanks to him up - on the harp, And sing to
3. In wis - dom by his might - y word The heav'ns were
4. His mer - cy and his right - eous - ness, His works on
5. O tru - ly is the na - tion blest Whose hope is

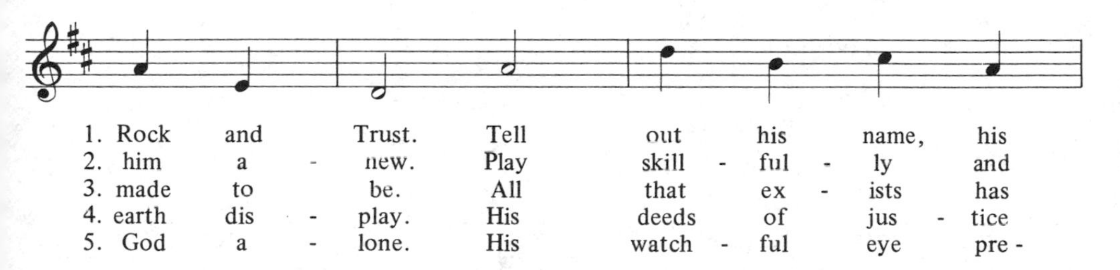
1. Rock and Trust. Tell out his name, his
2. him a - new. Play skill - ful - ly and
3. made to be. All that ex - ists has
4. earth dis - play. His deeds of jus - tice
5. God a - lone. His watch - ful eye pre -

1. deeds, his word; How faith - ful, sure and just!
2. shout a - loud That God, our Lord, is true.
3. sprung from him, And lives at his de - cree.
4. and of grace Re - veal his lov - ing way.
5. serves and keeps All those he calls his own.

6. Now let our hearts rejoice in him;
His love shall crown our land.
Salvation comes from God, our King,
To those within his hand.

7. Give glory to our faithful God;
Hosanna to his Son;
All praise to God, the Comforter;
The mighty Three in One.

Text: Psalm 33 paraphrase, J. Dunn.
Tune: *London New,* "Scottish Psalter", 1635.

289 Rejoice with Us in God the Trinity

ANTIPHON *Sung by Choir* Rejoice with us in God the Trinity,
The Three forever One, forever Three,
Fountain of Love, Giver of Unity!

VERSES *Sung by All*

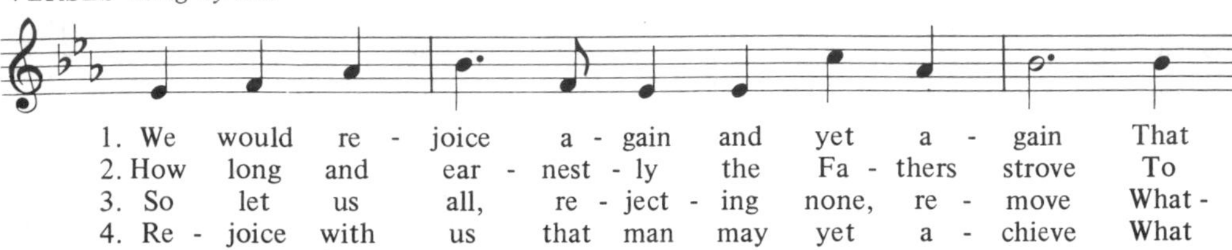
1. We would re - joice a - gain and yet a - gain That
2. How long and ear - nest - ly the Fa - thers strove To
3. So let us all, re - ject - ing none, re - move What -
4. Re - joice with us that man may yet a - chieve What

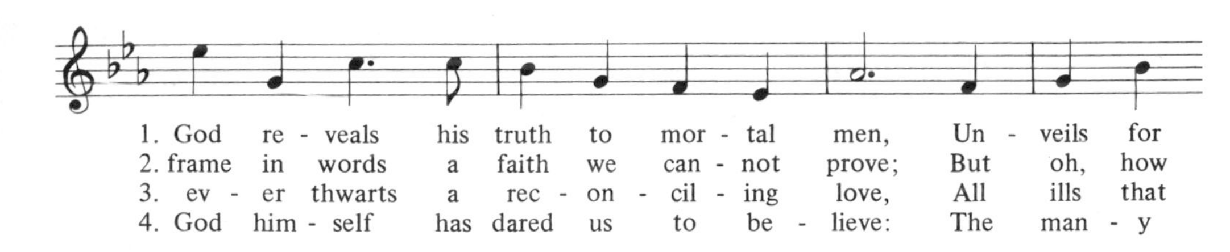
1. God re - veals his truth to mor - tal men, Un - veils for
2. frame in words a faith we can - not prove; But oh, how
3. ev - er thwarts a rec - on - cil - ing love, All ills that
4. God him - self has dared us to be - lieve: The man - y

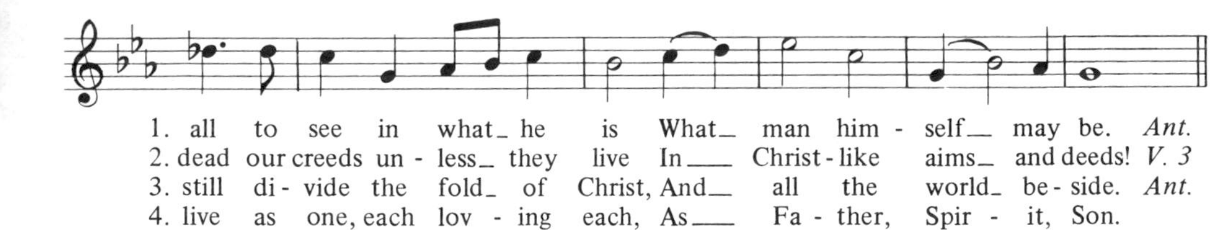
1. all to see in what_ he is What_ man him - self_ may be. Ant.
2. dead our creeds un - less_ they live In___ Christ - like aims_ and deeds! V. 3
3. still di - vide the fold_ of Christ, And_ all the world_ be - side. Ant.
4. live as one, each lov - ing each, As___ Fa - ther, Spir - it, Son.

Text: F.P. Green.
Tune: *Trinitas,* J. Wilson.

Rejoice, the Lord Is King

290

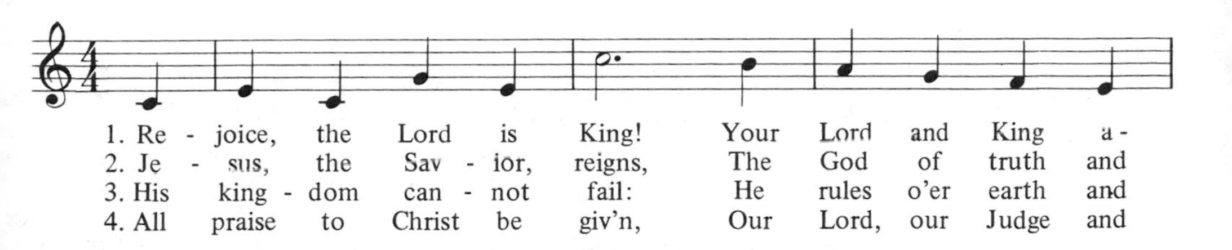
1. Re - joice, the Lord is King! Your Lord and King a -
2. Je - sus, the Sav - ior, reigns, The God of truth and
3. His king - dom can - not fail: He rules o'er earth and
4. All praise to Christ be giv'n, Our Lord, our Judge and

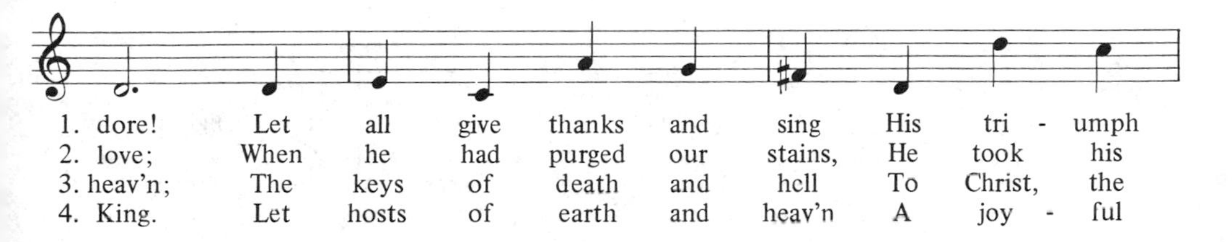
1. dore! Let all give thanks and sing His tri - umph
2. love; When he had purged our stains, He took his
3. heav'n; The keys of death and hell To Christ, the
4. King. Let hosts of earth and heav'n A joy - ful

1. ev - er - more.
2. seat a - bove.
3. Lord, are giv'n.
4. an - them sing.
Lift up your heart! Lift

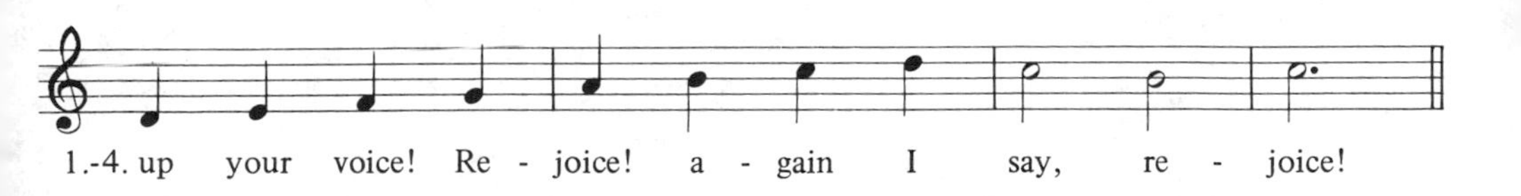
1.-4. up your voice! Re - joice! a - gain I say, re - joice!

Text: Verses 1-3 from "Hymns for Our Lord's Resurrection". C. Wesley, +1788, alt.
Verse 4, T. Marier.
Tune: *Darwall's 148th,* J. Darwall, +1789.

291

Safe in the Hands of God

Ps. 27

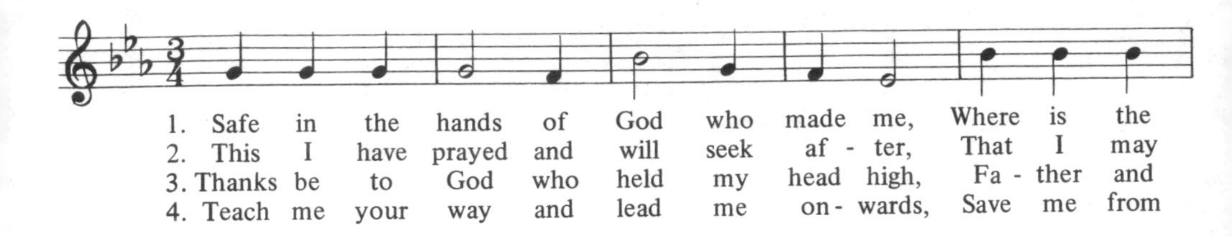
1. Safe in the hands of God who made me, Where is the
2. This I have prayed and will seek af - ter, That I may
3. Thanks be to God who held my head high, Fa - ther and
4. Teach me your way and lead me on- wards, Save me from

1. man ___ whom I should fear? God is my light and
2. walk ___ with God each day: Then will he give me
3. moth - er now to me, Since he has con - quered
4. those ___ who do me wrong, Give me the grace to

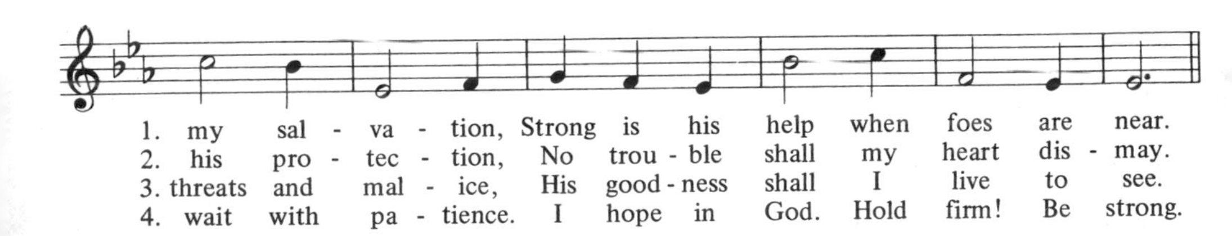
1. my sal - va - tion, Strong is his help when foes are near.
2. his pro - tec - tion, No trou - ble shall my heart dis - may.
3. threats and mal - ice, His good - ness shall I live to see.
4. wait with pa - tience. I hope in God. Hold firm! Be strong.

Text: Psalm 27 paraphrase, M. Perry. © by author in "Psalm Praise".
Used with permission.
Tune: *Safe in the Hands,* N. Warren. © by composer in "Psalm Praise".
Used with permission.

Send Forth From the Heav'ns

Ps. 104

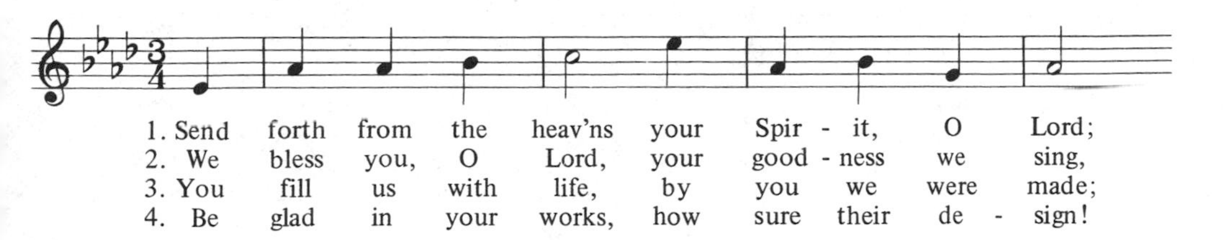
1. Send forth from the heav'ns your Spir - it, O Lord;
2. We bless you, O Lord, your good - ness we sing,
3. You fill us with life, by you we were made;
4. Be glad in your works, how sure their de - sign!

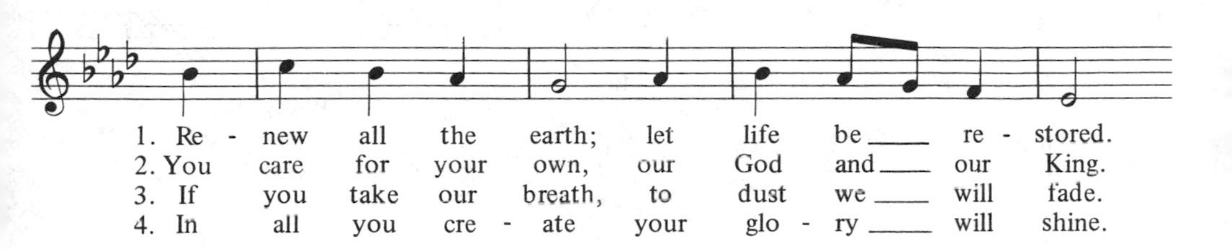
1. Re - new all the earth; let life be ___ re - stored.
2. You care for your own, our God and ___ our King.
3. If you take our breath, to dust we ___ will fade.
4. In all you cre - ate your glo - ry ___ will shine.

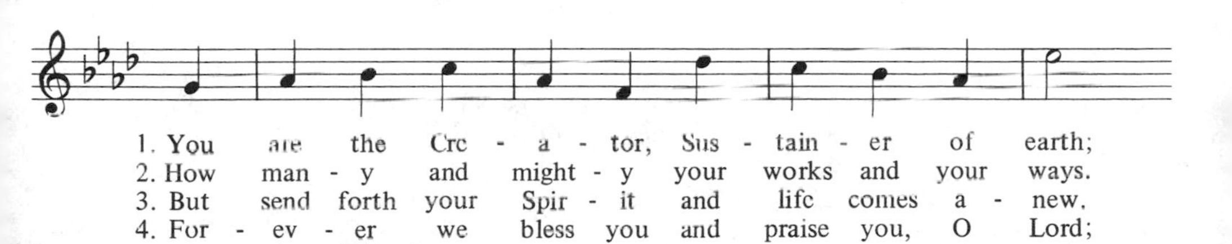
1. You are the Cre - a - tor, Sus - tain - er of earth;
2. How man - y and might - y your works and your ways.
3. But send forth your Spir - it and life comes a - new.
4. For - ev - er we bless you and praise you, O Lord;

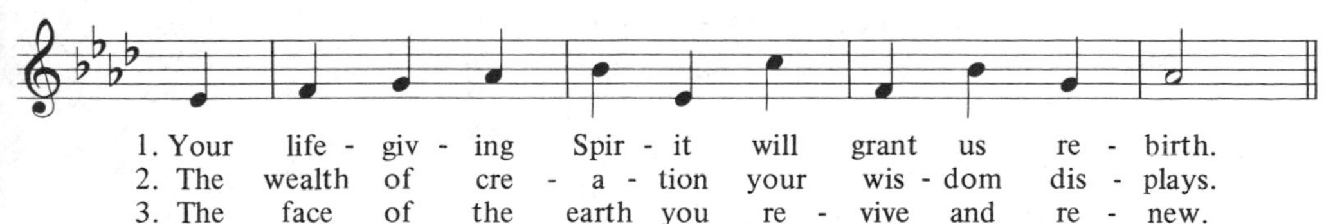
1. Your life - giv - ing Spir - it will grant us re - birth.
2. The wealth of cre - a - tion your wis - dom dis - plays.
3. The face of the earth you re - vive and re - new.
4. By all gen - er - a - tions your name be a - dored.

Text: Psalm 104 paraphrase, J. Dunn.
Tune: *Hanover*, attributed to W. Croft, +1727.

293 Set Her as a Seal upon Your Heart

1. Set her as a seal up - on your heart,
2. May you be a sign of life in Christ,
3. May Je - sus the Lord clothe you in love,
4. Set him as a seal up - on your heart,
1. As a seal of love be - gun.
2. And a wit - ness to his Word;
3. May he bless you with his peace;
4. All the mo - ments of your days.
1. Wear him as a ring up - on your hand
2. A pledge of the Cov - e - nant of Peace,
3. His love make you one through all your days,
4. Wear her as a ring up - on your hand,
1. For as long as time shall run.
2. And of un - ion with the Lord.
3. That your mar - riage nev - er cease.
4. Giv - ing God e - ter - nal praise.

Text: G. Truitt. Used with permission of author.
Tune: *Amor,* T. Marier.

Shepherd of Souls 294

1. Shep - herd of souls, re - fresh and bless
2. We would not live by bread a - lone,
3. Be known to us in break - ing bread,
4. Lord, sup with us in love di - vine;

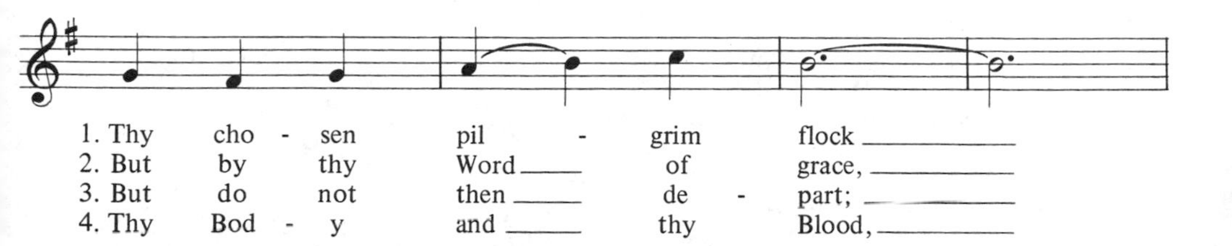
1. Thy cho - sen pil - grim flock
2. But by thy Word of grace,
3. But do not then de - part;
4. Thy Bod - y and thy Blood,

1. With man - na in the wil - der - ness,
2. In strength of which we trav - el on
3. O Lord, a - bide with us and spread
4. That liv - ing bread, that heav'n - ly wine,

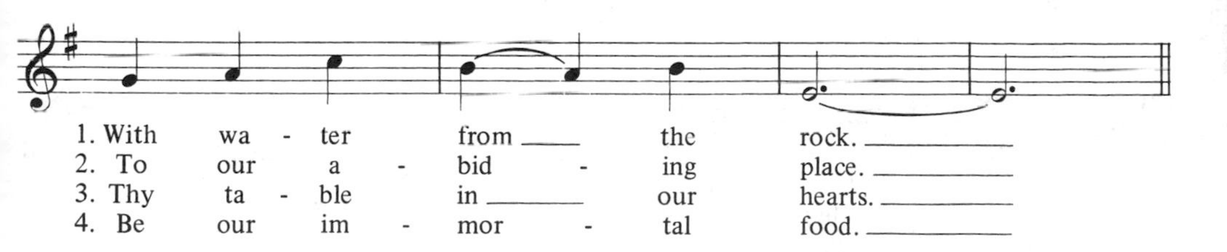
1. With wa - ter from the rock.
2. To our a - bid - ing place.
3. Thy ta - ble in our hearts.
4. Be our im - mor - tal food.

Text: J. Montgomery, +1854, alt.
Tune: *Pastor bonus,* T. Marier.

Silent Night, Holy Night!

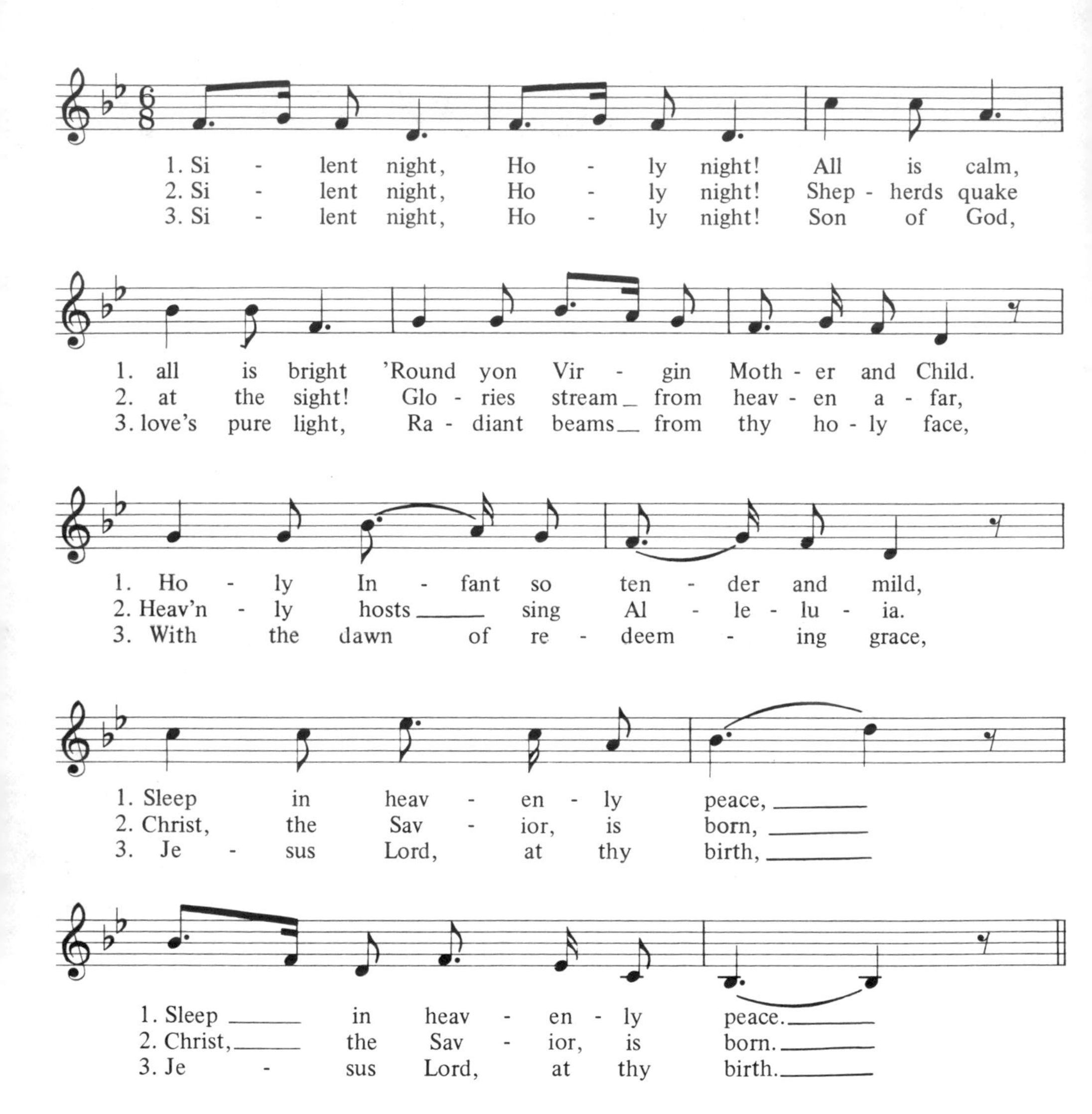
1. Si - lent night, Ho - ly night! All is calm,
2. Si - lent night, Ho - ly night! Shep - herds quake
3. Si - lent night, Ho - ly night! Son of God,
1. all is bright 'Round yon Vir - gin Moth - er and Child.
2. at the sight! Glo - ries stream _ from heav - en a - far,
3. love's pure light, Ra - diant beams _ from thy ho - ly face,
1. Ho - ly In - fant so ten - der and mild,
2. Heav'n - ly hosts _ sing Al - le - lu - ia.
3. With the dawn of re - deem - ing grace,
1. Sleep in heav - en - ly peace, _
2. Christ, the Sav - ior, is born, _
3. Je - sus Lord, at thy birth, _
1. Sleep _ in heav - en - ly peace. _
2. Christ, _ the Sav - ior, is born. _
3. Je - sus Lord, at thy birth. _

Text: J. Mohr, +1848. Trans. J.F. Young, +1885.
Tune: *Stille Nacht*, F. Gruber, +1864.

Sing, All Creation

296

Ps. 100

1. Sing, all cre - a - tion, sing to God in glad - ness!
2. Know that our God is Lord of all the a - ges!
3. En - ter his tem - ple, ring - ing out his prais - es!
4. Great in his good - ness is the Lord we wor - ship;
5. God in Three Per - sons, Fa - ther ev - er - last - ing;
1. Joy - ous - ly serve him, sing - ing hymns of hom - age!
2. He is our Mak - er; we are all his crea - tures,
3. Sing in thanks - giv - ing as you come be - fore him!
4. Stead - fast his kind - ness, love that knows no end - ing!
5. Son, co - e - ter - nal, ev - er bless - ed Spir - it;
1. Chant - ing his prais - es, come be - fore his
2. Peo - ple he fash - ioned, sheep he leads to
3. Bless - ing his boun - ty, glo - ri - fy his
4. Faith - ful his word is, change - less, ev - er -
5. To the Al - might - y, praise and ad - o -
1. pres - ence! Praise the Al - might - y.
2. pas - ture! Praise the Al - might - y.
3. great - ness! Praise the Al - might - y.
4. last - ing! Praise the Al - might - y.
5. ra - tion Now and for - ev - er.

Text: Verses 1-4, Psalm 100 paraphrase, J. Quinn, S.J. © 1969 James Quinn SJ, reprinted by permission of Geoffrey Chapman, a division of Cassell Ltd. vs. 5 J. Dunn, © by author. Used with permission.
Tune: *Coelites plaudant,* Rouen Melody, 17th Century.

297

Sion, at Thy Shining Gates

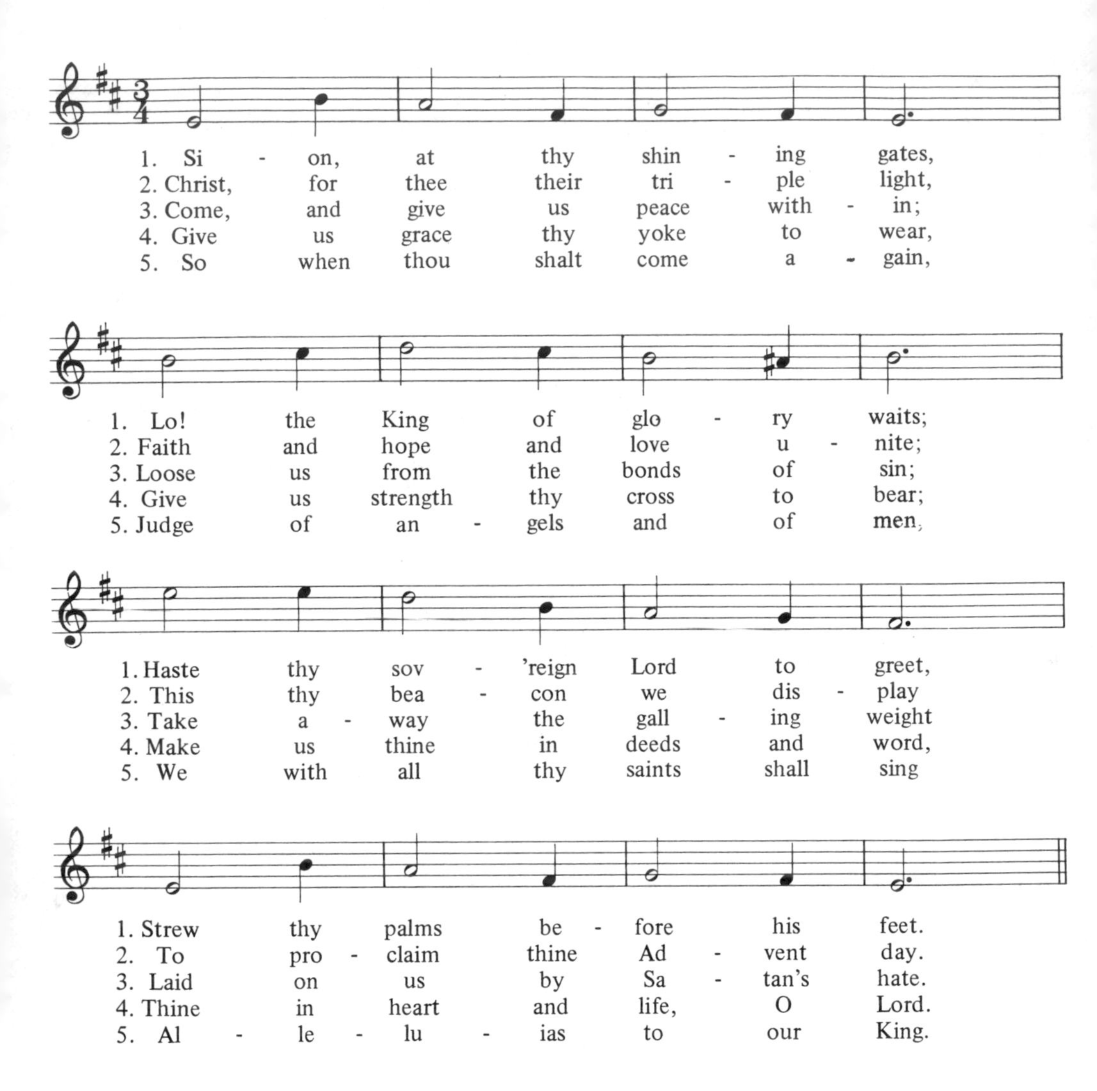

1. Si - on, at thy shin - ing gates,
2. Christ, for thee their tri - ple light,
3. Come, and give us peace with - in;
4. Give us grace thy yoke to wear,
5. So when thou shalt come a - gain,
1. Lo! the King of glo - ry waits;
2. Faith and hope and love u - nite;
3. Loose us from the bonds of sin;
4. Give us strength thy cross to bear;
5. Judge of an - gels and of men,
1. Haste thy sov - 'reign Lord to greet,
2. This thy bea - con we dis - play
3. Take a - way the gall - ing weight
4. Make us thine in deeds and word,
5. We with all thy saints shall sing
1. Strew thy palms be - fore his feet.
2. To pro - claim thine Ad - vent day.
3. Laid on us by Sa - tan's hate.
4. Thine in heart and life, O Lord.
5. Al - le - lu - ias to our King.

Text: B.H. Kennedy, +1889, alt.
Tune: *Nos respectu gratiae,* Böhm Brüder, 1566.

Sing, My Tongue, the Savior's Glory
Therefore, We Before Him Bending

1. Sing, my tongue, the Sav - ior's glo - ry, Of his flesh the
2. Of a pure and spot - less Vir - gin Born for us on
3. On the night of that Last Sup - per, Seat - ed with his
4. Word made flesh, the bread of na - ture By his word to
5. THERE-FORE, WE be - fore him bend - ing, This great sa - cra -
6. Glo - ry let us give and bless - ing To the Fa - ther
1. mys - t'ry sing; Of the blood all price ex - ceed - ing,
2. earth be - low, He as man, with man con - vers - ing,
3. cho - sen band, He, the Pas - chal Vic - tim eat - ing,
4. flesh he turns; Wine in - to his blood he chang - es,
5. ment re - vere; An - cient forms have seen their end - ing,
6. and the Son, Hon - or, might and praise ad - dress - ing,
1. Shed by our im - mor - tal King, Des - tined for the
2. Stayed the seeds of truth to sow; Then he closed in
3. First ful - fills the Law's com - mand; Then as food to
4. Though our sight no change dis - cerns. With our in - most
5. For the new - er rite is here; Faith, our out - ward
6. While e - ter - nal a - ges run; Ev - er too his
1. world's re - demp - tion, From a no - ble womb to spring.
2. sol - emn or - der Won - drous - ly his life of woe.
3. all his breth - ren Gives him - self with his own hand.
4. heart in ear - nest, Faith her les - son quick - ly learns.
5. sense be - friend - ing, Makes our in - ward vi - sion clear.
6. love con - fess - ing, Who from both with both is One.
6. A - men.

For Responses and Oration at Benediction see: "Now, My Tongue, the Mystery Telling".

Text: St. Thomas Aquinas, +1274. Trans. E. Caswall, +1878.
Tune: *Meinen Jesum lass ich nicht,* German, alt.

299 Sing of Mary, Pure and Lowly

1. Sing of __ Mar - y, __ pure and low - ly, Vir - gin _ Moth - er __ un - de - filed,
2. Sing of __ Je - sus, _ son of Mar - y, In the _ home at __ Naz - a - reth.
3. Glo - ry __ be to __ God the Fa - ther; Glo - ry __ be to __ God the Son;

1. Sing of __ God's own _ Son most ho - ly, Who be - came her _ on - ly child.
2. Toil and _ la - bor _ can - not wea - ry Love en - dur - ing _ un - to death.
3. Glo - ry __ be to __ God the Spir - it; Glo - ry __ to the _ Three in One.

1. Fair - est _ child of fair - est _ moth - er, God, the _ Lord, who came to _ earth,
2. Con - stant _ was the love he __ gave her, Though he __ went forth from her _ side,
3. From the _ heart of bless - ed __ Mar - y, From all __ saints the song as - cends,

1. Word made _ flesh, our _ ver - y broth - er, Takes our _ na - ture _ by his birth.
2. Forth to __ preach, and _ heal and suf - fer, Till on __ Cal - va - ry he died.
3. And the _ Church the __ strain re - ech - oes Un - to _ earth's re - mot - est ends.

Text: R.F. Palmer.
Tune: *Pleading Savior,* Plymouth Collection, 1855.

1. Songs of thank - ful - ness and praise, Je - sus, Lord, to thee we raise,
2. Man - i - fest at Jor - dan's stream, Proph-et, Priest, and King su - preme;
3. Man - i - fest in mak - ing whole Pal - sied limbs and wea - ry soul;
4. Grant us grace to see thee, Lord, Mir-rored in thy ho - ly Word;

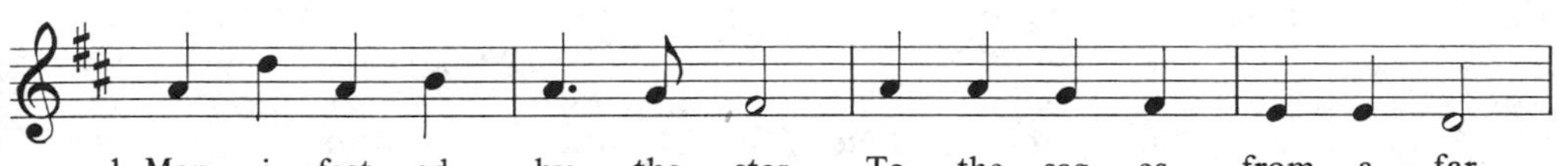

1. Man - i - fest - ed by the star To the sag - es from a - far,
2. And at Ca - na, wed - ding guest, In thy God - head man - i - fest;
3. Man - i - fest in val - iant fight, Quell - ing all the dev - il's might;
4. May we im - i - tate thee now And be pure as pure art thou,

1. Branch of roy - al Da - vid's stem In thy birth at Beth - le - hem;
2. Man - i - fest_ in power di - vine, Chang - ing wa - ter in - to wine;
3. Man - i - fest_ in gra - cious will, Ev - er bring - ing good from ill;
4. That we like_ to thee may be At thy great E - piph - a - ny;

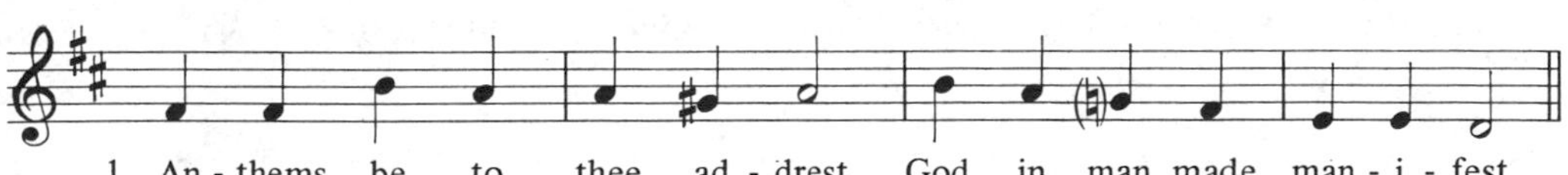

1. An - thems be to thee ad - drest, God in man made man - i - fest.
2. An - thems be to thee ad - drest, God in man made man - i - fest.
3. An - thems be to thee ad - drest, God in man made man - i - fest.
4. And may praise thee, ev - er blest, God in man made man - i - fest.

Text: C. Wordsworth, +1885.
Tune: *Salzburg*, J. Hintze, +1702.

301 Sing Praise to God Who Reigns Above

1. Sing praise to God who reigns a - bove, The
2. What God's al - might - y power hath made, His
3. Then all my glad - some way a - long, I
4. O ye who name Christ's ho - ly name, Give
1. God of all cre - a - tion, The God of power, the
2. gra - cious mer - cy keep - eth; By morn - ing glow or
3. sing a - loud thy prais - es, That all may hear the
4. God all praise and glo - ry; All ye who own his
1. God of love, The God of our sal - va - tion; To
2. eve - ning shade His watch - ful eye ne'er sleep - eth; With -
3. grate - ful song My voice re - joic - ing rais - es; Be
4. power pro-claim A - loud the won - drous sto - ry; Thro'
1. him whose bound - less love has won Sal - va - tion for us
2. in the king - dom of his might, Lo! all is just and
3. joy - ful in the Lord, my heart, Both soul and bod - y
4. earth and heav'n one song shall ring: "The Lord is God and
1. through his Son: To
2. all is right: To
3. take your part: To
4. he is King": To
God all praise and glo - ry.

Text: J.J. Schütz, +1690. Trans. F.E. Cox, +1897, alt.
Tune: *Was Gott tut das ist wohlgetan,* S. Gastorius, +c. 1650.

Sing of Christ, Proclaim His Glory

First Tune
1. Sing of Christ, pro - claim his glo - ry, Sing the res - ur -
2. O what glo - ry, far ex - ceed - ing All that eye has
3. Life e - ter - nal, heav'n re - joic - es! Je - sus lives who
4. Life e - ter - nal! O what won - ders Crowd on faith; what
1. rec - tion song! Death and sor - row, earth's dark sto - ry,
2. yet per - ceived! Ho - liest hearts for a - ges plead - ing,
3. once was dead; Join with all the heav'n - ly voic - es,
4. joy un - known, When a - midst earth's clos - ing thun - ders,
1. To the for - mer days be - long. All a - round the clouds are
2. Nev - er that full joy con - ceived. God has prom - ised, Christ pre -
3. Child of God, lift up your head! Pa - tri - archs from dis - tant
4. Saints shall stand be - fore the throne! O to en - ter that bright
1. break - ing, Soon the storms of time shall cease; In God's like - ness,
2. pares it, There on high our wel - come waits; Ev - 'ry hum - ble
3. a - ges, Saints all long - ing for their heav'n, Proph - ets, psalm - ists,
4. por - tal, See the glow - ing fir - ma - ment, O to know our
1. peo - ple wak - ing, Know the ev - er - last - ing peace.
2. spir - it shares it, Christ has passed th'e - ter - nal gates.
3. seers and sag - es, All a - wait the glo - ry giv'n.
4. God im - mor - tal, With the Christ whom he has sent"!

Text: W.J. Irons, +1883. Based on I Corinthians 15:20, alt.
Tune: *Austria*, F.J. Haydn, +1809.

303 Sing of Christ, Proclaim His Glory

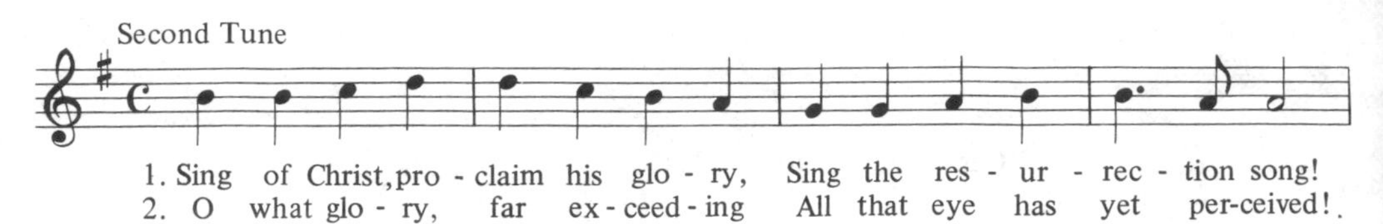
Second Tune

1. Sing of Christ, pro - claim his glo - ry, Sing the res - ur - rec - tion song!
2. O what glo - ry, far ex - ceed - ing All that eye has yet per-ceived!
3. Life e - ter - nal, heav'n re - joic - es! Je - sus lives who once was dead;
4. Life e - ter - nal! O what won-ders Crowd on faith; what joy un-known,

1. Death and sor - row, earth's dark sto - ry, To the for-mer days be - long.
2. Ho - liest hearts for a - ges plead - ing, Nev - er that full joy con-ceived.
3. Join with all the heav'n - ly voic - es, Child of God, lift up your head.
4. When a - midst earth's clos - ing thun - ders, Saints shall stand be - fore the throne!

1. All a - round the clouds are_ break-ing, Soon the_ storms of time shall cease;
2. God has prom - ised, Christ pre - pares it, There on_ high our wel-come waits;
3. Pa - tri - archs from dis - tant_ a - ges, Saints all_ long - ing for their heav'n,
4. O to en - ter that bright_por - tal, See the_ glow - ing fir - ma - ment,

1. In ___ God's like-ness, man a - wak - ing, Know the ev - er - last - ing peace.
2. Ev - 'ry hum-ble spir - it shares it, Christ has passed th'e - ter - nal gates.
3. Proph - ets, psalm-ists, seers and sag - es, All a - wait the glo - ry giv'n.
4. O _ to know our God im - mor - tal, With the Christ whom he has sent"!

Text: W.J. Irons, +1883. Based on I Corinthians 15:20, alt.
Tune: *Hymn to Joy,* L. van Beethoven, +1827.

Soul of Christ

304

1.-5.
6.
1. Soul of Christ, be my sanctifi - ca - tion;
2. Blood of Christ, fill all my veins;
3. Passion of Christ, my com - fort be,
4. In thy wounds I fain would hide,
5. Guard me when the foe as - sails me,
6. Bid me come to thee a - bove,
1. Body of Christ, be my sal - va - tion.
2. Water from Christ's side, wash out my stains.
3. O good Jesus, lis - ten to me.
4. Never to be part - ed from thy side.
5. Guide me when my feet shall fail me.
6. With thy saints to sing thy love forev- er. A - men.

Text: Attributed to St. Ignatius, †1556. Trans. anon.
Tune: Plainchant, Mode 2.

305

Soul of My Savior

1. Soul of my Sav - ior, sanc - ti - fy my breast!
2. Strength and pro - tec - tion may his Pas - sion be;
3. Guard and de - fend me from the foe ma - lign;

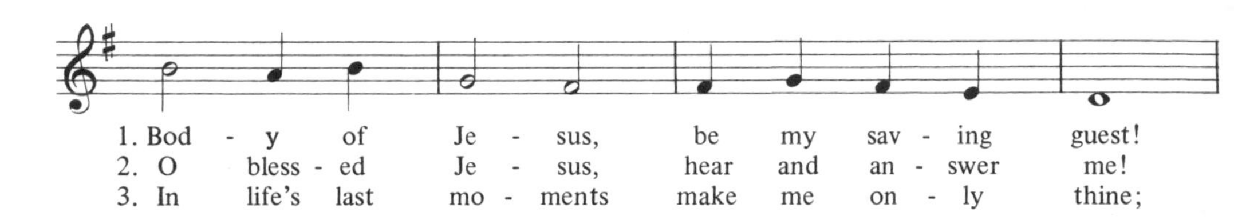
1. Bod - y of Je - sus, be my sav - ing guest!
2. O bless - ed Je - sus, hear and an - swer me!
3. In life's last mo - ments make me on - ly thine;

1. Blood of my Sav - ior, bathe me in thy tide!
2. Deep in thy wounds, Lord, hide and shel - ter me;
3. Call me and bid me come to thee on high,

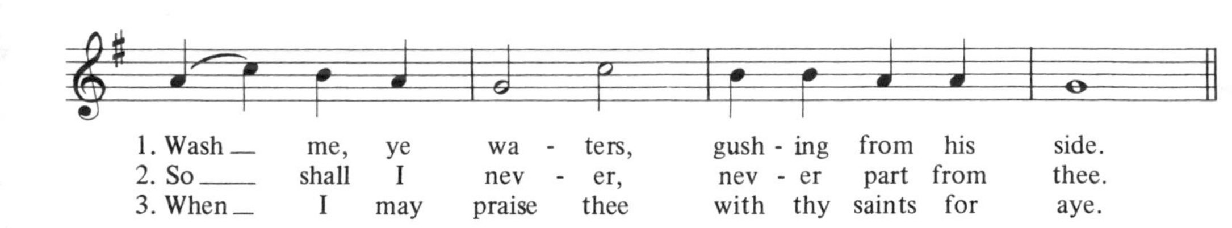
1. Wash _ me, ye wa - ters, gush - ing from his side.
2. So _ shall I nev - er, nev - er part from thee.
3. When _ I may praise thee with thy saints for aye.

Text: Latin, 14th Century, anon. Trans. anon.
Tune: *Anima Christi,* W.J. Maher, +1877.

Spirit Seeking Light and Beauty

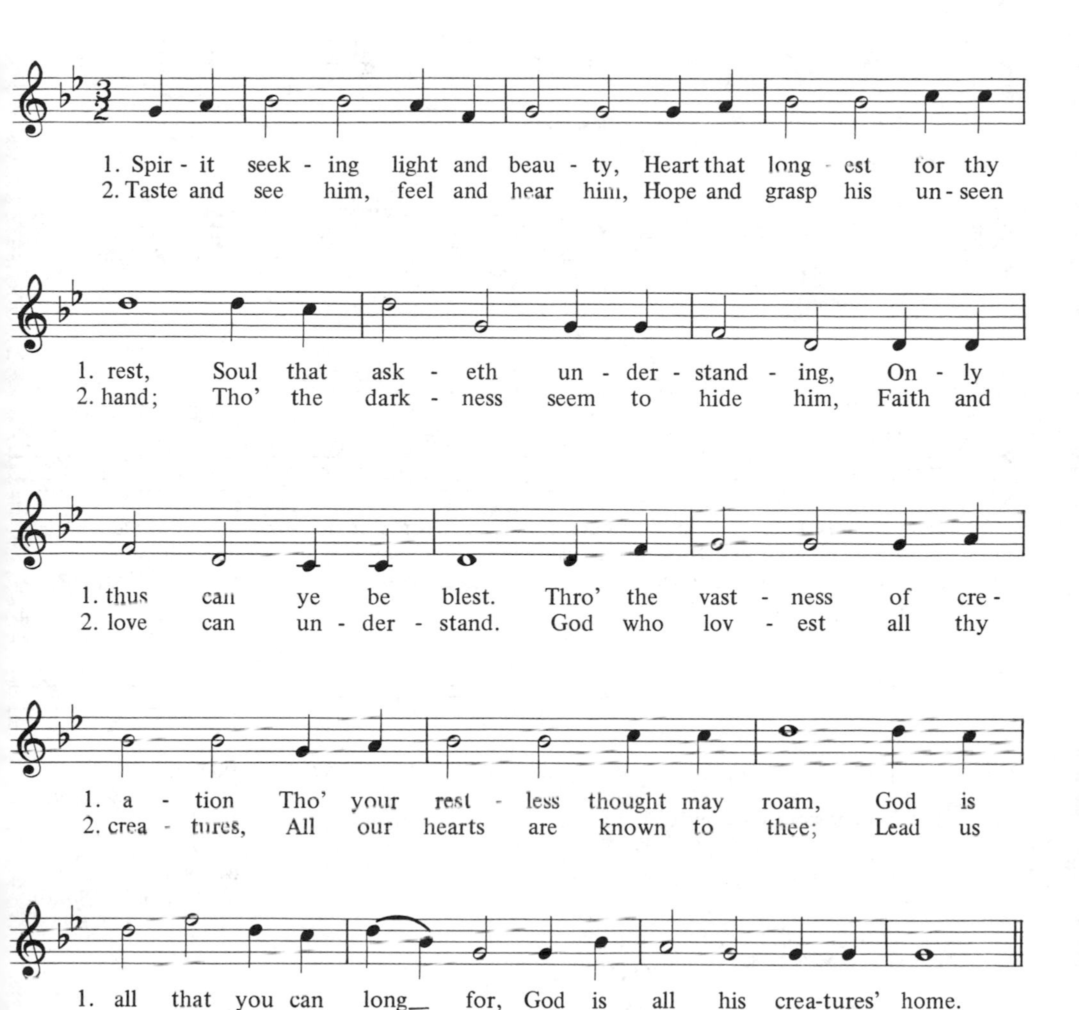
1. Spir - it seek - ing light and beau - ty, Heart that long - est for thy
2. Taste and see him, feel and hear him, Hope and grasp his un - seen
1. rest, Soul that ask - eth un - der - stand - ing, On - ly
2. hand; Tho' the dark - ness seem to hide him, Faith and
1. thus can ye be blest. Thro' the vast - ness of cre -
2. love can un - der - stand. God who lov - est all thy
1. a - tion Tho' your rest - less thought may roam, God is
2. crea - tures, All our hearts are known to thee; Lead us
1. all that you can long_ for, God is all his crea-tures' home.
2. thro' the land of shad - ows To thy blest e - ter - ni - ty.

Text: J. Stuart, +1914.
Tune: *Domnach Trionide*, Gaelic, from "Pius X Hymnal"

307 Springs of Water, Bless the Lord

ANTIPHON

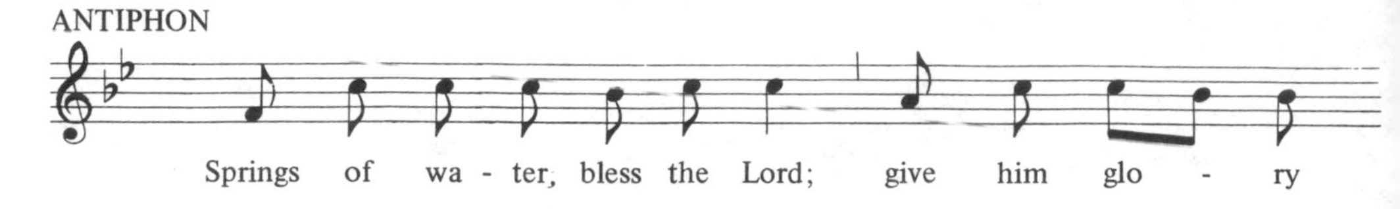

Springs of wa - ter, bless the Lord; give him glo - ry

and praise for - ev - er and ev - er.

I Saw Water - Psalm 118:1

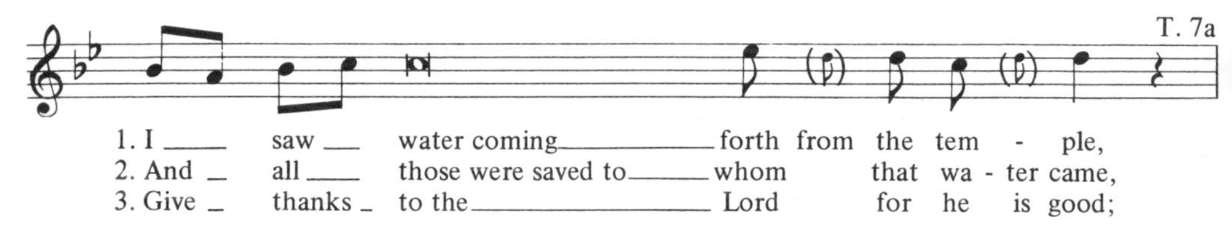

T. 7a
1. I saw water coming forth from the tem - ple,
2. And all those were saved to whom that wa - ter came,
3. Give thanks to the Lord for he is good;

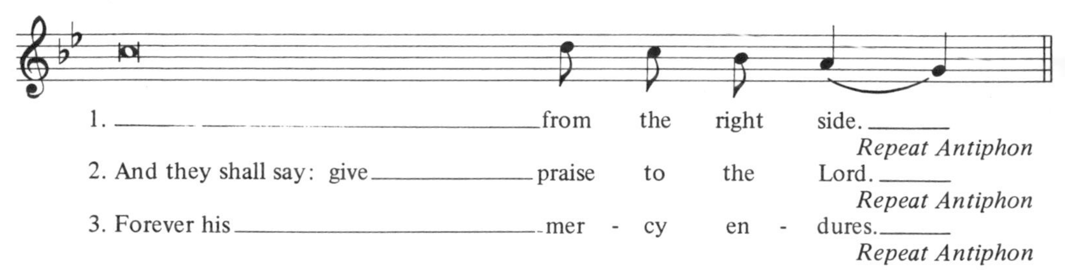

1. from the right side.
Repeat Antiphon
2. And they shall say: give praise to the Lord.
Repeat Antiphon
3. Forever his mer - cy en - dures.
Repeat Antiphon

Text: *Vidi aquam,* and Psalm 118:1. Trans. anon.
Tune: *Fontes aquarum,* T. Marier.

308 Alleluia

During Easter Season

ANTIPHON

Al - le - lu - ia, al - le - lu - ia, al - le - lu - ia.

"I saw water" – *as above*

Take Up Your Cross

1. Take up your cross, the Sav - ior said, If you would
2. Take up your cross, let not its weight Fill your weak
3. Take up your cross, then, in his strength, And ev - 'ry
4. Take up your cross, and fol - low Christ, Nor think till
5. To you, great Lord, the One in Three, All praise for -
1. my dis - ci - ple be; De - ny your - self, the
2. spir - it with a - larm; His strength shall bear your
3. dan - ger calm - ly brave, To guide you to a
4. death to lay it down; For on - ly he who
5. ev - er - more as - cend; O grant us here be -
1. world for - sake, And hum - bly fol - low af - ter me.
2. spir - it up, Shall brace your heart and nerve your arm.
3. bet - ter home, And vic - t'ry o - ver death and grave.
4. bears the cross May hope to wear the glo - rious crown.
5. low to see The heav'n ly life that knows no end.

Text: C. Everest, +1877. Adapted by A.G. Petti in "New Catholic Hymnal", © 1971 by Faber Music Limited.
Tune: *Angel's Song*, O. Gibbons, +1625.

310 Tell His Praise in Song and Story

Ps. 34

1. Tell his praise in song and sto - ry, Bless the Lord with
2. To the Lord whose love has found them Poor men cry in
3. Taste and see! in faith draw near him, Trust the Lord with
4. In our need he walks be - side us, Ears a - lert to

1. heart and voice; In my God is all my glo - ry, Come be -
2. their dis - tress; Swift his an - gels camped a - round them Prove him
3. all your powers; Seek and serve him, love and fear him, Life and
4. ev - 'ry cry; Watch - ful eye to love and guide us, Love that

1. fore him and re - joice. Join to praise his Name to - geth - er,
2. sure to save and bless. God it is who hears our cry - ing
3. all its joys are ours; True de - light in ho - ly liv - ing,
4. whis - pers "It is I." Good shall tri - umph, wrong be right - ed.

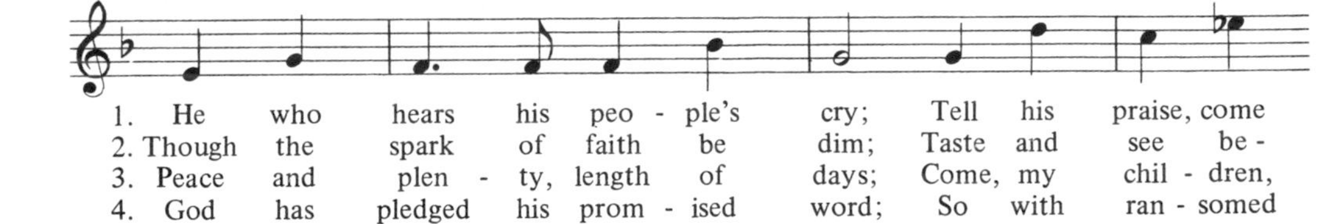

1. He who hears his peo - ple's cry; Tell his praise, come
2. Though the spark of faith be dim; Taste and see be -
3. Peace and plen - ty, length of days; Come, my chil - dren,
4. God has pledged his prom - ised word; So with ran - somed

1. wind or weath - er, Shin - ing fac - es lift - ed high.
2. yond de - ny - ing, Blest are those who trust in him.
3. with thanks - giv - ing Bless the Lord in songs of praise.
4. saints u - nit - ed Join to praise our liv - ing Lord.

Text: Psalm 34 paraphrase, T. Dudley-Smith.
Tune: *Rustington*, Sir C.H.H. Parry, +1918.

Tell Out, My Soul, the Greatness of the Lord

Magnificat

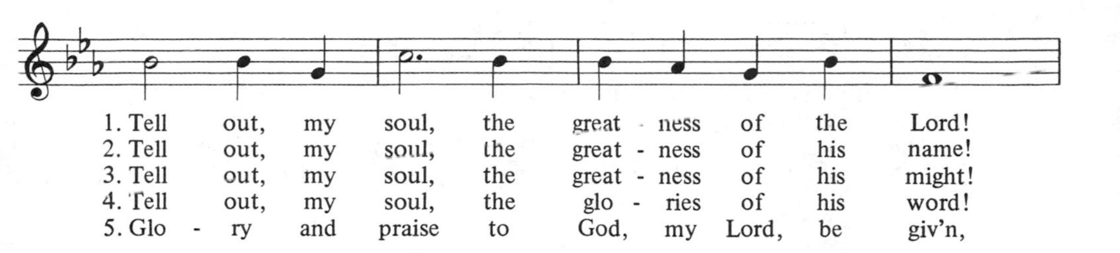
1. Tell out, my soul, the great - ness of the Lord!
2. Tell out, my soul, the great - ness of his name!
3. Tell out, my soul, the great - ness of his might!
4. Tell out, my soul, the glo - ries of his word!
5. Glo - ry and praise to God, my Lord, be giv'n,

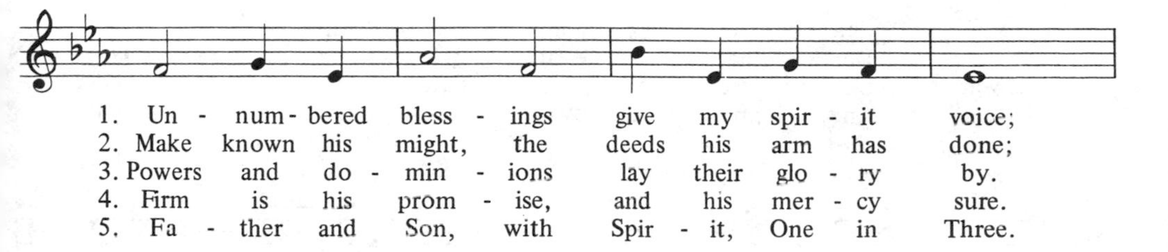
1. Un - num - bered bless - ings give my spir - it voice;
2. Make known his might, the deeds his arm has done;
3. Powers and do - min - ions lay their glo - ry by.
4. Firm is his prom - ise, and his mer - cy sure.
5. Fa - ther and Son, with Spir - it, One in Three.

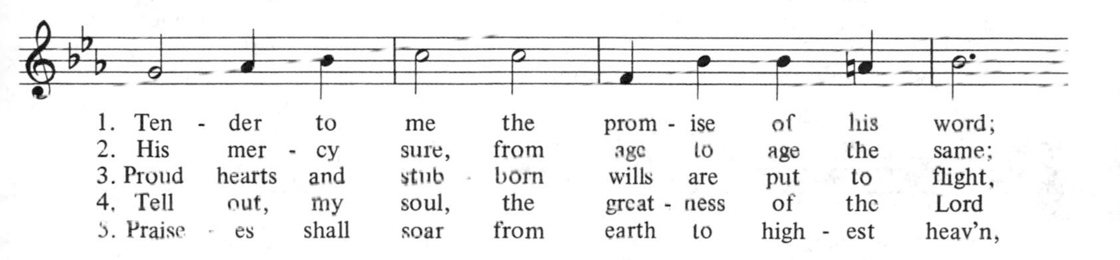
1. Ten - der to me the prom - ise of his word;
2. His mer - cy sure, from age to age the same;
3. Proud hearts and stub - born wills are put to flight,
4. Tell out, my soul, the great - ness of the Lord
5. Praise - es shall soar from earth to high - est heav'n,

1. In God my Sav - ior shall my heart re - joice.
2. His ho - ly name the Lord, the Might - y One.
3. The hun - gry fed, the hum - ble lift - ed high.
4. To chil - dren's chil - dren and for - ev - er - more.
5. From a - ges past and a - ges yet to be.

Text: *Magnificat,* Luke 1: 46-55 paraphrase, T. Dudley-Smith.

Tune: *Song 22,* O. Gibbons, 1625, var.

312 The Church's One Foundation

1. The Church's one foun - da - tion Is Je - sus Christ her
2. E - lect from ev - 'ry na - tion, Yet one o'er all the
3. 'Mid toil and trib - u - la - tion, And tu - mult of her
4. Yet she on earth hath un - ion With God, the Three in
1. Lord; She is his new cre - a - tion By
2. earth; Her char - ter of sal - va - tion, One
3. war, She waits the con - sum - ma - tion Of
4. One, And mys - tic sweet com - mun - ion With
1. wa - ter and the word; From heav'n he came and
2. Lord, one faith, one birth; One ho - ly name she
3. peace for - ev - er - more; Till with the vi - sion
4. those whose rest is won. O hap - py ones and
1. sought her To be his ho - ly bride; With
2. bless - es, Par - takes one ho - ly food, And
3. glo - rious, Her long - ing eyes are blest, And
4. ho - ly! Lord, give us grace that we Like
1. his own blood he bought her, And for her life he died.
2. to one hope she press - es, With ev - 'ry grace en - dued.
3. the great Church vic - to - rious Shall be the Church at rest.
4. them, the meek and low - ly, On high may dwell with thee.

Text: S.J. Stone, +1900, alt.
Tune: *Aurelia*, S.S. Wesley, +1876.

The Clouds of Night Are Passed Away

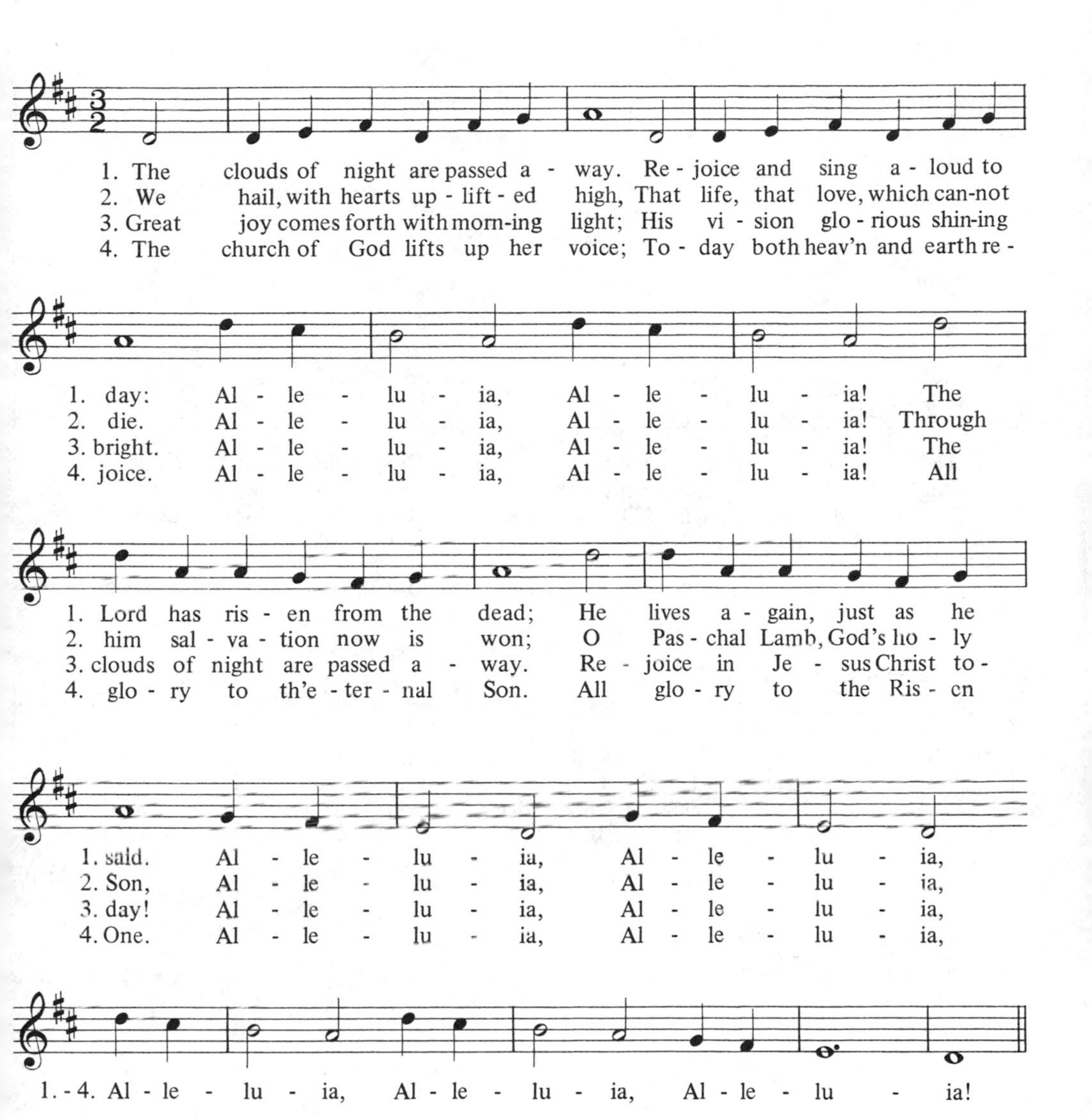
1. The clouds of night are passed a - way. Re - joice and sing a - loud to
2. We hail, with hearts up - lift - ed high, That life, that love, which can-not
3. Great joy comes forth with morn-ing light; His vi - sion glo - rious shin-ing
4. The church of God lifts up her voice; To - day both heav'n and earth re -
1. day: Al - le - lu - ia, Al - le - lu - ia! The
2. die. Al - le - lu - ia, Al - le - lu - ia! Through
3. bright. Al - le - lu - ia, Al - le - lu - ia! The
4. joice. Al - le - lu - ia, Al - le - lu - ia! All
1. Lord has ris - en from the dead; He lives a - gain, just as he
2. him sal - va - tion now is won; O Pas - chal Lamb, God's ho - ly
3. clouds of night are passed a - way. Re - joice in Je - sus Christ to -
4. glo - ry to th'e - ter - nal Son. All glo - ry to the Ris - en
1. said. Al - le - lu - ia, Al - le - lu - ia,
2. Son, Al - le - lu - ia, Al - le - lu - ia,
3. day! Al - le - lu - ia, Al - le - lu - ia,
4. One. Al - le - lu - ia, Al - le - lu - ia,
1.-4. Al - le - lu - ia, Al - le - lu - ia, Al - le - lu - ia!

Text: J. Dunn. © by author. Used with permission.
Tune: *Vigiles et sancti*, "Cologne Gesangbuch", 1623.

The Church Triumphant in Thy Love

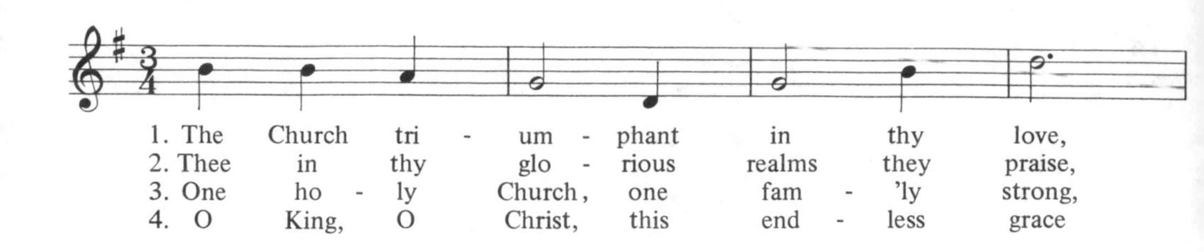
1. The Church tri - um - phant in thy love,
2. Thee in thy glo - rious realms they praise,
3. One ho - ly Church, one fam - 'ly strong,
4. O King, O Christ, this end - less grace

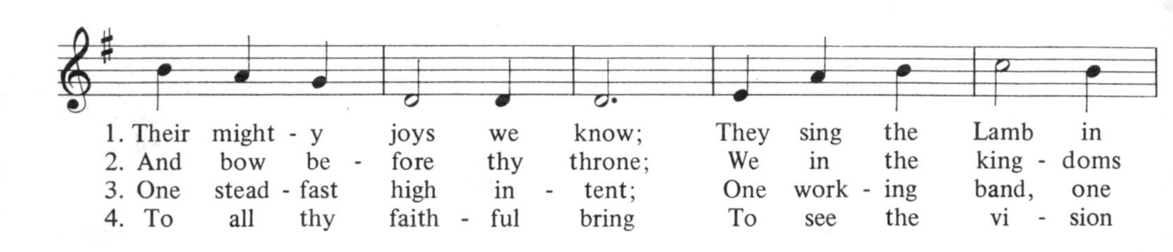
1. Their might - y joys we know; They sing the Lamb in
2. And bow be - fore thy throne; We in the king - doms
3. One stead - fast high in - tent; One work - ing band, one
4. To all thy faith - ful bring To see the vi - sion

1. hymns a - bove, And we in hymns be - low.
2. of thy grace: The king - doms are but one.
3. har - vest song, One King om - nip - o - tent.
4. of thy face In joy, O Christ, our King.

Text: Verses 1, 2, C. Wesley, +1788.
Verse 3, S. Johnson, +1882.
Verse 4, L. Muirhead, +1925.
Tune: *Gerontius,* J.B. Dykes, +1876.

The Day Is Surely Drawing Near

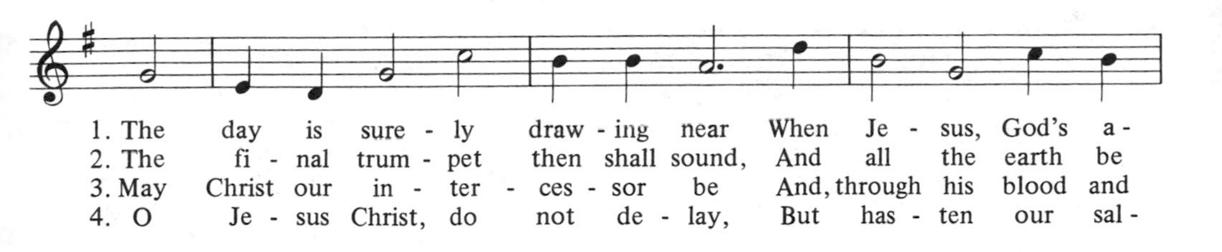
1. The day is sure - ly draw - ing near When Je - sus, God's a -
2. The fi - nal trum - pet then shall sound, And all the earth be
3. May Christ our in - ter - ces - sor be And, through his blood and
4. O Je - sus Christ, do not de - lay, But has - ten our sal -

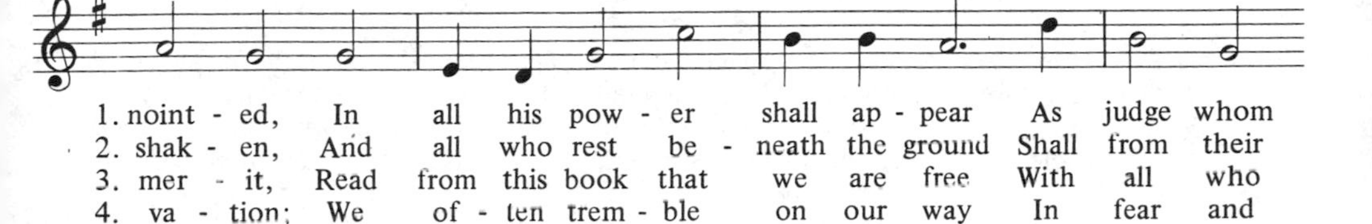
1. noint - ed, In all his pow - er shall ap - pear As judge whom
2. shak - en, And all who rest be - neath the ground Shall from their
3. mer - it, Read from this book that we are free With all who
4. va - tion; We of - ten trem - ble on our way In fear and

1. God ap - point - ed. Then fright shall ban - ish i - dle mirth, And hun - gry
2. sleep a - wak - en, But all who live will in that hour, By God's al -
3. life in - her - it. Then we shall see him face to face, With all his
4. trib - u - la - tion. Oh, hear and grant our fer - vent plea; Come, might - y

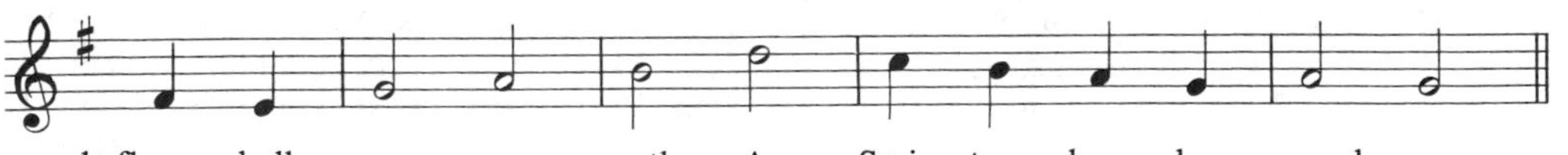

1. flames shall rav - age earth, As Scrip - ture long has warned us.
2. might - y, bound - less pow'r, Be changed at his com - mand - ing.
3. saints in that blest place Which he has pur - chased for us.
4. judge, and set us free From death and ev - 'ry e - vil.

Text: B. Ringwaldt, +c. 1600. Trans. P.A. Peter, +1917, adapt.
Tune: *Sei Lob und Ehr',* adapted from "Genevan Psalter" by J. Crüger, +1662.

The Day of Resurrection

1. The day of__ res - ur - rec - tion! Earth, spread_ the news a - broad;
2. Our hearts be__ free from e - vil That we__ may see a - right
3. His love is__ ev - er - last - ing; His mer - cies nev - er cease;
4. Now let the_ heav'ns be joy - ful, And earth_ her song be - gin;

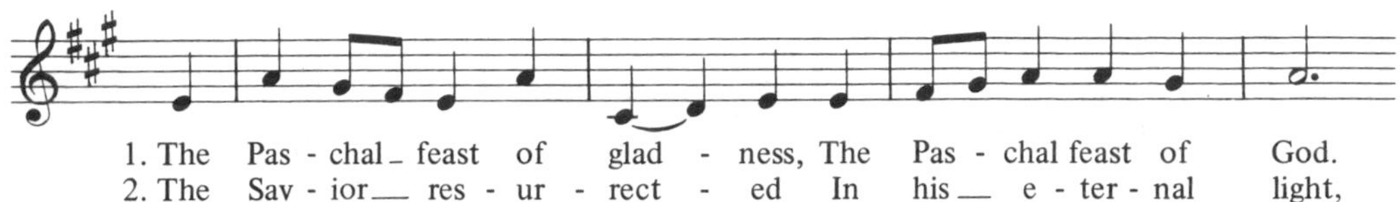

1. The Pas - chal_ feast of glad - ness, The Pas - chal feast of God.
2. The Sav - ior__ res - ur - rect - ed In his__ e - ter - nal light,
3. The res - ur - rect - ed Sav - ior, Will all__ our joys in - crease.
4. The whole world keep high tri - umph And all__ that is there - in;

1. From_ death to life e - ter - nal, From_ earth to heav-en's height
2. And__ hear his mes-sage plain - ly, De - liv-ered calm and clear:
3. He'll_ keep us in his fa - vor, Sup - ply - ing ho - ly grace,
4. Let__ all things in cre - a - tion Their_ notes of glad-ness blend,

1. Our Sav - ior__ Christ has brought_ us, The glo - rious Lord of Light.
2. "Re - joice with_ me in tri - umph, Be glad_ and do not fear."
3. To all his__ pil - grim peo - ple Who seek_ his heav'n-ly place.
4. For Christ the_ Lord has ris - en, Our joy__ that has no end.

Text: Verses 1, 2 and 4, St. John Damascene, +749. Trans. J.M. Neale, +1866, alt.
Verse 3, J. Dunn. © by author. Used with permission.
Tune: *Ellacombe,* "Würtemburg Gesangbuch", 1784.

Th' Eternal Gifts of Christ the King 317

1. Th'e - ter - nal gifts of Christ the King,
2. Their faith in Christ, the Lord, pre - vailed;
3. In them the Fa - ther's glo ry shone,
4. To thee, Re - deem - er, now we cry,
1. Th'a - pos - tles' glo - ry, let us sing,
2. Their hope, a light that nev - er failed;
3. In them the will of God the Son,
4. That thou wouldst join to them on high
1. And all, with hearts of glad - ness, raise
2. Their love a - blaze o'er path - ways trod
3. In them ex - ults the Ho - ly Ghost,
4. Thy ser - vants, who this grace im - plore,
1. Due hymns of thank - ful love and praise.
2. To lead them to th'e - ter - nal God.
3. Through them re - joice the heav'n - ly host.
4. For - ev - er and for - ev - er - more.

Text: St. Ambrose, +c. 397. Trans. J.M. Neale, +1866.
Tune: *The King's Majesty*, G. George,

318 The First Nowell

1. The first Now - ell the angel did say Was to
2. They look - èd up and saw a star Shin - ing
3. And by the light of that same star Three
4. This star drew nigh to the north - west; O'er
5. Then en - tered in those wise men three, Fell
6. Then let us all with one ac - cord Sing
1. cer - tain poor shep - herds in fields as they lay; In
2. in the East, be - yond them far; And
3. wise men came from coun - try far; To
4. Beth - le - hem it took its rest, And
5. rev - 'rent - ly up - on their knee, And
6. prais - es to our heav'n - ly Lord, That
1. fields where they lay keep - ing their sheep, On a
2. to the earth it gave great light, And
3. seek a king was their in - tent, And to
4. there it did both stop and stay Right
5. of - fered there in his pres - ence Their
6. hath made heav'n and earth of naught, And
1. cold win - ter's night that was so deep:
2. so it con - tin - ued both day and night:
3. fol - low the star where - ev - er it went.
4. o - ver the place where Je - sus lay.
5. gold and myrrh and frank - in - cense.
6. with his blood man - kind hath bought.
Now - ell, Now-ell, Now-ell, Now - ell, Born is the King of Is - ra - el.

Text: Old English Carol.
Tune: *The First Nowell,* traditional melody first published in 1833.

The Glory of These Forty Days

1. The glo - ry of these for - ty days
2. A - lone and fast ing Mo - ses saw
3. So Dan - iel trained his mys - tic sight,
4. Then grant us, Lord, like them to be
5. O Fa - ther, Son and Spir - it blest,
1. We cel - e - brate with songs of praise;
2. The lov - ing God who gave the law;
3. De - liv - ered from the li - on's might;
4. Full oft in fast and prayer with thee;
5. To thee be ev - 'ry prayer ad - drest,
1. For Christ, by whom all things were made,
2. And to E - li - jah fast - ing came
3. And John, the Bride - groom's friend, be - came
4. Our spir - its strength - ened with thy grace,
5. Who art in three - fold name a - dored,
1. Him - self has fast - ed and has prayed.
2. The steeds and char - i - ots of flame.
3. The her - ald of Mes - si - ah's name.
4. And give us joy to see thy face.
5. From age to age the on - ly Lord.

Text: 6th Century Office Hymn. Trans. M.F. Bell in "The English Hymnal".

Tune: *Agincourt*, 15th Century English melody, var.

320 The God of Abraham Praise

1. The God of A - braham praise, Who
2. There dwells the Lord, our King, The
3. The God who reigns on high The
4. The whole tri - um - phant host Give
1. reigns en - throned a - bove; An - cient of ev - er -
2. Lord, our Right - eous - ness, Tri - um - phant o'er the
3. great arch - an - gels sing, And "Ho - ly, Ho - ly,
4. thanks to God on high; "Hail, Fa - ther, Son and
1. last - ing days, And God of love; To
2. world and sin, The Prince of Peace; On
3. Ho - ly," cry, "Al - might - y King! Who
4. Ho - ly Ghost!" They ev - er cry. Hail
1. him up - lift your voice, At whose su - preme com -
2. Si - on's sa - cred height His king - dom he main -
3. was and is the same, And ev - er - more shall
4. A - braham's God and mine! I join the choir a -
1. mand From earth we rise and
2. tains, And glo - rious with his
3. be: E - ter - nal Fa - ther,
4. bove; All might and maj - es -
1. seek the joys At his right hand.
2. saints in light, For - ev - er reigns.
3. great Yah - weh, We wor - ship thee."
4. ty are thine, O fount of love.

Text: Jewish Doxology paraphrase, T. Olivers, +1799.
Verse 4, alt.
Tune: *Leoni,* traditional Hebrew melody, var.

The God Whom Earth and Sea and Sky 321

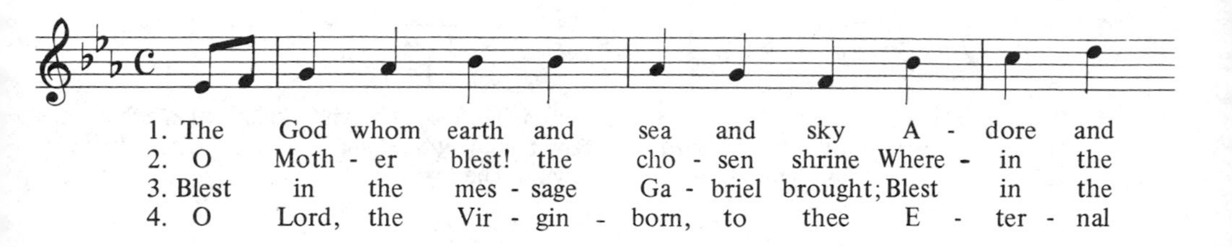
1. The God whom earth and sea and sky A - dore and
2. O Moth - er blest! the cho - sen shrine Where - in the
3. Blest in the mes - sage Ga - briel brought; Blest in the
4. O Lord, the Vir - gin - born, to thee E - ter - nal

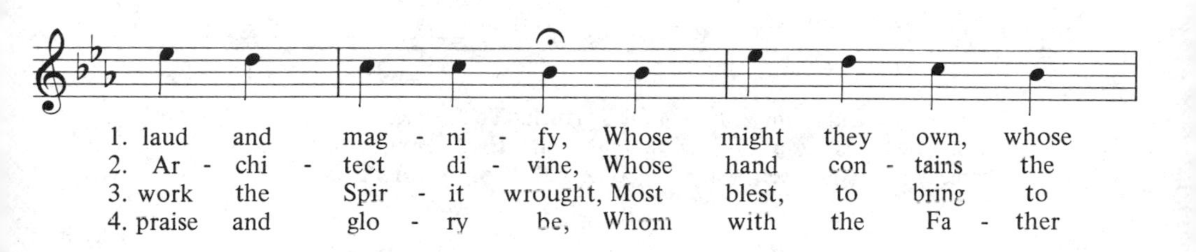
1. laud and mag - ni - fy, Whose might they own, whose
2. Ar - chi - tect di - vine, Whose hand con - tains the
3. work the Spir - it wrought, Most blest, to bring to
4. praise and glo - ry be, Whom with the Fa - ther

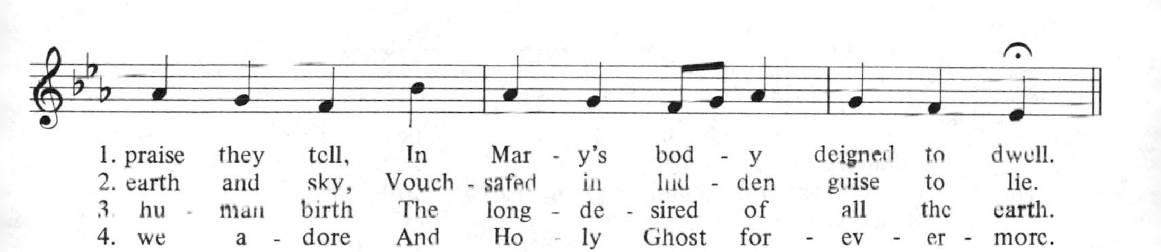
1. praise they tell, In Mar - y's bod - y deigned to dwell.
2. earth and sky, Vouch - safed in hid - den guise to lie.
3. hu - man birth The long - de - sired of all the earth.
4. we a - dore And Ho - ly Ghost for - ev - er - more.

Text: Venantius Fortunatus, +609. Trans. J.M. Neale, +1866, alt.

Tune: *Eisenach*, B. Gesius, +1613.

The Great Creator of the Worlds

1. The great Cre - a - tor of the worlds, The sov - 'reign God_ of_ heav'n,
2. He sent him not in wrath and pow'r, But grace and peace_ to_ bring;
3. He came as Sav - ior to his own, The way of love_ he_ trod;

1. His ho - ly and im - mor - tal_ truth To men_ on_ earth has giv'n.
2. In kind - ness, as a king might_send His son,_ him - self a king.
3. He came to win men by good_will, For force_ is_ not of God.

1. He sent no an - gel of his host To bear his might - y word,
2. He sent him down as send - ing God; As man he came to men;
3. Not to op - press, but sum - mon men Their tru - est life to find,

1. But him thro' whom the worlds were made, The ev - er - last - ing_ Lord.
2. As one with us he dwelt with us, And died and lives_ a - gain.
3. In love God sent his Son to save, Not to con - demn_ man - kind.

Text: F. Bland Tucker. Based on the Epistle to Diognetus, c. 150.

Tune: *Tregaron,* P. James.

The Great Forerunner of the Morn

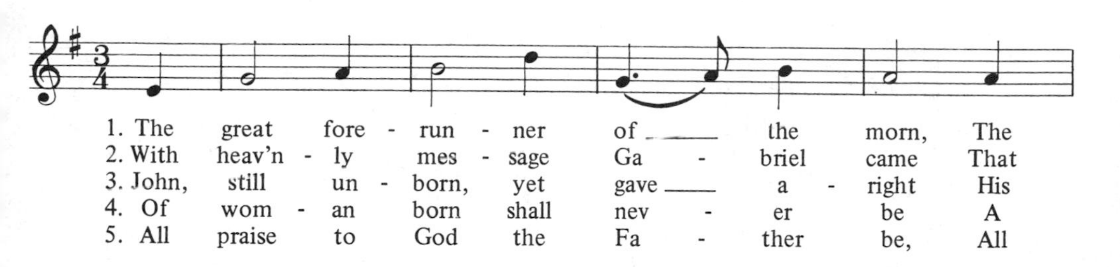
1. The great fore - run - ner of the morn, The
2. With heav'n - ly mes - sage Ga - briel came That
3. John, still un - born, yet gave a - right His
4. Of wom - an born shall nev - er be A
5. All praise to God the Fa - ther be, All

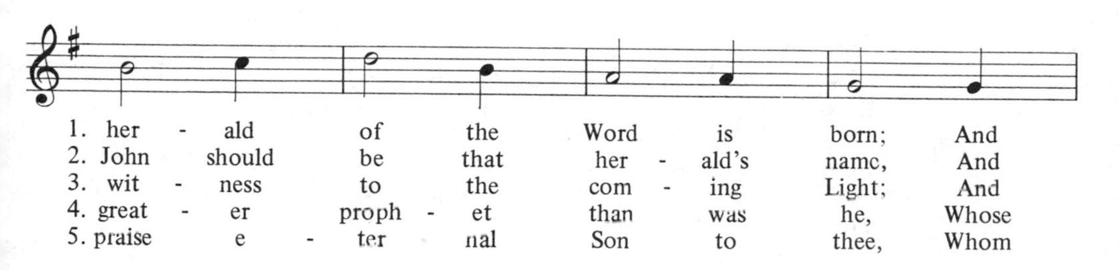
1. her - ald of the Word is born; And
2. John should be that her - ald's name, And
3. wit - ness to the com - ing Light; And
4. great - er proph - et than was he, Whose
5. praise e - ter nal Son to thee, Whom

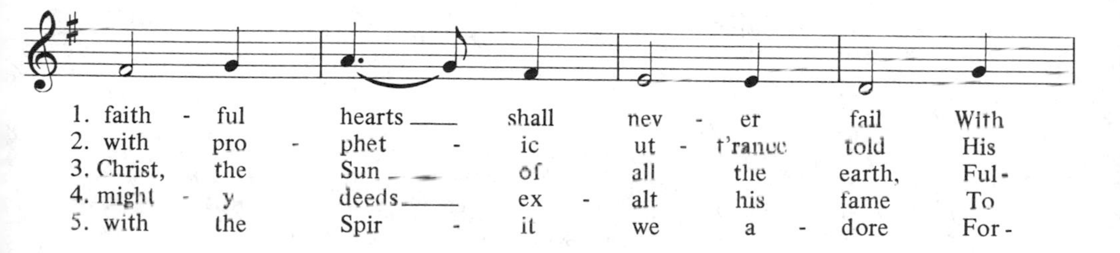
1. faith - ful hearts shall nev - er fail With
2. with pro - phet - ic ut - t'rance told His
3. Christ, the Sun of all the earth, Ful -
4. might - y deeds ex - alt his fame To
5. with the Spir - it we a - dore For -

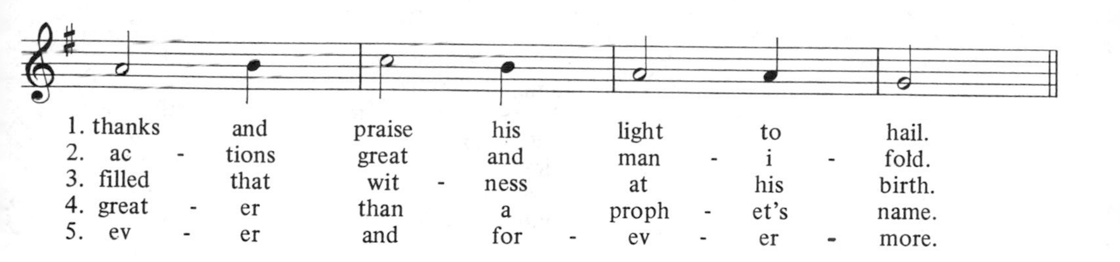
1. thanks and praise his light to hail.
2. ac - tions great and man - i - fold.
3. filled that wit - ness at his birth.
4. great - er than a proph - et's name.
5. ev - er and for - ev - er - more.

Text: The Venerable Bede, +735. Trans. by J.M. Neale, +1866.
Tune: *Sedulius*, "Nürnbergisches Gesangbuch", 1676.

324 The King of Love My Shepherd Is

Ps. 23

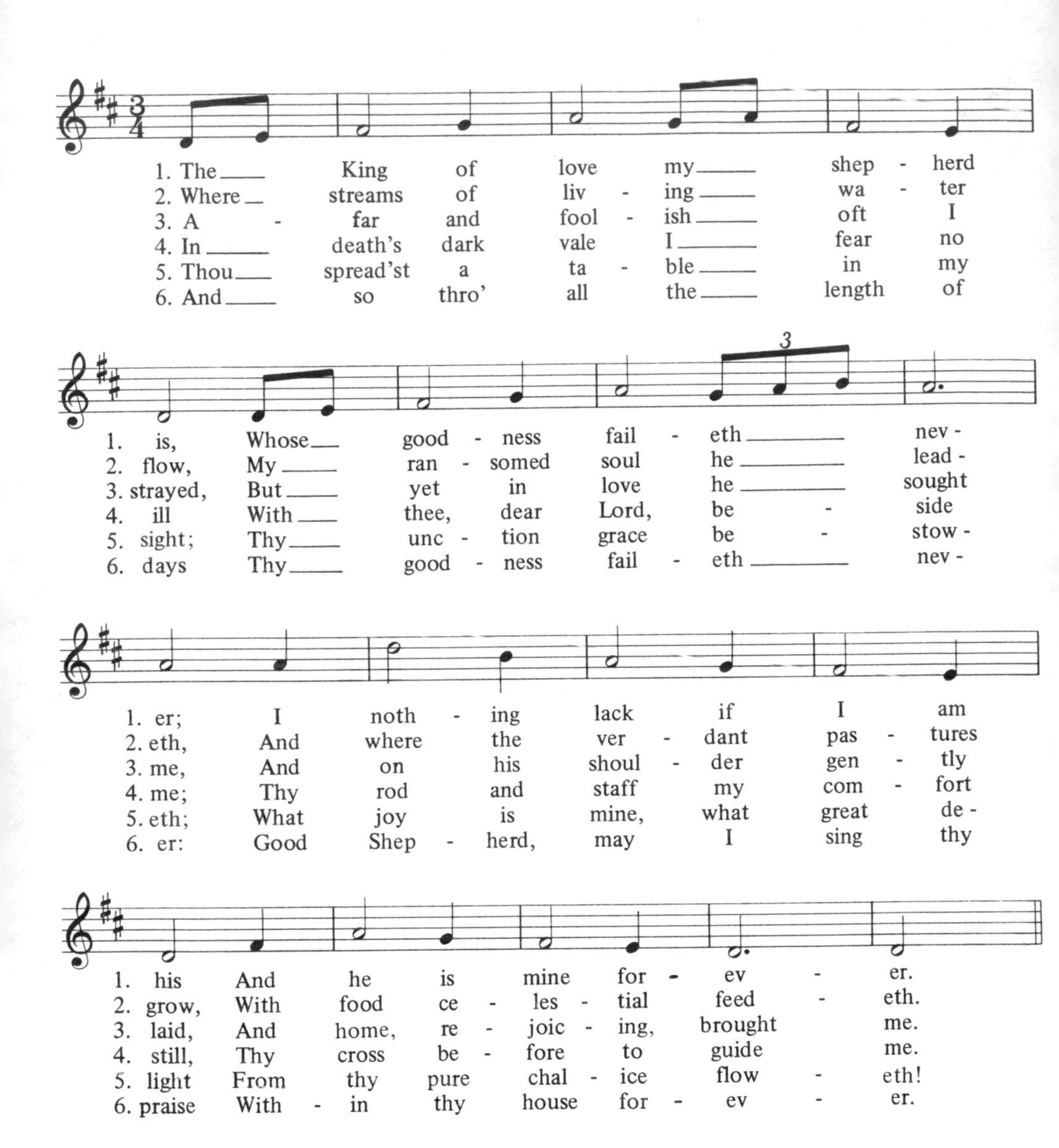

1. The King of love my shepherd is, Whose goodness faileth never; I nothing lack if I am his And he is mine forever.
2. Where streams of living water flow, My ransomed soul he leadeth, And where the verdant pastures grow, With food celestial feedeth.
3. Afar and foolish oft I strayed, But yet in love he sought me, And on his shoulder gently laid, And home, rejoicing, brought me.
4. In death's dark vale I fear no ill With thee, dear Lord, beside me; Thy rod and staff my comfort still, Thy cross before to guide me.
5. Thou spread'st a table in my sight; Thy unction grace bestoweth; What joy is mine, what great delight From thy pure chalice floweth!
6. And so thro' all the length of days Thy goodness faileth never: Good Shepherd, may I sing thy praise Within thy house forever.

Text: Psalm 23 paraphrase, H.W. Baker, +1877.
Tune: *St. Columba*, Irish.

The King Shall Come When Morning Dawns 325

1. The King shall come when morn - ing dawns And
2. Not as of old, a lit - tle child, To
3. The King shall come when morn - ing dawns And
4. And let the end - less bliss be - gin By
5. The King shall come when morn - ing dawns And

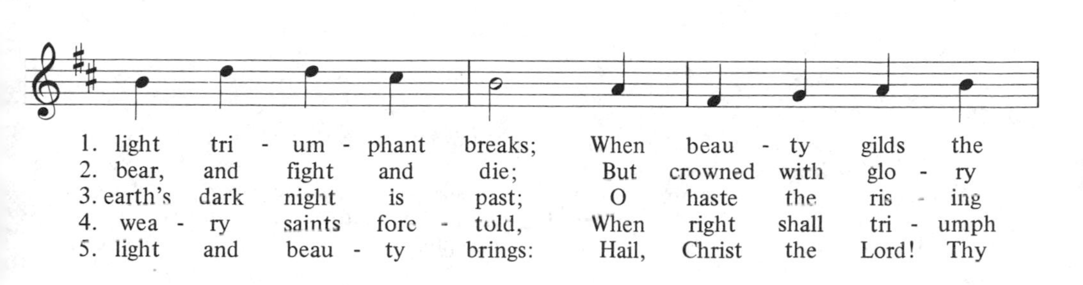
1. light tri - um - phant breaks; When beau - ty gilds the
2. bear, and fight and die; But crowned with glo - ry
3. earth's dark night is past; O haste the ris - ing
4. wea - ry saints fore - told, When right shall tri - umph
5. light and beau - ty brings: Hail, Christ the Lord! Thy

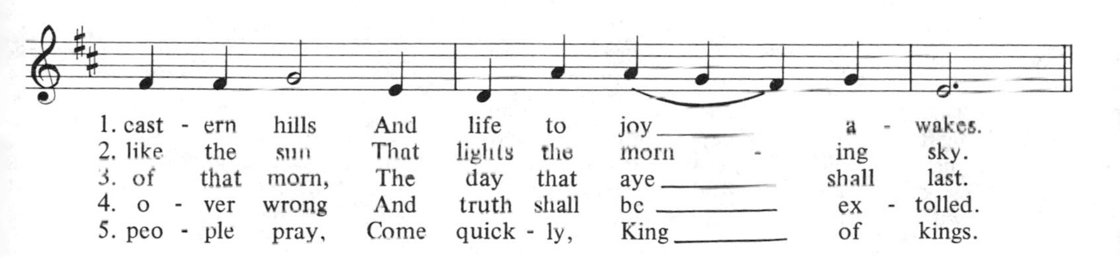
1. east - ern hills And life to joy a - wakes.
2. like the sun That lights the morn - ing sky.
3. of that morn, The day that aye shall last.
4. o - ver wrong And truth shall be ex - tolled.
5. peo - ple pray, Come quick - ly, King of kings.

Text: Trans. from Greek by J. Brownlie, +1925.
Tune: *In Adventu*, T. Marier.

The Lord Is King

1. The Lord is King, lift up your voice; In
2. The east - ern sag - es saw from far, And
3. With - in the Jor - dan's sa - cred flood The
4. And lo! a mir - a - cle di - vine When
5. To Je - su, glo - ry ev - er be For

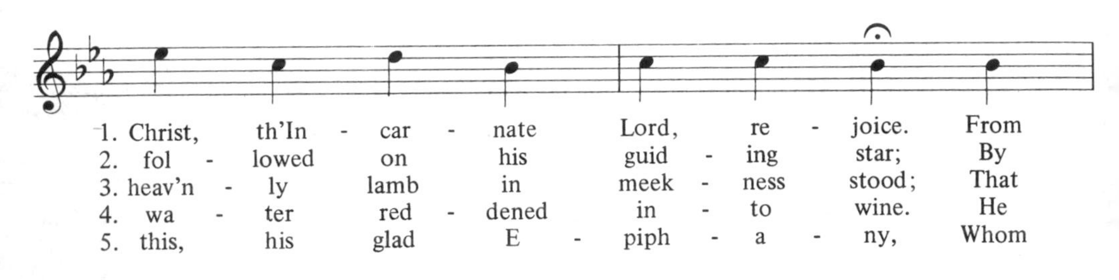
1. Christ, th'In - car - nate Lord, re - joice. From
2. fol - lowed on his guid - ing star; By
3. heav'n - ly lamb in meek - ness stood; That
4. wa - ter red - dened in - to wine. He
5. this, his glad E - piph - a - ny, Whom

1. land to land let prais - es ring As
2. light their way to Light they trod, And
3. he who knew no sin that day, His
4. spoke the word and forth it flowed In
5. with the Fa - ther all a - dore, And

1. earth and heav'n con - fess him King.
2. by their gifts con - fessed their God.
3. peo - ple's sin might wash a - way.
4. streams that na - ture ne'er be - stowed.
5. Ho - ly Spir - it ev - er - more.

Text: Verse 1, J. Conder, +1855, alt.
Verses 2-5, Caelius Sedulius, c. 450, alt. Trans. from "Hymns Ancient and Modern." Used with permission.
Tune: *Pearsall,* R.L. Pearsall, +1856.

The Perfect Law of God

Ps. 19

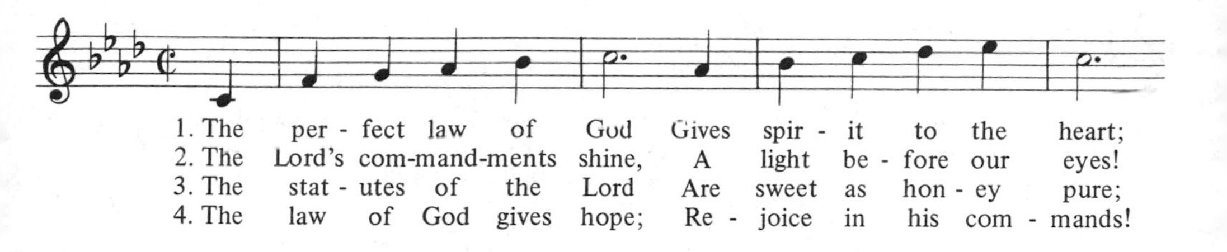
1. The per - fect law of God Gives spir - it to the heart;
2. The Lord's com-mand-ments shine, A light be - fore our eyes!
3. The stat - utes of the Lord Are sweet as hon - ey pure;
4. The law of God gives hope; Re - joice in his com - mands!

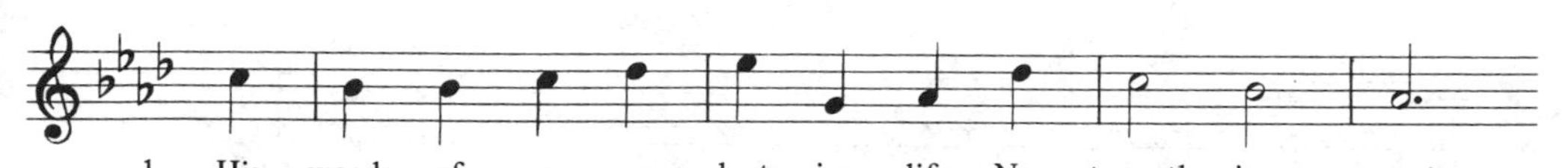
1. His words of ev - er - last - ing life New strength im - part.
2. His tes - ti - mo - ny sure will make The sim - ple wise.
3. His words of love with - in our hearts Make us se - cure.
4. Through heav'n and earth his faith - ful word For - ev - er stands.

1. Re - fresh - ing to the soul, His laws are right and true;
2. How per - fect is his word And all his judg-ments just!
3. More pre - cious in our sight Than heaps of fin - est gold,
4. His pre - cepts be our rock And help in all our days;

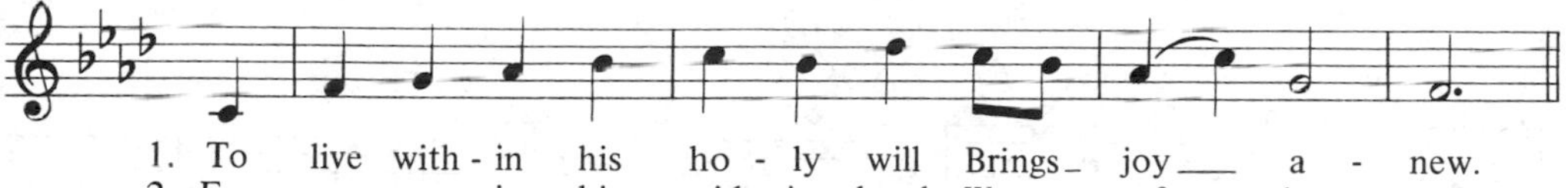
1. To live with - in his ho - ly will Brings joy a - new.
2. For - ev - er in his guid - ing hand We safe - ly trust.
3. They prom - ise ev - er - last - ing life And joy un - told.
4. Our Sav - ior and re - deem - ing Lord, Our God al - ways!

Text: Psalm 19 paraphrase, J. Dunn.
Tune: *Leoni,* traditional Hebrew melody, var.

328 The Royal Banners Forward Go

1. The roy - al ban - ners for - ward go;
2. Where deep for us the spear was dyed,
3. Ful - filled is all that Da - vid told
4. O Tree of beau - ty! Tree of light!

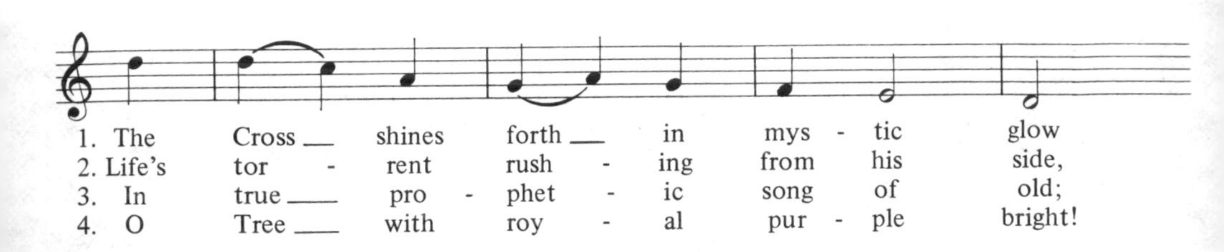
1. The Cross shines forth in mys - tic glow
2. Life's tor - rent rush - ing from his side,
3. In true pro - phet - ic song of old;
4. O Tree with roy - al pur - ple bright!

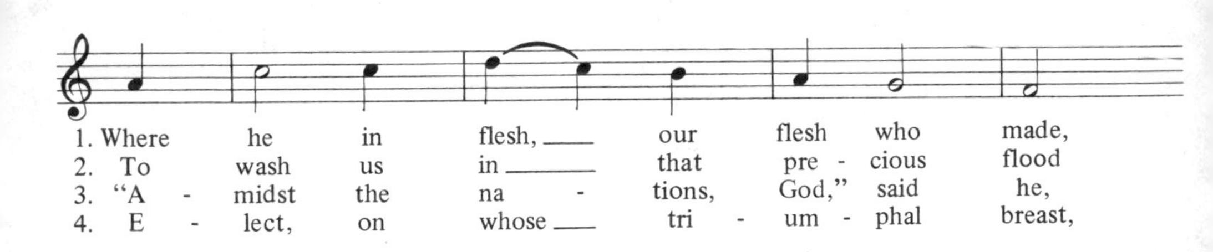
1. Where he in flesh, our flesh who made,
2. To wash us in that pre - cious flood
3. "A - midst the na - tions, God," said he,
4. E - lect, on whose tri - um - phal breast,

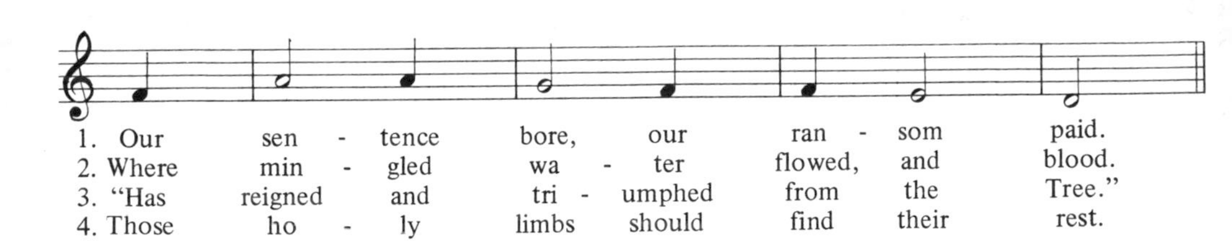
1. Our sen - tence bore, our ran - som paid.
2. Where min - gled wa - ter flowed, and blood.
3. "Has reigned and tri - umphed from the Tree."
4. Those ho - ly limbs should find their rest.

Text: *Vexilla Regis,* Venantius Fortunatus, +609. Trans. J.M. Neale, +1866, alt.
Tune: *Agincourt,* 15th Century English melody, var.

This Is the Day the Lord Created

329

Ps. 118

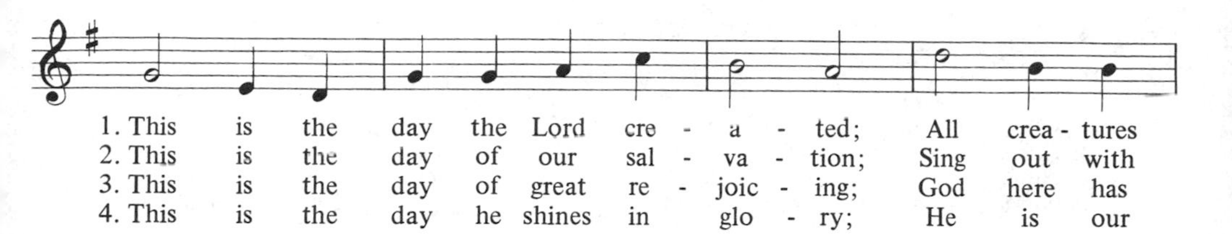

1. This is the day the Lord cre - a - ted; All crea - tures
2. This is the day of our sal - va - tion; Sing out with
3. This is the day of great re - joic - ing; God here has
4. This is the day he shines in glo - ry; He is our

1. come, re - joice and sing! Thank him for his e - ter - nal good - ness;
2. hymns of ju - bi - lee! God's might - y arm has struck with pow - er;
3. made sal - va - tion known. See how the stone the build - ers ban - ished
4. Sav - ior and our Light. Tru - ly our health and our sal - va - tion,

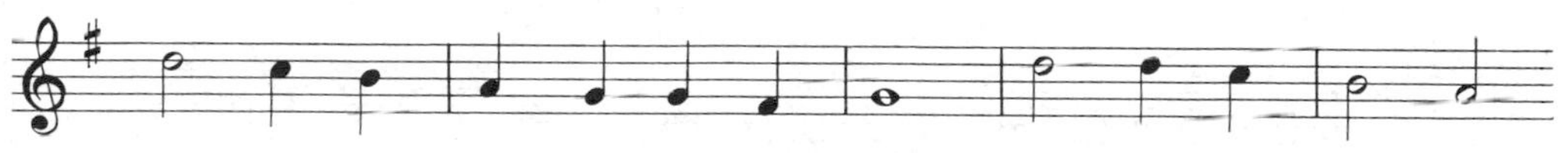

1. Praise him, the ev - er - last - ing King. Is - rael sa - lutes his
2. Shout psalms of joy and vic - to - ry. We shall not die but
3. Now has be - come the cor - ner - stone. This has been done by
4. Look on his strength with great de - light. Thank him for his e -

1. kind com - pas - sion; Brings hon - or to his ho - ly name. Let all who
2. live be - fore him, And all his might - y works de - clare. Come now and
3. God al - might - y; To all our eyes a won - drous sight. Thank him for
4. ter - nal good - ness; Praise him, the ev - er - last - ing King. This is the

1. fear him know his mer - cy; Stead - fast, his love re - mains the same.
2. joy - ful - ly a - dore him, All who his vic - to - ry will share.
3. all his deeds of mer - cy; Praise the tri - um - phant Lord of might.
4. day the Lord cre - a - ted; All crea - tures now re - joice and sing!

Text: Psalm 118 paraphrase, J. Dunn.
Tune: *Rendez à Dieu,* L. Bourgeois, +1561.

Think of the Son of God

1. Think of the Son of God, how he
2. Think of the spear the sol - dier bore,
3. Think up - on Christ who gave his blood,
4. Think of re - pent - ance time - ly made,
1. Died on the tree our souls to save;
2. Think how it tore his ho - ly side;
3. Poured in a flood our souls to win;
4. Think like a shade our time flits, too;
1. Think of the nails that pierced him through,
2. Think of the bit - ter gall for drink,
3. Think of the min - gled tide that gushed
4. Think up - on Death with poi - soned dart,
1. Think of him, too, in low - ly grave.
2. Think of it, think, for us he died.
3. Forth at the thrust to wash our sin.
4. Pierc - ing the heart and bod - y through.

Text: Gaelic anon. Trans. D. Hyde, +1949.
Tune: *Emendar,* T. Marier. From "Pius X Hymnal", © 1953 by Summy-Birch Music division of Birch Tree Group Ltd. Used with permission.

Thou Art the Star of Morning

331

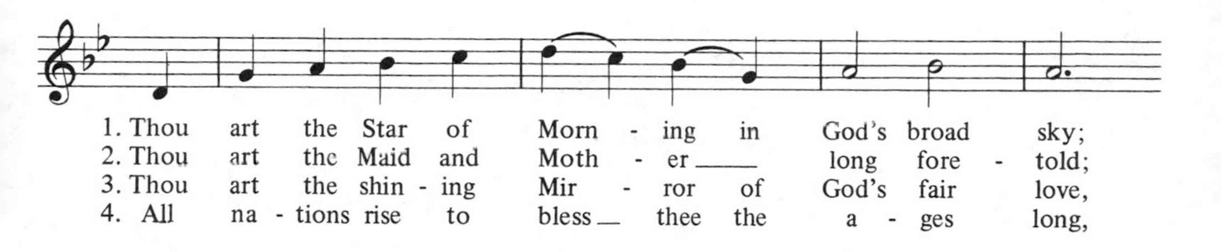
1. Thou art the Star of Morn - ing in God's broad sky;
2. Thou art the Maid and Moth - er long fore - told;
3. Thou art the shin - ing Mir - ror of God's fair love,
4. All na - tions rise to bless thee the a - ges long,

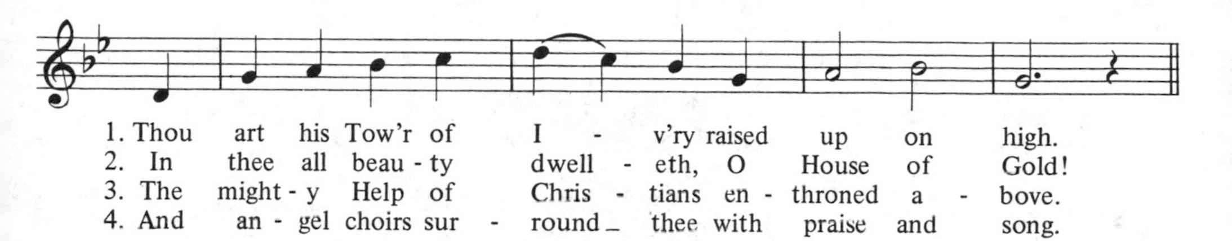
1. Thou art his Tow'r of I - v'ry raised up on high.
2. In thee all beau - ty dwell - eth, O House of Gold!
3. The might - y Help of Chris - tians en - throned a - bove.
4. And an - gel choirs sur - round thee with praise and song.

REFRAIN

1.-4. Hail, Heav - en's Queen! O lux cae - le - sti - a!
O heavenly light!

1.-4. Thou giv - er of all glad - ness, O ple - na gra - ti - a!
O full of grace!

Text: H. Condon. From "Pius X Hymnal",
Tune: *Je sais, Vierge Marie,* French Noel.

332

To Bless the Earth

Ps. 65

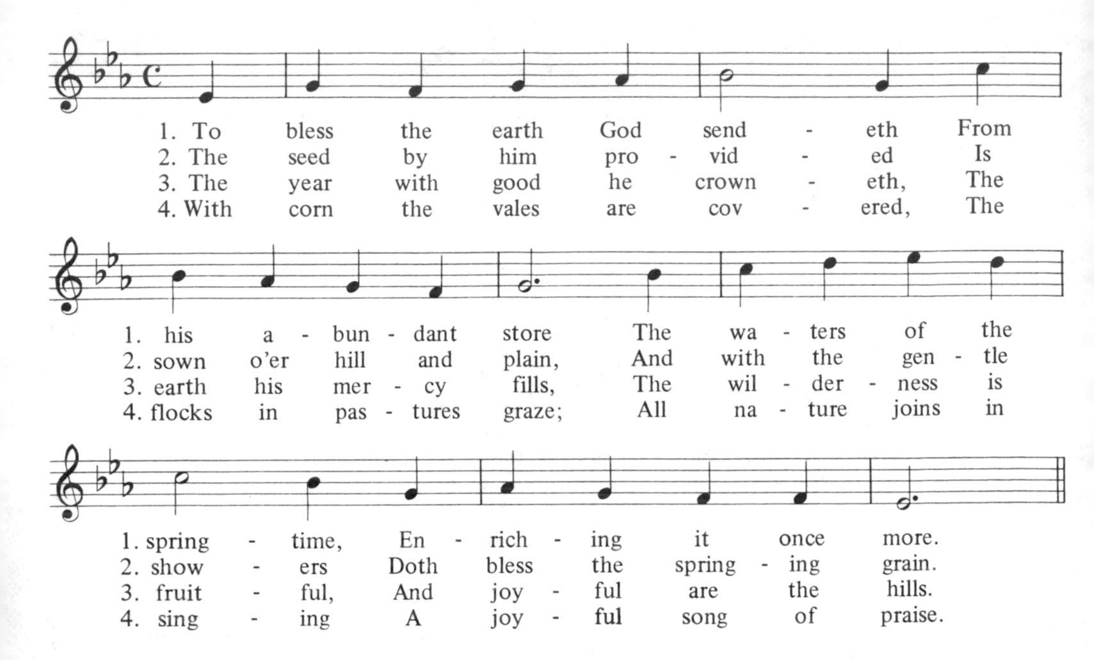
1. To bless the earth God send - eth From
2. The seed by him pro - vid - ed Is
3. The year with good he crown - eth, The
4. With corn the vales are cov - ered, The
1. his a - bun - dant store The wa - ters of the
2. sown o'er hill and plain, And with the gen - tle
3. earth his mer - cy fills, The wil - der - ness is
4. flocks in pas - tures graze; All na - ture joins in
1. spring - time, En - rich - ing it once more.
2. show - ers Doth bless the spring - ing grain.
3. fruit - ful, And joy - ful are the hills.
4. sing - ing A joy - ful song of praise.

Text: Psalm 65 paraphrase, anon.
Tune: *Christus der ist mein Leben,* M. Vulpius, +1615.

To the Name of Our Salvation

1. To the name of our sal - va tion Laud and hon - or
2. Je - sus is the name we treas - ure, Name be - yond what
3. 'Tis the name for ad - o - ra - tion, Name for songs of
4. 'Tis the name that who - so preach - eth Speaks like mu - sic
5. Praise the Fa - ther of sal - va - tion; Sing ho - san - nas
1. let us pay, Which for man - y a gen - er - a - tion
2. words can tell; Name of glad - ness, pass - ing meas - ure,
3. vic - to - ry; Name of ho - ly med - i - ta - tion
4. to the ear; Who in prayer this name be - seech - eth
5. to his Son; Praise the spir - it of cre - a - tion;
1. All in God's fore - knowl - edge lay,
2. Ear and heart de - light - ing well;
3. In this vale of mis - er - y;
4. Sweet - est com - fort find - eth near;
5. Ev - er three and ev - er one.
1. But with ho - ly ex - ul - ta - tion We may sing a - loud to - day.
2. Name of sweet - ness, name we treas - ure Sav - ing us from sin and hell.
3. Name for joy - ful ven - er - a - tion By the cit - i - zens on high.
4. Who its per - fect wis - dom reach - eth Heav'n - ly joy pos - sess - eth here.
5. Sing out thanks and ad - o - ra - tion While un - end - ing a - ges run.

Text: Verses 1-4, 15th Century anon. Trans. J.M. Neale, +1866, alt.
Verse 5, J. Dunn, © by author. Used with permission.
Tune: *Regent Square,* H.T. Smart, +1879.

334 To Christ, the Prince of Peace

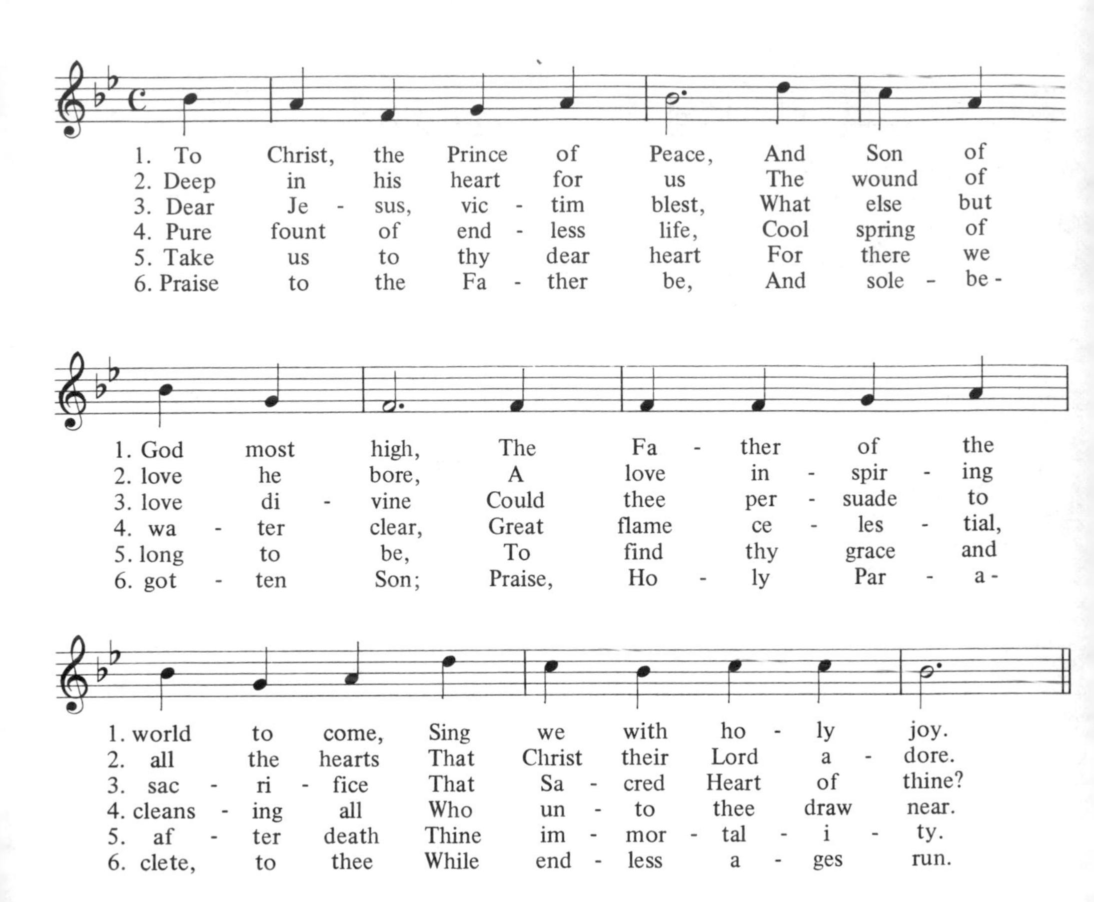
1. To Christ, the Prince of Peace, And Son of
2. Deep in his heart for us The wound of
3. Dear Je - sus, vic - tim blest, What else but
4. Pure fount of end - less life, Cool spring of
5. Take us to thy dear heart For there we
6. Praise to the Fa - ther be, And sole - be -
1. God most high, The Fa - ther of the
2. love he bore, A love in - spir - ing
3. love di - vine Could thee per - suade to
4. wa - ter clear, Great flame ce - les - tial,
5. long to be, To find thy grace and
6. got - ten Son; Praise, Ho - ly Par - a -
1. world to come, Sing we with ho - ly joy.
2. all the hearts That Christ their Lord a - dore.
3. sac - ri - fice That Sa - cred Heart of thine?
4. cleans - ing all Who un - to thee draw near.
5. af - ter death Thine im - mor - tal - i - ty.
6. clete, to thee While end - less a - ges run.

Text: *Summi parentis Filio.* Trans. E. Caswall, +1878. Adapted by A.G. Petti in "New Catholic Hymnal",
Tune: *Narenza,* Leisentritt's "Catholicum Hymnologium Germanicum", 1587. Adapted by W.H. Havergal, +1870.

To God with Gladness Sing

335

Ps. 95

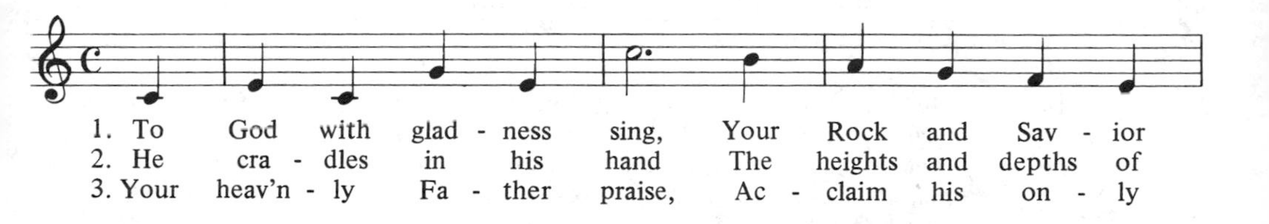

1. To God with glad - ness sing, Your Rock and Sav - ior
2. He cra - dles in his hand The heights and depths of
3. Your heav'n - ly Fa - ther praise, Ac - claim his on - ly

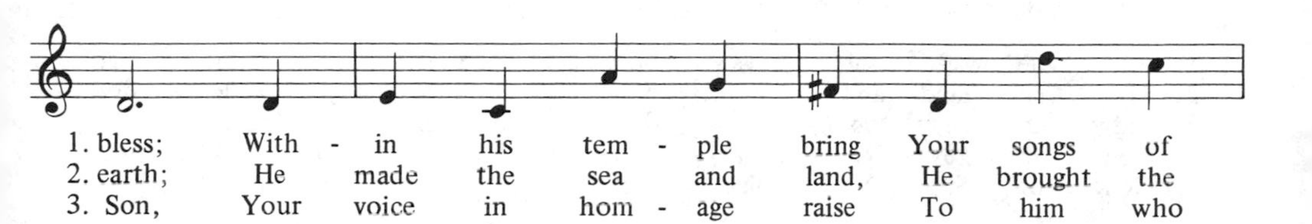

1. bless; With - in his tem - ple bring Your songs of
2. earth; He made the sea and land, He brought the
3. Son, Your voice in hom - age raise To him who

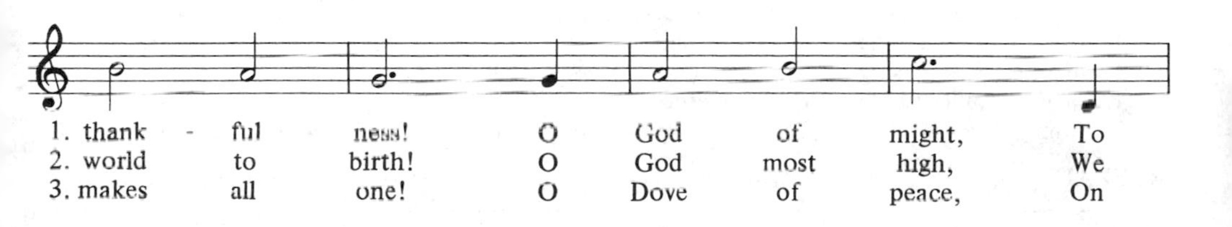

1. thank - ful ness! O God of might, To
2. world to birth! O God most high, We
3. makes all one! O Dove of peace, On

1. you we sing, En - throned as King On heav - en's height!
2. are your sheep, On us you keep Your shep - herd's eye!
3. us de - scend That strife may end And joy in - crease!

Text: Psalm 95 paraphrase, J. Quinn. © 1969 James Quinn SJ, reprinted by permission of Geoffrey Chapman, a division of Cassell, Ltd.
Tune: *Darwall's 148th,* J. Darwall, +1789.

336 To Jesus Christ, Our Sov'reign King

1. To Je - sus Christ, our sov - 'reign King, Who
2. Thy reign ex - tend, O King be - nign, To
3. To thee and to thy Church, great King, We
4. Thy maj - es - ty shall be the praise And
5. May God the Fa - ther, God the Son And
1. is the world's sal - va - tion, All praise and hom - age
2. ev - 'ry land and na - tion, For in thy king - dom,
3. pledge our hearts' ob - la - tion, Un - til be - fore thy
4. thanks of ev - 'ry na - tion; To thee the world with
5. God the Spir - it bless us! Let all the world praise
1. do we bring And thanks and ad - o - ra - tion.
2. Lord di - vine, A - lone we find sal - va - tion.
3. throne we sing In end - less ju - bi - la - tion.
4. joy shall raise The voice of ex - ul - ta - tion.
5. him a - lone, Let sol - emn awe pos - sess us.
REFRAIN
1.-5. Christ Je - sus, Vic - tor! Christ Je - sus, Rul - er!

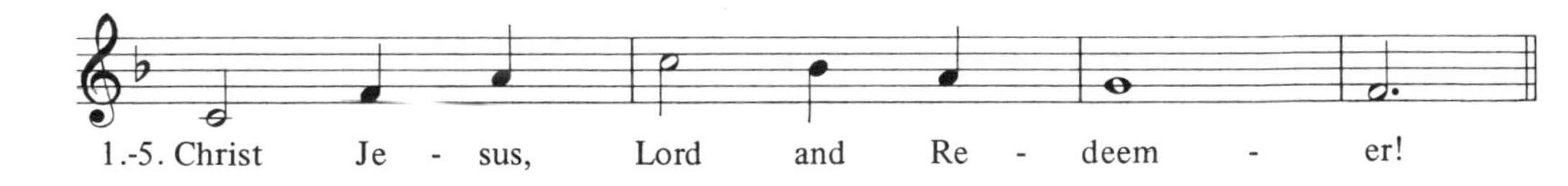
1.-5. Christ Je - sus, Lord and Re - deem - er!

Text: M. Hellriegel, +1981. Used with permission.
Tune: *Christus Rex,* Mainz Melody.

To You I lift My Soul

Ps. 25

1. To you I lift my soul; My trust is in your
2. To you I lift my soul; You are my Sav - ior,
3. To you I lift my soul; I trust your guid - ing

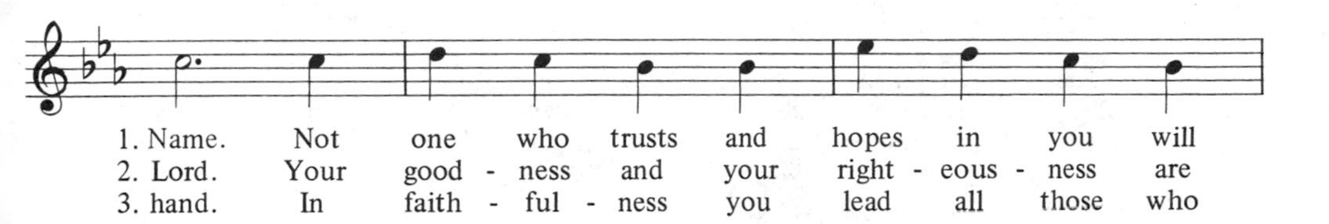
1. Name. Not one who trusts and hopes in you will
2. Lord. Your good - ness and your right - eous - ness are
3. hand. In faith - ful - ness you lead all those who

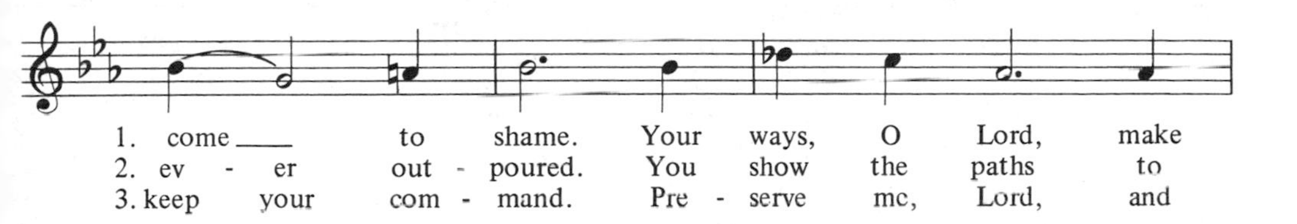
1. come ___ to shame. Your ways, O Lord, make
2. ev - er out - poured. You show the paths to
3. keep your com - mand. Pre - serve me, Lord, and

1. known to me, Make clear your truth, en - light - en me.
2. those who stray; The meek and hum - ble learn your way.
3. care for me; In you my hope will ev - er be.

338

Up, Awake, from Highest Steeple

1. "Up, a - wake," from high - est stee - ple
2. Sy - on hears the watch - men sound - ing,
3. Now let ev - 'ry tongue a - dore thee!
1. The watch - men cry, "A - wake, ye peo - ple;
2. Her heart with deep de - light is bound - ing;
3. Let men and an - gels sing be - fore thee;
1. O Sa - lem, from thy slum - ber rise!"
2. A - non she wakes; a - way she wends,
3. Let harps and cym - bals now u - nite!
1. Hear those clar - ion voic - es knell - ing,
2. Comes her Spouse from heav'n all glo - rious,
3. All thy gates with pearl are glo - rious
1. The hour of mid - night loud forth - tell - ing;
2. In grace al - might, in truth vic - to - rious,
3. Where we par - take through faith vic - to - rious,

1. Say, where are ye, O vir - gins wise?
2. Her light doth shine, her star ____ as - cends.
3. With an - gels ’round thy throne __ of light.
REFRAIN
1.-3. No mor - tal eye hath seen, no mor - tal
1.-3. ear hath heard Such won - drous things; There -

1.-3. fore with joy our ____ song shall soar In

1.-3. praise to God for - ev - er - more.

Text: P. Nicolai, +1608. Trans. anon.
Tune: *Wachet auf,* P. Nicolai, +1608.

339 'Twas in the Moon of Wintertime

1. 'Twas in the moon of win - ter - time When all the birds had fled, That
2. With - in a lodge of bro - ken bark The ten - der Babe was found, A
3. The ear- liest moon of win - ter - time Is not so round and fair As
4. O chil-dren of the for - est free, O sons of Man - i - tou, The

1. might - y Git - chi - Man - i - tou Sent an - gel choirs in - stead; Be -
2. rag - ged robe of rab - bit skin En-wrapp'd his beau - ty 'round; But
3. was the ring of glo - ry on The help - less in - fant there. The
4. Ho - ly Child of earth and heav'n Is born to - day for you. Come

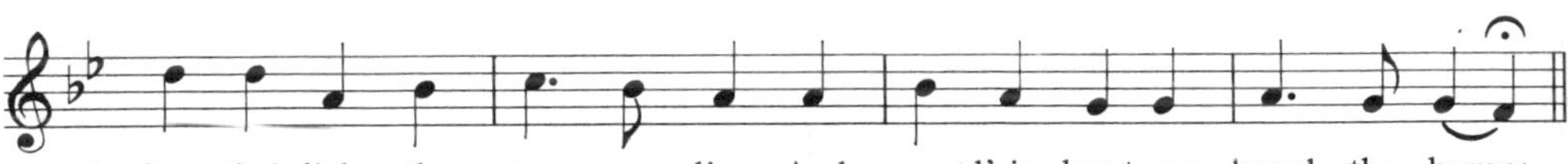

1. fore their light the stars grew dim, And won-d'ring hunt- ers heard the hymn:__
2. as the hunt - er braves drew nigh, The an - gel song rang loud and high:__
3. chiefs from far be - fore him knelt With gifts of fox and bea - ver pelt.__
4. kneel be - fore the ra - diant boy; Who brings you beau - ty, peace and joy.__

REFRAIN

1.-4. Je - sus, your King is born, Je - sus is born, In ex - cel - sis glo - ri - a.__

Text: St. John de Brebeuf, +1649. Trans. J.E. Middleton, +1960.

Tune: *Une jeune pucelle*, French Carol.

OI

Veni Creator Spiritus

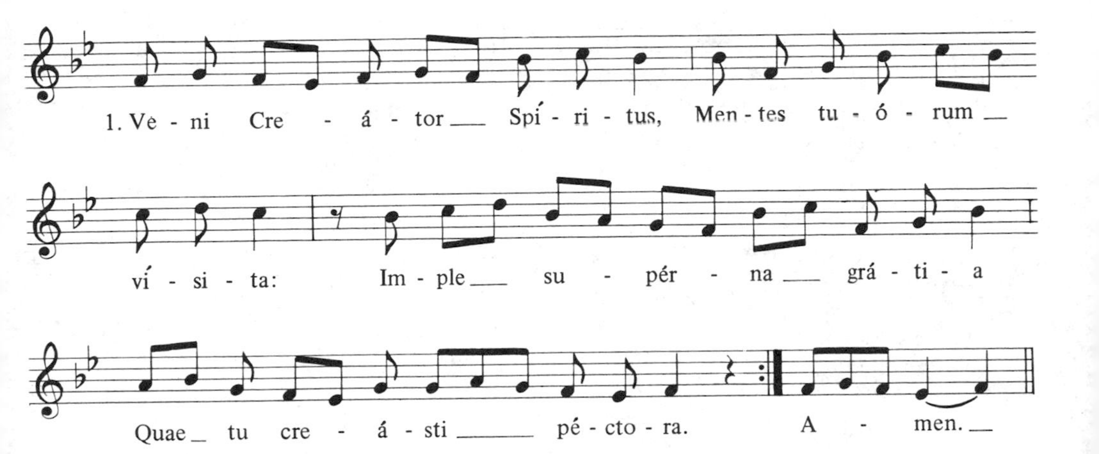
1. Ve - ni Cre - á - tor Spí - ri - tus, Men - tes tu - ó - rum
ví - si - ta: Im - ple su - pér - na grá - ti - a
Quae tu cre - á - sti pé - cto - ra. A - men.

2. Qui díceris Paráclitus,
Altíssimi dónum Dei,
Fons vivus, ignis, cáritas,
Et spiritális únctio.

3. Tu septifórmis múnere,
Dígitus patérnae déxterae,
Tu rite promíssum Patris,
Sermóne ditans gúttura.

4. Accénde lumen sénsibus,
Infúnde amórem córdibus,
Infírma nostri córporis
Virtúte fírmans pérpeti.

5. Hostem repéllas lóngius,
Pacémque dones prótinus:
Ductóre sic te praévio,
Vitémus omne nóxium.

6. Per te sciámus da Patrem,
Noscámus atque Fílium,
Teque utriúsque Spíritum
Credámus omni témpore.

7. Deo Patri sit glória,
Et Fílio, qui a mórtuis,
Surréxit, ac Paráclito,
In saeculórum saécula. Amen.

For translation see "Come, Holy Ghost, Creator Blest".

Text: Ascribed to Rabanus Maurus, +856.
Tune: *Veni Creator,* Plainchant, Mode 8.

341 Veni Sancte Spiritus

Sequence for Pentecost Sunday

1. Ve - ni San - cte Spí - ri - tus, Et e - mít - te caé - li - tus
2. Ve - ni pa - ter paú - pe - rum, Ve - ni da - tor mú - ne - rum,

1. Lu - cis tu - ae rá - di - um. 3. Con - so - lá - tor ó - pti - me,
2. Ve - ni lu - men cór - di - um. 4. In la - bó - re ré - qui - es,

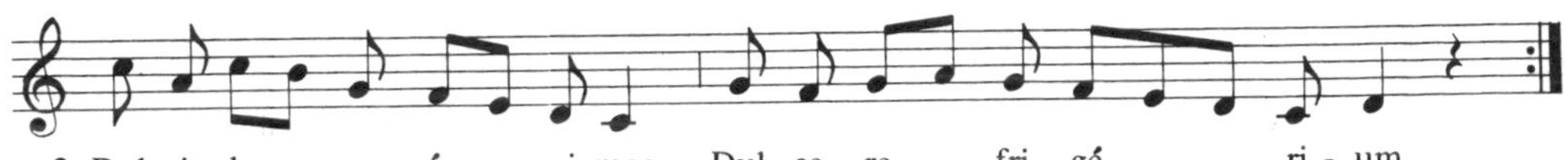
3. Dul - cis ho - spes á - ni - mae, Dul - ce re - fri - gé - ri - um.
4. In ae - stu tem - pé - ri - es, In fle - tu so - lá - ti - um.

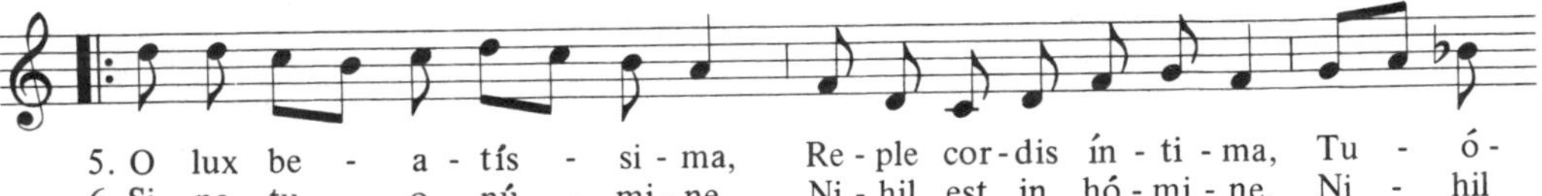
5. O lux be - a - tís - si - ma, Re - ple cor - dis ín - ti - ma, Tu - ó -
6. Si - ne tu - o nú - mi - ne, Ni - hil est in hó - mi - ne, Ni - hil

5. rum fi - dé - li - um. 7. La - va quod est sór - di - dum, Ri - ga
6. est in - nó - xi - um. 8. Fle - cte quod est rí - gi - dum, Fo - ve

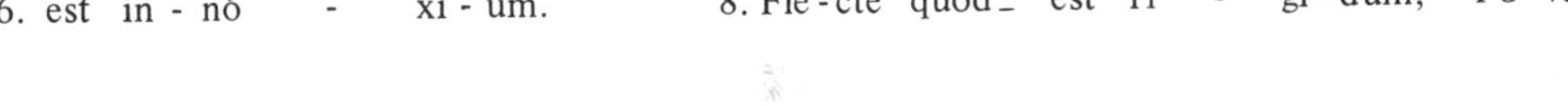

7. quod est á - ri - dum, Sa - na quod est saú - ci - um. 9. Da tu - is
8. quod est frí - gi - dum, Re - ge quod est dé - vi - um. 10. Da vir - tu -

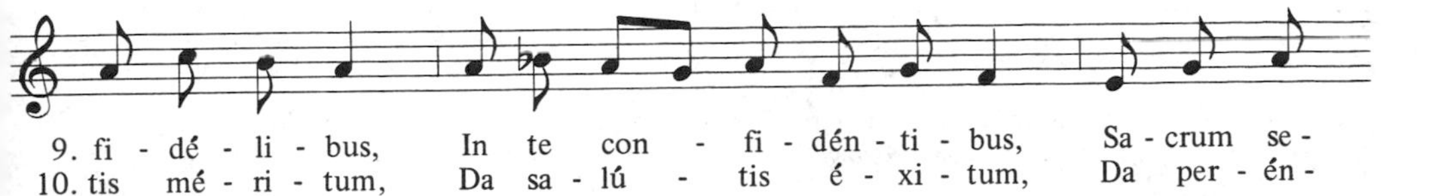
9. fi - dé - li - bus, In te con - fi - dén - ti - bus, Sa - crum se -
10. tis mé - ri - tum, Da sa - lú - tis é - xi - tum, Da per - én -

9. pte - ná - ri - um.
10. ne gaú - di - um. A - men. Al - le - lú - ia.

For translation see "Holy Spirit, Come and Shine".

Text: Ascribed to Innocent III, +1216.
Tune: *Veni Sancte Spiritus,* Plainchant, Mode 1.

Victimae Paschali Laudes **342**

Sequence for Easter Sunday

1. Ví - cti - mae Pa - schá - li lau - des im - mó - lent Chri - sti - á - ni.

Christians, offer your thankful praises to the paschal victim!

2. A - gnus re - dé - mit o - ves: Chri - stus ín - no - cens Pa - tri re - con - ci - li -

A lamb the sheep redeemeth: Christ, who only is sinless reconcileth

á - vit pec - ca - tó - res. 3. Mors et vi - ta du - él - lo con - fli - xé - re mi - rán -

sinners to the Father. *Death and life have contended in that combat stupendous:*

do: dux vi - tae mór - tu - us re - gnat vi - vus. 4. Dic no - bis Ma - rí - a, ___
The prince of life who died, reigns immortal. Speak, Mary, declaring

quid vi - dí - sti in vi - a? 5. Se - púl-chrum Chri - sti vi - vén - tis, et
what thou sawest wayfaring. "The Tomb of Christ, who is living, the glory of Jesus'

gló - ri - am vi - di re - sur - gén - tis. 6. An - gé - li - cos te - stes, ___
resurrection: Bright angels attesting,

su - dá - ri - um, et ve - stes. 7. Sur - ré - xit Chri - stus spes me - a:
the shroud and napkin resting. Yes, Christ, my hope, is arisen:

prae - cé - det su - os in Ga - li - laé - am. 8. Sci - mus Chri - stum sur - re -
to Galilee he goes before you." Christ indeed from death is

xís - se a mór - tu - is ve - re: tu no - bis vi - ctor Rex, mi - se - ré - re.
risen, our new life obtaining. Have mercy, victor King, ever reigning.

A - men. ___ Al - le - lú - ia.

Text: From Liturgy of Easter Sunday. Ascribed to Wipo, 11th Century. Trans. anon.
Tune: *Victimae paschali,* Plainchant, Mode 1.

We Find Thee, Lord, in Others' Need

343

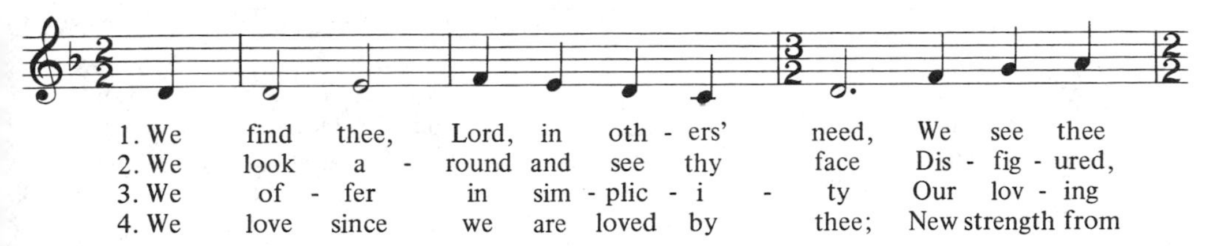
1. We find thee, Lord, in oth - ers' need, We see thee
2. We look a - round and see thy face Dis - fig - ured,
3. We of - fer in sim - plic - i - ty Our lov - ing
4. We love since we are loved by thee; New strength from

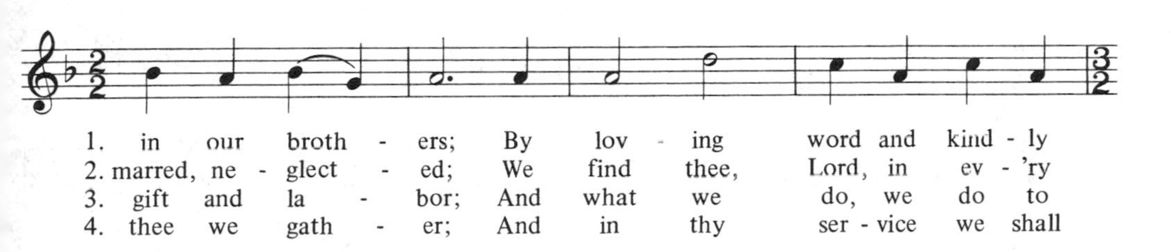
1. in our broth - ers; By lov - ing word and kind - ly
2. marred, ne - glect - ed; We find thee, Lord, in ev - 'ry
3. gift and la - bor; And what we do, we do to
4. thee we gath - er; And in thy ser - vice we shall

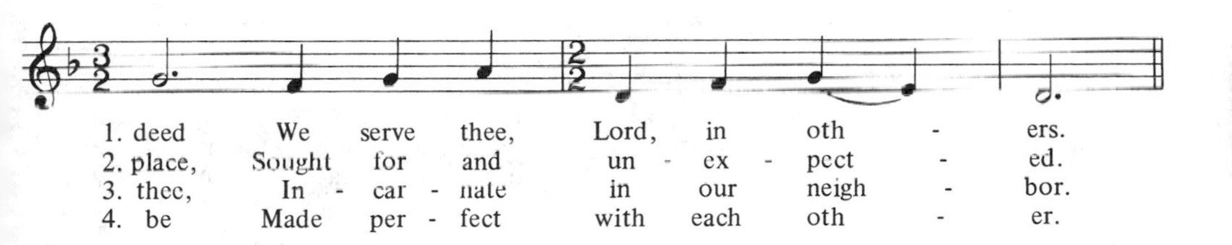
1. deed We serve thee, Lord, in oth - ers.
2. place, Sought for and un - ex - pect - ed.
3. thee, In - car - nate in our neigh - bor.
4. be Made per - fect with each oth - er.

Text: G. Ambrose.
Tune: *Freuen wir uns all in ein,* M. Weisse, +1534, alt.

344 We Gather Together

1. We gath - er to - geth - er to ask the Lord's
2. Be - side us to guide us, our God with us
3. We all do ex - tol thee, O lead - er tri -
1. bless - ing, He chas - tens and has - tens his
2. join - ing, Or - dain - ing, main - tain - ing his
3. um - phant, And pray that thou still our de -
1. will to make known; The wick - ed op -
2. king - dom di - vine; So from the be -
3. fend - er wilt be. Let thy con - gre-
1. press - ing now cease from dis - tress - ing; Sing
2. gin - ning the fight we were win - ning; Thou,
3. ga - tion es - cape trib - u - la - tion; Thy
1. prais - es to his name, he for - gets not his own.
2. Lord, wast at our side, all glo - ry be thine.
3. name be ev - er praised! O Lord, make us free.

Text: *"Nederlandtsch Gedenklanck"*, 1626. Trans. T. Baker, +1934.
Used with permission of G. Schirmer Co., Inc., N.Y.
Tune: *Kremser,* also from "Nederlandtsch Gedenklanck", 1626.

We Give Immortal Praise

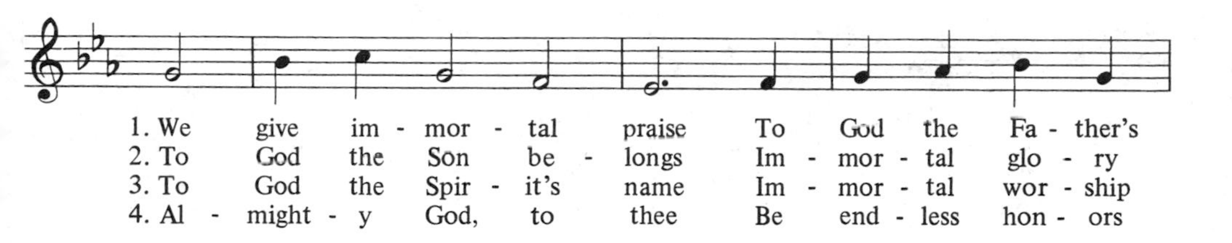
1. We give im - mor - tal praise To God the Fa - ther's
2. To God the Son be - longs Im - mor - tal glo - ry
3. To God the Spir - it's name Im - mor - tal wor - ship
4. Al - might - y God, to thee Be end - less hon - ors

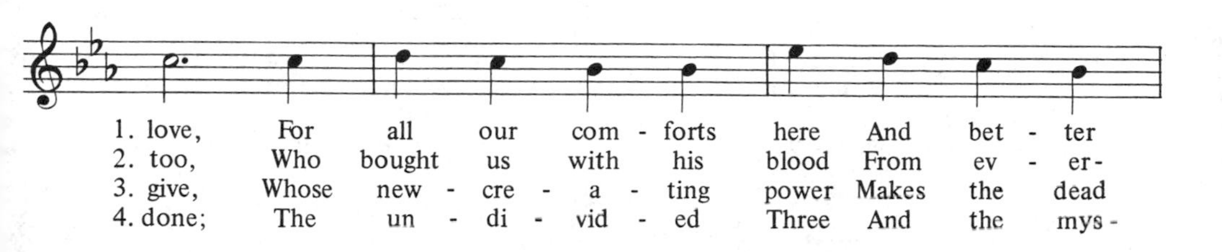
1. love, For all our com - forts here And bet - ter
2. too, Who bought us with his blood From ev - er-
3. give, Whose new - cre - a - ting power Makes the dead
4. done; The un - di - vid - ed Three And the mys-

1. hopes a - bove; He sent his own e-
2. last - ing woe: And now he lives, and
3. sin - ner live: His work com - pletes the
4. te - rious One: Where rea - son fails with

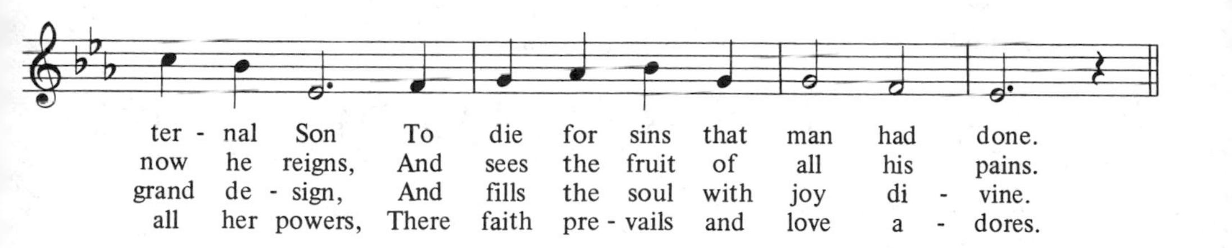
ter - nal Son To die for sins that man had done.
now he reigns, And sees the fruit of all his pains.
grand de - sign, And fills the soul with joy di - vine.
all her powers, There faith pre - vails and love a - dores.

Text: I. Watts, +1748.
Tune: *Love Unknown*, J. Ireland, +1962.

346 We Love Your Temple Lord

1. We love your— tem - ple, Lord, For there your hon - or
2. We love the— sa - cred font, Whose sav - ing wa - ters
3. We love your words of life, The words that grant us
4. Lord Je - sus,— give us grace On earth to love and
1. ev - er dwells; The joy of your a - bode All
2. o - ver - flow And pour as ev - er wont Your
3. your own peace, Of com - fort in the strife, And
4. praise you more, In heav'n to see your face, And
1. earth - ly joy for us ex - cels. It is the house of
2. bless - ing on us here be - low. We love your ta - ble,
3. won - drous joys that nev - er— cease. We love to sing be -
4. with your lov - ing saints a - dore. Be - fore you, Lord, we
1. prayer, Where - in your ser - vants meet; And
2. Lord, Where nour - ished here on earth Our
3. low For mer - cies free - ly giv'n; But
4. bow, E - ter - nal One in Three; For
1. you, O Lord, are there, Your cho - sen— ones to greet.
2. lives are new re - stored, Our souls find— new re - birth.
3. oh, we long to know The tri - umph— song of heav'n.
4. thus it was, is now, And ev - er - more shall be.

Text: W. Bullock, +1874, and H.W. Baker, +1877.

Tune: *Darmstadt,* Ahasuerus Fritsch's "Himmels-Lust", 1679.

We Rejoice, God's Holy People

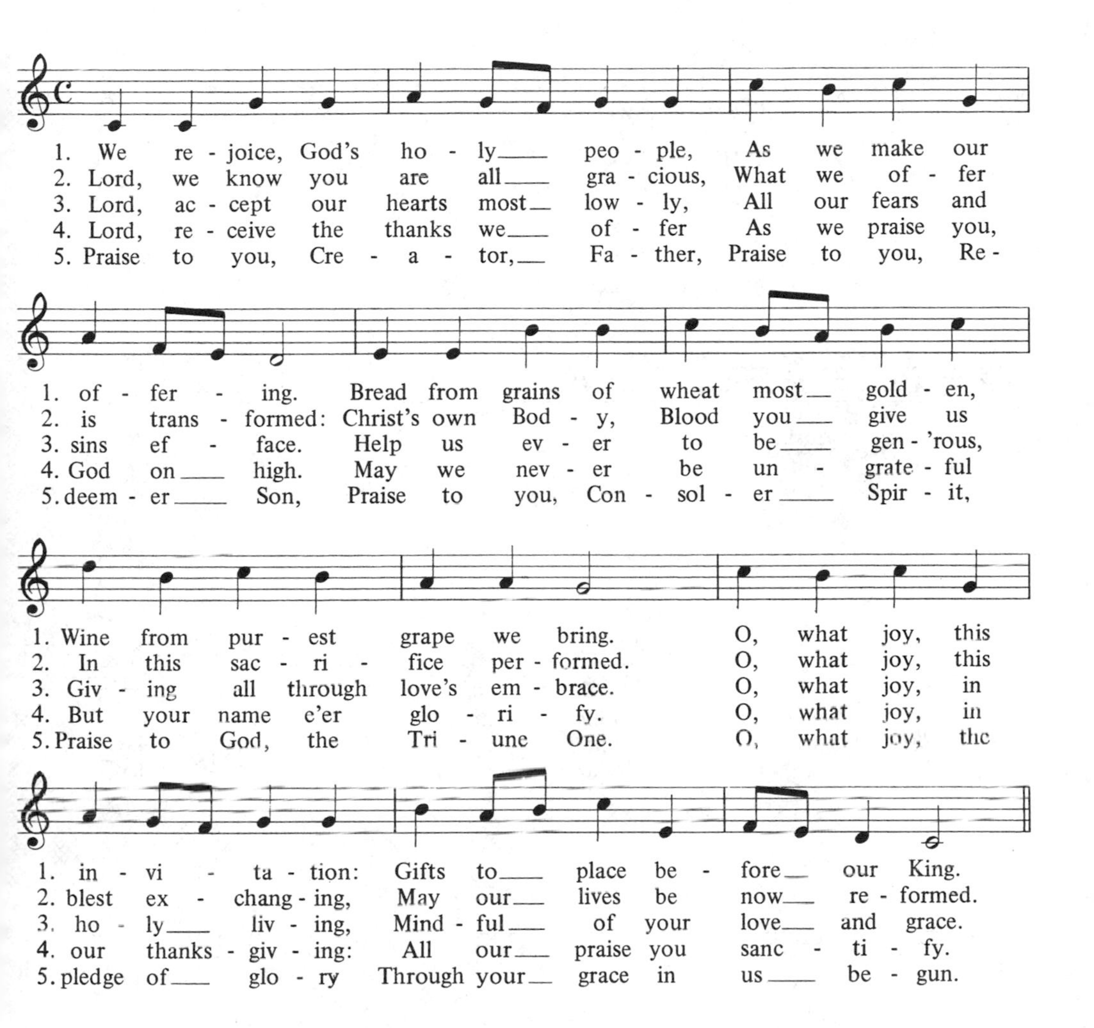
1. We re - joice, God's ho - ly peo - ple, As we make our
2. Lord, we know you are all gra - cious, What we of - fer
3. Lord, ac - cept our hearts most low - ly, All our fears and
4. Lord, re - ceive the thanks we of - fer As we praise you,
5. Praise to you, Cre - a - tor, Fa - ther, Praise to you, Re -
1. of - fer - ing. Bread from grains of wheat most gold - en,
2. is trans - formed: Christ's own Bod - y, Blood you give us
3. sins ef - face. Help us ev - er to be gen - 'rous,
4. God on high. May we nev - er be un - grate - ful
5. deem - er Son, Praise to you, Con - sol - er Spir - it,
1. Wine from pur - est grape we bring. O, what joy, this
2. In this sac - ri - fice per - formed. O, what joy, this
3. Giv - ing all through love's em - brace. O, what joy, in
4. But your name e'er glo - ri - fy. O, what joy, in
5. Praise to God, the Tri - une One. O, what joy, the
1. in - vi - ta - tion: Gifts to place be - fore our King.
2. blest ex - chang - ing, May our lives be now re - formed.
3. ho - ly liv - ing, Mind - ful of your love and grace.
4. our thanks - giv - ing: All our praise you sanc - ti - fy.
5. pledge of glo - ry Through your grace in us be - gun.

Text: N. Herman, C.P. From "Psalms and Hymns for Ecumenical Worship",

Tune: *Offeramus*, T. Marier, from "Psalms and Hymns for Ecumenical Worship",
permission as above.

We Praise You, Father, for Your Gift

1. We praise you, Fa - ther, for your gift
2. With - in your hands we rest se - cure:
3. Your glo - ry may we ev - er seek

1. Of dusk and night - fall o - ver earth,
2. In qui - et sleep our strength re - new;
3. In rest as in ac - tiv - i - ty,

1. Fore - shad - ow - ing the mys - ter - y
2. Yet give your peo - ple hearts that wake
3. Un - til its full - ness is re - vealed,

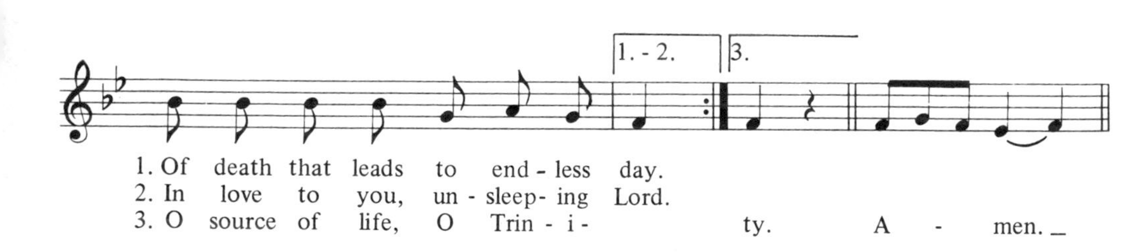
1. - 2.
3.
1. Of death that leads to end - less day.
2. In love to you, un - sleep- ing Lord.
3. O source of life, O Trin - i - ty. A - men.

Tune: *Te lucis ante terminum,* Plainchant, Mode 8.

What Shall I Render to the Lord

349

Ps. 116

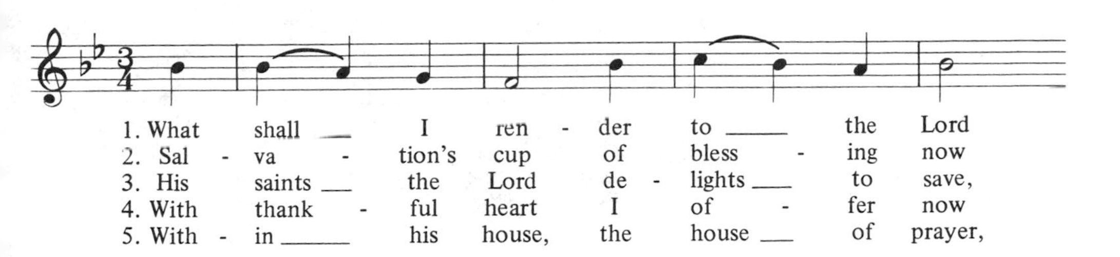
1. What shall I ren - der to the Lord
2. Sal - va - tion's cup of bless - ing now
3. His saints the Lord de - lights to save,
4. With thank - ful heart I of - fer now
5. With - in his house, the house of prayer,

1. For all his ben - e - fits to me?
2. I take and call up - on God's name;
3. Their death is pre - cious in his sight;
4. My gift, and call up - on God's name;
5. I ded - i cate my - self to God;

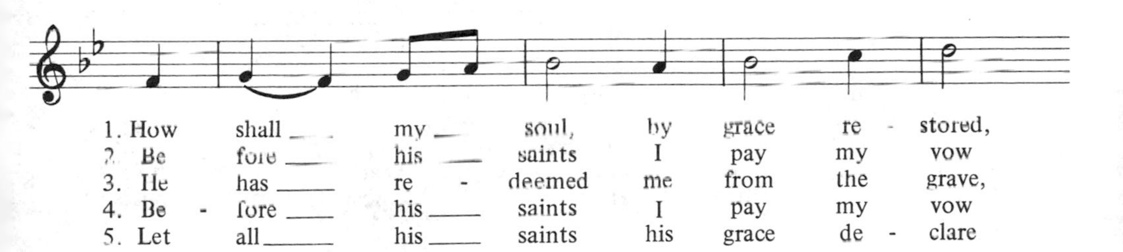
1. How shall my soul, by grace re - stored,
2. Be fore his saints I pay my vow
3. He has re - deemed me from the grave,
4. Be - fore his saints I pay my vow
5. Let all his saints his grace de - clare

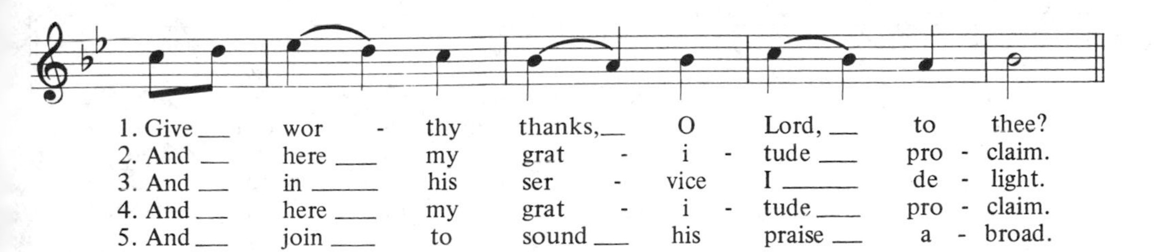
1. Give wor - thy thanks, O Lord, to thee?
2. And here my grat - i - tude pro - claim.
3. And in his ser - vice I de - light.
4. And here my grat - i - tude pro - claim.
5. And join to sound his praise a - broad.

Text: Psalm 116 paraphrase, "Psalter Hymnal", 1959.
Tune: *Wareham,* W. Knapp, +1768.

What Star Is This

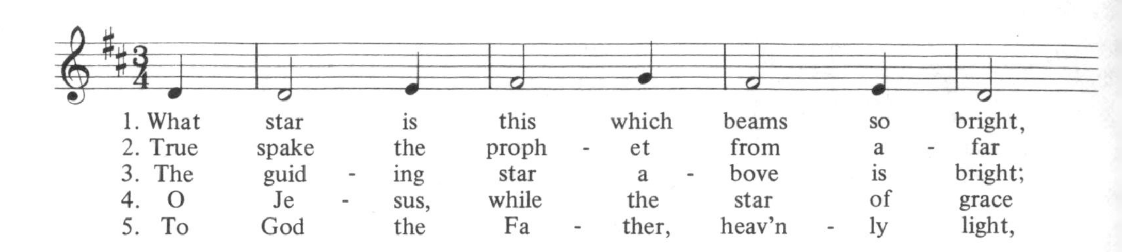
1. What star is this which beams so bright,
2. True spake the proph - et from a - far
3. The guid - ing star a - bove is bright;
4. O Je - sus, while the star of grace
5. To God the Fa - ther, heav'n - ly light,

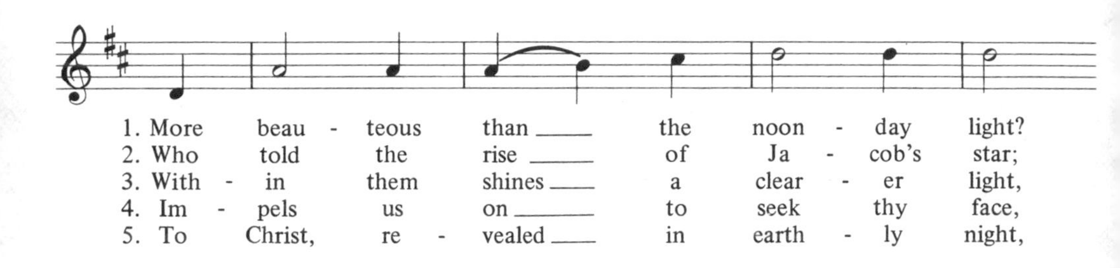
1. More beau - teous than the noon - day light?
2. Who told the rise of Ja - cob's star;
3. With - in them shines a clear - er light,
4. Im - pels us on to seek thy face,
5. To Christ, re - vealed in earth - ly night,

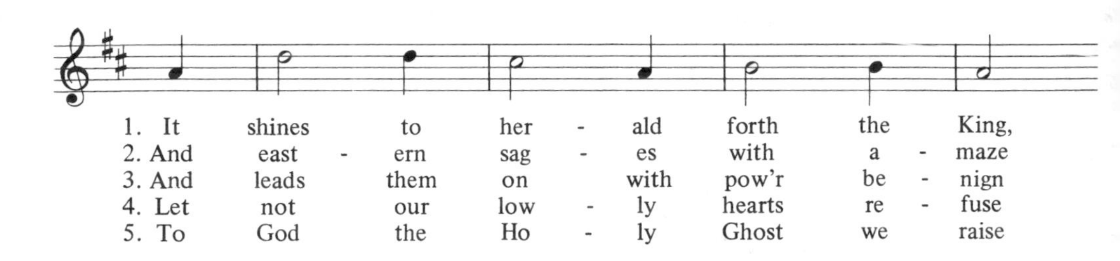
1. It shines to her - ald forth the King,
2. And east - ern sag - es with a - maze
3. And leads them on with pow'r be - nign
4. Let not our low - ly hearts re - fuse
5. To God the Ho - ly Ghost we raise

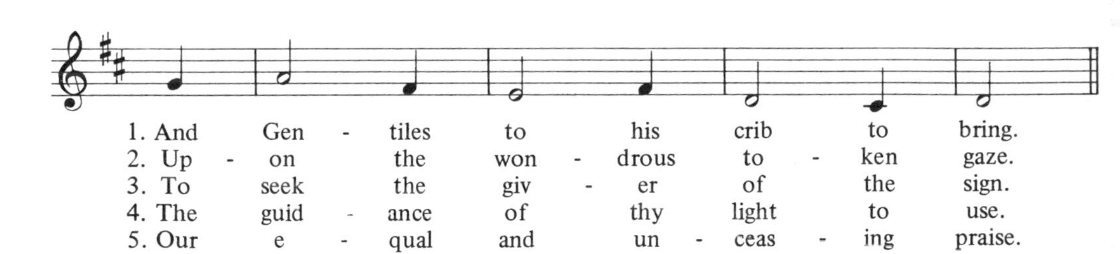
1. And Gen - tiles to his crib to bring.
2. Up - on the won - drous to - ken gaze.
3. To seek the giv - er of the sign.
4. The guid - ance of thy light to use.
5. Our e - qual and un - ceas - ing praise.

Text: C. Coffin, +1749. Trans. J. Chandler, +1876, alt.
Tune: *Puer nobis,* attributed to M. Praetorius, +1609.

Where Abideth Charity and Love

351

ANTIPHON

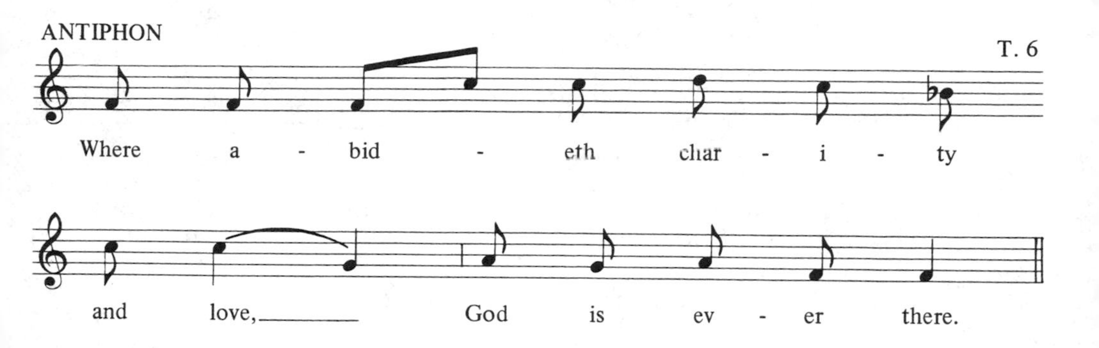
T. 6
Where a - bid - eth char - i - ty
and love, God is ev - er there.

All together one in love of Christ, our blessed Lord,
Let us sing in exultation of one accord.
Live we in holy fear and gentle love our life in God,
And give we to one another our hearts in truth.

All repeat ANTIPHON

And whenever we are come together in mind and heart,
There is no fear of quarreling among us to drive apart.
Cease all angry thoughts and bitter words, all evils end,
And Christ, our brother, comes to live among us, our guest and friend.

All repeat ANTIPHON

And when we shall see the saints in heaven, our brothers too,
There will Christ in glory shine among us, our life anew.
O joy that knows no bound nor fear of ending at love so true,
Through all the ages of eternity, world without end. Amen.

All repeat ANTIPHON

Text: Holy Thursday Liturgy. Trans. J. Nolan.
Setting: *Ubi caritas,* T. Marier, from "Cantus Populi",

352 With All My Powers of Heart and Tongue

Ps. 138

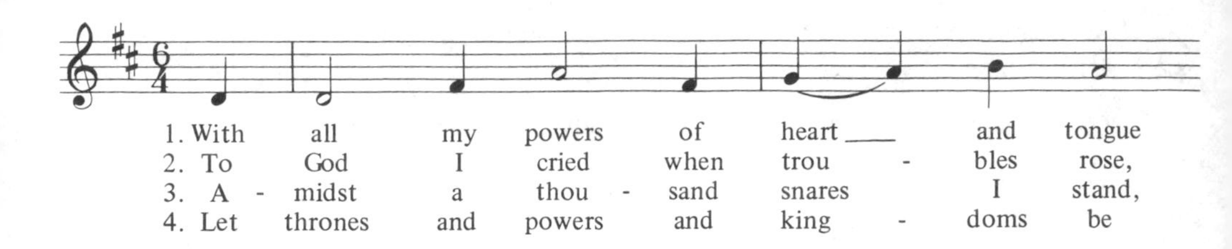
1. With all my powers of heart and tongue
2. To God I cried when trou - bles rose,
3. A - midst a thou - sand snares I stand,
4. Let thrones and powers and king - doms be

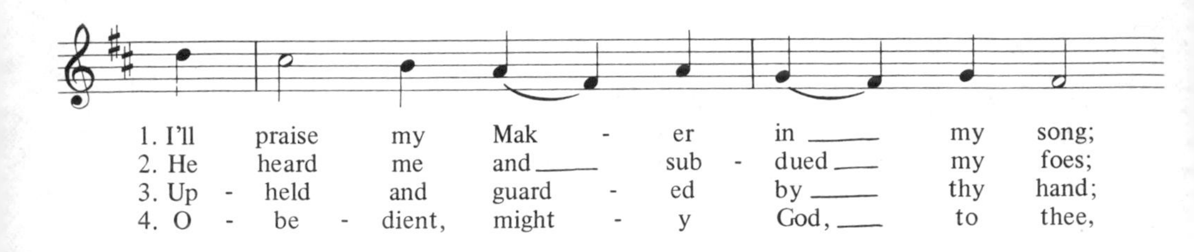
1. I'll praise my Mak - er in my song;
2. He heard me and sub - dued my foes;
3. Up - held and guard - ed by thy hand;
4. O - be - dient, might - y God, to thee,

1. The heavens shall hear the psalm I raise,
2. He did my ris - ing fears con - trol,
3. Thy words my weak - ened soul re - vive
4. And o - ver land and stream and main,

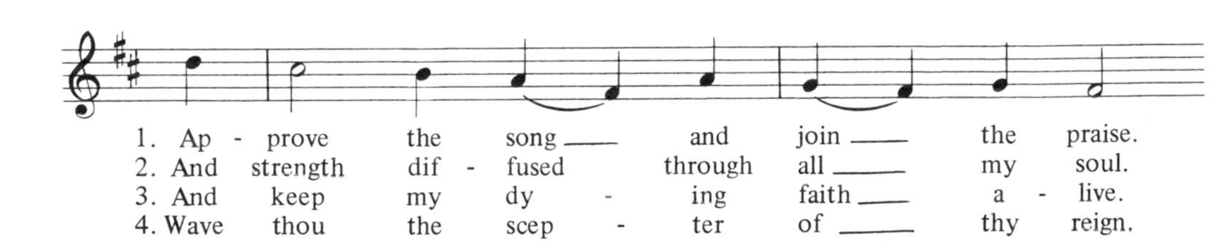
1. Ap - prove the song and join the praise.
2. And strength dif - fused through all my soul.
3. And keep my dy - ing faith a - live.
4. Wave thou the scep - ter of thy reign.

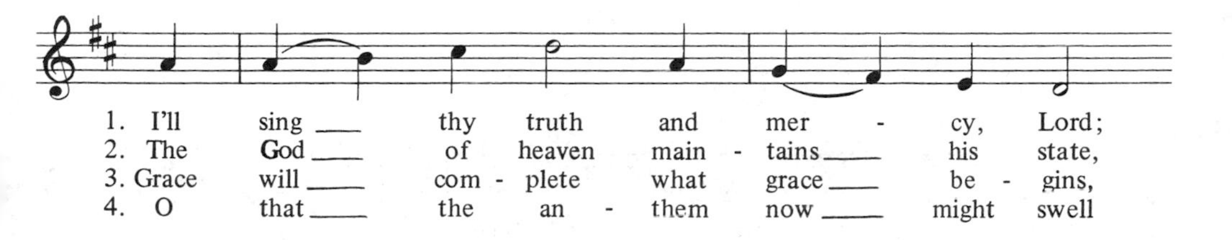
1. I'll sing thy truth and mer - cy, Lord;
2. The God of heaven main - tains his state,
3. Grace will com - plete what grace be - gins,
4. O that the an - them now might swell

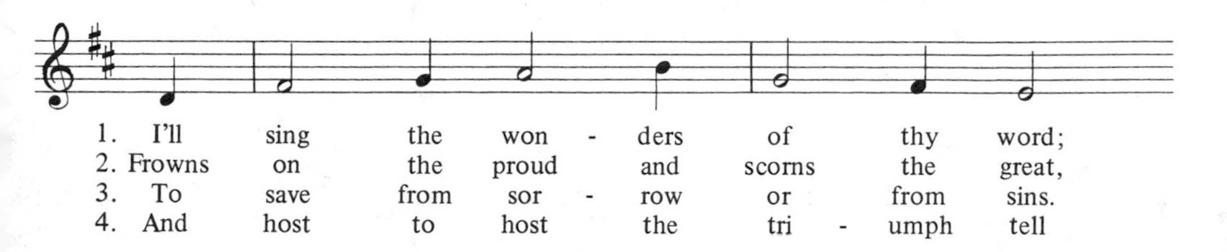
1. I'll sing the won - ders of thy word;
2. Frowns on the proud and scorns the great,
3. To save from sor - row or from sins.
4. And host to host the tri - umph tell

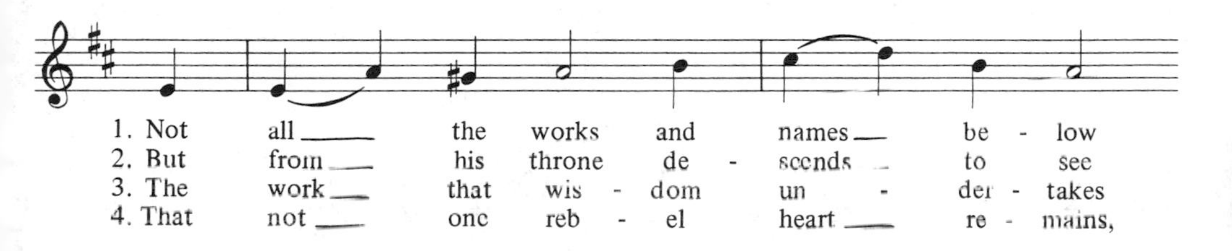
1. Not all the works and names be - low
2. But from his throne de - scends to see
3. The work that wis - dom un - der - takes
4. That not one reb - el heart re - mains,

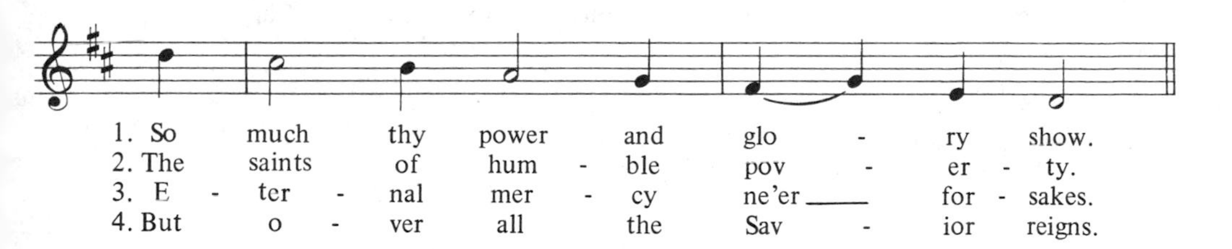
1. So much thy power and glo - ry show.
2. The saints of hum - ble pov - er - ty.
3. E - ter - nal mer - cy ne'er for - sakes.
4. But o - ver all the Sav - ior reigns.

Text: Psalm 138 paraphrase, I. Watts, +1748.
Tune: *Rottenburg*, from "Rottenburg Gesangbuch", 1865.

353 Within the Shelter of the Lord

Ps. 91

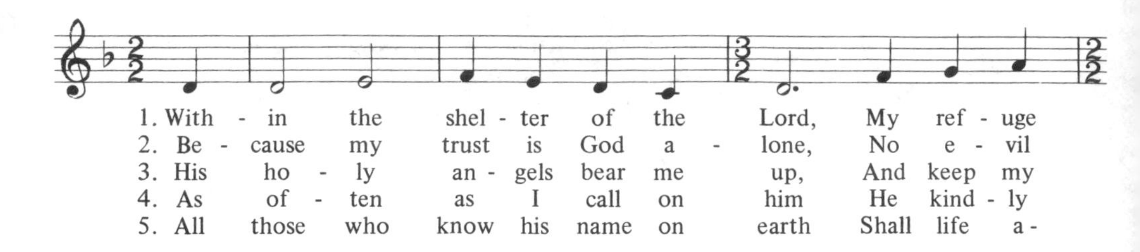

1. With - in the shel - ter of the Lord, My ref - uge
2. Be - cause my trust is God a - lone, No e - vil
3. His ho - ly an - gels bear me up, And keep my
4. As of - ten as I call on him He kind - ly
5. All those who know his name on earth Shall life a -

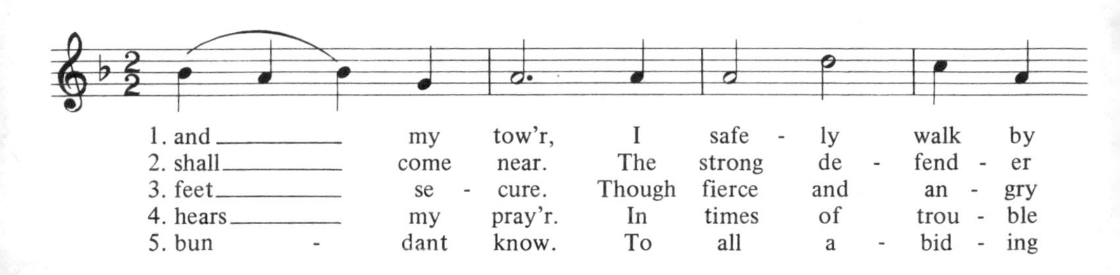

1. and my tow'r, I safe - ly walk by
2. shall come near. The strong de - fend - er
3. feet se - cure. Though fierce and an - gry
4. hears my pray'r. In times of trou - ble
5. bun - dant know. To all a - bid - ing

1. day and night Be - neath his guid - ing pow'r.
2. of my home, With him I have no fear.
3. foes as - sail, In him my way is sure.
4. and dis - tress He keeps me in his care.
5. in his love, Sal - va - tion will he show.

Text: Psalm 91 paraphrase, J. Dunn.
Tune: *Freuen wir uns all in ein,* M. Weisse, +1534, alt.

With Joy We Go up to the House of the Lord

Ps. 122

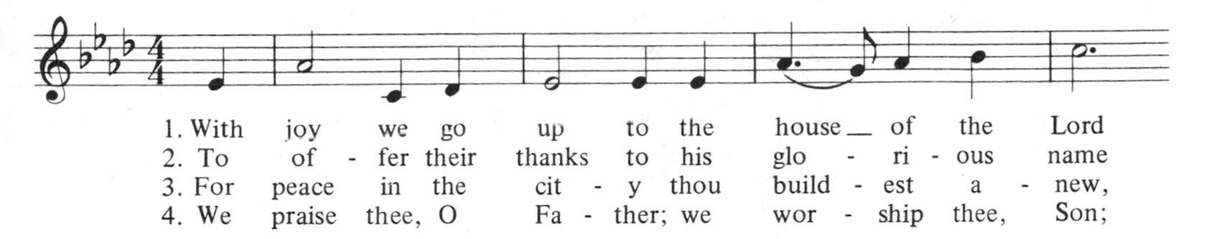
1. With joy we go up to the house of the Lord
2. To of - fer their thanks to his glo - ri - ous name
3. For peace in the cit - y thou build - est a - new,
4. We praise thee, O Fa - ther; we wor - ship thee, Son;

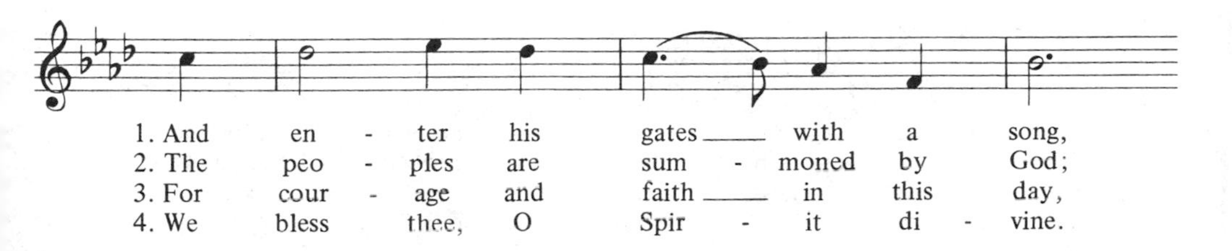
1. And en - ter his gates with a song,
2. The peo - ples are sum - moned by God;
3. For cour - age and faith in this day,
4. We bless thee, O Spir - it di - vine.

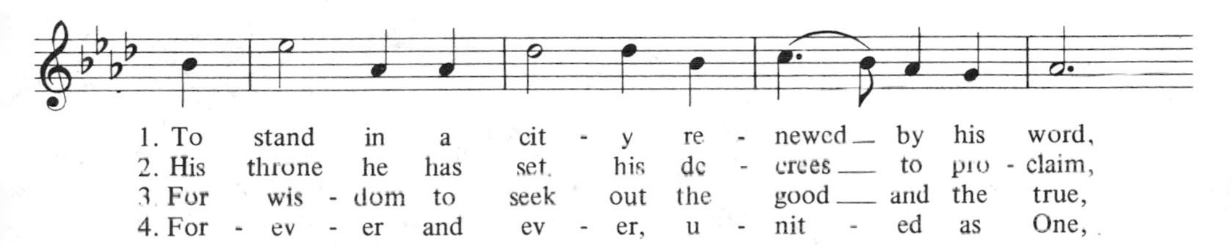
1. To stand in a cit - y re - newed by his word,
2. His throne he has set, his de - crees to pro - claim,
3. For wis - dom to seek out the good and the true,
4. For - ev - er and ev - er, u - nit - ed as One,

1. The cit - y where all men be - long.
2. His judg - ments are gone out a - broad.
3. O Lord of the na - tions, we pray.
4. All glo - ry and hon - or be thine.

Text: Psalm 122 paraphrase, J.W. Grant.
Verse 4, J. Dunn.
Tune: *Laetatus*, T. Marier.

355 Word of God, Come Down on Earth

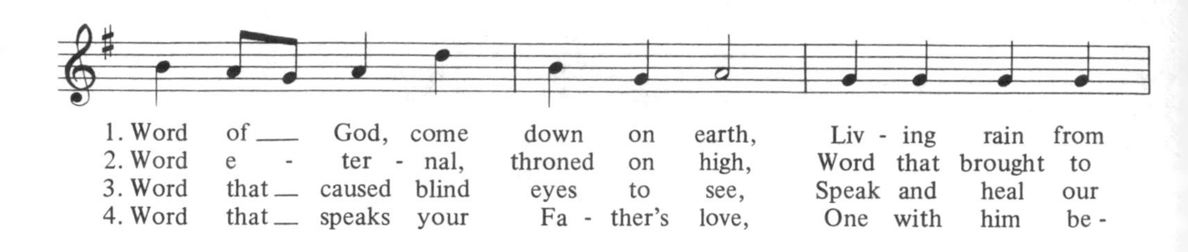
1. Word of ___ God, come down on earth, Liv - ing rain from
2. Word e - ter - nal, throned on high, Word that brought to
3. Word that ___ caused blind eyes to see, Speak and heal our
4. Word that ___ speaks your Fa - ther's love, One with him be -

1. heav'n de - scend - ing: Touch our ___ hearts and bring to birth
2. life cre - a - tion, Word that ___ came from heav'n to die,
3. mor - tal blind - ness; Deaf we ___ are: our heal - er be;
4. yond all tell - ing, Word that ___ sends us from a - bove

1. Faith and hope and love un - end - ing. Word al - might - y,
2. Cru - ci - fied for our sal - va - tion, Sav - ing Word, the
3. Loose our tongues to tell your kind - ness. Be our Word in
4. God the Spir - it, with us dwell - ing. Word of truth, to

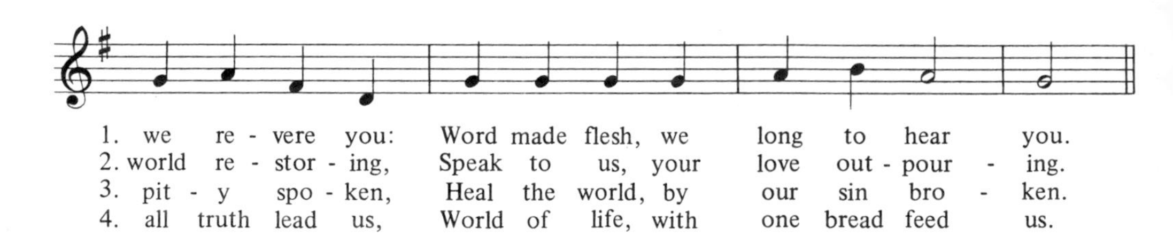
1. we re - vere you: Word made flesh, we long to hear you.
2. world re - stor - ing, Speak to us, your love out - pour - ing.
3. pit - y spo - ken, Heal the world, by our sin bro - ken.
4. all truth lead us, World of life, with one bread feed us.

Text: J. Quinn, S.J.
Tune: *Liebster Jesu,* J.R. Ahle, +1673.

Ye Holy Angels Bright

1. Ye ho - ly an - gels bright, Who wait at God's right hand,
2. Ye bless - ed souls at rest, Who ran this earth - ly race
3. Ye saints who toil be - low, A - dore your heav'n - ly King,
4. My soul, take now thy part, Re - joice in God a - bove:

1. Or through the realms of light Fly at your Lord's com - mand,
2. And now, from sin re - leased, Be - hold the Sav - ior's face,
3. And on - ward as ye go Some joy - ful an - them sing;
4. And with a well- tuned heart Sing thou the songs of love.

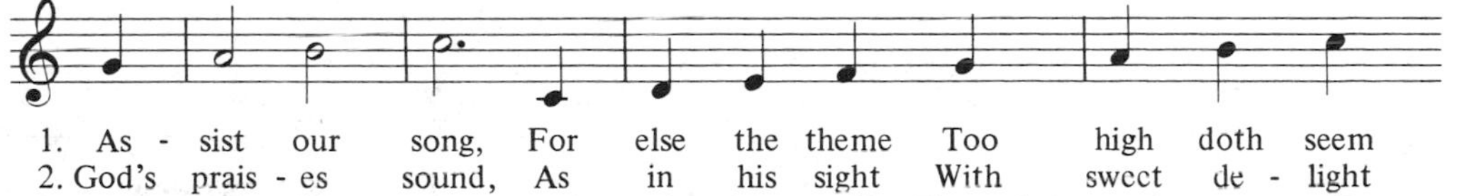

1. As - sist our song, For else the theme Too high doth seem
2. God's prais - es sound, As in his sight With sweet de - light
3. Take what he gives And praise him still, Through good or ill,
4. Let all thy days Till life shall end, What - e'er he send,

1. For mor - tal tongue.
2. Ye do a - bound.
3. Who ev - er lives.
4. Be filled with praise.

Text: R. Baxter, +1691, and J.H. Gurney, +1862, alt.
Tune: *Darwall's 148th,* J. Darwall, +1789.

Ye Servants of God, Your Master Proclaim

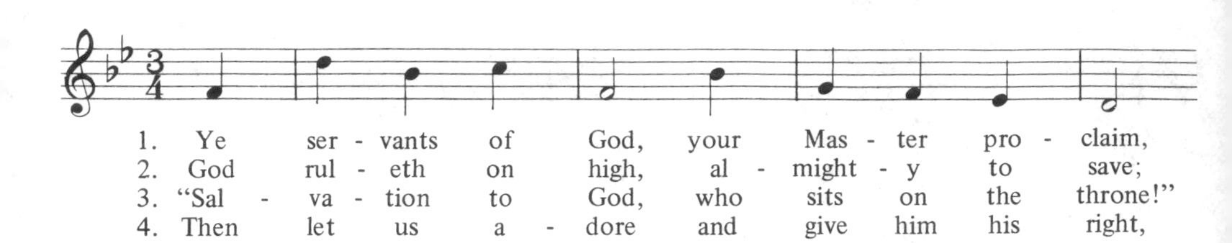
1. Ye ser - vants of God, your Mas - ter pro - claim,
2. God rul - eth on high, al - might - y to save;
3. "Sal - va - tion to God, who sits on the throne!"
4. Then let us a - dore and give him his right,

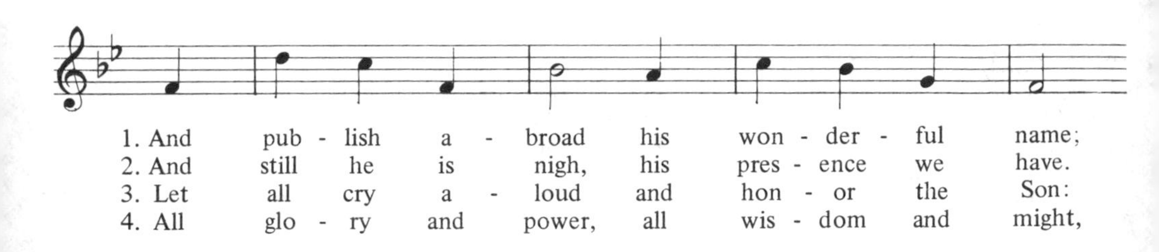
1. And pub - lish a - broad his won - der - ful name;
2. And still he is nigh, his pres - ence we have.
3. Let all cry a - loud and hon - or the Son:
4. All glo - ry and power, all wis - dom and might,

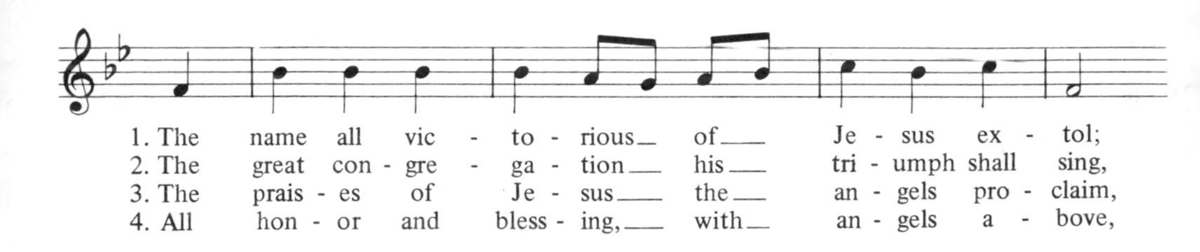
1. The name all vic - to - rious of Je - sus ex - tol;
2. The great con - gre - ga - tion his tri - umph shall sing,
3. The prais - es of Je - sus the an - gels pro - claim,
4. All hon - or and bless - ing, with an - gels a - bove,

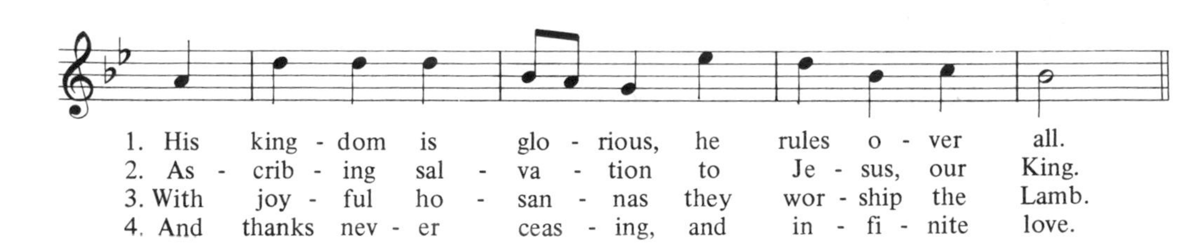
1. His king - dom is glo - rious, he rules o - ver all.
2. As - crib - ing sal - va - tion to Je - sus, our King.
3. With joy - ful ho - san - nas they wor - ship the Lamb.
4. And thanks nev - er ceas - ing, and in - fi - nite love.

Text: C. Wesley, +1788, alt.
Tune: *Laudate Dominum,* C.H.H. Parry, +1918.

Ye Sons and Daughters of the Lord 358

REFRAIN
Fine
Al - le - lu - ia, Al - le - lu - ia, Al - le - lu - ia!
1. Ye sons and daugh - ters of the Lord,
2. All in the ear - ly morn - ing grey,
3. Of spic - es pure a pre - cious store,
4. An an - gel clad in white they see,
*5. That night th'a - pos - tles met in fear,
1. The King of Glo - ry, King a - dored,
2. Went ho - ly wom - en on their way
3. In their pure hands these wom - en bore,
4. Who sat and spake un - to the three:
*5. But Christ did in their midst ap - pear:
Repeat Refrain
1. This day him - self from death re - stored. Al - le - lu - ia!
2. To see the tomb where Je - sus lay. Al - le - lu - ia!
3. To a - noint the sa - cred bod - y o'er. Al - le - lu - ia!
4. "Your Lord hath gone to Gal - i - lee." Al - le - lu - ia!
*5. "My peace," he saith, "be on all here." Al - le - lu - ia!

*6. When Thomas first the tidings heard,
How they had seen the risen Lord,
He doubted the disciples' word.
Alleluia!

*7. "My piercéd side, O Thomas, see;
My hands, my feet, I show to thee;
Not faithless, but believing be."
Alleluia!

*8. No longer Thomas then denied,
He saw the feet, the hands, the side;
"Thou art my Lord and God," he cried.
Alleluia!

*9. How blest are they who have not seen
And yet whose faith has constant been,
For they eternal life shall win.
Alleluia!

10. On this most holy day of days,
To God your hearts and voices raise
In laud, and jubilee, and praise.
Alleluia!

*Verses suitable for the Second Sunday of Easter.

Text: J. Tisserand, +1494.
Verses 1-5 trans. E. Caswall, +1878.
Verses 6-10, J.M. Neale, +1866.
Tune: *O filii et filiae,* French Melody, Mode 2.

359 Ye Watchers and Ye Holy Ones

1. Ye watch - ers and ye ho - ly ones, Bright
2. O high - er than the cher - u - bim, More
3. Re - spond, ye souls, in end - less rest, Ye
4. O friends, in glad - ness let us sing, Su -
1. ser - aphs, cher - u - bim and thrones, Raise the
2. glo - rious than the ser - a - phim, Lead their
3. pa - tri - archs and proph - ets blest, Al - le -
4. per - nal an - thems ech - o - ing, Al - le -
1. glad strain, Al - le - lu - ia! Cry out, do - min - ions,
2. prais - es, Al - le - lu - ia! Thou bear - er of th'e -
3. lu - ia, Al - le - lu - ia! Ye ho - ly twelve, ye
4. lu - ia, Al - le - lu - ia! To God the Fa - ther,
1. prince - doms, pow'rs, Vir - tues, arch - an - gels, an - gels' choirs,
2. ter - nal Word, Most gra - cious, mag - ni - fy the Lord,
3. mar - tyrs strong, All saints tri - um - phant, raise the song:
4. God the Son, And God the Spir - it, Three in One,
1.- 4. Al - le - lu - ia, Al - le - lu - ia, Al - le -
1.- 4. lu - ia, Al - le - lu - ia, Al - le - lu - ia!

Text: A. Riley, +1945.
Tune: *Vigiles et sancti,* "Cologne Gesangbuch", 1623.

You Satisfy the Hungry Heart

Gift of Finest Wheat

REFRAIN
You sat - is - fy the hun - gry heart With gift of fin - est wheat;
Come, give to us, O ___ sav - ing Lord, The bread of life to eat.
Fine
1. As when the shep - herd calls his sheep They
2. With joy - ful lips we sing to you Our
3. Is not the cup we bless and share The
4. The mys - t'ry of your pres - ence, Lord, No
5. You give your - self to us, O Lord; Then
1. know and heed his voice; So when you call your
2. praise and grat - i - tude, That you should count us
3. blood of Christ out - poured? Do not one cup, one
4. mor - tal tongue can tell: Whom all the world can -
5. self - less let us be, To serve each oth - er
Repeat Refrain
1. fam - 'ly Lord, We fol - low and re - joice.
2. wor - thy, Lord, To share this heav'n - ly food.
3. loaf de - clare, Our one - ness in the Lord?
4. not con - tain Comes in our hearts to dwell.
5. in your name In truth and char - i - ty.

Text: O. Westendorf.
Tune: *Finest Wheat,* R.E. Kreutz.

361

You Are God: We Praise You

Te Deum

ANTIPHON

All the world worships you, the everlasting Father.

Verses – Cantor and Schola or All, alternating

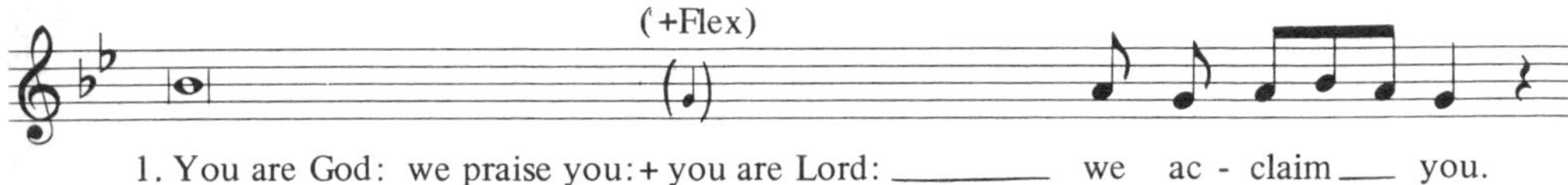
(+Flex)

1. You are God: we praise you: + you are Lord: we ac - claim you.
3. The glorious company of apostles praise you. + The noble fellowship of proph-ets praise you.
5. You, Christ, are the King of glo - ry,
7. You are seated at God's right hand in glo - ry.

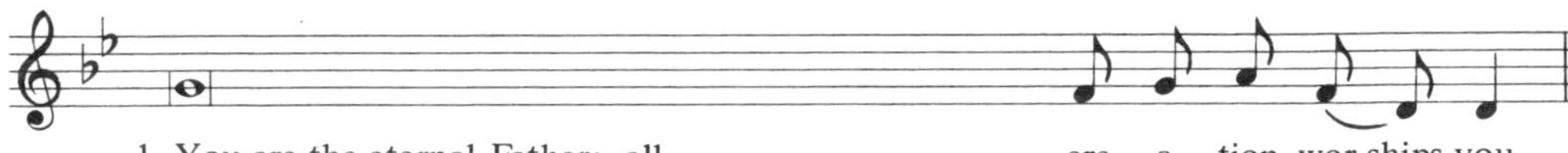

1. You are the eternal Father: all cre - a - tion wor-ships you.
3. The white-robed army of mar-tyrs praise you.
5. The eternal Son of the Fa - ther.
7. We believe that you will come and be our judge.

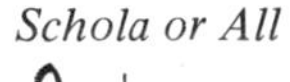
Schola or All

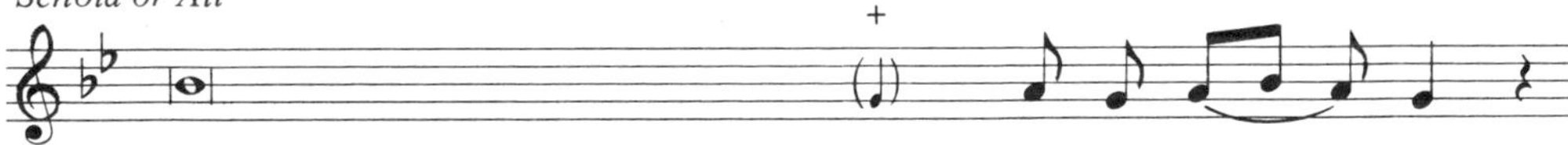
+

2. To you all angels, all the powers of heaven, + cherubim and seraphim, sing in end - less praise:
4. Throughout the world the holy Church acclaims you: + Father of majes - ty un - bound - ed,
6. When you became man to set us free you did not spurn the Vir - gin's womb.
8. Come then, Lord, and help your people, + bought with the price of your own blood,

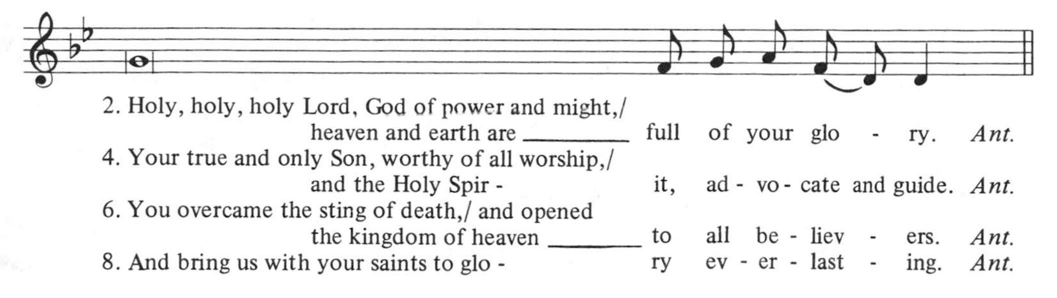
2. Holy, holy, holy Lord, God of power and might,/
heaven and earth are full of your glo - ry. Ant.
4. Your true and only Son, worthy of all worship,/
and the Holy Spir - it, ad - vo - cate and guide. Ant.
6. You overcame the sting of death,/ and opened
the kingdom of heaven to all be - liev - ers. Ant.
8. And bring us with your saints to glo - ry ev - er - last - ing. Ant.

CONCLUSION

Optional Versicles and Responses

Cel. or Schola

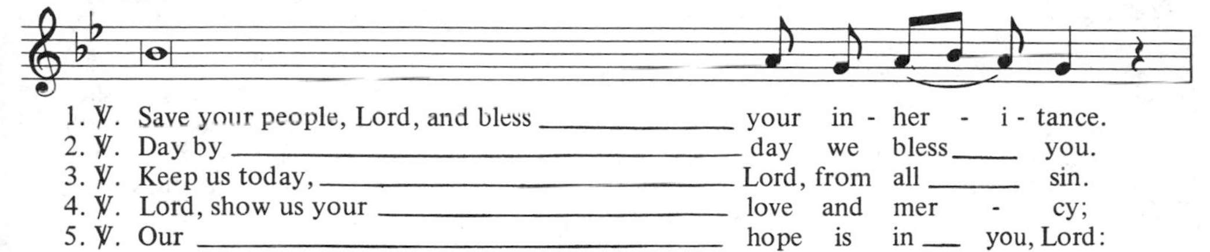
1. ℣. Save your people, Lord, and bless your in - her - i - tance.
2. ℣. Day by day we bless you.
3. ℣. Keep us today, Lord, from all sin.
4. ℣. Lord, show us your love and mer - cy;
5. ℣. Our hope is in you, Lord:

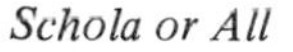
Schola or All

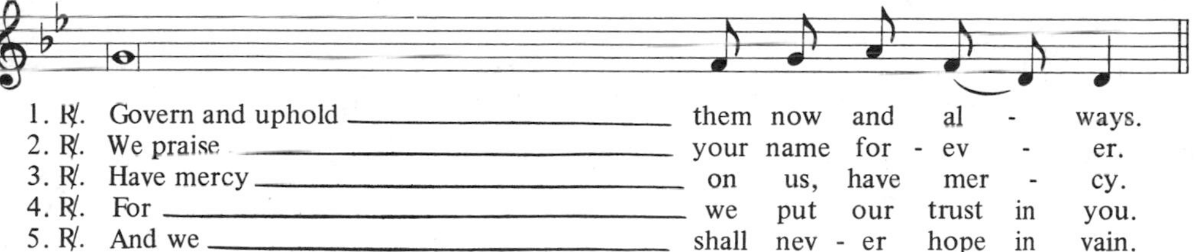
1. ℟. Govern and uphold them now and al - ways.
2. ℟. We praise your name for - ev - er.
3. ℟. Have mercy on us, have mer - cy.
4. ℟. For we put our trust in you.
5. ℟. And we shall nev - er hope in vain.

Repeat Antiphon

Text: *Te Deum,* attributed to St. Nicetas, +415. Trans.

Tune: *Te Deum Laudamus,* Gregorian Chant (Old Roman Version), adapt. T. Marier.

362 You Called Me, Father, by My Name

1. You called me, Fa - ther, by my name When
2. You give me free - dom to be - lieve; To -
3. With - in the cir - cle of the faith, As
4. In all the ten - sions of my life, Be -
5. So help me in my un - be - lief And

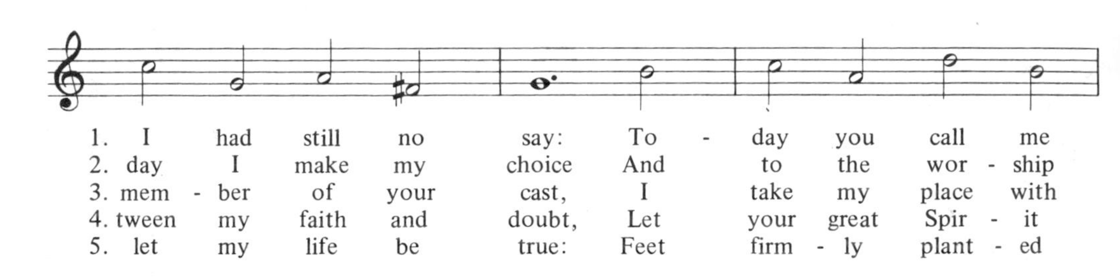
1. I had still no say: To - day you call me
2. day I make my choice And to the wor - ship
3. mem - ber of your cast, I take my place with
4. tween my faith and doubt, Let your great Spir - it
5. let my life be true: Feet firm - ly plant - ed

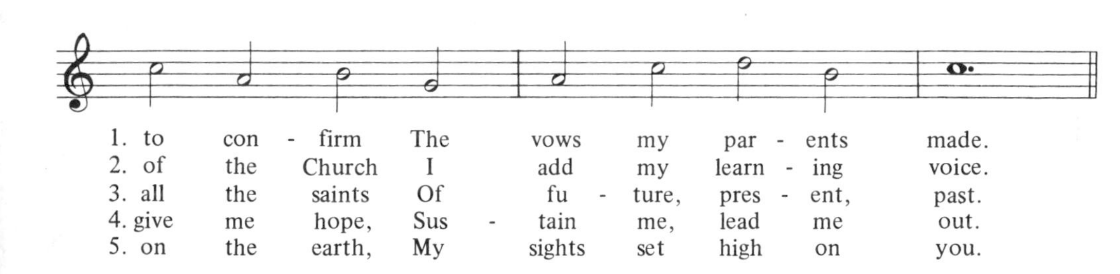
1. to con - firm The vows my par - ents made.
2. of the Church I add my learn - ing voice.
3. all the saints Of fu - ture, pres - ent, past.
4. give me hope, Sus - tain me, lead me out.
5. on the earth, My sights set high on you.

Text: F. Kaan.
Tune: *St. Anne*, W. Croft, +1727.

Ps. 1
Happy Are They Who Follow Not the Counsel of the Wicked

ANTIPHON: Happy are they who hope in the Lord

T. 8G
Hap - py are they who hope in the Lord.

PSALM 1: 1-2. 3a-3b. 4. 6.

Happy are they who follow not the counsel of the wicked
nor walk in the way of sinners,
Nor sit in the company of the insolent,
But delight in the law of the Lord
and meditate on his law day and night.

All repeat ANTIPHON

They are like trees planted near running water
That yield their fruit in due season,
And whose leaves never fade.
Whatever they do prospers.

All repeat ANTIPHON

Not so the wicked, not so;
They are like chaff which the wind drives away.
For the Lord watches over the way of the just,
But the way of the wicked vanishes.

All repeat ANTIPHON

364

Ps. 4
O My Just God, When I Call, Answer Me

ANTIPHON: O Lord, let your face shine on us

T.2
O Lord, let your face shine on us.

PSALM 4: 2. 4. 7-8. 9.

O my just God, when I call, answer me,
When I am afflicted you come to my help;
Have pity on me,
And hear my prayer!

All repeat ANTIPHON

Know that the Lord does wonders for his faithful one;
When I call upon him, the Lord will hear me.
Let the light of your countenance shine upon us, O Lord!
You put gladness in my heart.

All repeat ANTIPHON

As soon as I lie down,
I fall peacefully asleep,
For you alone, O Lord,
Make me dwell in safety.

All repeat ANTIPHON

Ps. 8
When I Behold Your Heavens

ANTIPHON: O Lord, our God, how wonderful your name

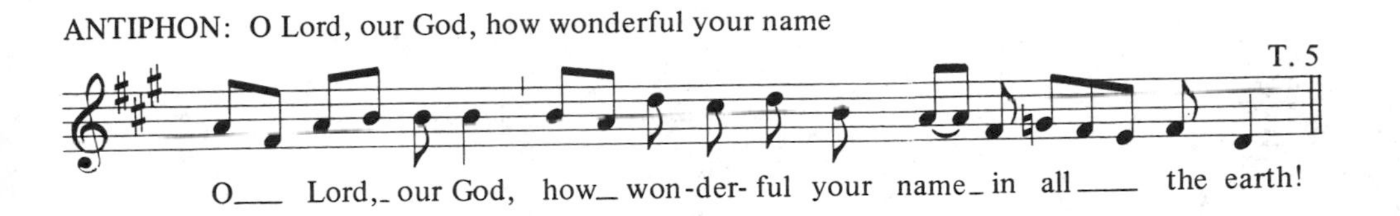
T. 5
O___ Lord,_ our God, how_ won-der- ful your name_ in all___ the earth!

PSALM 8: 4-5. 6-7. 8-9.

When I behold your heavens which you have made,
The moon and the stars which you set in place,
What is man that you should think of him,
Or the son of man that you should care for him?

All repeat ANTIPHON

You have made him little less than the angels,
And crowned him with glory and honor.
Over the works of your hands you have given him dominion,
Putting all things under his feet:

All repeat ANTIPHON

All sheep and oxen,
Yes, and the beasts of the fields,
All birds and fishes,
And whatever swims the paths of the seas.

All repeat ANTIPHON

366

Ps. 13
But I Have Trusted in Thy Steadfast Love

ANTIPHON: With delight I rejoice in the Lord

T. 6
With de - light I re - joice in the Lord.

PSALM 13: 5. 6.

Though I have trusted in thy steadfast love;
In thy salvation my heart shall rejoice.

All repeat ANTIPHON

I will sing to the Lord,
Because he has been good to me.

All repeat ANTIPHON

Ps. 15
They Who Walk Blamelessly

ANTIPHON: They who do justice will live

T.6
They who do — jus - tice will live — in the pres-ence of the Lord.

PSALM 15: 2-3.3-4.4-5.

They who walk blamelessly
And do what is right;
Who think the truth in their hearts
And slander not with their tongues;

All repeat ANTIPHON

Who harm not their neighbors,
And do not spread rumors about their friends;
By whom the reprobate is despised,
While they honor those who fear the Lord;

All repeat ANTIPHON

Who lend not their money at usury
And against the innocent accept no bribe;
Whoever does these things
Shall never be disturbed.

All repeat ANTIPHON

368

Ps. 16
Keep Me, O God, for in You I Take Refuge

ANTIPHONS: A You are my inheritance, O Lord
B Lord, you will show us the path of life
C Keep me safe, O God; you are my hope

T.6
A You___ are___ my in - her - i - tance,___ O___ Lord.
B Lord,___ you___ will___ show___ us___ the path___ of life.

T. 6
C Keep me safe,___ O God; you___ are___ my hope.

PSALM 16: 1-2. 5. 7-8. 9. 11.

Keep me safe, O God, for in you I take refuge;
I say to the Lord, "My Lord are you."
O Lord, my allotted portion and my cup,
You it is who hold fast my lot.

All repeat ANTIPHON

I bless the Lord who counsels me;
My heart exhorts me even in the night.
I set the Lord ever before me;
With him at my right hand I shall not be disturbed.

All repeat ANTIPHON

Therefore my heart is glad and my soul rejoices,
My body, too, abides in confidence.
You will show me the path to life, fullness of joy in your presence,
The delights forever at your right hand.

All repeat ANTIPHON

Ps. 17
Hear, O Lord, a Just Cause

ANTIPHON: O Lord, when your glory appears

T.Per.
O Lord, when your glo - ry ap-pears, my joy will be full.

PSALM 17: 1. 5-6. 8. 15.

Hear, O Lord, a just cause;
Listen to my plea;
Hearken to my prayer
From lips without deceit.

All repeat ANTIPHON

My steps have been steadfast in your paths,
From your way I have not strayed.
I call upon you, for you will answer me, O God;
Listen to me; hear my word.

All repeat ANTIPHON

Keep me as the apple of your eye,
Hide me in the shadow of your wings.
But I shall behold your face in righteousness;
I shall be content in your presence when I awake.

All repeat ANTIPHON

370

Ps. 18
I Love You, O Lord, My Strength

ANTIPHON: I love you, O Lord, my strength

T.7c
I love you, O Lord, my strength.

PSALM 18: 2-3. 3-4. 47. 50-51.

I love you, O Lord, my strength,
O Lord, my fortress, my deliverer, my rock;
My God, my rock of refuge,
The horn of my salvation, my stronghold and my shield!

All repeat ANTIPHON

I exclaim, praised be the Lord,
And from my enemies I am safe.
The Lord lives! And blessed be my Rock!
May God, my Savior, be extolled!

All repeat ANTIPHON

Among the nations I will extol you, Lord,
And sing praises to your name.
You gave great victories to your king
And showed kindness to your anointed one.

All repeat ANTIPHON

Ps. 19(I) 371

The Law of the Lord Is Perfect

ANTIPHON: Lord, you have the words of everlasting life

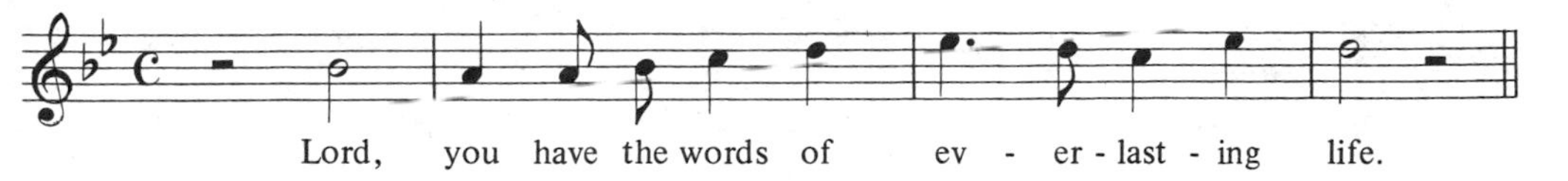
Lord, you have the words of ev - er - last - ing life.

PSALM 19: 8. 9. 10. 11.

The law of the Lord is perfect,
Refreshing the soul;
The decree of the Lord is trustworthy,
Giving wisdom to the simple.
The precepts of the Lord are right,
Rejoicing the heart;
The command of the Lord is clear,
enlightening the eye.

All repeat ANTIPHON

The fear of the Lord is pure,
Enduring forever;
The ordinances of the Lord are true,
All of them are just.
They are more precious than gold,
Than a heap of purest gold;
Sweeter also than syrup
Or honey from the comb.

All repeat ANTIPHON *below*

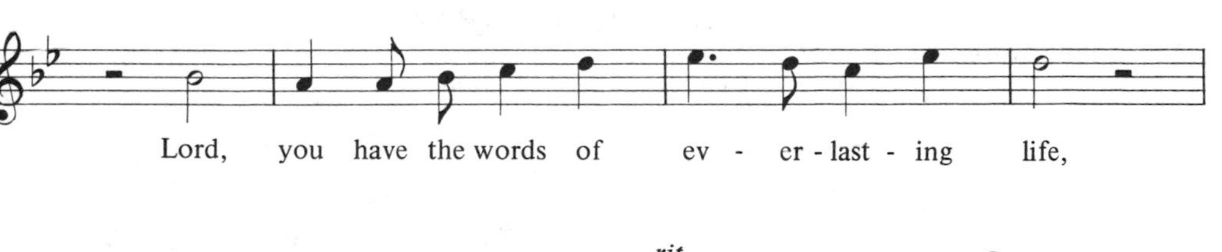
Lord, you have the words of ev - er - last - ing life,
rit.
ev - er - last - ing life.

Ps. 19(II)
The Law of the Lord Is Perfect

ANTIPHONS: A You, Lord, have the words of everlasting life
B Your words, Lord, are spirit and life

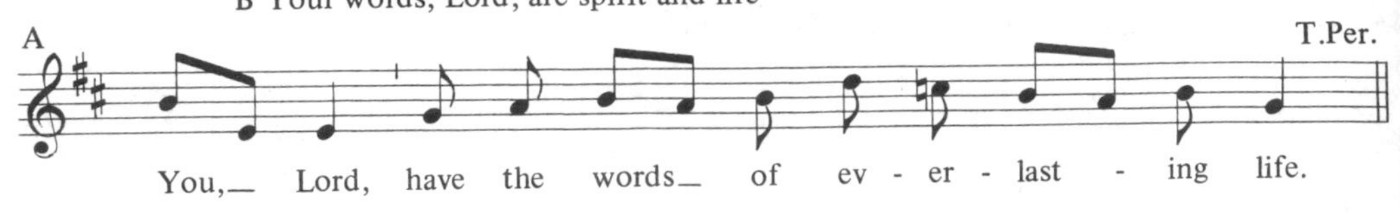
A
T.Per.
You, Lord, have the words of ev - er - last - ing life.

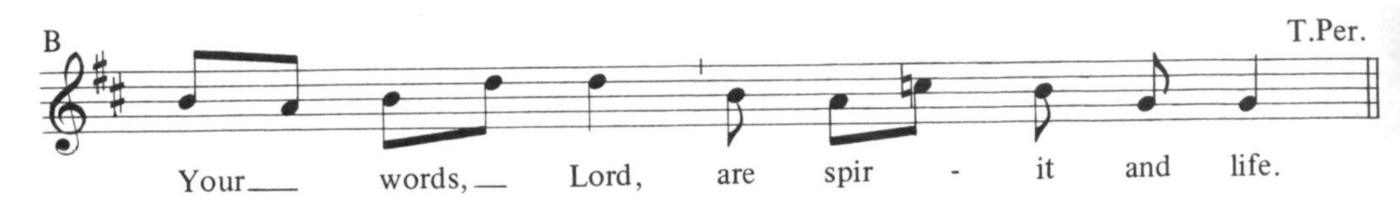
B
T.Per.
Your words, Lord, are spir - it and life.

PSALM 19: 8-9. 10-11. 15.

The law of the Lord is perfect,
Refreshing the soul;
The decree of the Lord is trustworthy,
Making the simple wise.
The precepts of the Lord are right,
Rejoicing the heart;
The command of the Lord is clear,
Enlightening the eye.

All repeat ANTIPHON

The fear of the Lord is pure,
Enduring forever;
The ordinances of the Lord are true,
All of them are just.
They are more precious than gold,
Than a heap of purest gold;
Sweeter also than syrup
Or honey from the comb.

All repeat ANTIPHON

Let the words of my mouth and the thought of my
heart find favor before you,
My redeemer and my rock, O Lord.

All repeat ANTIPHON

Ps. 19(III)
The Heavens Declare the Glory of God

ANTIPHONS: A Their message goes out to all the earth
B The precepts of the Lord give joy to the heart

A
T.5
Their mes - sage goes out to all the earth.
B
T.5
The pre - cepts of the Lord give joy to the heart.

PSALM 19: 2–3. 4–5. 8. 10. 12–13. 14.

A The heavens declare the glory of God,
And the firmament proclaims his handiwork.
Day pours out the word to day,
And night to night imparts knowledge.

All repeat ANTIPHON A

Not a discourse nor a word
Whose voice is not heard.
Through all the earth their voice resounds,
And to the ends of the world their message.

All repeat ANTIPHON A

B The law of the Lord is perfect, refreshing the soul;
The decree of the Lord is trustworthy,
giving wisdom to the simple.
The fear of the Lord is pure, enduring forever;
The ordinances of the Lord are true,
all of them just.

All repeat ANTIPHON B

Though your servant is careful to observe them,
In keeping them very diligent,
Yet who can detect failings?
From my unknown faults cleanse me.

All repeat ANTIPHON B

Restrain your servant from wanton sin;
Let it not rule over me.
Then I shall be blameless
And of serious sin innocent.

All repeat ANTIPHON B

374

Ps. 22(I)
All You Who See Me Scoff at Me

ANTIPHON: My God, my God, why have you forsaken me?

Graduale Simplex

My___ God,___ my___ God,___ why have you for - sak - en___ me?

PSALM 22: 8-9. 17-18a. 19-20. 23-24.

All you who see me scoff at me;
They mock me with parted lips, they wag their heads:
"He relied on the Lord; let him deliver him,
Let him rescue him if he loves him."

All repeat ANTIPHON

Indeed, many dogs surround me,
A pack of evildoers closes in upon me;
They have pierced my hands and feet;
I can count all my bones.

All repeat ANTIPHON

They divide my garments among them,
And for my vesture they cast lots.
But you, O Lord, be not far from me;
O my help, hasten to aid me.

All repeat ANTIPHON

I will proclaim your name to my brethren;
In the midst of the assembly I will praise you:
"You who fear the Lord, praise him;
All you descendants of Jacob, give glory to him."

All repeat ANTIPHON

Ps. 22(II)
I Will Fulfill My Vows

ANTIPHON: In the assembly of your people, I will praise you, Lord

T.3a
In the as-sem-bly of your peo - ple, I will praise you, Lord.

PSALM 22: 26-28. 31-32.

I will fulfill my vows before those who fear the Lord.
The lowly shall eat their fill;
They who seek the Lord shall praise him:
"Merry may your hearts ever be."

All repeat ANTIPHON

All the ends of the earth
Shall remember the Lord and turn to him;
All the families of nations
Shall bow down before him.

All repeat ANTIPHON

And for him my soul shall live;
My descendants shall serve him.
Let the coming generations be told of the Lord
That they may proclaim to a people yet to be born
the justice he has shown.

All repeat ANTIPHON

Ps. 23(I)
The Lord Is My Shepherd

ANTIPHONS: A The Lord is my shepherd
B I shall live in the house of the Lord

A
T.2
The Lord_ is my_ shep - herd; there_ is noth - ing I_____ shall want.

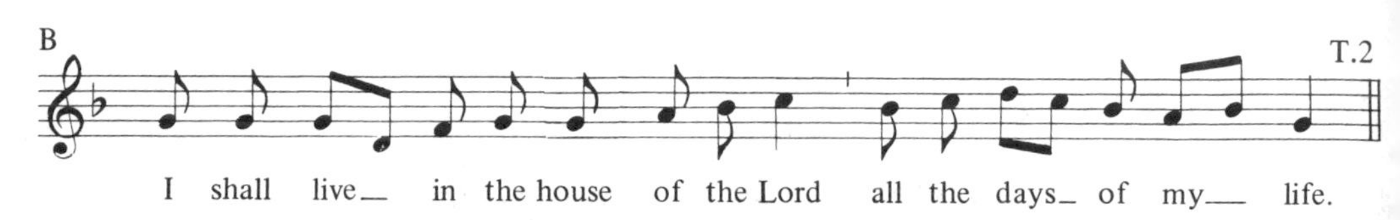
B
T.2
I shall live_ in the house of the Lord all the days_ of my_ life.

PSALM 23: 1-6.

The Lord is my shepherd;
I shall not want.
He gives me rest in green pastures;
He leads me to waters of peace.

All repeat ANTIPHON

He refreshes my soul;
He guides me by right paths for his name's sake.
Though I walk in a death-dark valley,
I fear no harm.

All repeat ANTIPHON

For you are with me;
Your rod and your staff reassure me.
You spread a table before me
In the sight of my enemies.

All repeat ANTIPHON

You perfume my head with oil,
And my cup brims over.
Yes, goodness and mercy will follow me all the days of my life,
And I shall dwell in the house of the Lord forever.

All repeat ANTIPHON

Ps. 23(II)

The Lord Is My Shepherd

ANTIPHON: I am the Good Shepherd

Sr. Theophane Hytrek

2
I am the Good Shep - herd, I pas - ture my sheep, For

them I lay down my life, al - le - lu - ia.

PSALM 23: 1.2.4.5.6.

The Lord is my shepherd; there is nothing I shall want.
Fresh and green are the pastures where he gives me repose.

All repeat ANTIPHON

Near restful waters he leads me, to revive my drooping spirit.
He guides me along the right path, he is true to his name.

All repeat ANTIPHON

If I should walk in the valley of darkness, no evil would I fear.
You are there with your crook and your staff,
with these you give me comfort.

All repeat ANTIPHON

You have prepared a banquet for me in the sight of my foes.
My head you have anointed with oil;
my cup is overflowing.

All repeat ANTIPHON

Surely, goodness and kindness shall follow me all the days of my life.
In the Lord's own house shall I dwell forever and ever.

All repeat ANTIPHON

DOX.: Give praise to the Father Almighty, to the Son, Christ the Lord,
To the Spirit who dwells in our hearts both now and forever.

All repeat ANTIPHON

378

Ps. 23(III)
Dominus Pascit Me

ANTIPHON: Panem caeli dedit eis: Alleluia

Gregorian Chant
T.6
Pa-nem cae-li de-dit e-is: al-le-lú-ia, al-le-lú-ia.
He gave them bread from heaven: praise God.

PSALM 23: 1-6.

Dóminus pascit me: nihil mihi de-est;
In páscuis viréntibus cubáre me facit.
Ad aquas, ubi quiéscam, condúcit me;
Réficit ánimam meam.

All repeat ANTIPHON

Dedúcit me per sémitas rectas
Propter nomen suum.
Etsi incédam in valle tenebrósa,
Non timébo mala, quia tu mecum es.

All repeat ANTIPHON

Virga tua et báculus tuus:
Haec me consolántur.
Paras mihi mensam
Spectántibus adversáriis meis;

All repeat ANTIPHON

Inungis oleo caput meum;
Calix meus ubérrimus est.
Benígnitas et grátia me sequéntur
Cunctis diébus vitae meae,

All repeat ANTIPHON

Et habitábo in domo Dómini
In longíssima témpora.

All repeat ANTIPHON

Glória Patri, et Fílio,
Et Spirítui Sancto.
Sicut erat in princípio, et nunc et semper,
Et in sáecula saeculórum. Amen.

All repeat ANTIPHON

*Psalm 22 in Latin psalter.

For translation, see preceding psalm setting.

Ps. 24(1) 379
The Lord's Are the Earth and Its Fullness

ANTIPHONS: A Let the Lord enter
B Here, Lord, are your people

A

Let the Lord_ en - ter; he__ is King__ of glo - ry.

B

T.Per.
Here,_ Lord,_ are your peo - ple, that long_ to see__ you__ face_ to__ face.

PSALM 24: 1-2. 3-4. 5-6.

The Lord's are the earth and its fullness;
The world and those who dwell in it.
For he founded it upon the seas
And upon the rivers he established it.

All repeat ANTIPHON

Who can ascend the mountain of the Lord;
Or who may stand in his holy place?
They whose hands are without sin, whose hearts are clean,
Who desire not what is vain.

All repeat ANTIPHON

They shall receive a blessing from the Lord,
From God their Savior, a reward.
Such is the race that seeks for him,
That seeks the face of Jacob's God.

All repeat ANTIPHON

380

Ps. 24(II)
Lift Up Your Heads, O Gates!

ANTIPHON: Who is this King of glory?

T.5
Who is this King of glo - ry? It is the Lord.

PSALM 24: 7-8. 9-10.

Lift up your heads, O gates! and be lifted up,
O ancient doors!
That the King of glory may come in.
Who is the King of glory?
The Lord, strong and mighty, the Lord,
mighty in battle!

All repeat ANTIPHON

Lift up your heads, O gates! and be lifted up,
O ancient doors!
That the King of glory may come in.
Who is this King of glory?
The Lord of hosts, he is the King of glory!

All repeat ANTIPHON

Ps. 25(I)

Make Known Your Ways to Me, O Lord

ANTIPHONS: A To you do I lift up my soul
B Teach me your ways, O Lord

A
T. 3a
To you do I lift up my soul, O Lord, my God.

B
T. 3a
Teach me your ways, O Lord.

PSALM 25: 4-5. 5-6. 8-9. 10. 14.

Make known your ways to me, O Lord;
Teach me your paths.
Guide me in your truth and teach me,
For you are my Savior and my God.

All repeat ANTIPHON

Remember that your compassion, O Lord,
And your kindness are of old.
Remember me in your kindness,
Because of your goodness, O Lord.

All repeat ANTIPHON

The Lord is good and upright;
Thus to sinners he shows the way.
He guides the humble to justice;
He teaches the humble his way.

All repeat ANTIPHON

Kindness and constancy are the pathways of the Lord
Toward those who keep his covenant and his decrees.
The friendship of the Lord is with those who fear him,
An his covenant he makes known to them.

All repeat ANTIPHON

382

Ps. 25(II)
Make Known Your Ways to Me, O Lord

ANTIPHONS: A Your ways, Lord, are love and truth
B Remember your mercies, Lord

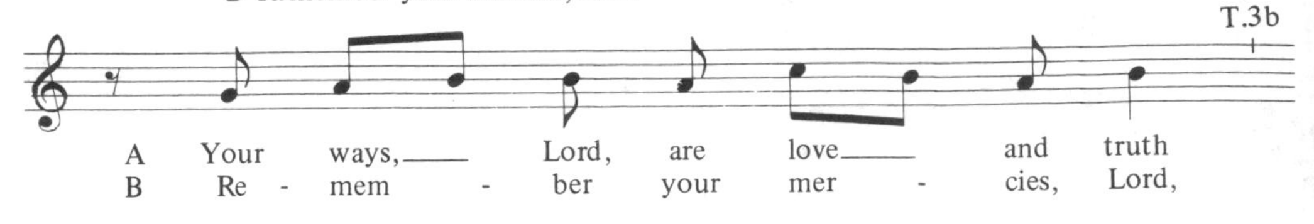
T.3b
A Your ways, Lord, are love and truth
B Re - mem - ber your mer - cies, Lord,

to those who keep your cov - e - nant.
toward those who keep your cov - e - nant.

PSALM 25: 4-10. 14.

Make known your ways to me, O Lord;
Teach me your paths;
Guide me in your truth and teach me,
For you are God, my Savior.

All repeat ANTIPHON

Remember that your compassion, O Lord,
And your kindness are from of old.
Remember me in your kindness,
Because of your goodness, O Lord.

All repeat ANTIPHON

The Lord is good and upright;
Thus to sinners he shows the way.
He guides the humble to justice;
He teaches the humble his way.

All repeat ANTIPHON

Kindness and constancy are the pathways of the Lord
Toward those who keep his covenant and his decrees.
The friendship of the Lord is with those who fear him,
And he makes known to them his covenant.

All repeat ANTIPHON

Ps. 25(III)

To You, O Lord, I Lift Up My Soul

ANTIPHON: And forgive all our sins, O Lord

T.4g
And for - give all our sins, O Lord.

PSALM 25: 1-2. 6. 7. 11. 16. 17.

To you, O Lord, I lift up my soul.
I trust you, let me not be disappointed.
Remember your mercy, Lord,
And the love you have shown from of old.

All repeat ANTIPHON

Do not remember the sins of my youth.
In your love remember me.
Lord, for the sake of your name forgive my guilt
For it is great.

All repeat ANTIPHON

Turn to me and have mercy
For I am lonely and poor.
Relieve the anguish of my heart
And set me free from my distress.

All repeat ANTIPHON

384

Ps. 27(I)
The Lord Is My Light and My Salvation

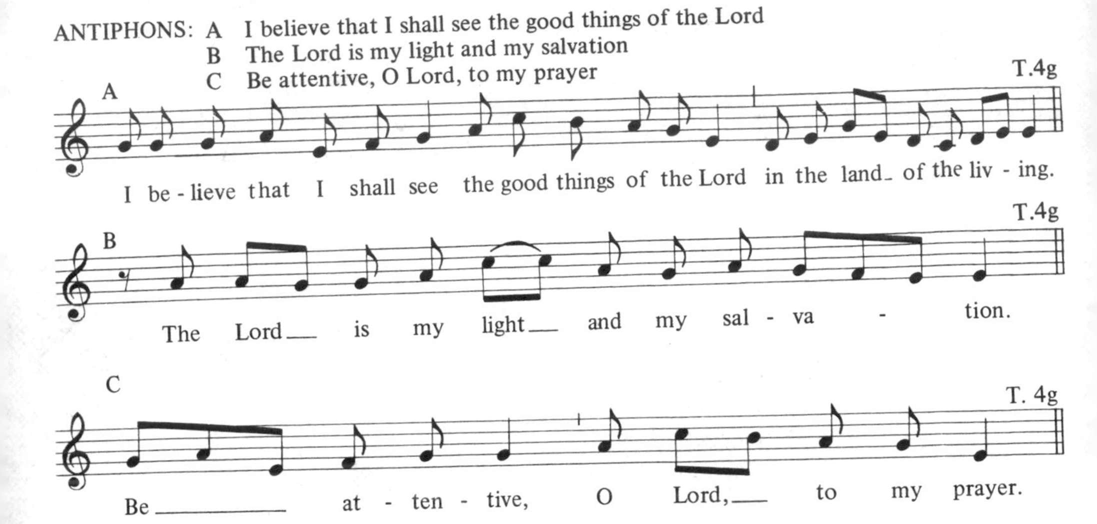
ANTIPHONS: A I believe that I shall see the good things of the Lord
B The Lord is my light and my salvation
C Be attentive, O Lord, to my prayer
A
T.4g
I be - lieve that I shall see the good things of the Lord in the land_ of the liv - ing.
B
T.4g
The Lord__ is my light__ and my sal - va - tion.
C
T. 4g
Be ______ at - ten - tive, O Lord,__ to my prayer.

PSALM 27: 1. 4. 13–14.

The Lord is my light and my salvation;
  Whom should I fear?
The Lord is my life's refuge;
  Of whom whould I be afraid?

All repeat ANTIPHON

One thing I ask of the Lord; this I seek:
  To dwell in the house of the Lord all the days of my life,
To behold the Lord's beauty,
  To gaze on his temple.

All repeat ANTIPHON

I believe I shall see the bounty of the Lord
  In the land of the living.
Wait for the Lord with courage;
  Wait for the Lord and be stouthearted.

All repeat ANTIPHON

Ps. 27(II)
The Lord Is My Light and My Salvation

RESPONSE: The Lord is near to those who call on him

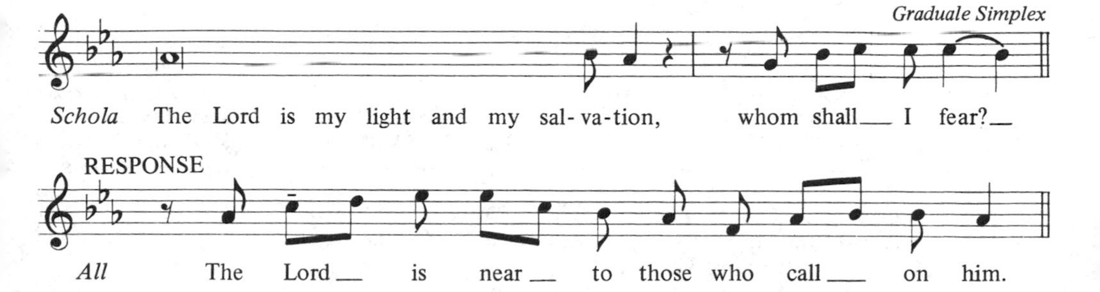
Graduale Simplex
Schola The Lord is my light and my sal- va-tion, whom shall I fear?
RESPONSE
All The Lord is near to those who call on him.

PSALM 27: 2.4.13.14.

The Lord is my life's stronghold,
Of whom shall I be afraid?

All repeat RESPONSE

One thing I ask of the Lord, this I seek:
To dwell in the house of the Lord all the days of my life;

All repeat RESPONSE

To behold the Lord's beauty,
To gaze on his temple.

All repeat RESPONSE

I am sure that in the land of the living
I shall see the goodness of the Lord.

All repeat RESPONSE

Wait for the Lord with courage;
Wait for the Lord and be strong of heart.

Schola The Lord is...
All repeat RESPONSE

Ps. 29
Declare to the Lord, O Daughters and Sons of God

RESPONSE: Alleluia

PSALM 29: 1-5. 10. 11.

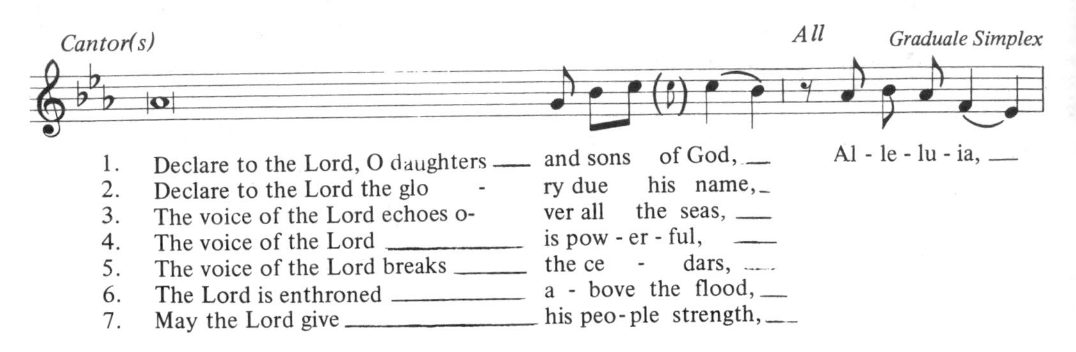
Cantor(s)
All
Graduale Simplex
1. Declare to the Lord, O daughters — and sons of God, — Al - le - lu - ia, —
2. Declare to the Lord the glo - ry due his name, —
3. The voice of the Lord echoes o- ver all the seas, —
4. The voice of the Lord — is pow - er - ful, —
5. The voice of the Lord breaks — the ce - dars, —
6. The Lord is enthroned — a - bove the flood, —
7. May the Lord give — his peo - ple strength, —

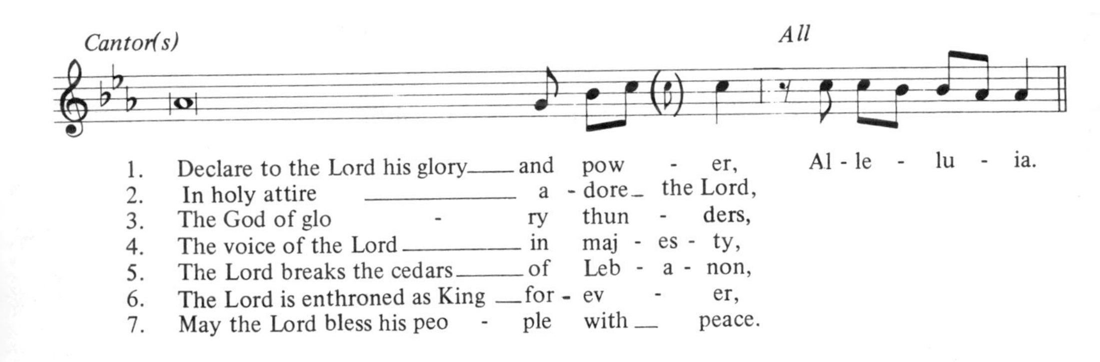
Cantor(s)
All
1. Declare to the Lord his glory — and pow - er, Al - le - lu - ia.
2. In holy attire — a - dore — the Lord,
3. The God of glo - ry thun - ders,
4. The voice of the Lord — in maj - es - ty,
5. The Lord breaks the cedars — of Leb - a - non,
6. The Lord is enthroned as King — for - ev - er,
7. May the Lord bless his peo - ple with — peace.

Ps. 30
I Will Extol You, O Lord

ANTIPHON: I will praise you, Lord, for you have rescued me

T. 6
I will praise— you,— Lord, for you— have res - cued me.

PSALM 30: 2. 4. 5-6. 11. 12a-13b.

I will extol you, O Lord, for you drew me clear
And did not let my enemies rejoice over me.
O Lord, you brought me up from the netherworld;
You preserved me from among those
going down into the pit.

All repeat ANTIPHON

Sing praise to the Lord, you his faithful ones,
And to his holy name give thanks.
For his anger lasts but a moment; his good will a lifetime.
Weeping enters in at nightfall, but rejoicing
comes with the dawn.

All repeat ANTIPHON

O Lord, hear and have pity on me;
Be my helper, O Lord.
You changed my mourning into dancing;
O Lord, my God, forever will I give you thanks.

All repeat ANTIPHON

388

Ps. 31
In You, O Lord, I Take My Refuge

ANTIPHONS: A Father, I put my life in your hands
B Lord, be my rock of safety

Joseph Policelli

A
T. 4g
Fa - ther, I put my life in your hands.

B
T. 4g
Lord, ______ be my rock of safe - ty.

PSALM 31 A: 2.6.12.13.15.16.17.25.
B: 2-3a.3b.4.17.25.

A B In you, O Lord, I take refuge; let me never be put to shame.
In your justice rescue me.
Into your hands I commend my spirit;
You will redeem me, O Lord, O faithful God.
All repeat ANTIPHON

A For all my foes I am an object of reproach, a laughing stock
to my neighbors, and a dread to my friends;
They who see me abroad flee from me.
I am forgotten like the unremembered dead;
I am like a dish that is broken.
All repeat ANTIPHON

A But my trust is in you, O Lord;
I say, "You are my God."
In your hands is my destiny;
Rescue me from the clutches of my enemies
and my persecutors.
All repeat ANTIPHON

B In you, O Lord, I take refuge;
Let me never be put to shame.
In your justice rescue me,
Incline your ear to me, make haste to deliver me.
All repeat ANTIPHON

B Be my rock of refuge,
A stronghold to give me safety.
You are my rock and my fortress;
For your name's sake you will lead and guide me.
All repeat ANTIPHON

A B Let your face shine upon your servant;
Save me in your kindness.
Take courage and be stouthearted,
All you who hope in the Lord.
All repeat ANTIPHON

Ps. 32

Happy Are They Whose Sins Are Forgiven

ANTIPHONS: A Lord, forgive the wrong I have done
B I turn to you, Lord, in time of trouble

A
T.6
Lord, for - give the wrong I have done.

B
T.6
I turn to you, Lord, in time of trou - ble,

and you fill me with the joy of sal - va - tion.

PSALM 32: 1-2. 5a-b. 7. 11.

Happy are they whose sins are forgiven,
Whose trangressions are pardoned.
Happy are they whom the Lord does not accuse of doing wrong,
Who are free from all deceit.

All repeat ANTIPHON

Then I confessed my sin to you;
My wrongdoings I did not conceal.
I decided to confess them to you,
And all my transgressions you forgave.

All repeat ANTIPHON

You are my hiding place; you will save me from trouble.
Because you protect me, I sing aloud of your salvation.
All who are righteous be glad and rejoice, because of what the
Lord has done!
All who obey him, shout for joy!

All repeat ANTIPHON

Ps. 33
Upright Is the Word of the Lord

ANTIPHONS: A O how blessed the people
B Lord, let your mercy be on us

A
T. 7a
O how blessed the peo - ple the Lord_ has cho - sen___ to be___ his own.

B
T. 7a
Lord,_ let___ your mer-cy be on us_____ as we place_ our trust_ in you.

PSALM 33: 4-5.6.9.18.19.20.22.

Upright is the word of the Lord,
And trustworthy are all his works.
He loves justice and right;
Of the kindness of the Lord the earth is full.

All repeat ANTIPHON

By the word of the Lord the heavens were made;
By the breath of his mouth all their host.
For he spoke and it was made;
He commanded and it stood forth.

All repeat ANTIPHON

See, the eyes of the Lord are upon those who fear him,
Upon those who hope for his loving care,
In spite of famine to preserve them,
And to deliver them from death.

All repeat ANTIPHON

Our soul waits for the Lord
Who is our help and our shield.
May your kindness, O Lord,
Be upon us who have placed our trust in you.

All repeat ANTIPHON

Ps. 34(I)
I Will Bless the Lord at All Times

ANTIPHONS: A Taste and see the goodness of the Lord
B I will bless the Lord at all times

A
T. 1g
Taste ___ and see the good - ness of ___ the Lord.
B
T. 1g
I will bless ___ the Lord at all ___ times.

PSALM 34: 2-9.

I will bless the Lord at all times;
His praise shall be ever in my mouth.
Let my soul glory in the Lord;
The lowly will hear me and be glad.

All repeat ANTIPHON

With me glorify the Lord,
Let us together extol his name.
I sought the Lord and he answered me,
An delivered me from all my fears.

All repeat ANTIPHON

Look to him that you may be radiant with joy,
And your faces may not blush with shame.
The Lord heard when the afflicted ones called out,
And from all their distress he saved them.

All repeat ANTIPHON

The angel of the Lord encamps around those who fear him
And delivers them.
Taste and see how good the Lord is;
Happy are they who take refuge in him.

All repeat ANTIPHON

Ps. 34(II)
I Will Bless the Lord at All Times

ANTIPHONS: A The Lord hears the cry of the poor
B Taste and see the goodness of the Lord

A
T. 4g
The Lord hears the cry of the poor.
B
T. 4g
Taste and see the good - ness of the Lord.

PSALM 34: 1-2.10-11.12-13.14-15.17-18.19.23.

AB I will bless the Lord at all times;
His praise shall be ever in my mouth.
Let my soul glory in the Lord;
The lowly will hear me and be glad.

All repeat ANTIPHON

B Fear the Lord, you his holy ones,
For nought is lacking to those who fear him.
The great grow poor and hungry;
But those who seek the Lord want for no good thing.

All repeat ANTIPHON

B Come, children, hear me;
I will teach you the fear of the Lord.
Which of you desires life,
And takes delight in prosperous days?

All repeat ANTIPHON

B Keep your tongue from evil
And your lips from speaking guile.
Turn from evil and do good;
Seek peace and follow after it.

All repeat ANTIPHON

A The Lord confronts the evil doers,
To destroy remembrance of them from the earth.
When the just cry out, the Lord hears them,
And from all their distress he rescues them.

All repeat ANTIPHON

A The Lord is close to the brokenhearted;
And those who are crushed in spirit he saves.
The Lord redeems the lives of his servants;
No one incurs guilt who takes refuge in him.

All repeat ANTIPHON

Ps. 34(III)
I Will Bless the Lord at All Times

ANTIPHON: The angel of the Lord will rescue those who fear him

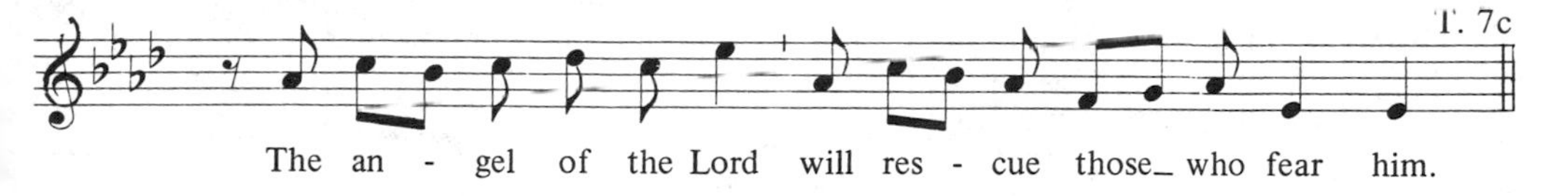
T. 7c
The an - gel of the Lord will res - cue those_ who fear him.

PSALM 34: 2-9.

I will bless the Lord at all times;
His praise shall be ever in my mouth.
Let my soul glory in the Lord;
The lowly will hear me and be glad.

All repeat ANTIPHON

With me glorify the Lord,
Let us together extol his name.
I sought the Lord and he answered me
And delivered me from all my fears.

All repeat ANTIPHON

Look to him that you may be radiant with joy,
And your faces may not blush with shame.
The Lord heard when the afflicted ones called out,
And saved them from all their distress.

All repeat ANTIPHON

The angel of the Lord encamps around those who fear him,
And delivers them.
Taste and see how good the Lord is,
Happy are they who take refuge in him.

All repeat ANTIPHON

Ps. 40
For the Lord I Waited Patiently

A
T. 4g
I come to do your will, Lord, this is my de - light.
B
T. 4g
Lord, come to my aid.

PSALM 40: 1.3.6–9.16.

For the Lord I waited patiently;
He inclined to me and heard my cry.
In my mouth he put a new song,
A song of praise to our God.

All repeat ANTIPHON

Sacrifice and offering you do not desire;
But you have given me an open ear.
Burnt offering and sin offering
You have not required.

All repeat ANTIPHON

Then I said, "Lo, I come.
In the roll of the book it is said of me:
To do your will, my God, is my delight;
Your law is written in my heart."

All repeat ANTIPHON

I have told the glad news of deliverance
In the great congregation;
Lo, I have not restrained my lips,
As you know, O Lord.

All repeat ANTIPHON

May all who are seeking you
Shout for joy and be glad in you.
May they always say who love your saving help:
"Glory to the Lord!"

All repeat ANTIPHON

Ps. 41

Happy Are They Who Have Regard for the Lowly

ANTIPHON: Lord, heal my soul, for I have sinned against you

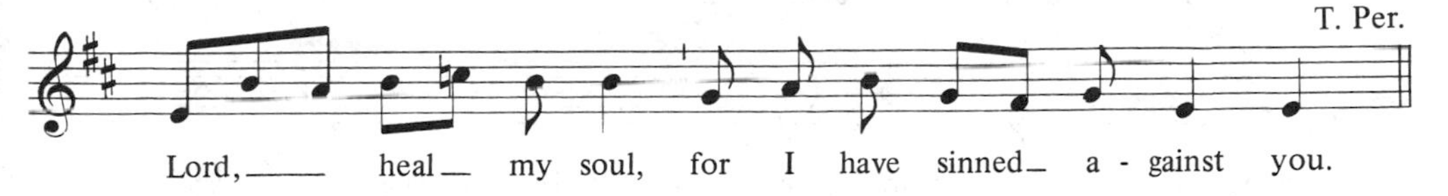
T. Per.
Lord, heal my soul, for I have sinned a - gainst you.

PSALM 41: 2-3.4-5.13-14.

Happy are they who have regard for the lowly and the poor;
In the day of misfortune the Lord will deliver them.
The Lord will keep and preserve them;
he will make them happy on the earth,
And his enemies will not do with them what they please.

All repeat ANTIPHON

On their sick beds the Lord will help them;
He will take away their ailments when they are ill.
Once I said, "O Lord, have pity on me;
Heal me, though against you I have sinned."

All repeat ANTIPHON

You sustain me because I do what is right,
And in your presence forever you let me stand.
Blessed be the Lord, the God of Israel,
From all eternity and forever. Amen.

All repeat ANTIPHON

396

Pss. 42-43
My Soul Thirsts for God

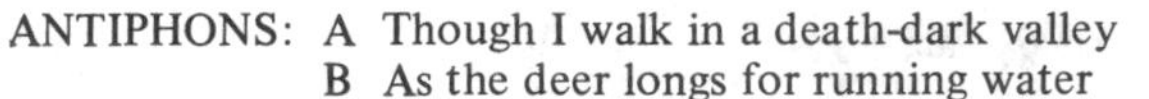
ANTIPHONS: A Though I walk in a death-dark valley
B As the deer longs for running water

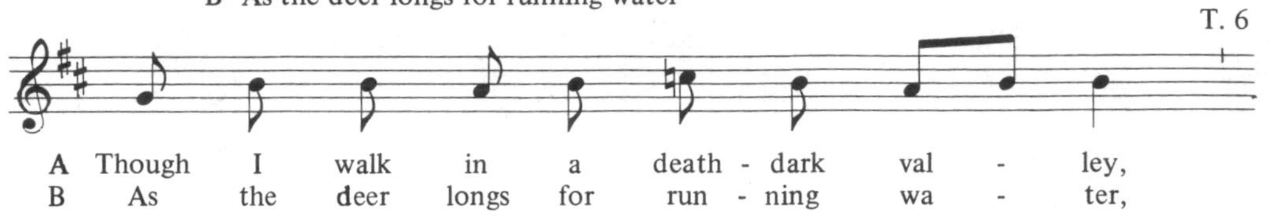
T. 6
A Though I walk in a death - dark val - ley,
B As the deer longs for run - ning wa - ter,

A I fear no harm, for you are with me.
B my soul, O Lord, is long - ing for you.

PSALM 42: 3.5.
PSALM 43: 3. 4.

My soul thirsts for God, for the living God.
When shall I come and behold the face of God?
I went with the throng and led them in procession to
the house of God,
A multitude keeping festival with glad shouts and
songs of joy and praise.

All repeat ANTIPHON

Send out your light and truth, let them lead me;
Let them bring me to your holy hill and to your
dwelling place.
Then will I go to the altar of God because you give me joy;
And I will praise you on the harp, O God, my God.

All repeat ANTIPHON

Ps. 45
My Heart Overflows with a Goodly Theme

ANTIPHONS: A The queen stands at your right hand
B The bridegroom is here

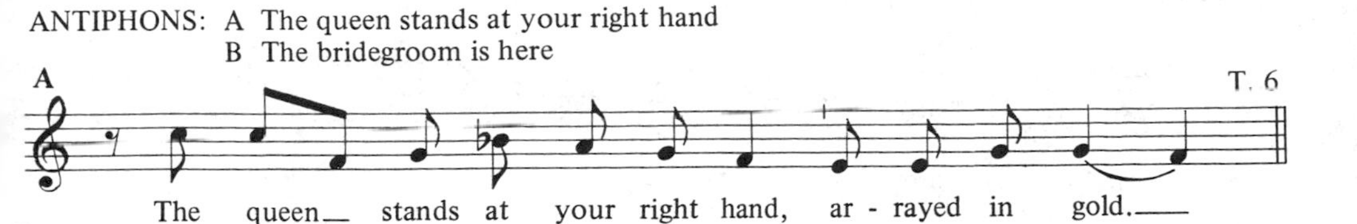
A
T. 6
The queen_ stands at your right hand, ar - rayed in gold.___

B
T. 6
The bride - groom is here; let us go out_ to meet_ Christ_ the Lord.

PSALM 45: 2a-3. 10-11.12.16.

*My heart overflows with a goodly theme;
As I sing my ode to the king.
Grace is poured out upon your lips;
Thus forever has God blessed you.

All repeat ANTIPHON

The daughters of kings come to meet you;
In gold of Ophir the queen takes her place
at your right hand.
Hear, O daughter and see;
Forget your people and your father's house.

All repeat ANTIPHON

So shall the king desire your beauty;
And you must worship him for he is your Lord.
They are borne in with gladness and joy;
They enter the palace of the king.

All repeat ANTIPHON

* This verse may be omitted.

398

Ps. 47
All You Peoples, Clap Your Hands

ANTIPHON: God mounts his throne amid shouts of joy

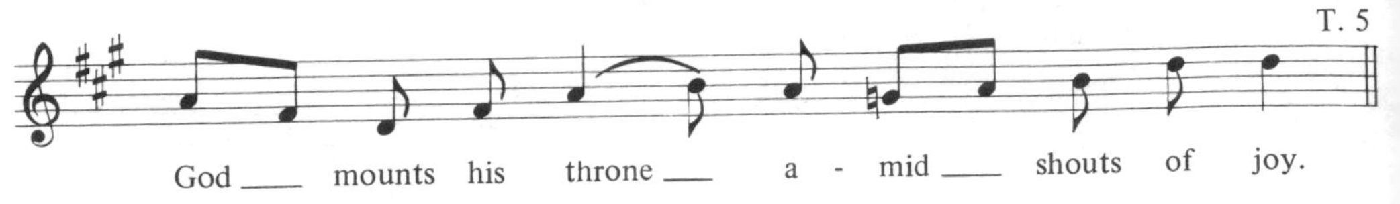
T. 5
God mounts his throne a - mid shouts of joy.

PSALM 47: 2-3.6-7.8-9.

All you peoples, clap your hands;
Shout to God with cries of gladness,
For the Lord, the Most High, the awesome,
Is the great king over all the earth.

All repeat ANTIPHON

God mounts his throne amid shouts of joy;
The Lord amid trumpet blasts.
Sing praise to God, sing praise;
Sing praise to our king.

All repeat ANTIPHON

For king of all the earth is God;
Sing hymns of praise.
God reigns over the nations;
God sits upon his holy throne.

All repeat ANTIPHON

Ps. 50
God the Lord Has Spoken

399

ANTIPHON: To the upright I will show the saving power of God

T. 1g
To the up - right I will show the sav - ing power of God.

PSALM 50: 1.8.12-13.14-15.

God the Lord has spoken and summoned the earth,
From the rising of the sun to its setting.
"Not for your sacrifices do I rebuke you,
For your holocausts are before me always."

All repeat ANTIPHON

"If I were hungry I should not tell you,
For mine are the world and its fullness.
Do I eat the flesh of strong bulls,
Or is the blood of goats my drink?"

All repeat ANTIPHON

"Offer praise to God as your sacrifice
And fulfill your vows to the Most High;
Then in time of distress call upon me;
I will rescue you, and you shall glorify me."

All repeat ANTIPHON

400 Ps. 51(I)
Have Mercy on Me, O God, in Your Goodness

ANTIPHON: Remember your love and have mercy on me

T. 3a
Re - mem - ber your love and have mer - cy on me.

PSALM 51: 3-4.5-6.12-13.14.17.

Have mercy on me, O God, in your goodness;
In the greatness of your compassion
wipe out my offense.
Thoroughly wash me from my guilt
And cleanse me of my sin.
For I acknowledge my offense
And my sin is always before me:
"Against you only have I sinned
And done what is evil in your sight."

All repeat ANTIPHON

A clean heart create for me, O God,
And a steadfast spirit renew within me.
Cast me not out from your presence,
And your holy spirit take not from me.
Give me back the joy of your salvation
And a willing spirit sustain in me.

All repeat ANTIPHON

O Lord, open my lips
And my mouth shall proclaim your praise.

All repeat ANTIPHON

Ps. 51(II)
Have Mercy on Me, O God, in Your Goodness

ANTIPHONS: A Create a clean heart in me, O God
B I shall arise and return to my father

A
T. 3a
Cre - ate a clean heart in me, O God.

B
T. 3a
I shall a - rise and re - turn to my fa - ther.

PSALM 51: 3-4.5-6a.12.13-14.15.17.

Have mercy on me, O God, in your goodness;
In the greatness of your compassion
wipe out my offense.
Thoroughly wash me from my guilt
And cleanse me of my sin.

All repeat ANTIPHON

For I acknowledge my offense and my sin is always before me:
"Against you only have I sinned
and done what is evil in your sight."
A clean heart create for me, O God,
And a steadfast spirit renew within me.

All repeat ANTIPHON

Cast me not out from your presence,
And your holy spirit take not from me.
Give me back the joy of your salvation,
And a willing spirit sustain in me.

All repeat ANTIPHON

I will teach transgressors your ways,
And sinners shall return to you.
O Lord, open my lips
And my mouth shall proclaim your praise.

All repeat ANTIPHON

402

Ps. 54
O God, by Your Name Save Me

ANTIPHON: The Lord upholds my life

T. 8G
The Lord up - holds my life.

PSALM 54: 3-4.5.6.8.

O God, by your name save me,
And by your might defend my cause.
O God, hear my prayer;
Hearken to the words of my mouth.

All repeat ANTIPHON

For the arrogant have risen up against me,
and the ruthless seek my life;
They set not God before their eyes.
Behold, God is my helper;
The Lord sustains my life.

All repeat ANTIPHON

Freely I will offer you sacrifice;
I will praise your name, O Lord, for its goodness.

All repeat ANTIPHON

Ps. 62
Only in God Is My Soul at Rest

ANTIPHON: Rest in God alone, O my soul

Graduale Simplex
Rest in God a - lone, O my soul.

PSALM 62: 2-3.6-7.8-9.

Only in God is my soul at rest;
From him comes my salvation.
He only is my rock and my salvation, my stronghold;
I shall not be disturbed at all.

All repeat ANTIPHON

Only in God be at rest, my soul,
For my hope comes from him.
He only is my rock and my salvation, my stronghold;
I shall not be disturbed.

All repeat ANTIPHON

With God is my safety and my glory, he is my rock of strength;
My refuge is in God.
Trust in him at all times, O my people!
Pour out your hearts before him.

All repeat ANTIPHON

404

Ps. 63
O God, You Are My God Whom I Seek

ANTIPHON: My soul is thirsting for you, O Lord, my God

T. 2
My soul is thirst - ing for you, O Lord, my God.

PSALM 63: 2.3-4.5-6.8-9.

O God, you are my God whom I seek; for you my flesh pines,
And my soul thirsts like the earth,
parched, lifeless and without water.
Thus in the sanctuary have I gazed toward you
To see your glory and your power.

All repeat ANTIPHON

For your kindness is a greater good than life;
You my lips shall glorify.
Thus will I bless you while I live;
Lifting up my hands, I will call upon your name.

All repeat ANTIPHON

As with the riches of a banquet shall my soul be satisfied,
And with exultant lips my mouth shall praise you.
My soul clings fast to you;
Your right hand upholds me.

All repeat ANTIPHON

Ps 65

405

O God, in Zion People Must Praise You

ANTIPHON: The seed that falls on good ground

T. 3a
The seed that falls on good ground will yield a fruit-ful har - vest.

PSALM 65: 1.9a.9b.10a.10b.11.12.13.

O God, in Zion
People must praise you.
You show your care for the land by sending it rain;
You make it fertile and rich.

All repeat ANTIPHON

The streams you have given never run dry;
They provide the earth with crops.
You send abundant rain on the plowed fields
And with water you soak them.

All repeat ANTIPHON

You soften the soil with showers
And cause the young plants to grow.
What a rich harvest your goodness provides!
There is plenty wherever you go.

All repeat ANTIPHON

With flocks the pastures are filled;
The hillsides are filled with joy.
The hillsides are covered with sheep;
the valleys are full of wheat.
They shout and sing for joy.

All repeat ANTIPHON

406

Ps. 66
Shout to God with Joy, All the World

RESPONSE: Give him glorious praise

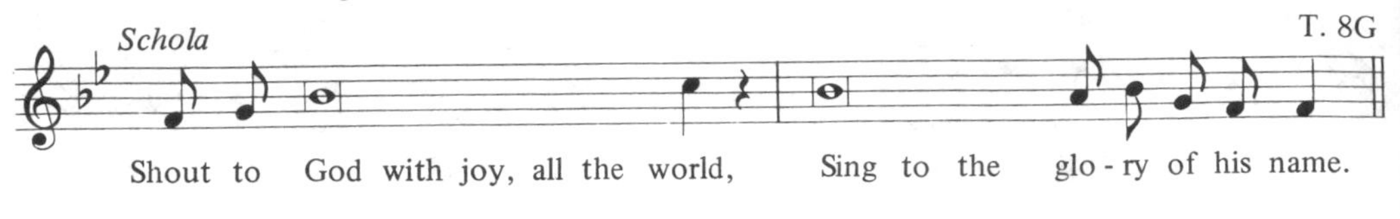
Schola
T. 8G
Shout to God with joy, all the world, Sing to the glo - ry of his name.

RESPONSE
All Give him glo - rious praise.

PSALM 66: 1-2.3-6.20.

Say to God: "How astounding are your deeds, O Lord,
So vast your power, your enemies pay you homage.
All on earth bow down to you and sing,
They sing praise to your name."

All repeat RESPONSE

Come and see the works of the Lord,
His astounding deeds among all people.
He changed the sea to firm earth;
Let them cross the river dry shod.

All repeat RESPONSE

By his power he rules forever, his eyes are watching the nations;
Let rebels not rise against him.
Blest be God who did not reject my prayer,
Nor withhold his love from me.

All repeat RESPONSE

Ps. 67
May God Have Pity on Us

ANTIPHONS: A O God, let all the nations praise you
B May God bless us in his mercy

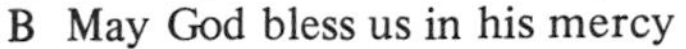

A
T. 5
O God, let all the na - tions praise you!

B
T. 5
May God bless us in his mer - cy.

PSALM 67: 2-3.4-5.6.8.

May God have pity on us and bless us;
May he let his face shine upon us.
So may your way be known upon earth;
Among all nations, your salvation.

All repeat ANTIPHON

May the peoples praise you, O God;
May all the peoples praise you!
May the nations be glad and exult
Because you rule the peoples with equity;

All repeat ANTIPHON

May the peoples praise you, O God;
May all peoples praise you!
May God bless us,
And may peoples everywhere honor him.

All repeat ANTIPHON

408

Ps. 68
The Just Rejoice

ANTIPHON: O God, in your goodness

T. 5
O— God,– in your good-ness you have made— a home— for— the poor.

PSALM 68: 4-5.6-7.10-11.

The just rejoice and exult before God;
They are glad and rejoice.
Sing to God, chant praise to his name,
Whose name is the Lord.

All repeat ANTIPHON

The father of orphans and protector of widows
Is God in his holy dwelling.
God gives a home to the forsaken;
To prosperity he leads forth the prisoners.

All repeat ANTIPHON

A bountiful rain you showered down, O God,
Upon your inheritance;
You restored the land when it languished, in it your flock
found a dwelling;
In your goodness, O God, you provided it for the needy.

All repeat ANTIPHON

Ps. 69

I Pray to You for the Time of Your Favor, O God!

ANTIPHONS: A In your great love, Lord, answer me
B Turn to the Lord in your need

A
T. Per.
In your great love, Lord, an - swer me.

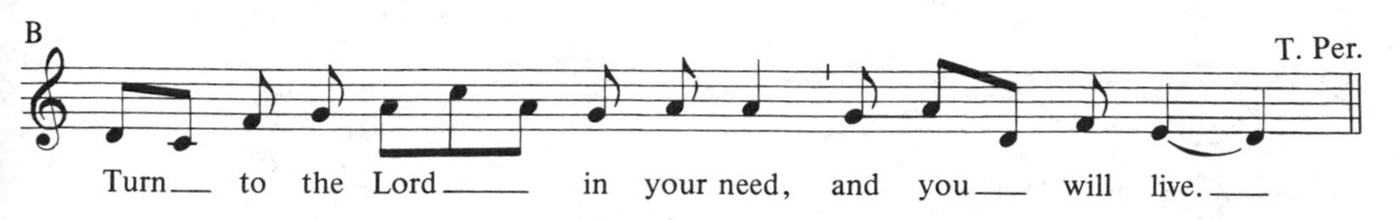
B
T. Per.
Turn to the Lord in your need, and you will live.

PSALM 69: 14.17.30-31.33-34.

I pray to you for the time of your favor, O God!
In your great kindness answer me
with your constant help.
Answer me, O Lord, for your kindness is bounteous:
In your great mercy turn toward me.

All repeat ANTIPHON

I am afflicted and in pain;
Let your saving help, O God, protect me.
I will praise the name of God in song,
With thanksgiving I will glorify him.

All repeat ANTIPHON

"See and be glad, you lowly ones;
May your hearts be merry who seek God!
For the Lord hears the poor,
And he spurns not his own who are in bonds."

All repeat ANTIPHON

410

Ps. 71
In You, O Lord, I Take Refuge

ANTIPHONS: A I will sing of your salvation
B Since my mother's womb, you have been my strength.

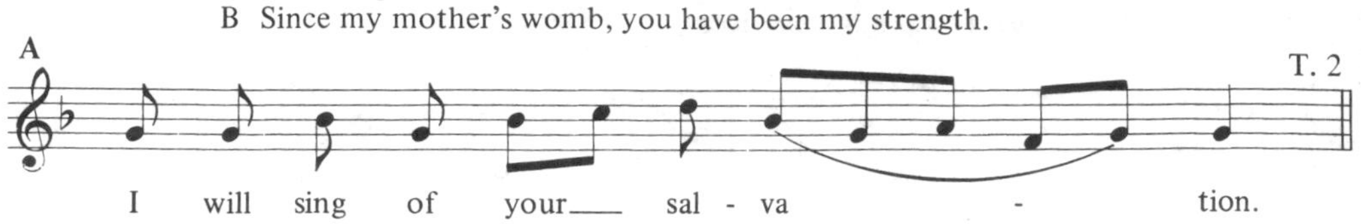
A
T. 2
I will sing of your___ sal - va - tion.

B
T. 2
Since__ my moth-er's womb,_____ you___ have been__ my strength.

PSALM 71: 1-2.3-4.5-6.15.17.

In you, O Lord, I take refuge;
Let me never be put to shame.
In your justice rescue me and deliver me;
Listen to me and save me.

All repeat ANTIPHON

Be my rock of refuge,
A stronghold to give me safety,
For you are my rock and my fortress.
O my God, rescue me from the hand of the wicked.

All repeat ANTIPHON

For you are my hope, O Lord;
My trust, O God, from my youth.
On you I depend from birth;
From my mother's womb you are my strength.

All repeat ANTIPHON

My mouth shall declare your justice,
Your salvation day by day.
O God, from my youth you have taught me,
And till the present I proclaim your wondrous deeds.

All repeat ANTIPHON

Ps. 72

O God, with Your Judgment Endow the King

411

ANTIPHONS: A Ev'ry nation on earth will serve him
B Justice shall flourish in his time

A
T. 7a
Ev - 'ry na - tion on earth will serve him.

B
T. 7a
Jus - tice shall flour - ish in his time, and full-ness of peace for - ev - er.

PSALM 72: 1-2.8.10.11-12.13.17a.

O God, with your judgment endow the king,
And with your justice, the king's son;
He shall govern your people with justice
And with right judgment your afflicted ones.

All repeat ANTIPHON

May he rule from sea to sea
And from the river to the ends of the earth.
The kings of Tarshish and the Isles will pay tribute to him,
The kings of Seba and Arabia offer gifts.

All repeat ANTIPHON

All kings will pay him homage,
All peoples proclaim his wondrous deeds.
For he will rescue the poor when they cry out,
And save the lives of those in need.

All repeat ANTIPHON

He will have pity on the lowly and the poor;
The lives of the poor he shall save.
Blessed forever be his glorious name;
With his glory may the whole earth be filled.

All repeat ANTIPHON

412

Ps. 78(I)
What We Have Heard and Know

ANTIPHON: The Lord gave them bread from heaven

T. 7c
The Lord gave them bread from heav - en.

PSALM 78: 3-4.23-24.25.54.

What we have heard and know,
And what our fathers declared to us,
We will declare to the generation to come the glorious deeds
of the Lord and his strength
And the wonders that he wrought.

All repeat ANTIPHON

He commanded the skies above
And he opened heaven's doors;
He rained manna upon them for food
And gave them heavenly bread.

All repeat ANTIPHON

They ate the bread of angels.
Food in abundance he sent them
And to his holy land he brought them,
To the mountains his right hand had won.

All repeat ANTIPHON

Ps. 78(II)
Give Ear, O My People, to My Teaching

ANTIPHON: Do not forget the works of the Lord

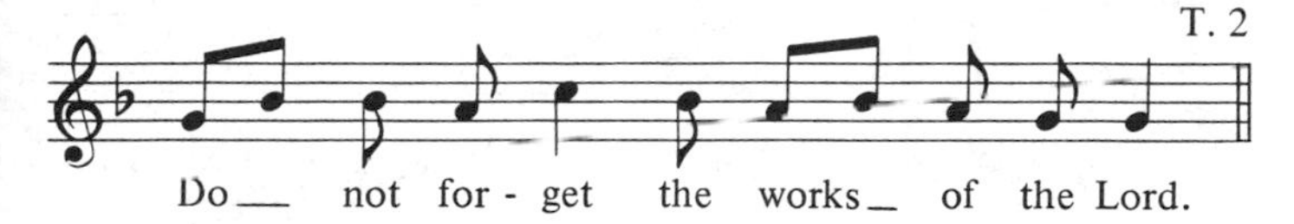
T. 2
Do not for - get the works of the Lord.

PSALM 78: 1-2.34-35.36-37.38.

Give ear, O my people, to my teaching;
Incline your ears to the words of my mouth.
I will open my mouth in a parable;
I will utter dark sayings from of old.

All repeat ANTIPHON

When he slew them, they sought for him;
They repented and sought God earnestly.
They remembered that God was their rock,
The Most High God, their redeemer.

All repeat ANTIPHON

But they flattered him with their mouths;
They lied to him with their tongues.
Their heart was not steadfast toward him;
They were not true to his covenant.

All repeat ANTIPHON

Yet he, being compassionate, forgave their iniquity,
And did not destroy them;
He restrained his anger often,
And did not stir up all his wrath.

All repeat ANTIPHON

414

Ps. 80(I)
Give Ear, O Shepherd of Israel

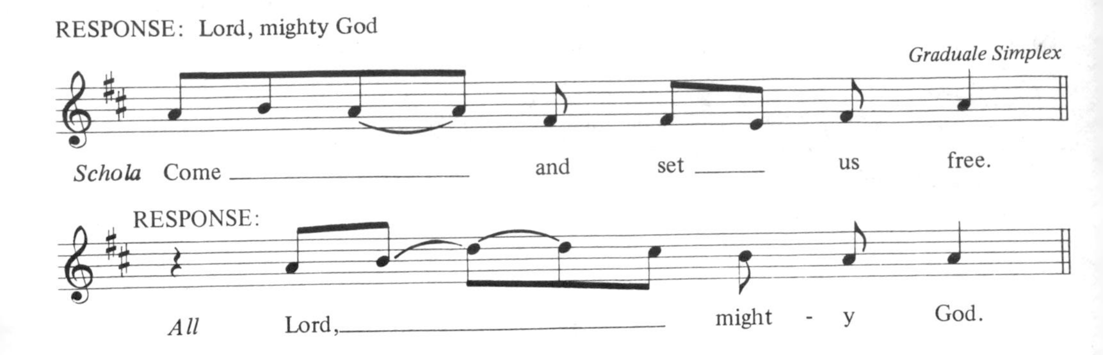
RESPONSE: Lord, mighty God
Graduale Simplex
Schola Come and set us free.
RESPONSE:
All Lord, might - y God.

PSALM 80: 1.2.14.15.17.18.

Give ear, O Shepherd of Israel,
Thou who art enthroned upon the cherubim, shine forth.
All repeat RESPONSE

Stir up thy might,
And come to save us.
All repeat RESPONSE

Turn again, O God of hosts!
Look down from heaven and see;
All repeat RESPONSE

Have regard for this vine,
The stock which thy right hand planted.
All repeat RESPONSE

But let thy hand be upon the man of thy right hand,
The son of man whom thou hast made strong for thyself.
All repeat RESPONSE

Then we will never turn back from thee;
Give us life and we will call on thy name.
Cantor or Schola: Come,...
All repeat RESPONSE

Ps. 80(II)
From Egypt You Took a Vine

ANTIPHON: The vineyard of the Lord is the house of Israel

T. 2
The vine - yard of the Lord is the house of Is - ra - el.

PSALM 80: 9.12.13-14.15-16.19-20.

From Egypt you took a vine,
You drove out the heathen to replant it.
Its leaves reach to the sea,
Its shoots to the river.

All repeat ANTIPHON

Why have you broken down its fences?
All who go by pluck its fruit;
The wild boar tramples it down,
Cattle use it for pasture.

All repeat ANTIPHON

Return, O God of hosts,
Look down from heaven and see, and visit this vine:
Protect it, for your right hand planted it,
This shoot that you made so strong.

All repeat ANTIPHON

We will turn away from you no more;
You will give us life, and we shall invoke your name.
O Lord of hosts, restore us,
Let your face shine out on us that we may be saved.

All repeat ANTIPHON

416

Ps. 81
Take Up a Melody and Sound the Timbrel

ANTIPHON: Sing with joy to God, our help

T. 5
Sing with joy to God, our help.

PSALM 81: 3-4.5-6a.6c-8.10-11.

Take up a melody and sound the timbrel,
The pleasant harp and lyre.
Blow the trumpet for the festival,
When the moon is new and when the moon is full.

All repeat ANTIPHON

For it is a statute in Israel,
An ordinance of the God of Jacob,
Who made it a decree for Joseph
When he came forth from the land of Egypt.

All repeat ANTIPHON

I hear an unfamiliar voice saying:
"I took the heavy burden from your back;
From the work-basket your hands were freed.
In distress you called and I delivered you."

All repeat ANTIPHON

"There shall be no strange god among you,
Nor shall you worship an alien god.
I am the Lord your God,
Who led you forth from the land of Egypt."

All repeat ANTIPHON

Ps. 84(I)
How Lovely Is Your Dwelling Place

RESPONSE: I long for the house of the Lord

Cantor(s): How lovely is your dwelling place, O Lord of hosts!
For the courts of the Lord my soul is longing and sighing.

RESPONSE

T. 5
All I long for the house of the Lord.

PSALM 84: 1-5.10.12.13.

My heart and my flesh cry out for joy
To the living God.
Even the sparrow finds a home,
And the swallow a nest to shelter her young,

All repeat RESPONSE

Your altars, O Lord of hosts,
My king and my God:
Blessed are they who dwell in your house, O Lord,
Without ceasing they praise you.

All repeat RESPONSE

O Lord of hosts, hear my prayer,
Hearken, O God of Jacob!
O God, our shield, behold,
Look on the face of your anointed!

All repeat RESPONSE

For the Lord God is a sun and a shield,
The Lord bestows grace and glory.
The Lord denies nothing good to those who walk in innocence.
Happy are they who trust in you, O Lord of hosts!

All repeat RESPONSE

418

Ps. 84(II)
How Lovely Is Your Dwelling Place

ANTIPHON: You open your hand and fill ev'ry creature

T. 5
You o - pen your hand and fill ev - 'ry
crea - ture with your kind - ness.

PSALM 84: 2-6. 10-12.

How lovely is your dwelling place,
O Lord of hosts!
My soul is longing and sighing
For the courts of the Lord.
My heart and my flesh cry out for joy
To the living God.

All repeat ANTIPHON

Even the sparrow finds a home,
And the swallow a nest to shelter her young,
Your altars, O Lord of hosts,
My king and my God!
Blessed are they who dwell in your house, O Lord,
Without ceasing they praise you.

All repeat ANTIPHON

Blessed are they who find strength in you
When they set their hearts on the sacred journey.
O God, our shield, behold,
Look on the face of your anointed!
Far better one day in your courts
Than a thousand elsewhere.

All repeat ANTIPHON

Far better to lie at the threshold of my God's house,
Than to dwell in the tents of the wicked.
For the Lord God is a sun and a shield;
The Lord bestows grace and glory.
The Lord denies nothing good
To those who walk in innocence.

All repeat ANTIPHON

Ps. 85
I Will Hear What the Lord God Proclaims

ANTIPHONS: A O Lord, come, let us see your kindness
B Grant peace, O Lord, to all who wait for you

A
T. 1D
O Lord, come, let us see your kind - ness, and grant us your sal - va - tion.

B
T. 1D
Grant peace, O Lord, to all who wait for you.

PSALM 85: 9-10.11-12.13-14.

I will hear what the Lord God proclaims,
A voice that speaks of peace.
His help is near to those who fear him
And his glory will dwell in our land.

All repeat ANTIPHON

Mercy and faithfulness have met,
Peace and justice have embraced.
From the earth shall spring faithfulness
And justice from heaven look down.

All repeat ANTIPHON

The Lord will grant us prosperity,
And our earth shall yield its fruit.
Justice shall march before him
And peace shall follow his steps.

All repeat ANTIPHON

420

Ps. 86
You, O Lord, Are Good and Forgiving

ANTIPHON: You, O Lord, are good and forgiving

T. 3a
You,— O Lord,— are — good — and — for - giv - ing.

PSALM 86: 5-6.9-10.15-16.

You, O Lord, are good and forgiving,
Abounding in kindness to all who call on you.
O Lord, hearken to my prayer
And listen to my cry for help.

All repeat ANTIPHON

All nations you have made shall come and worship you, O Lord,
And shall glorify your name.
For you alone are God;
You are great and you do wondrous deeds.

All repeat ANTIPHON

You are merciful and gracious, O Lord,
Slow to anger, always faithful and kind.
Turn toward me and have pity on me;
And to your servant give your strength.

All repeat ANTIPHON

Ps. 89 I Will Sing of Your Steadfast Love

ANTIPHONS: A I will sing the goodness of the Lord
B The son of David will live forever

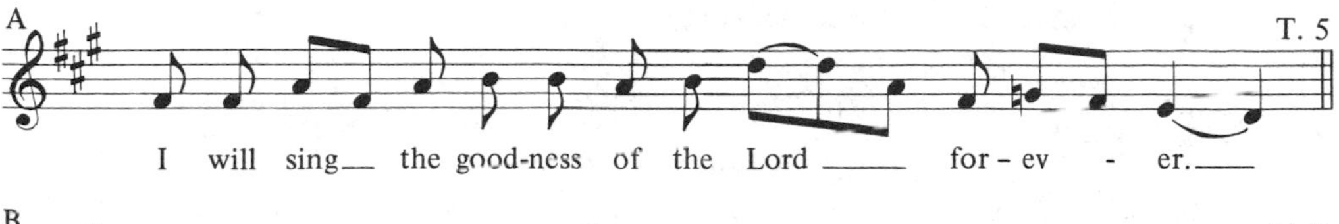
A
T. 5
I will sing__ the good-ness of the Lord ____ for - ev - er.____

B
T. 5
The son of Da - vid will live for - ev - er.

PSALM 89: 1-4.15-16.20-21.26.28.

AB I will sing of your steadfast love, O Lord, forever;
I will proclaim your faithfulness
to all generations.
For your steadfast love was established forever;
Your faithfulness is as firm as the heavens.

All repeat ANTIPHON

AB You have said, "I have made a covenant with my chosen one,
To my servant, David, I have sworn:
I will establish your descendants forever,
And for all generations build your throne."

All repeat ANTIPHON

A Happy the people who know the joyful shout,
O Lord, they walk in the light of your countenance.
They rejoice all the day at your name,
And they are exalted through your justice.

All repeat ANTIPHON

B *"I have found David, my servant;
With holy oil I have anointed him,
That my hand may be always with him,
And that my arm may make him strong.

All repeat ANTIPHON

B *He shall cry to me, You are my father,
The rock of my salvation and my God.
For him I will keep my steadfast love forever,
And for him my covenant will stand firm."

All repeat ANTIPHON

*Verses appropriate for Mass of Chrism on Holy Thursday.

422 Ps. 90
O Lord, You Have Been Our Refuge

ANTIPHONS: A In ev'ry age, O Lord, you have been our refuge
B Fill us with your love, O Lord
C Lord, give success to the work of our hands

A
T. 4g
In ev - 'ry age, O Lord,___ you have been_ our ref - uge.
B
T. 4g
Fill us with_ your love,___ O Lord, and we will sing___ for joy!___
C
T. 4g
Lord,___ give___ suc - cess___ to the work___ of our___ hands.

PSALM 90: 1-2.3-4.12.14.16.17.

O Lord, you have been our refuge
Through all generations.
Before the mountains were begotten and the earth and
the world were brought forth,
From everlasting to everlasting you are God.

All repeat ANTIPHON

You turn us back to dust
Saying, "Return, O children of earth."
For a thousand years in your sight are as yesterday,
now that it is past,
Or as a watch of the night.

All repeat ANTIPHON

Teach us to number our days aright,
That we may gain wisdom of heart.
Fill us at daybreak with your kindness,
That we may shout for joy and gladness all our days.

All repeat ANTIPHON

Let your work be seen by your servants
And your glory by their children;
And may the gracious care of the Lord our God be ours;
Prosper the work of our hands!

All repeat ANTIPHON

Ps 91
You Who Dwell in the Shelter of the Most High

ANTIPHONS: A When I am troubled, Lord, be my refuge
B He has placed his angels over you

A
T. 4g
When I am trou - bled, Lord, be my ref - uge.
B
T. 4g
He has placed his an-gels o - ver you to guard you in all your ways.

PSALM 91: 1-2.10-11.12-13. 14. 16.

You who dwell in the shelter of the Most High,
Who abide in the shadow of the Almighty,
Say to the Lord, "My refuge and my fortress,
My God in whom I trust."

All repeat ANTIPHON

No evil shall befall you,
Nor shall affliction come near your tent,
For to his angels he has given command about you,
That they guard you in all your ways.

All repeat ANTIPHON

Upon their hands they shall bear you up,
Lest you dash your foot against a stone.
You shall tread upon the asp and the viper;
You shall trample down the lion and the dragon.

All repeat ANTIPHON

Because he clings to me I will deliver him;
I will set him on high because he acknowledges my name.
I will gratify him with length of days
And I will show him my salvation.

All repeat ANTIPHON

Ps. 92
It Is Good to Give Thanks to the Lord

ANTIPHON: O Lord, it is good to give thanks and sing your praise, Most High

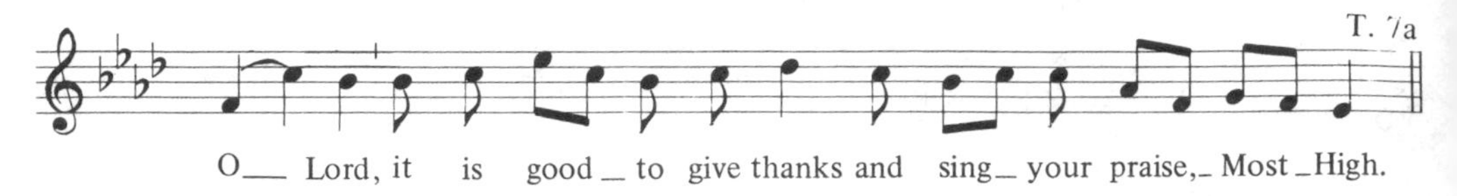
T. 7a
O___ Lord, it is good _ to give thanks and sing_ your praise,_ Most _High.

PSALM 92: 2. 3. 13-16.

It is good to give thanks to the Lord,
To sing praise to your name, Most High,
To proclaim your kindness at dawn
And your faithfulness throughout the night.

All repeat ANTIPHON

The just shall flourish like the palm tree,
Like the cedar of Lebanon shall they grow.
They that are planted in the house of the Lord
Shall flourish in the courts of our God.

All repeat ANTIPHON

They shall bear fruit even in old age;
Vigorous and sturdy shall they be,
Declaring how just is the Lord,
My rock, in whom there is no wrong.

All repeat ANTIPHON

Ps. 93
The Lord Is King

ANTIPHON: Christ, Lord of Glory

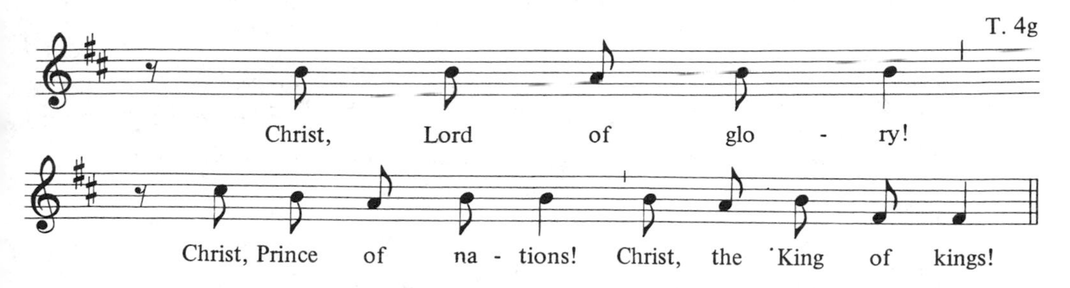
T. 4g
Christ, Lord of glo - ry!
Christ, Prince of na - tions! Christ, the King of kings!

PSALM 93: 1.2.4.5.

The Lord is king;
He is robed in majesty.
The Lord is king, in splendor robed;
Robed is the Lord and girt about with strength.

All repeat ANTIPHON

He has made the world firm,
Not to be moved.
From of old your throne stands firm;
From everlasting you are, O Lord.

All repeat ANTIPHON

More powerful than the roar of many waters and more powerful than the breakers of the sea,
Powerful on high is the Lord.
Your decrees are worthy of trust indeed;
Holiness befits your house, O Lord, for length of days.

All repeat ANTIPHON

Text of Antiphon: Joseph Nolan

426

Ps. 95
Come, Let Us Sing Joyfully to the Lord

ANTIPHONS: A If today you hear his voice, harden not your hearts
B Let us come before the Lord and praise him

A
T. 1g
If — to - day — you — hear — his voice, hard - en not your hearts.

B
T. 1g
Let us come — be - fore — the Lord and praise — him.

PSALM 95: 1-2.6-7.8-9.

AB Come, let us sing joyfully to the Lord;
Let us acclaim the rock of our salvation.
Let us greet him with thanksgiving;
Let us joyfully sing psalms to him.

All repeat ANTIPHON

AB Come, let us bow down and worship him;
Let us kneel before the Lord who made us.
For he is our God,
And we are the people he shepherds, the flock he guides.

All repeat ANTIPHON

A Oh, that today you would hear his voice:
"Harden not your hearts as at Meribah,
as in the day of Massah in the desert,
Where your fathers tempted me;
They tested me though they had seen my works."

All repeat ANTIPHON

Ps. 96(I)
Sing to the Lord a New Song

427

ANITPHONS: A Today is born our Savior, Christ the Lord
B Proclaim his marvelous deeds to all the nations

A
T. 7a
To - day__ is born__ our__ Sav - ior,__ Christ__ the Lord.

B
T. 7a
Pro - claim__ his mar - vel - ous deeds__ to all__ the na - tions.

PSALM 96: 1.2.3.7-8.11.12.13.

AB Sing to the Lord a new song;
Sing to the Lord, all you lands.
Sing to the Lord; bless his name;
Announce his salvation day after day.

All repeat ANTIPHON

AB Tell his glory throughout the world,
Among all peoples, his wondrous deeds.
Let the heavens be glad and the earth rejoice;
Let the sea and what fills it resound.

All repeat ANTIPHON

B You families of nations, give to the Lord,
Give to the Lord glory and praise;
Give to the Lord
The glory due his name!

All repeat ANTIPHON

A Let the plains be joyful and all that is in them!
Then shall the trees of the forest sing for joy.
They shall exult before the Lord for he comes,
For he comes to rule the earth.

All repeat ANTIPHON

A With justice he shall rule the world,
And the peoples with his truth.

All repeat ANTIPHON

428 Ps. 96(II)
Sing to the Lord a New Song

ANTIPHONS: A Go forth into the world and teach all nations
B Give to the Lord glory and honor

A
T. 7a
Go forth in - to the world and teach all na - tions.
B
T. 7a
Give to the Lord glo - ry and hon - or.

PSALM 96: 1.3.4-5.7-8.9.10.

Sing to the Lord a new song;
Sing to the Lord, all you lands.
Tell his glory throughout the world;
Among all peoples, his wondrous deeds.

All repeat ANTIPHON

For great is the Lord and highly to be praised;
Awesome is he beyond all gods.
For all the gods of the nations are things of nought,
But the heavens the Lord made.

All repeat ANTIPHON

You families of nations, give to the Lord,
Give to the Lord glory and praise;
Give to the Lord the glory due his name!
Bring gifts and enter his courts.

All repeat ANTIPHON

Worship the Lord in holy attire;
Tremble before him, all the earth;
Say among the nations: the Lord is king,
He governs the peoples with equity.

All repeat ANTIPHON

Ps. 96(III) 429
Sing to the Lord, O Bless His Name

ANTIPHON: Sing a new song to the Lord

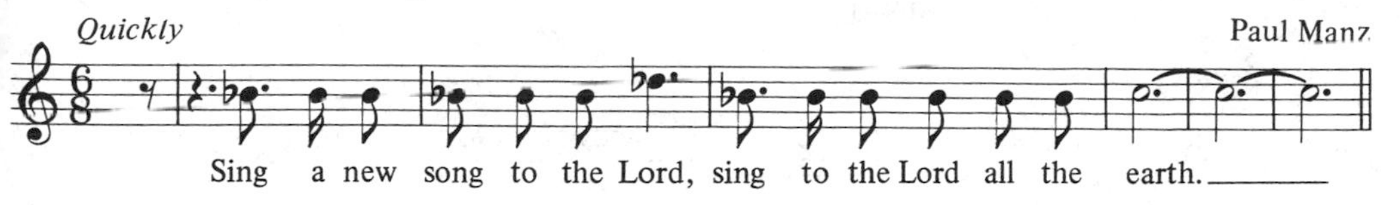
Quickly
Paul Manz
Sing a new song to the Lord, sing to the Lord all the earth.

PSALM 96: 1-3.7-9.

Sing to the Lord, O bless his name;
Go tell his salvation from day to day.

All repeat ANTIPHON

Declare his glory among the nations,
His marvelous works from day to day!

All repeat ANTIPHON

Ascribe to the Lord the glory of his name,
Bring an off'ring and come unto his courts.
Ascribe to the Lord all strength.

All repeat ANTIPHON

Worship the Lord in great array, fear him, ye folk on earth;
Bring him the glory he deserves and come adore him.

All repeat ANTIPHON

DOX. Glory be to the Father and to the Son, and to the Holy Spirit,
As it was in the beginning, is now, and ever shall be world without end.

ANTIPHON Last time only

Sing a new song to the Lord, sing to the Lord all the earth.
Al - le - lu - ia! Al - le - lu - ia! A - men.

430

Ps. 96(IV)
Sing to the Lord, O Bless His Name

RESPONSE: Alleluia

PSALM 96: 2. 3. 8. 9.

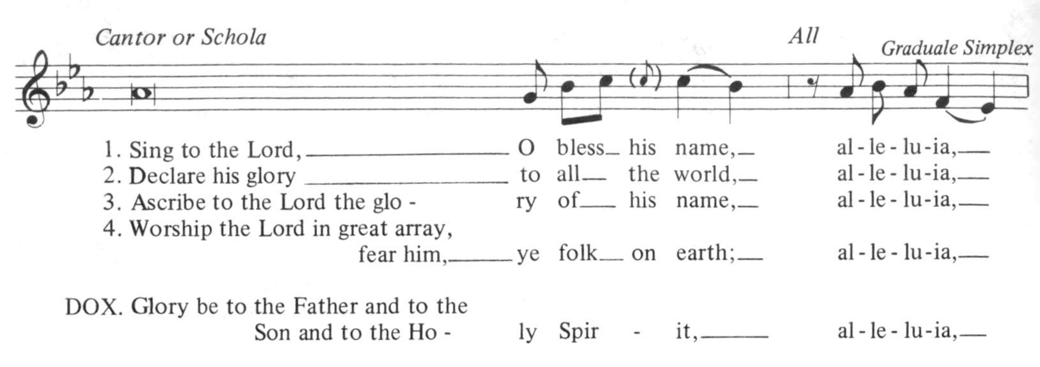
Cantor or Schola
All
Graduale Simplex
1. Sing to the Lord, O bless his name, al-le-lu-ia,
2. Declare his glory to all the world, al-le-lu-ia,
3. Ascribe to the Lord the glo-ry of his name, al-le-lu-ia,
4. Worship the Lord in great array, fear him, ye folk on earth; al-le-lu-ia,
DOX. Glory be to the Father and to the Son and to the Ho-ly Spir-it, al-le-lu-ia,

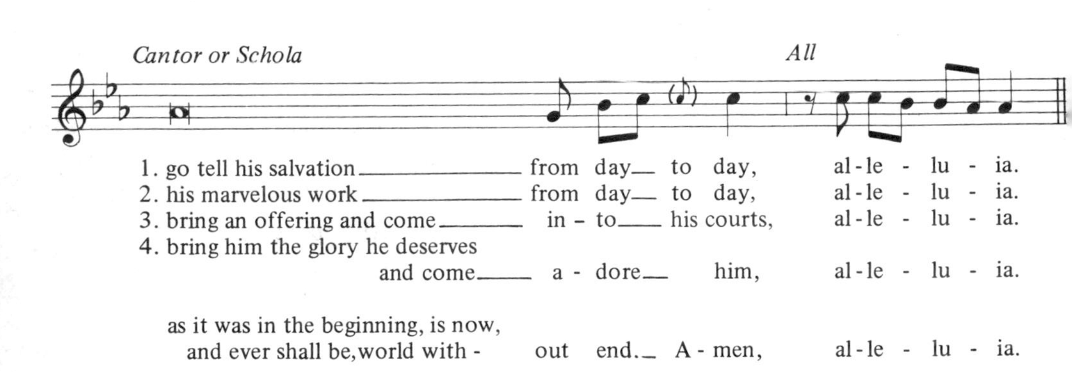
Cantor or Schola
All
1. go tell his salvation from day to day, al-le-lu-ia.
2. his marvelous work from day to day, al-le-lu-ia.
3. bring an offering and come in-to his courts, al-le-lu-ia.
4. bring him the glory he deserves and come a-dore him, al-le-lu-ia.
as it was in the beginning, is now, and ever shall be, world with-out end. A-men, al-le-lu-ia.

Ps. 97
The Lord Is King

ANTIPHONS: A A light will shine on us this day: the Lord is born for us
B The Lord is king, the most high over all the earth
C Let the good rejoice in the Lord

A T. 7c

A light will shine— on us this day: the Lord—— is born— for us.

B T. 7c

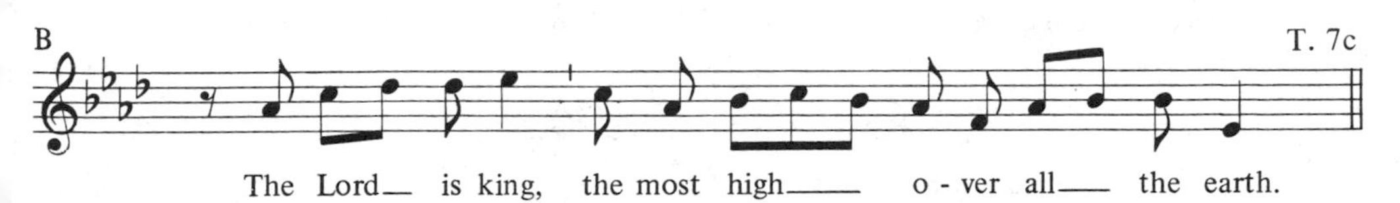
The Lord— is king, the most high—— o - ver all—— the earth.

C T. 7c

Let— the good— re - joice,—— re - joice—— in—— the Lord.

PSALM 97: 1-2.6.9.11.12.

The Lord is king; let the earth rejoice;
Let the many isles be glad.
Justice and judgment
Are the foundation of his throne.

All repeat ANTIPHON

The heavens proclaim his righteousness,
And his glory all peoples see.
You, Lord, are the most high over all the earth,
And exalted far above all gods.

All repeat ANTIPHON

Light dawns for the just,
And gladness for the upright in heart.
Be glad in the Lord, ye just;
And give thanks to his holy name.

All repeat ANTIPHON

432

Ps. 98(I)
Sing to the Lord a New Song

ANTIPHON: All the ends of the earth

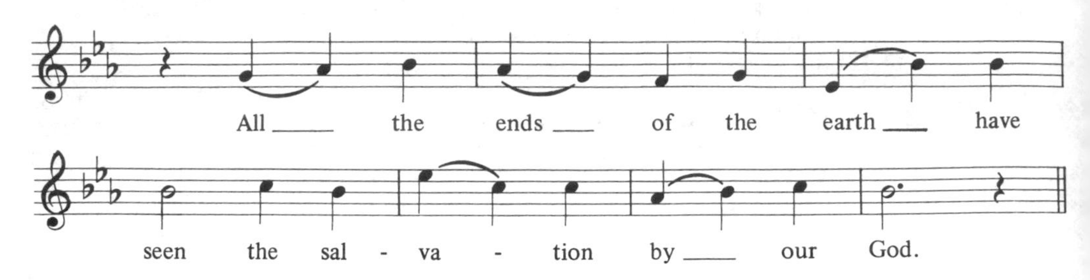
All the ends of the earth have
seen the sal - va - tion by our God.

PSALM 98: 1.2-3a.3b-4.5.6.

Sing to the Lord a new song
For he has done wondrous deeds;
His right hand has won victory for him,
His holy arm.

All repeat ANTIPHON

The Lord has made his salvation known;
In sight of the nations he has revealed his justice.
He has remembered his kindness and his faithfulness
Toward the house of Israel.

All repeat ANTIPHON

All the ends of the earth have seen
The salvation by our God.
Sing joyfully to the Lord, all you lands;
Break into song; sing praise.

All repeat ANTIPHON

Sing praise to the Lord with the harp,
With the harp and melodious song.
With trumpets and the sound of the horn
Sing joyfully before the King, the Lord.

ANTIPHON *last time only*

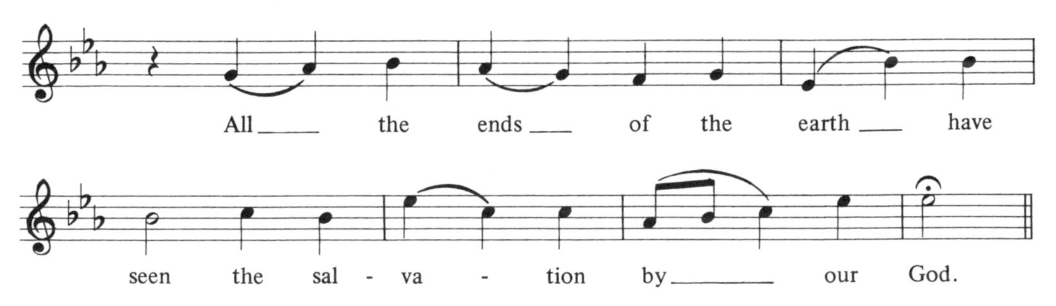
All the ends of the earth have
seen the sal - va - tion by our God.

Ps. 98(II) 433
Sing to the Lord a New Song

ANTIPHONS: A The Lord has revealed to the nations
B The Lord comes to rule the world with justice

A

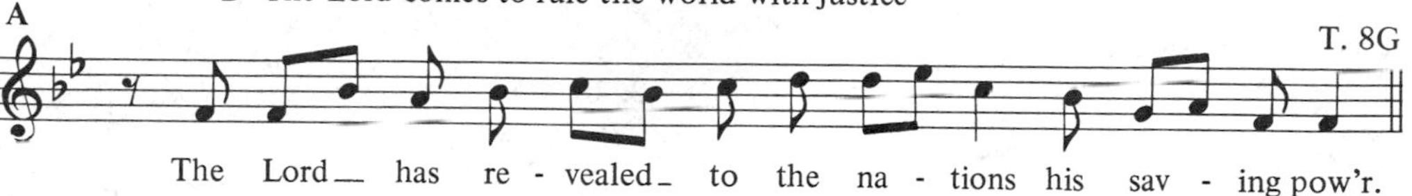
T. 8G
The Lord_ has re - vealed_ to the na - tions his sav - ing pow'r.

B

T. 8G
The Lord_ comes_ to rule_ the world_ with_ jus - tice.

PSALM 98: 1a-1b.2-3a.3b-4.5-6.9.

A Sing to the Lord a new song
For he has done wondrous deeds;
His right hand for him has won victory,
His holy arm.

All repeat ANTIPHON

A The Lord has made his salvation known;
In the sight of the nations he has revealed his justice.
He has remembered his kindness and his faithfulness
Toward the house of Israel.

All repeat ANTIPHON

A All the ends of the earth have seen
The salvation by our God.
Sing joyfully to the Lord, all you lands;
Break into song; sing praise.

All repeat ANTIPHON

AB Sing praise to the Lord with the harp,
With the harp and melodious song.
With the sound of the horn and the trumpets,
Sing joyfully before the King, the Lord.

All repeat ANTIPHON

AB Let them sing before the Lord,
For he comes to rule the earth.
With justice he will rule the world
And the peoples with equity.

All repeat ANTIPHON

434

Ps. 98(III)
Sing to the Lord a New Song

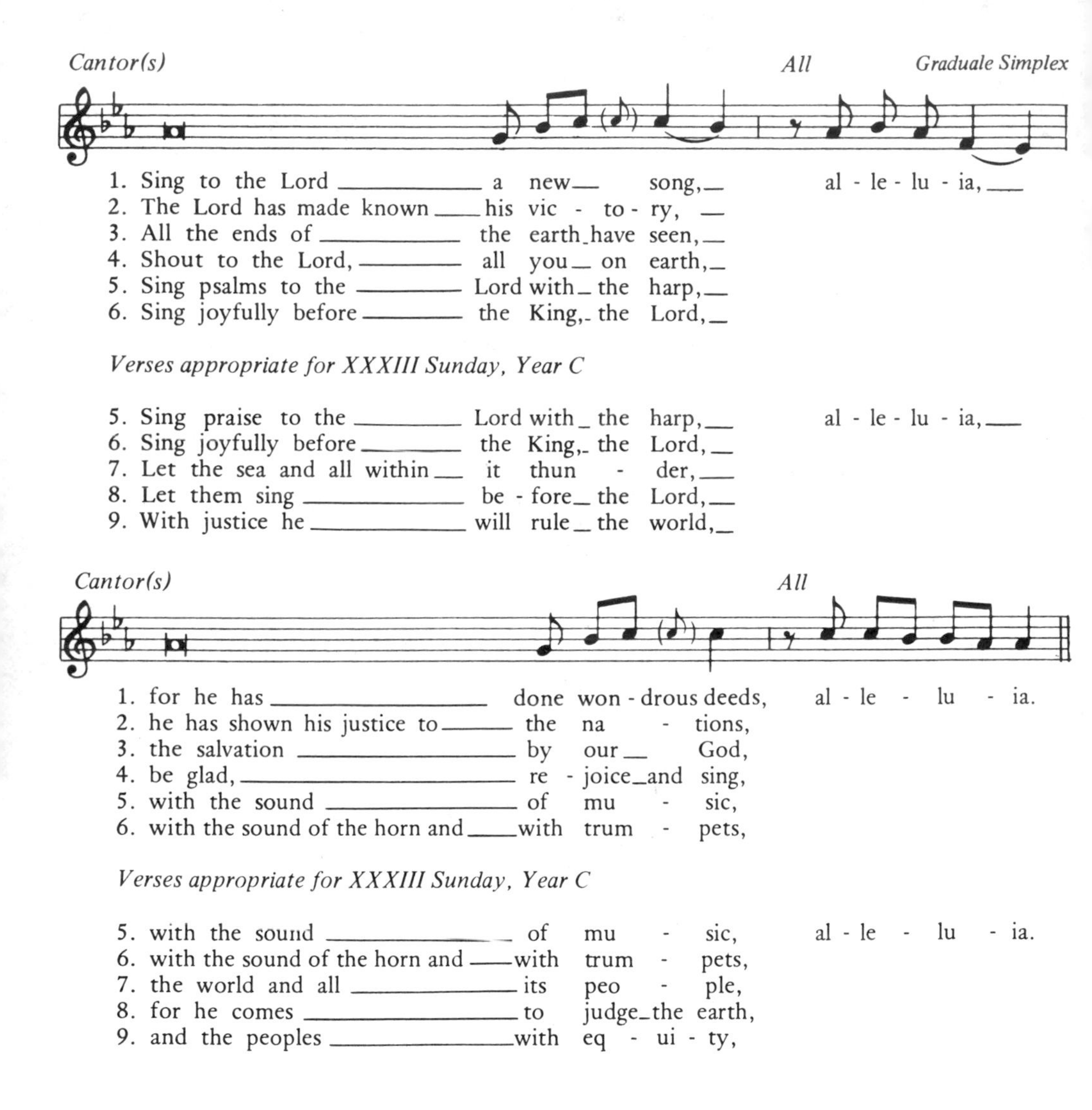
RESPONSE: Alleluia
PSALM 98: 1a. 2. 3b. 4-9.
Cantor(s)
All
Graduale Simplex
1. Sing to the Lord a new song, al - le - lu - ia,
2. The Lord has made known his vic - to - ry,
3. All the ends of the earth have seen,
4. Shout to the Lord, all you on earth,
5. Sing psalms to the Lord with the harp,
6. Sing joyfully before the King, the Lord,
Verses appropriate for XXXIII Sunday, Year C
5. Sing praise to the Lord with the harp, al - le - lu - ia,
6. Sing joyfully before the King, the Lord,
7. Let the sea and all within it thun - der,
8. Let them sing be - fore the Lord,
9. With justice he will rule the world,
Cantor(s)
All
1. for he has done won - drous deeds, al - le - lu - ia.
2. he has shown his justice to the na - tions,
3. the salvation by our God,
4. be glad, re - joice and sing,
5. with the sound of mu - sic,
6. with the sound of the horn and with trum - pets,
Verses appropriate for XXXIII Sunday, Year C
5. with the sound of mu - sic, al - le - lu - ia.
6. with the sound of the horn and with trum - pets,
7. the world and all its peo - ple,
8. for he comes to judge the earth,
9. and the peoples with eq - ui - ty,

Ps. 100
Sing with Joy to the Lord, All Ye Lands

ANTIPHONS: A We are his people
B Sing with joy to the Lord, all ye lands

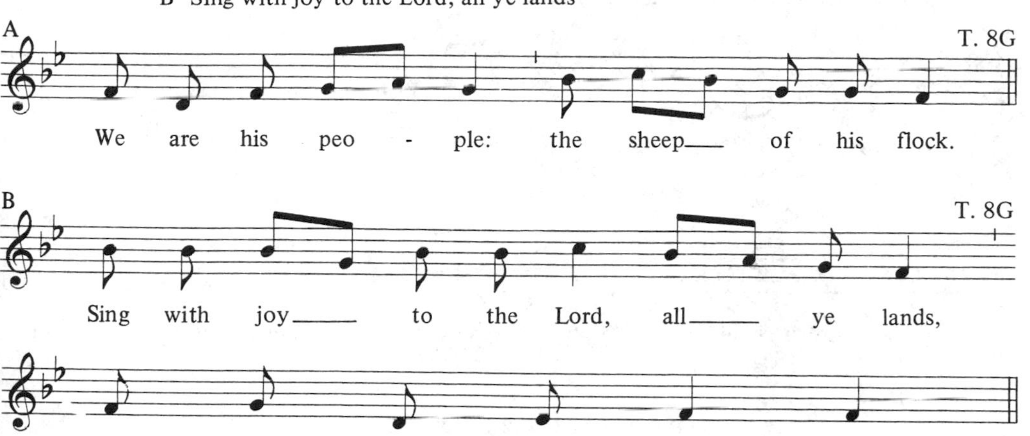
A
T. 8G
We are his peo - ple: the sheep of his flock.
B
T. 8G
Sing with joy to the Lord, all ye lands,
serve the Lord with glad - ness.

PSALM 100: 2.3.5.

Sing with joy to the Lord, all ye lands; serve the Lord with gladness;
Come into his presence rejoicing.
Know that the Lord he is God, he made us and we are his;
We are his people and the sheep of his pasture.

All repeat ANTIPHON

Come into his gates with thanksgiving, into his courts with hymns of praise;
Give thanks to him and bless his name.
For the Lord is good, his mercy is everlasting,
His faithfulness endures from generation to generation.

All repeat ANTIPHON

436

Ps. 103(I)
Bless the Lord, O My Soul

ANTIPHONS: A Bless the Lord, O my soul
B The Lord is kind and merciful

A
T. 7d
Bless the Lord, O_ my soul,___ give thanks_ to him and bless his ho - ly name._

B
T. 7d
The Lord_ is kind_ and mer-ci - ful,___ slow_to an - ger and rich in com-pas - sion.

PSALM 103: 1-2.3-4.8.10.12-13.

Bless the Lord, O my soul;
And all my being, bless his holy name.
Bless the Lord, O my soul,
And all his benefits do not forget.

All repeat ANTIPHON

He pardons all your iniquities,
He heals all your ills.
He redeems your life from destruction,
He crowns you with kindness and loving care.

All repeat ANTIPHON

Merciful and gracious is the Lord,
Slow to anger and abounding in steadfast love.
He does not deal with us according to our sins,
Nor repay us according to our faults.

All repeat ANTIPHON

As far as the east is from the west,
So far has he put our transgressions from us.
As a father has compassion on his children,
So the Lord has compassion on those who fear him.

All repeat ANTIPHON

Ps. 103(II)
Bless the Lord, O My Soul

ANTIPHON: The Lord has set his throne in heaven

T. Per.
The___ Lord___ has set___ his throne___ in heav - en.

PSALM 103: 1-2.11-12.19-20.

Bless the Lord, O my soul,
His kingdom and my being, bless his holy name.
Bless the Lord, O my soul,
And forget not all his benefits.

All repeat ANTIPHON

For as the heavens are high above the earth,
So surpassing is his kindness toward those who fear him.
As far as the east is from the west,
So far has he put our transgressions from us.

All repeat ANTIPHON

The Lord has established his throne in heaven,
And his kingdom rules over all.
Bless the Lord, all you his angels,
you mighty in strength who do his bidding,
Obeying his spoken word.

All repeat ANTIPHON

438

Ps. 104(I)
Bless the Lord, O My Soul

ANTIPHON: Send forth your Spirit, Lord

T. 7a
Send forth your Spir - it, Lord,_ and_ re - new__ the face_ of the earth.

PSALM 104: 1-2.5-6.10.12.13-14.24.35.

Bless the Lord, O my soul!
O Lord, my God, you are great indeed!
With majesty and glory you are clothed,
Robed in light as with a cloak.

All repeat ANTIPHON

You fixed the earth upon its foundation,
Not to be moved forever;
With water, as with a garment, you covered it;
Above the mountains the water stood.

All repeat ANTIPHON

Into the watercourses you send forth springs
That flow among the hills.
Beside them the birds of heaven dwell;
From among the branches they send forth their song.

All repeat ANTIPHON

You water the mountains from your palace;
The earth is replete with the fruit of your works.
You raise grass for the cattle, and vegetation for our use,
Producing bread from the earth.

All repeat ANTIPHON

How manifold are your works, O Lord!
In wisdom you have wrought them all.
Of your creatures the earth is full.
Bless the Lord, O my soul! Praise the Lord!

All repeat ANTIPHON

Ps. 104(II)
Bless the Lord, O My Soul

439

ANTIPHONS A Send forth your Spirit, Lord
B The Spirit of God is upon me

A
T. 7a
Send forth your Spir - it, Lord,_ and_ re - new_ the face_ of the earth.
B
T. 7a
The Spir - it of God is up-on_ me be-cause_ the Lord_ has a - noint - ed_ me.

PSALM 104: 1.24.29-30.31.34.

Bless the Lord, O my soul!
O Lord, my God, you are great indeed!
How manifold are your works, O Lord!
Of your creatures the earth is full.

All repeat ANTIPHON

If you take away their breath,
They perish and return to their dust.
When you send forth your Spirit,
They are created and you renew the face of the earth.

All repeat ANTIPHON

May the glory of the Lord endure forever;
May the Lord be glad in his works!
Pleasing to him be my theme;
I will be glad in the Lord.

All repeat ANTIPHON

440

Ps. 107
They Who Sailed the Sea in Ships

ANTIPHON: Give thanks to the Lord, his love is everlasting

T. 6
Give thanks___ to the Lord,___ his love___ is ev - er - last - ing.

PSALM 107: 23-24.25-26.28-29.30-31.

They who sailed the sea in ships,
Earning their living on the sea,
Saw what the Lord has done
And his wonders in the abyss.

All repeat ANTIPHON

His command raised up a stormy wind
Which tossed its waves on high.
They mounted up to heaven; to the depths they sank;
Their hearts melted away in their plight.

All repeat ANTIPHON

They cried to the Lord in their distress;
He rescued them from their plight.
He hushed the storm to a gentle breeze,
And the billows of the sea were stilled.

All repeat ANTIPHON

They rejoiced that they were calmed;
He brought them safely to their port.
Let them give thanks to the Lord for his kindness
And his wondrous deeds for the children of earth.

All repeat ANTIPHON

Ps. 110
The Lord Says to My Lord

RESPONSE: You are a priest forever in the line of Melchizedek

Cantor(s)
Antiphonale Romanum
The Lord says to my Lord: "Sit at my right hand."

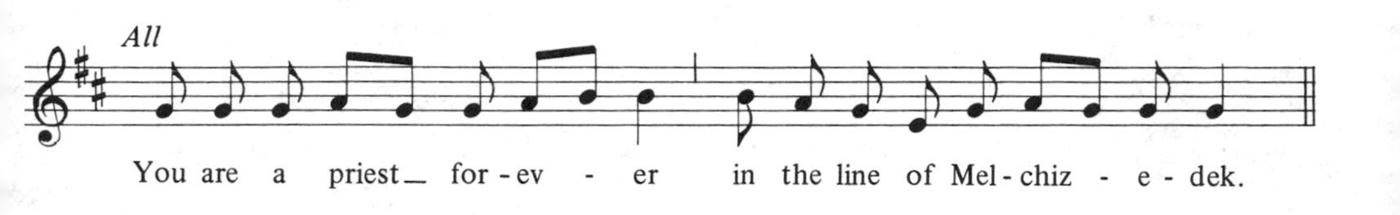
All
You are a priest for - ev - er in the line of Mel - chiz - e - dek.

PSALM 110: 1.2.3a.3b.4.

The Lord says to my Lord: "Sit at my right hand,
Till I put your enemies under your feet."
The Lord sends forth your might scepter from Sion:
"Rule in the midst of your foes!"

All repeat RESPONSE

Your people will offer themselves freely
On the day you lead your host upon the sacred hills.
From the womb of the morning
Like dew your youth will come to you.

All repeat RESPONSE

The Lord has sworn and will not change his mind:
"You are a priest forever in the line of Melchizedek."

Cantor(s) The Lord...

All repeat RESPONSE

442

Ps. 112
Happy Are They Who Fear the Lord

ANTIPHONS: A The just one is a light in darkness to the upright
B Happy are they who fear the Lord
C Happy are they who are merciful

A
T. 6
The just one is a light in dark - ness to the up - right.

B
T. 6
Hap - py are they who fear ___ the Lord.
C
T. 6
Hap - py are they who are mer - ci - ful and lend ___ to those in need.

PSALM 112: 1-2.3-4.5-6.7-8.9-10.

Happy are they who fear the Lord,
Who greatly delight in his commands.
Their posterity shall be mighty upon the earth;
The upright generations shall be blessed.

All repeat ANTIPHON

Their generosity shall endure forever;
Wealth and riches shall be always in their house.
They dawn through the darkness, a light for the upright.
They are gracious and just and merciful.

All repeat ANTIPHON

Well for them who are gracious and lend,
Who with justice conduct their affairs.
The just shall be in everlasting remembrance;
They shall never be moved.

All repeat ANTIPHON

An evil report they shall not fear;
Trusting in the Lord, their hearts are firm.
Their hearts are steadfast; they shall not fear
Till they look down upon their foes.

All repeat ANTIPHON

They give to the poor lavishly; their generosity shall endure forever;
With honor they shall be exalted and glorified.
The wicked shall see it and be vexed;
they shall gnash their teeth and pine away;
The desire of the wicked shall come to nought.

All repeat ANTIPHON

Ps. 113 443

Praise the Lord, You His Servants

ANTIPHONS: A Praise the Lord who lifts up the poor
B The Lord will give him a seat with the leaders of his people
C Blessed be the name of the Lord forever

A

T. 4g
Praise the Lord who lifts up the poor.

B

T. 4g
The Lord will give him a seat with the lead - ers of his peo - ple.

C

T. 4g
Bless - ed be the name of the Lord for - ev - er.

PSALM 113: 1-2.4-6.7-8.

Praise the Lord, you his servants,
Praise the Lord's name.
Blessed be the Lord's name
Both now and forever.

All repeat ANTIPHON

The Lord is high above all nations;
His glory is above the heavens.
Who is like the Lord, our God, who is enthroned on high
And looks down upon the heavens and the earth below?

All repeat ANTIPHON

He raises up the lowly from the dust;
He lifts up the poor from their misery
To seat them with princes,
With the princes of his own people.

All repeat ANTIPHON

444

Ps. 116(I)
What Shall I Render to the Lord

ANTIPHONS: A Gracious is the Lord and just
B I will take the cup of salvation

A
J. Gerald Phillips
T. 7a
Gra - cious is the Lord and just, mer - ci - ful is our God.

B
T. 7a
I will take the cup of sal - va - tion and call on the name of the Lord.

PSALM 116: 12-17.

What shall I render to the Lord
For all he has given to me?
I will take the cup of salvation
And invoke the name of the Lord.

All repeat ANTIPHON

In the presence of all his people
I will fulfill my vows to the Lord.
Great price in the eyes of the Lord
Has the death of his faithful ones.

All repeat ANTIPHON

I am your servant, the son of your handmaid;
You have loosèd my bonds.
I will offer the sacrifice of praise
And call on the name of the Lord.

All repeat ANTIPHON

Ps. 116(II)
I Love the Lord

ANTIPHONS: A The cup of blessing
B I shall walk before the Lord

A
T. 1D
The cup— of bless - ing is a shar - ing in the blood— of Christ.

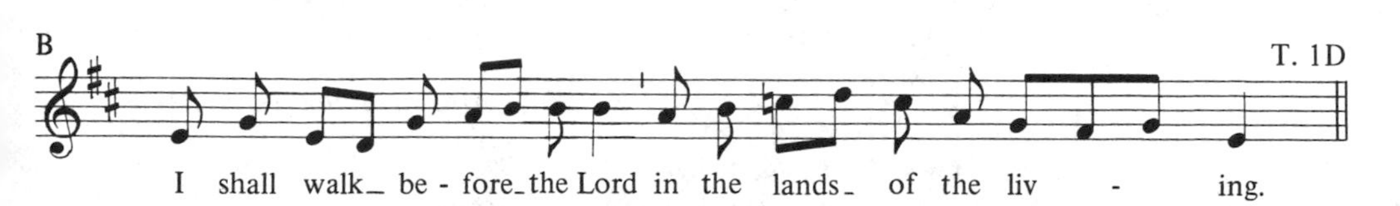
B
T. 1D
I shall walk— be - fore—the Lord in the lands— of the liv - ing.

PSALM 116: 1-2.5.9.12-13.14.17.

B I love the Lord because he has heard my voice in supplication,
Because he has inclined his ear to me
on the day I called him.
The cords of death encompassed me,
And I called upon the name of the Lord,
"O Lord, save my life."

All repeat ANTIPHON

B Gracious is the Lord and just;
Yes, our God is merciful.
For he has freed my soul from death,
My eyes from tears, my feet from stumbling.

All repeat ANTIPHON

A What shall I render to the Lord
For all the good he has done for me?
I will take the cup of salvation
And call upon the Lord's name.

All repeat ANTIPHON

AB Precious in the eyes of the Lord
Is the death of his faithful ones.
O Lord, I am your servant, the son of your handmaid;
You have loosed my bonds.

All repeat ANTIPHON

AB To you will I offer the sacrifice of thanksgiving,
I will call upon the Lord's name.
My vows to the Lord I will pay
In the presence of all his people.

All repeat ANTIPHON

446

Ps. 117(I)
All You Nations, Praise the Lord

ANTIPHON: Go out to all the world

T. 1g
Go out to all the world, and tell the Good News.

*PSALM 117: 1-2.

All you nations, praise the Lord;
Glorify him, all ye peoples!

All repeat ANTIPHON

For steadfast is his kindness toward us
And the fidelity of the Lord endures forever.

All repeat ANTIPHON

447

Ps. 117(II)
Laudate Dominum

ANTIPHON: Alleluia

Gregorian Chant T. 6

Al - le - lú - ia, al - le - lú - ia, al - le - lú - ia.

*PSALM 117: 1-2.

Laudáte Dóminum, omnes gentes:
Laudáte eum, omnes pópuli.
Quóniam confirmáta est super nos misericórdia ejus:
Et véritas Dómini manet in aetérnum.

All repeat ANTIPHON

DOX. Glória Patri, et Fílio,
Et Spirítui Sancto.
Sicut erat in princípio, et nunc, et semper,
Et sáecula saeculórum. Amen.

All repeat ANTIPHON

*Listed as Psalm 116 in the Latin psalter.

Ps. 117(III)
Laudate Dominum, Omnes Gentes

ANTIPHONS: A Adorémus in aetérnum
B Atténde, Dómine

A

Gregorian Chant T. 5

Ad - o - ré - mus_ in ae - tér - num san-ctís - si - mum_ Sa - cra-mén - tum.

Tr. Let us adore the Most Blessed Sacrament forever.

B

T. 5

At-tén-de, Dó-mi-ne, et mi - se - ré - re, qui - a pec-cá - vi-mus ti - bi.

Tr. Hear us, O Lord, and have mercy, for we have sinned against thee.

*PSALM 117: 1-2.

Laudáte Dóminum, omnes gentes:
Laudáte eum, omnes pópuli.
Quóniam confirmáta est super nos misericórdia ejus:
Et véritas Dómini manet in aetérnum.

All repeat ANTIPHON

DOX. Glória Patri, et Fílio,
Et Spirítui Sancto.
Sicut erat in princípio, et nunc, et semper,
Et in saécula saeculórum. Amen.

All repeat ANTIPHON

* *Listed as Psalm 116 in Latin psalter. For translation see* No. 446.

449

Ps. 117(IV)
Laudate Dominum, Omnes Gentes

ANTIPHONS: A Roráte caeli
B Cor Jesu

A

Gregorian Chant T. 1D
Ro-rá - te, cae-li, dé - su-per,— et nu-bes plu - ant ju - stum.
Drop down dew, ye heavens, from above, and let the clouds rain down the just one.

B

Gregorian Chant T. 1D
Cor Je-su sa-cra-tís - si-mum, mi-se-ré - re no - bis.
Most Sacred Heart of Jesus, have mercy on us.

*PSALM 117: 1-2.

Laudáte Dóminum, omnes gentes:
Laudáte eum, omnes pópuli.
Quóniam confirmáta est super nos misericórdia ejus:
Et véritas Dómini manet in aetérnum.

All repeat ANTIPHON

DOX. Glória Patri, et Fílio,
Et Spirítui Sancto.
Sicut erat in princípio, et nunc, et semper,
Et in saécula saeculórum. Amen.

All repeat ANTIPHON

* *Listed as Psalm 116 in Latin psalter. For translation see* No. 446.

Ps. 118(I)
Give Thanks to the Lord for He Is Good

ANTIPHONS: A Alleluia
B Give thanks to the Lord for he is good
C The stone rejected by the builders
D This is the day the Lord has made

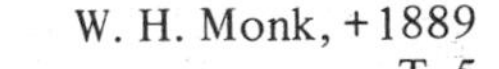
W. H. Monk, +1889

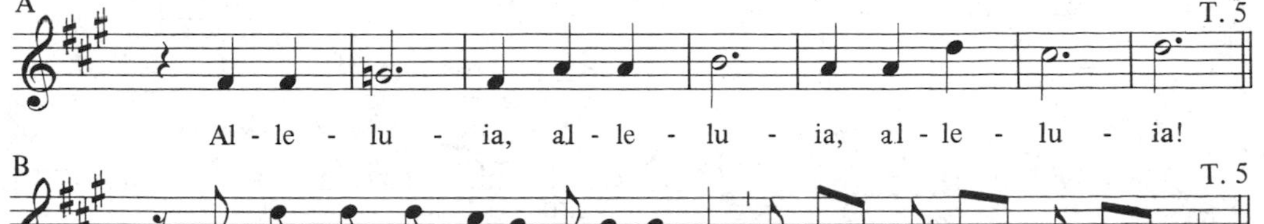
A
T. 5
Al - le - lu - ia, al - le - lu - ia, al - le - lu - ia!

B T. 5

Give thanks to the Lord_ for he is good, his love_ is ev - er - last - ing.

C
T. 5
The stone_ re - ject - ed by the build - ers has_ be-come the cor - ner - stone.

D
T. 5
This is the day_ the Lord_ has made; let us re - joice_ and be glad.

PSALM 118: 1-2.16-17.22-23.

Give thanks to the Lord for he is good,
For his mercy endures forever.
Let the house of Israel say,
"His mercy endures forever."

All repeat ANTIPHON

The right hand of the Lord has struck with power;
The right hand of the Lord is exalted.
I shall not die, but live,
And declare the works of the Lord.

All repeat ANTIPHON

The stone which the builders rejected
Has become the cornerstone.
By the Lord has this been done;
It is wonderful in our eyes.

All repeat ANTIPHON

451

Ps. 118(II)
Give Thanks to the Lord for He Is Good

ANTIPHON: This is the day the Lord has made

This is the day the Lord has made; let us re-
joice and be glad. glad.
last time

PSALM 118: 1-2.16-17.22-23.

Give thanks to the Lord for he is good,
For his mercy endures forever.
Let the house of Israel say:
"His mercy endures forever."

All repeat ANTIPHON

The right hand of the Lord has struck with pow'r;
The right hand of the Lord is exalted.
I shall not die, but live,
And declare the works of the Lord.

All repeat ANTIPHON

The stone which the builders rejected
Has become the cornerstone.
By the Lord has this been done;
It is wonderful in our eyes.

All repeat ANTIPHON

Ps. 119(I)
How Blessed Are They

ANTIPHON: How blessed are they who walk in the law of the Lord

T. 1g
How blessed are they who walk

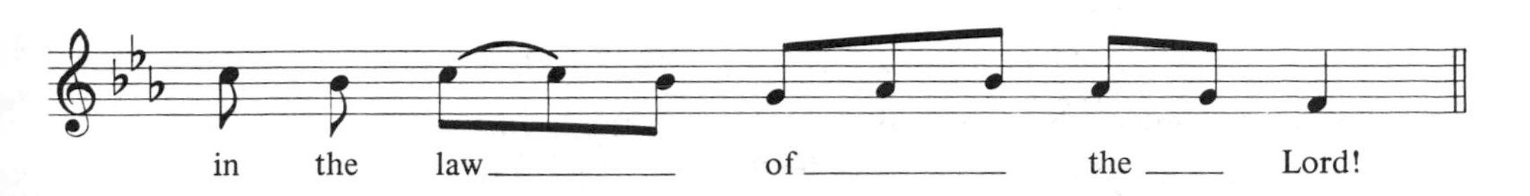
in the law of the Lord!

PSALM 119: 1-7.17-18.34.

How blessed are they who treasure his mandates,
Who seek him with all their hearts,
Not doing what is evil
But walking in his ways!
You have given your precepts
To be guarded with all care.

All repeat ANTIPHON

Oh, that my ways were laid straight
Toward observing your decrees.
Then need I not be ashamed
In studying your commandments.
I will give you thanks with a true heart
For teaching me the edicts of your justice.

All repeat ANTIPHON

Grant your servant the grace to live
And I will keep your word;
Open my eyes
To consider the wonders of your law.
Give me understanding that I may keep your law
And observe it with all my heart.

All repeat ANTIPHON

453

Ps. 119(II)
How Blessed Are They

ANTIPHON: I love your commands, O Lord, my God

T. 1g
I love your com - mands, O Lord my God.

PSALM 119: 1-2.57.72.76-77.127-128.129-130.

How blessed are they who walk in the law of the Lord,
Whose way is blameless.
Blessed are they who observe his decrees,
Who seek him with all their hearts.

All repeat ANTIPHON

You are all I want, O Lord,
I promise to obey your laws.
The law of your mouth is to me more precious
Than thousands of gold and silver pieces.

All repeat ANTIPHON

Let your kindness comfort me
According to your promise to your servants.
Let your compassion come to me that I may live,
For your law is my delight.

All repeat ANTIPHON

For I love your commands,
More than the finest gold.
For I go forward in all your precepts;
I hate ev'ry false way.

All repeat ANTIPHON

Your decrees are wonderful;
I obey them with all my heart.
The revelation of your words sheds light,
Giving understanding to the simple.

All repeat ANTIPHON

Ps. 121
I Lift Up My Eyes Toward the Mountains

ANTIPHON: Our help is from the Lord who made heav'n and earth

T. 1D
Our help is from the Lord who made heav'n and earth.

PSALM 121: 1-2.3-4.5-6.7-8.

I lift my eyes toward the mountains;
Whence shall my help come?
My help is from the Lord,
Who made heaven and earth.

All repeat ANTIPHON

May he not suffer your foot to slip;
May he who guards you slumber not:
Indeed he neither slumbers nor sleeps,
The guardian of Israel.

All repeat ANTIPHON

The Lord is your guardian; the Lord is your shade;
He is beside you at your right hand.
The sun shall not harm you by day,
Nor the moon by night.

All repeat ANTIPHON

From all evil the Lord will guard you;
He will guard your life.
He will guard your coming and going,
Both now and forever.

All repeat ANTIPHON

Ps. 122
I Rejoiced Because They Said to Me

RESPONSE: We will go up to the house of the Lord

T. 5
Schola I re - joiced ___ be - cause they said ___ to me,
RESPONSE
All "We will go up ___ to the house ___ of ___ the Lord."

PSALM 122: 1-9.

And now we have set foot within your gates,
O Jerusalem.
Jerusalem, built as a city
With compact unity.

All repeat RESPONSE

To it the tribes of the Lord go up
To give thanks to the name of the Lord
according to the decree for Israel.
In it are set up judgment seats,
Seats for the house of David.

All repeat RESPONSE

Pray for the peace of Jerusalem!
May those who love you prosper!
May peace be within your walls,
Prosperity in your buildings.

All repeat RESPONSE

Because of my relatives and friends I will say,
"Peace be within you!"
Because of the house of the Lord, our God,
For your good I will pray.

Schola I rejoiced. . .
All repeat RESPONSE

Ps. 123
To You I Lift Up My Eyes

ANTIPHON: Our eyes are fixed on the Lord, pleading for his mercy

T. 2
Our eyes— are fixed on the Lord,— plead - ing for— his mer - cy.

PSALM 123: 1–4.

To you I lift up my eyes
Who are enthroned in heaven,
Behold, as the eyes of servants
Are on the hands of their masters.

All repeat ANTIPHON

As the eyes of a maid
Are on the hands of her mistress,
So our eyes are on the Lord, our God,
Till he have pity on us.

All repeat ANTIPHON

Have mercy on us, O Lord, have mercy,
For we are more than sated with contempt;
Our souls are more than sated with the mockery of the arrogant,
With the contempt of the proud.

All repeat ANTIPHON

457

Ps. 124
If It Had Not Been the Lord

ANTIPHON: Our soul has escaped like a bird from the hunter's net

T. 2
Our soul_ has_ es - caped_ like_ a bird_ from the hunt-er's net.

PSALM 124: 2-3.4-5.7b-8.

If it had not been the Lord who was on our side,
When enemies rose up against us,
Then they would have swallowed us up alive,
When their anger was kindled against us.

All repeat ANTIPHON

Then the flood would have swept us away,
The torrent would have gone over us;
The raging waters
Would then have gone over us.

All repeat ANTIPHON

The snare is broken,
And we have escaped!
Our help is in the name of the Lord,
Who made heaven and earth.

All repeat ANTIPHON

Ps. 126 **458**

When the Lord Brought Back the Captives

ANTIPHONS: A The Lord has done great things for us
B Those who sow in tears shall reap in joy

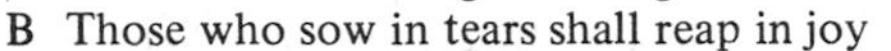

A

T. 6
The Lord has done great things for us; we are filled _ with joy;

B

T. 6
Those who sow ___ in tears shall reap ___ in joy.

PSALM 126: 1-6.

When the Lord brought back the captives of Sion,
We were like those in a dream.
Then our mouth was filled with laughter
And our tongue with shouts of joy.

All repeat ANTIPHON

Then they said among the nations,
"The Lord has done great things for them."
The Lord has done great things for us;
We are glad indeed.

All repeat ANTIPHON

O Lord, restore our fortunes,
Like the torrents in the southern desert.
Those who sow in tears
Shall reap in joy.

All repeat ANTIPHON

Although they go forth weeping,
Carrying the seed to be sown,
They shall come back rejoicing,
Carrying their sheaves.

All repeat ANTIPHON

Ps. 128
Happy Are You Who Fear the Lord

ANTIPHONS: A Happy are you who fear the Lord
B May the Lord bless us all the days of our lives

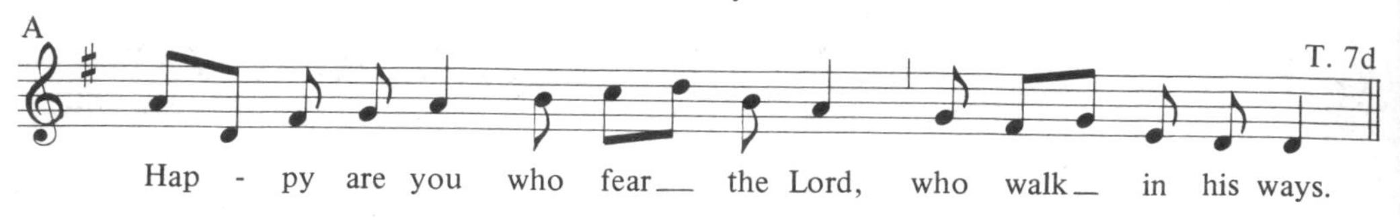
A
T. 7d
Hap - py are you who fear_ the Lord, who walk_ in his ways.

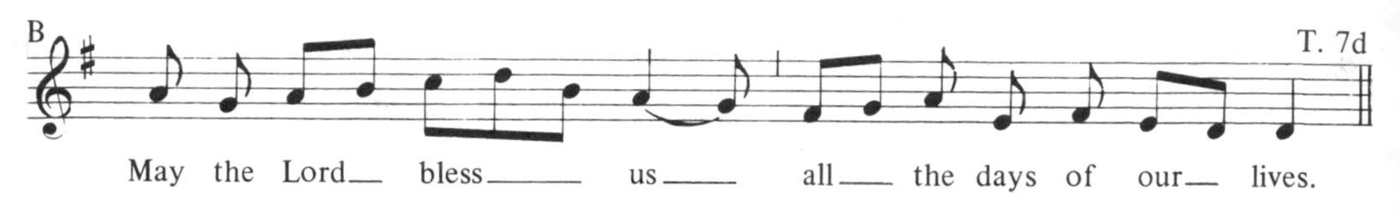
B
T. 7d
May the Lord_ bless_ us_ all_ the days of our_ lives.

PSALM 128: 1-6.

Happy are you who fear the Lord,
Who walk in his ways!
For you shall eat the fruit of your handiwork;
Favored and happy shall you be.

All repeat ANTIPHON

Your wife shall be like a fruitful vine in the
recesses of your home;
Your children around your table like olive plants.
Behold, thus is the man blessed
Who fears the Lord.

All repeat ANTIPHON

The Lord bless you from Zion:
May you see the prosperity of Jerusalem
all the days of your life;
May you see your children's children.
Peace be upon Israel!

All repeat ANTIPHON

Ps. 130
Out of the Depths I Cry to You

ANTIPHONS: A With the Lord there is mercy
B I hope in the Lord and I trust in his word

A
T. Per.
With the Lord there is mer - cy and full-ness of re - demp - tion.
B
T. Per.
I hope in the Lord and I trust in his word.

PSALM 130: 1-2.3-4.4-6.7-8.

Out of the depths I cry to you, O Lord;
Lord, hear my voice!
Let your ears be attentive
To my call for help.

All repeat ANTIPHON

If you, O Lord, will mark iniquities,
Lord, who can stand?
But with you is forgiveness,
That you may be revered.

All repeat ANTIPHON

I trust in the Lord;
My soul trusts in his word.
My soul waits for the Lord
more than sentinels wait for the dawn.
Let Israel wait for the Lord.

All repeat ANTIPHON

For with the Lord is kindness,
And fullness of redemption is with him.
And Israel he will redeem
From all their sinful ways.

All repeat ANTIPHON

461

Ps. 131
My Heart Is Not Proud, O Lord

ANTIPHON: In you, O Lord, I have found my peace

Graduale Simplex
In you, O Lord, I have found my peace.

PSALM 131: 1.2.3.

My heart is not proud, O Lord,
Nor haughty are my eyes;
I busy not myself with great things,
Nor with things too sublime for me.

All repeat ANTIPHON

Nay rather, I have quieted and stilled my soul
Like a weaned child.
Like a weaned child on its mother's lap,
So is my soul within me.

All repeat ANTIPHON

Hope in the Lord, O Israel,
Both now and forever.

All repeat ANTIPHON

Ps. 132 462
Lo, We Heard of It in Ephrathah

ANTIPHONS: A Lord, go up to the place of your rest
B God will give him the throne of David, his father

A
T. 7c
Lord, go up_ to the place_ of your rest,_ you_ and the ark_ of your ho-li-ness.

B
T. 7c
God_ will give_ him the throne_ of Da - vid, his fa - ther.

PSALM 132: 6.7.9.10.11.13.14.17.18.

A Lo, we heard of it in Ephrathah;
We found it in the fields of Jaar.
"Let us go to his dwelling place;
Let us worship at his feet."

All repeat ANTIPHON

A Let thy priests be clothed with righteousness,
And let thy saints shout for joy.
For thy servant David's sake
Do not turn away the face of thy anointed one.

All repeat ANTIPHON

B The Lord swore to David a sure oath
From which he will not turn back:
"One of the sons of your body
I will set on your throne."

All repeat ANTIPHON

AB For the Lord has chosen Zion;
He has desired it for his dwelling place,
"Forever this is my resting place;
For I have desired it, here will I dwell.

All repeat ANTIPHON

B "There will I make a horn to sprout for David;
For my anointed I have prepared a lamp.
His enemies I will clothe with shame,
But his crown will shed its luster upon himself."

All repeat ANTIPHON

463 Ps. 136(I)

Give Thanks to the Lord for He Is Good

REFRAINS: His love is everlasting
For his mercy endures forever

REFRAIN

1. Cantor(s)
All
His love_ is ev - er - last - ing. His love_ is ev - er - last - ing.

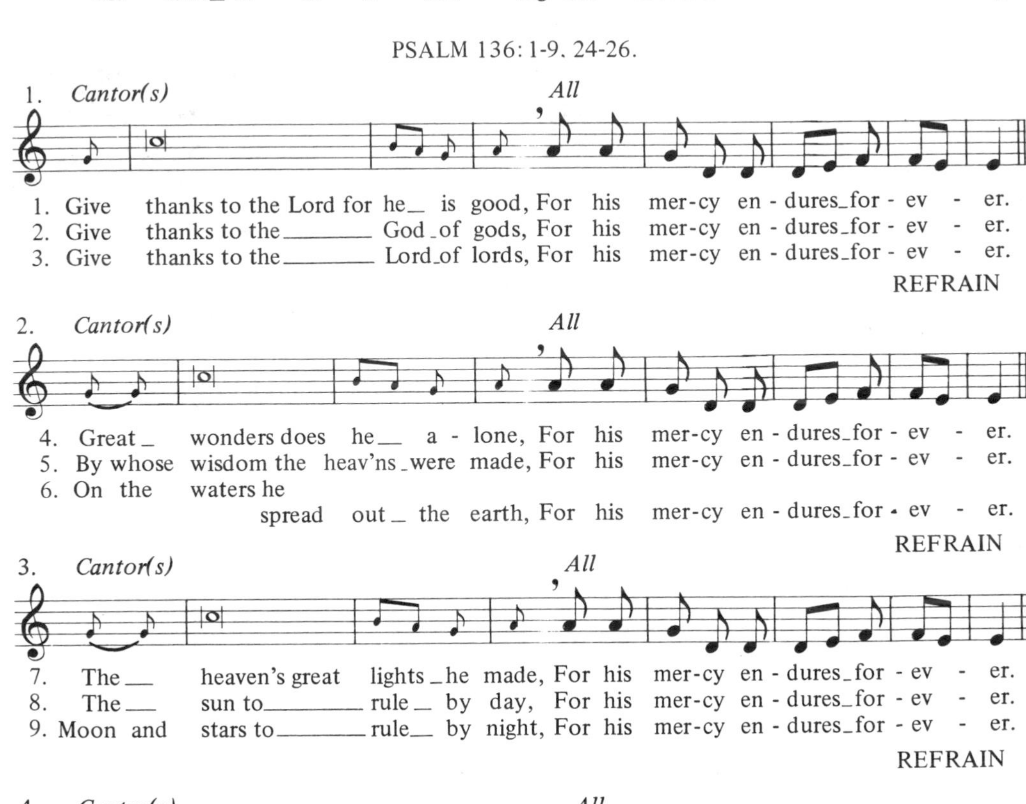
PSALM 136: 1-9. 24-26.
1. Cantor(s)
All
1. Give thanks to the Lord for he_ is good, For his mer-cy en - dures_for - ev - er.
2. Give thanks to the_____ God_of gods, For his mer-cy en - dures_for - ev - er.
3. Give thanks to the_____ Lord_of lords, For his mer-cy en - dures_for - ev - er.
REFRAIN
2. Cantor(s)
All
4. Great_ wonders does he_ a - lone, For his mer-cy en - dures_for - ev - er.
5. By whose wisdom the heav'ns_were made, For his mer-cy en - dures_for - ev - er.
6. On the waters he
spread out_ the earth, For his mer-cy en - dures_for - ev - er.
REFRAIN
3. Cantor(s)
All
7. The_ heaven's great lights_he made, For his mer-cy en - dures_for - ev - er.
8. The_ sun to_____ rule_ by day, For his mer-cy en - dures_for - ev - er.
9. Moon and stars to_____ rule_ by night, For his mer-cy en - dures_for - ev - er.
REFRAIN

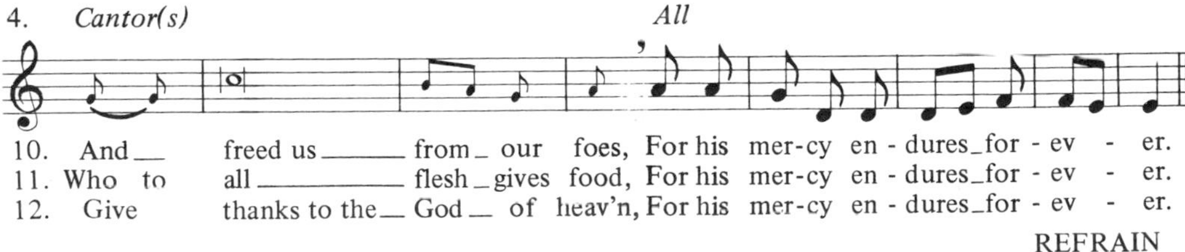
4. Cantor(s)
All
10. And_ freed us_____ from_ our foes, For his mer-cy en - dures_for - ev - er.
11. Who to all_____ flesh_gives food, For his mer-cy en - dures_for - ev - er.
12. Give thanks to the_ God_ of heav'n, For his mer-cy en - dures_for - ev - er.
REFRAIN

Ps. 136(II)
Give Thanks to the Lord for He Is Good

464

REFRAINS: His love is everlasting
For his mercy endures forever

REFRAIN

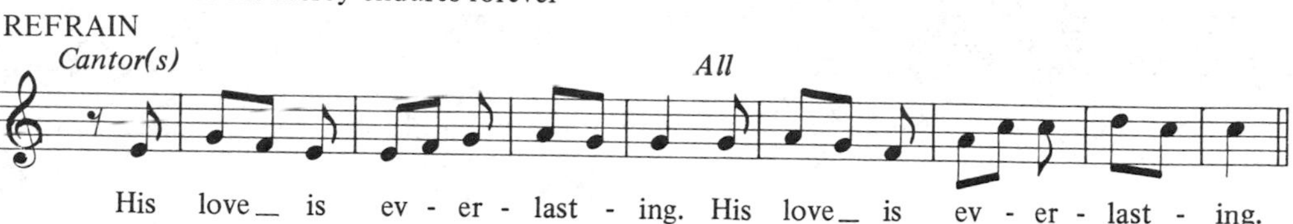

Cantor(s)
All
His love_ is ev - er - last - ing. His love_ is ev - er - last - ing.

PSALM 136: 1. 3. 16. 21-26.

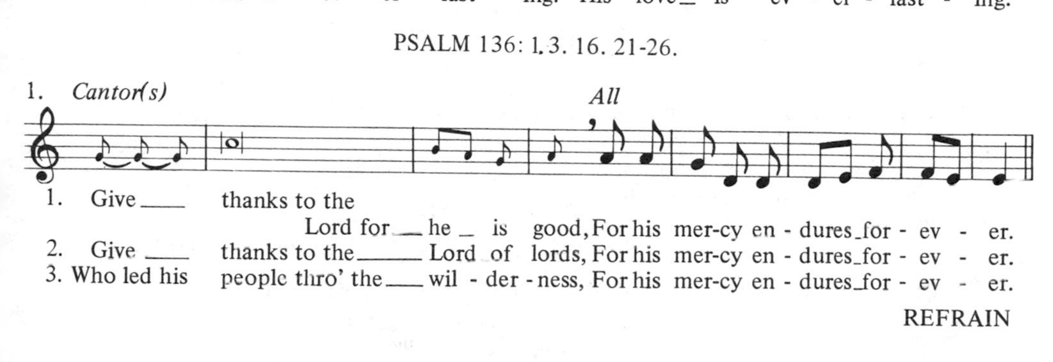

1. Cantor(s)
All
1. Give___ thanks to the Lord for___ he_ is good, For his mer-cy en - dures_for - ev - er.
2. Give___ thanks to the___ Lord of lords, For his mer-cy en - dures_for - ev - er.
3. Who led his people thro' the___ wil - der - ness, For his mer-cy en - dures_for - ev - er.
REFRAIN

2. Cantor(s)
All

4. And ___ made their land a her - i - tage, For his mer-cy en - dures_for - ev - er.
5. The ___ heritage of his servant Is - ra - el, For his mer-cy en - dures_for - ev - er.
6. In our ab - jection he re - mem-bered us, For his mer-cy en - dures_for - ev - er.

REFRAIN

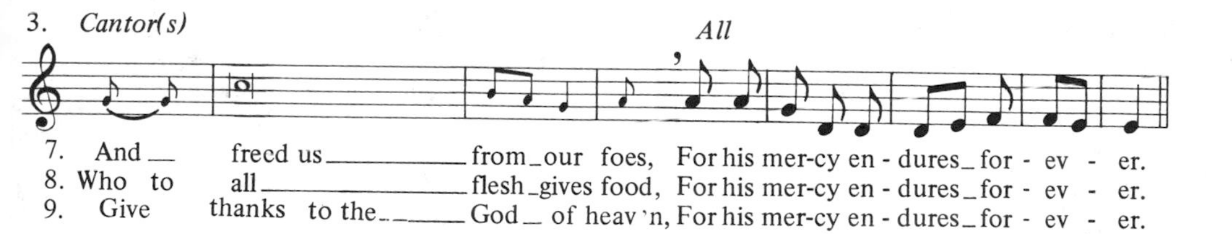

3. Cantor(s)
All
7. And_ freed us___ from_our foes, For his mer-cy en - dures_ for - ev - er.
8. Who to all___ flesh_gives food, For his mer-cy en - dures_ for - ev - er.
9. Give thanks to the___ God_ of heav'n, For his mer-cy en - dures_ for - ev - er.

REFRAIN

Ps. 137
By the Streams of Babylon

ANTIPHON: Let my tongue be silenced

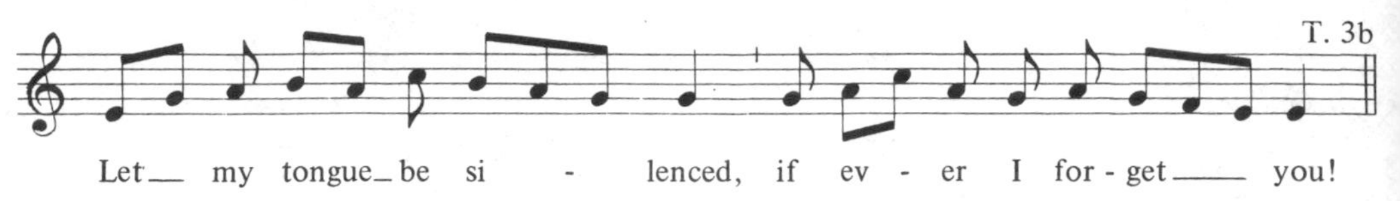
T. 3b
Let my tongue be si - lenced, if ev - er I for - get you!

PSALM 137: 1-2.3-4.5-6.

By the streams of Babylon we sat and wept
When we remembered you, Zion.
On the aspens of the land
We hung up our harps.

All repeat ANTIPHON

Though there our captors asked of us the lyrics of our songs,
And our despoilers urged us to be joyous:
"Sing for us a song of Zion!"
How could we sing the Lord's song
In a foreign land?

All repeat ANTIPHON

Jerusalem, if I forget you,
May my right hand be forgotten!
May my tongue cleave to my palate if I remember you not,
If I place not Jerusalem ahead of my joy.

All repeat ANTIPHON

Ps. 138(I)
I Will Give Thanks to You

ANTIPHONS: A Lord, I thank you for your faithfulness and love
B In the sight of the angels

A
T. 8G
Lord, I thank_ you for your faith - ful - ness___ and___ love.

B
T. 8G
In the sight_ of the an - gels I will sing_ your prais - es, Lord.

PSALM 138: 1-5.7-8.

I will give thanks to you, O Lord, with all my heart,
For you have heard the words of my mouth;
In the presence of the angels
I will sing your praise.

All repeat ANTIPHON

I will worship at your holy temple and give thanks to your name,
because of your truth and your kindness;
For you have made your name and your promise great
above all things.
When I called you answered me;
You built up strength within me.

All repeat ANTIPHON

All the kings of the earth shall give thanks to you, O Lord,
When they hear the words of your mouth;
And of the ways of the Lord they shall sing:
"Great is the glory of the Lord."

All repeat ANTIPHON

Your right hand saves me.
The Lord will complete what he has done for me.
You kindness, O Lord, endures forever;
Forsake not the work of your hands.

All repeat ANTIPHON

467

Ps. 138(II)
I Will Give Thanks to You

ANTIPHONS: A Lord, your love is eternal
B Lord, on the day I called for help

A
T. 8G
Lord, your love_ is e - ter - nal; do not_ for - sake_ the work of your hands.

B
T. 8G
Lord,_ on the day_ I called_ for help, you an - swered me.

PSALM 138: 1-2.2-3.6-7.7-8.

I will give thanks to you, O Lord, with all my heart,
For you have heard the words of my mouth;
In the presence of the angels
I will sing your praise.

All repeat ANTIPHON

I will worship at your holy temple and give thanks to your name,
because of your truth and your kindness;
For you have made your name and your promise great
above all things.
When I called, you answered me;
You built up strength within me.

All repeat ANTIPHON

The Lord is exalted, yet he sees the lowly,
And the proud he knows from afar.
Though I walk amid distress, you preserve me;
You raise your hand against the anger of my enemies.

All repeat ANTIPHON

You stretch out your hand and save me.
The Lord will complete what he has done for me.
Your kindness, O Lord, endures forever;
Do not forsake the work of your hands.

All repeat ANTIPHON

Ps. 139
O Lord, You Have Probed Me

ANTIPHONS: A I give you thanks
B Guide me, O Lord, along the everlasting way

A
T. 8G
I give you thanks that I___ am won - der - ful - ly made.

B
T. 8G
Guide___ me,_ O Lord, a - long___ the ev - er - last - ing way.

PSALM 139: 1.2.7-10.13.14.

O Lord, you have probed me and you know me;
you know when I sit and when I stand;
From afar you understand my thoughts.
Where can I go from your spirit?
From your presence where can I flee?

All repeat ANTIPHON

If I go up to the heavens, you are there;
If I sink to the nether world, you are present there.
If I take the wings of dawn, if I settle at the farthest limits of the sea,
Even there your hand shall guide me,
and your right hand hold me fast.

All repeat ANTIPHON

Truly, you have formed my inmost being;
You knit me in my mother's womb.
I give you thanks that I am fearfully, wonderfully made;
Wonderful are your works.

All repeat ANTIPHON

469

Ps. 145(I)
I Will Extol You, O My God and King

RESPONSES: A You open your hand to feed us, Lord
B The Lord is compassionate

Cantor or Schola I will extol you, O my God and King!

A

Graduale Simplex
You o - pen your hand_ to feed us, Lord, and an - swer all_ our needs.

B

Graduale Simplex
The Lord_ is com - pas - sion - ate to all_ his crea - tures.

PSALM 145: 2.3.8.9.15-18.

B Every day I will bless you,
And forever I will praise your name.
All repeat RESPONSE

B Great is the Lord and highly to be praised;
Unsearchable is the greatness of the Lord.
All repeat RESPONSE

AB The Lord is gracious and merciful,
Slow to anger and abounding in steadfast love.
All repeat RESPONSE

AB The Lord is good to all
And compassionate toward all his works.
All repeat RESPONSE

A The eyes of all look hopefully to you,
And in due season you give them their food.
All repeat RESPONSE

A You open your hand
And satisfy the desire of ev'ry living thing.
All repeat RESPONSE

AB The Lord is just in all his ways
And holy in all his works.
All repeat RESPONSE

AB The Lord is near to all who call on him,
To all who call upon him in truth.
Cantor "I will extol..."
All repeat RESPONSE

Ps. 145(II)

I Will Extol You, O My God and King

ANTIPHONS: A I will praise your name forever
B Your friends tell the glory of your kingship, Lord

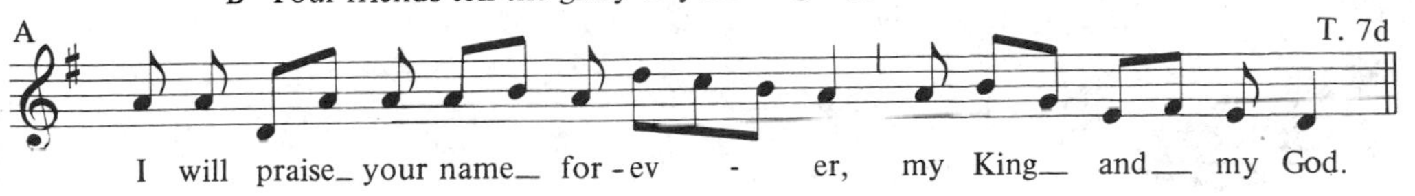
A
T. 7d
I will praise_ your name_ for-ev - er, my King_ and_ my God.

B
T. 7d
Your friends_ tell the glo - ry of your king - ship, Lord.

PSALM 145: 1-2.8-13.17.18.

A I will extol you, O my God and King,
And forever and ever I will bless your name.
Every day I will bless you,
And forever and ever I will praise your name.

All repeat ANTIPHON

A The Lord is gracious and merciful,
Slow to anger and abounding in steadfast love.
The Lord is good to all,
And his compassion is over all that he has made.

All repeat ANTIPHON

AB All your works shall give thanks to you, O Lord,
And all your saints shall bless you.
Of the glory of the kingdom they shall speak,
And tell of your power.

All repeat ANTIPHON

AB To make known to all people your mighty deeds,
And the glorious splendor of the kingdom that is yours.
Your kingdom is eternal,
And forever you are king.

All repeat ANTIPHON

B The Lord is just in all his ways
And holy in all his works.
The Lord is near to those who call on him,
To all who call upon him in truth.

All repeat ANTIPHON

471

Ps. 146
Forever the Lord God Keeps His Faith

ANTIPHONS: A Lord, come and save us
B Praise the Lord, O my soul
C Happy the poor in spirit

A
T. 5
Lord, come and save us.
B
T. 5
Praise the Lord, O my soul!
C
T. 5
Hap - py the poor in spir - it, the king-dom of heav - en is theirs.

PSALM 146: 6.7.8.9.10.

Forever the Lord God keeps faith,
Secures justice for the oppressed;
Gives food to the hungry.
The Lord sets captives free.

All repeat ANTIPHON

The Lord gives sight to the blind;
The Lord raises up those that were bowed down;
The Lord loves the just;
The Lord protects strangers.

All repeat ANTIPHON

The fatherless and widows he sustains,
But the way of the wicked he thwarts.
The Lord shall reign forever;
Your God, O Sion, through all generations.

All repeat ANTIPHON

Ps. 147(I)
Praise the Lord for He Is Good

ANTIPHONS: A The Word of God became man and lived among us
B Praise the Lord, Jerusalem

A
T. 8G
The Word of God be - came man and lived a - mong us.

B
T. 8G
Praise the Lord, Je - ru - sa - lem.

PSALM 147: 1.13.14-15.19-20.

Praise the Lord for he is good,
Sing praise to our God for he is gracious.
For he has strengthened the bars of your gates;
He has blessed your children within you.

All repeat ANTIPHON

He has granted peace in your borders;
With the best of wheat he fills you.
He sends forth his command to the earth;
Swiftly runs his word!

All repeat ANTIPHON

He has proclaimed his word to Jacob,
His statutes and his ordinances to Israel.
He has not done thus for any other nation;
His ordinances he has not made known to them.

All repeat ANTIPHON

473

Ps. 147(II)
Praise the Lord for He Is Good

ANTIPHON: Praise the Lord who heals the broken-hearted
T. 5
Praise the Lord who heals the bro - ken-heart - ed.

PSALM 147: 1-2.3-4.5-6.

Praise the Lord for he is good; sing praise to our God
for he is gracious;
It is fitting to praise him.
The Lord rebuilds Jerusalem;
He gathers the dispersed of Israel.

All repeat ANTIPHON

He heals the broken-hearted
And binds up their wounds.
He tells the number of stars;
He calls each by name.

All repeat ANTIPHON

Great is our Lord and mighty in power;
There is no limit to his wisdom.
The Lord sustains the lowly;
The wicked he casts to the ground.

All repeat ANTIPHON

Exodus 15

My Strength and My Courage Is the Lord

ANTIPHONS: A I will sing to the Lord
B Pharaoh's chariots he has cast into the sea

A
T. 7c
I will sing to the Lord for he is glo - rious - ly tri - um - phant.

B
T. 7c
Phar - aoh's char - i - ots he has cast in - to the sea.

EXODUS 15: 2-6.17.18.

My strength and my courage is the Lord,
And he has been my savior.
He is my God, I praise him; the God of my father, I extol him.
The Lord is a warrior, Lord is his name.

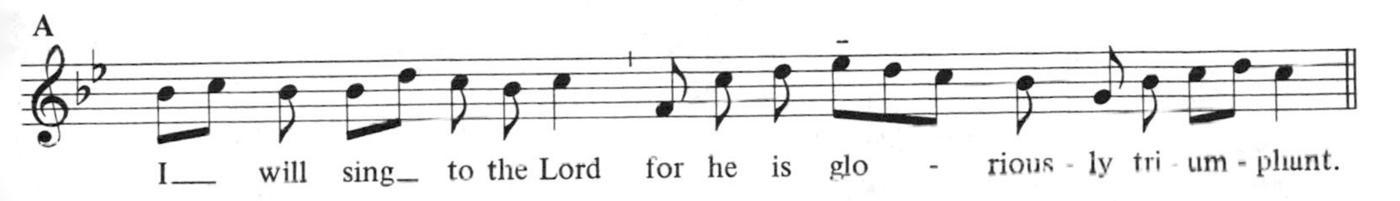
A
I will sing to the Lord for he is glo - rious - ly tri - um - phant.

Pharaoh's chariots and army he hurled into the sea;
The elite of his officers were submerged in the Red Sea.
The flood waters covered them,
They sank into the depths like a stone.

B
Phar - aoh's char - i - ots he has cast in - to the sea.

Your right hand, O Lord, magnificent in power,
Your right hand has shattered the enemy, O Lord.
You brought in the people you redeemed
And planted them on the mountain of your inheritance.
Forever and ever the Lord will reign.

All repeat: "I will sing. . ."
"Pharaoh's chariots. . ."

475

Daniel 3
Blessed Are You, O Lord

RESPONSE: Glory and praise forever!

Graduale Simplex
Cantor or Schola:
Blessed are you, O Lord.

RESPONSE

Graduale Simplex
All
Glo - ry and praise for - ev - er!

DANIEL 3: 52a.52b.53.54.55.56.

Blessed are you, O Lord, the God of our fathers,
Praiseworthy and exalted above all forever;

All repeat RESPONSE

And blessed is your holy and glorious name,
Praiseworthy and exalted above all for all ages.

All repeat RESPONSE

Blessed are you in the temple of your holy glory,
Praiseworthy and glorious above all forever.

All repeat RESPONSE

Blessed are you on the throne of your kingdom,
Praiseworthy and exalted above all forever.

All repeat RESPONSE

Blessed are you who look into the depths from your throne
upon the cherubim,
Praiseworthy and exalted above all forever.

All repeat RESPONSE

Blessed are you in in the firmament of heaven,
Praiseworthy and glorious forever.

Cantor or Schola "Blessed are you, O Lord."
All "Glory and praise forever!"

Isaiah 12
Behold, God Is My Salvation

ANTIPHONS: A With joy you will draw water
B In your midst is the great and Holy One of Israel

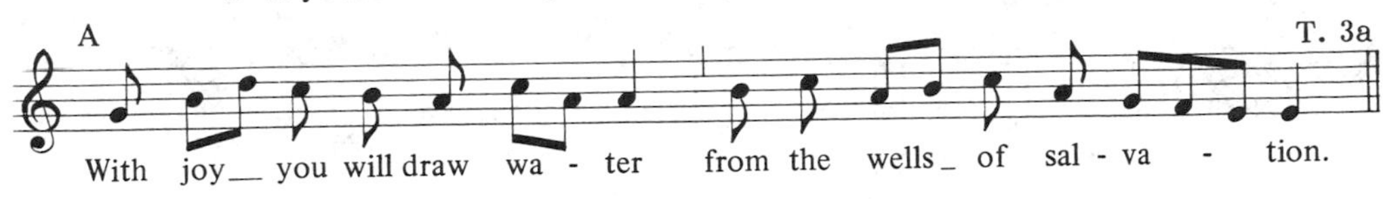
A
T. 3a
With joy__ you will draw wa - ter from the wells_ of sal - va - tion.

B
T. 3a
In your midst is the great and Ho - ly One of Is - ra - el.

ISAIAH 12: 2-6.

Behold, God is my salvation;
I will trust and will not be afraid;
For the Lord is my strength and my song,
And he has been my saving Lord.

All repeat ANTIPHON

With joy you will draw water from the wells of salvation.
Give thanks to the Lord, call upon his name.
Among the nations make known his deeds,
Proclaim how exalted is his name.

All repeat ANTIPHON

Sing praises to the Lord, for he has done gloriously;
Let this be known in all the earth.
Inhabitants of Sion, shout and sing for joy,
For great in your midst is the Holy One of Israel.

All repeat ANTIPHON

477

Luke 1
My Soul Magnifies the Lord
Mary's Canticle - Magnificat

ANTIPHONS: A Hail Mary, full of grace
B My soul rejoices in my God

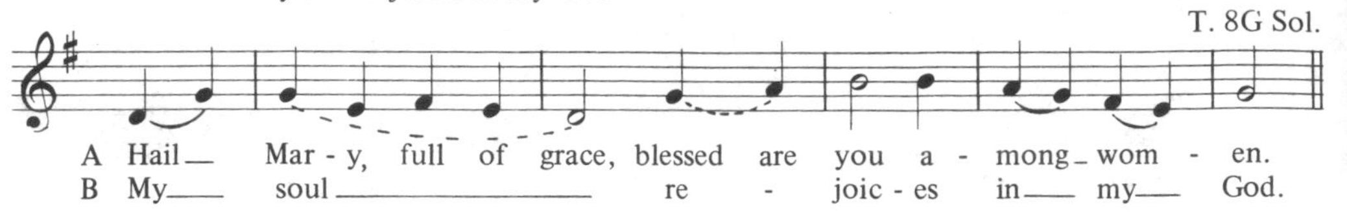
T. 8G Sol.
A Hail— Mar - y, full of grace, blessed are you a - mong – wom - en.
B My— soul— re - joic - es in— my— God.

LUKE 1: 46-55.

My soul magnifies the Lord
And my spirit rejoices in God, my Savior,
For he has regarded the lowliness of his handmaiden;
For behold, henceforth all generations will
call me blessed.

All repeat ANTIPHON

For he who is mighty has done great things for me,
And holy is his name.
And his mercy is on those who fear him
From generation to generation.

All repeat ANTIPHON

He has shown strength with his arm;
he has confused the proud in their inmost thoughts;
He has put down the mighty from their thrones
and exalted those of low degree;
He has filled the hungry with good things
And the rich he has sent empty away.

All repeat ANTIPHON

He has helped Israel, his servant,
In remembrance of his mercy;
As he promised to our fathers,
To Abraham and his seed forever.

All repeat ANTIPHON

DOX. Glory be to the Father, and to the Son,
And to the Holy Spirit.
As it was in the beginning, is now, and ever shall be,
World without end. Amen.

All repeat ANTIPHON

MORNING PRAYER

A Core Music Program

Order of Service

478

INVITATORY	Beginning of the Hours
	PSALM 95 and seasonal antiphons *See* PSALMS 100. 24 or 67 for alternate psalm settings
HYMN	O GOD OF LIGHT
PSALMODY	PSALM 63 and antiphon
	Old Testament Canticle DANIEL 3, CANTICLE OF THE THREE CHILDREN
	Psalm of praise PSALM 149 and antiphon *See* PSALM 24 (1), 27 or 47 for alternate psalm settings
READINGS	A reading is given for Sunday and each weekday Alternate readings at the discretion of the leader
	Homily may follow
RESPONSORY	CHRIST, SON OF THE LIVING GOD
GOSPEL CANTICLE	CANTICLE OF ZECHARIAH with seasonal antiphons
INTERCESSIONS	At the option of the leader
THE LORD'S PRAYER	*See* Nos. 30, 31 or 69 (PATER NOSTER) omit Embolism
DISMISSAL	

479

MORNING PRAYER

Invitatory

Beginning of the Hours

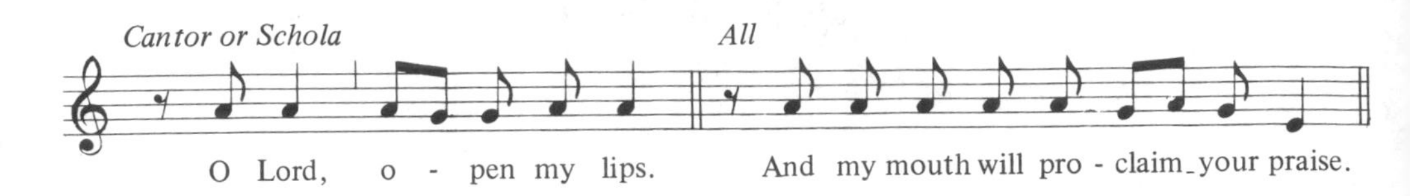
Cantor or Schola
All
O Lord, o - pen my lips.
And my mouth will pro - claim_your praise.

480

Ps. 95
Come, Let Us Sing to the Lord

Ps. 100 or Ps. 24, *with appropriate antiphon, may be substituted. Cf.* PSALTER

SEASONAL ANTIPHONS

A Ordinary Time

Come,_ let us sing to the Lord, the Rock_ of our sal - va - tion.

B Advent

Come,_ let us wor - ship the Lord, the King_ who is to come.

C Christmastide

Christ is born for us; Come,_ let us a - dore_____ him.

D Lent

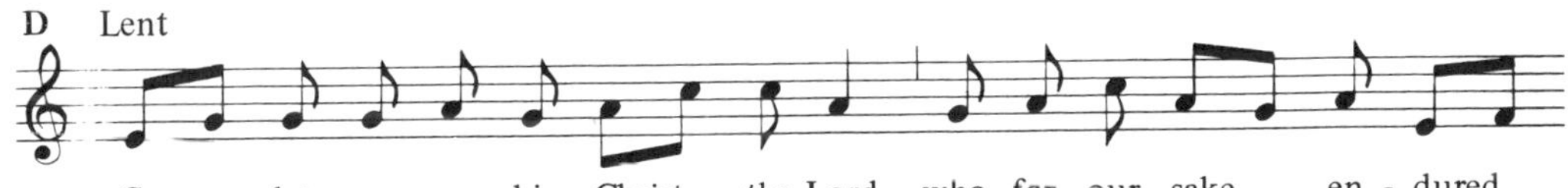
Come,_ let us wor-ship Christ_ the Lord, who for our sake_ en - dured_

temp - ta - tion and suf - fer - ing.
E Eastertide
The Lord_ is ris - en. Al - le - lu - ia!

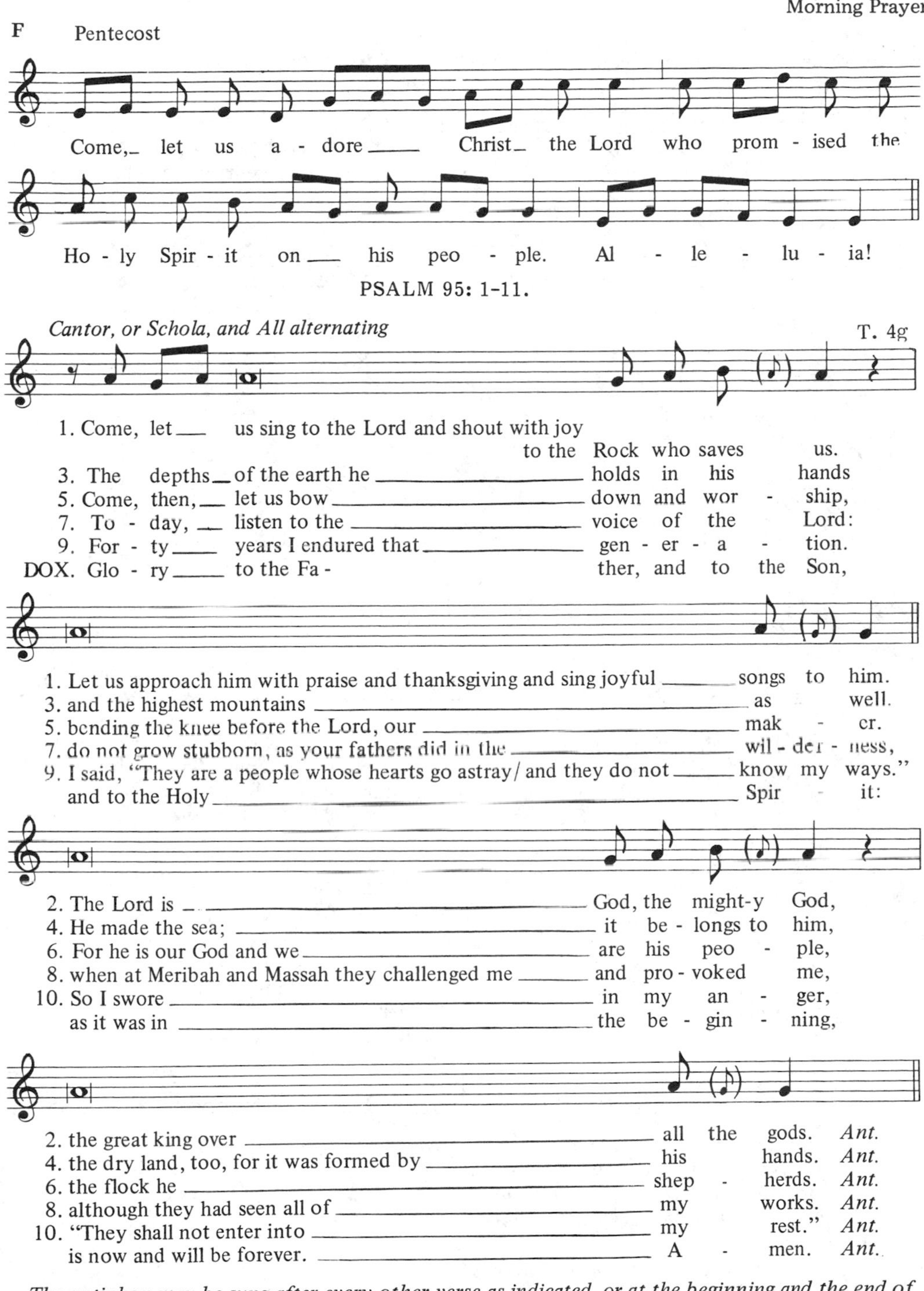
F Pentecost
Come, let us adore Christ the Lord who promised the
Holy Spirit on his people. Alleluia!
PSALM 95: 1-11.
Cantor, or Schola, and All alternating
T. 4g
1. Come, let us sing to the Lord and shout with joy to the Rock who saves us.
3. The depths of the earth he holds in his hands
5. Come, then, let us bow down and wor - ship,
7. To - day, listen to the voice of the Lord:
9. For - ty years I endured that gen - er - a - tion.
DOX. Glo - ry to the Fa - ther, and to the Son,
1. Let us approach him with praise and thanksgiving and sing joyful songs to him.
3. and the highest mountains as well.
5. bending the knee before the Lord, our mak - er.
7. do not grow stubborn, as your fathers did in the wil - der - ness,
9. I said, "They are a people whose hearts go astray/ and they do not know my ways."
and to the Holy Spir - it:
2. The Lord is God, the might-y God,
4. He made the sea; it be - longs to him,
6. For he is our God and we are his peo - ple,
8. when at Meribah and Massah they challenged me and pro - voked me,
10. So I swore in my an - ger,
as it was in the be - gin - ning,
2. the great king over all the gods. Ant.
4. the dry land, too, for it was formed by his hands. Ant.
6. the flock he shep - herds. Ant.
8. although they had seen all of my works. Ant.
10. "They shall not enter into my rest." Ant.
is now and will be forever. A - men. Ant.

The antiphon may be sung after every other verse as indicated, or at the beginning and the end of the psalm.

When Morning Prayer begins here, the above INVITATORY is omitted.
Cantor or Schola
All
Lord God, come to my as - sist - ance. O Lord, make haste to help_ me.
DOXOLOGY
Glo - ry to the Fa - ther, and to the Son, and to the Ho - ly Spir - it:
as it was in the be - gin - ning, is now, and will be for ev - er. A - men.
Omit during Lent
Al - le - lu - ia.
481
O God of Light
1. O God of light, the dawn - ing day Gives us new prom -
2. Your bless - ings, Fa - ther, nev - er fail: Your Son who is
3. Make us the ser - vants of your peace, Re - new our strength,
4. To Fa - ther, Son and Spir - it blest, One on - ly God,
1. ise of your love. Each fresh be - gin - ning is your gift,
2. our dai - ly Bread, The Ho - ly Spir - it of your love,
3. re - move all fear; Be with us, Lord, through - out this day,
4. we hum - bly pray: Show us the splen - dor of your light
1.-3.
4.
1. Like gen - tle dew from heav'n a - bove.
2. By whom each day your sons are led.
3. For all is joy if you are near.
4. In death the dawn of per - fect day. A - men.

Text: J. Quinn, S. J. © 1969 by J. Quinn SJ, printed by permission of Geoffrey Chapman, a division of Cassell Ltd., London.
Tune: *Te lucis ante terminum,* Plainchant, Mode 8.

Ps. 63
O God, You Are My God

ANTIPHON: As the morning breaks, I look for you, O God

I. *Cantor or Schola* II. *All*

T. 5
As the morn - ing breaks,_I look_for you, O God, to be my strength this day.

Omit during Lent

Al - le - lu - ia.

PSALM 63: 2-9.

O God, you are my God, for you I long;
For you my soul is thirsting.
My body pines for you
Like a dry, weary land without water.

All repeat ANTIPHON

So I gaze on you in the sanctuary
To see your strength and your glory.
For your love is better than life,
My lips will speak your praise.

All repeat ANTIPHON

So I will bless you all my life,
In your name I will lift up my hands.
My soul shall be filled as with a banquet,
My mouth shall praise you with joy.

All repeat ANTIPHON

On my bed I remember you. On you I muse through the night
for you have been my help;
In the shadow of your wings I rejoice.
My soul clings to you;
Your right hand holds me fast.

All repeat ANTIPHON

DOXOLOGY
Glory to the Father, and to the Son,
And to the Holy Spirit:
As it was in the beginning, is now,
And will be forever. Amen.

All repeat ANTIPHON

483

Daniel 3
Angels of the Lord, Bless the Lord

Canticle of the Three Children

RESPONSE: Praise and exalt him above all forever

Cantor or Schola
Bless the Lord, all ___ you works ___ of ___ the Lord.
All
Praise ___ and ex - alt ___ him ___ a - bove ___ all ___ for - ev - er.

DANIEL 3: 57-88. 56.

Cantor, or Schola, and All alternating
T. 8G
1. Angels of the Lord, ___ bless the Lord. All you waters above the heavens, bless the Lord.
2. Sun and moon, ___ bless the Lord. Stars of heaven, ___ bless the Lord.
3. All you winds, ___ bless the Lord. Fire and heat, ___ bless the Lord.
4. Dew and rain, ___ bless the Lord. Frost and chill, ___ bless the Lord.
5. Nights and days, ___ bless the Lord. Light and darkness, bless the Lord.
1. All you hosts of the ___ Lord, bless the Lord.
2. Every shower and ___ dew, bless the Lord.
3. Cold and ___ chill, bless the Lord.
4. Ice and ___ snow, bless the Lord.
5. Lightnings and ___ clouds, bless the Lord.

Cantor or Schola
Let ___ the earth ___ bless ___ the Lord.
All
Praise ___ and ex - alt ___ him ___ a - bove ___ all ___ for - ev - er.

Cantor, or Schola, and All alternating
6. Mountains and hills, bless the Lord.
7. Seas and rivers, bless the Lord.
8.
6. Everything growing from the earth, bless the Lord.
7. You dolphins and all water creatures, bless the Lord.
8. All you beasts, wild and tame, bless the Lord.
6. Ye springs, bless the Lord.
7. All you birds of the air, bless the Lord.
8. You children of men, bless the Lord.
Cantor or Schola
O Is - ra - el, bless the Lord.
All
Praise and ex - alt him a - bove all for - ev - er.
Cantor, or Schola, and All alternating
9. Priests of the Lord, bless the Lord. Servants of the Lord, bless the Lord.
10. Holy ones of humble heart, bless the Lord.

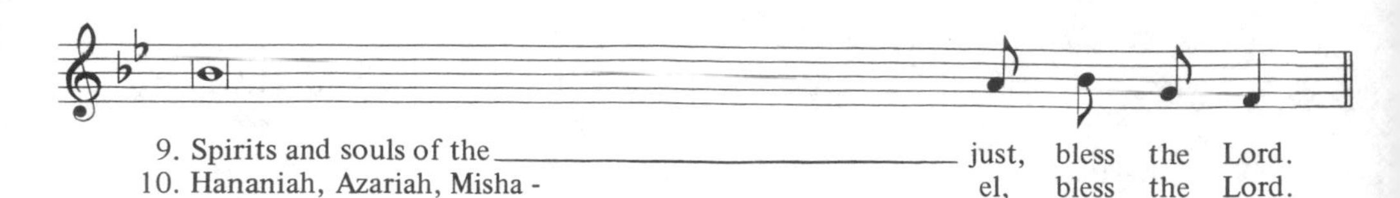
9. Spirits and souls of the just, bless the Lord.
10. Hananiah, Azariah, Misha - el, bless the Lord.

All
Praise and ex - alt him a - bove all for ev - er.

DOXOLOGY

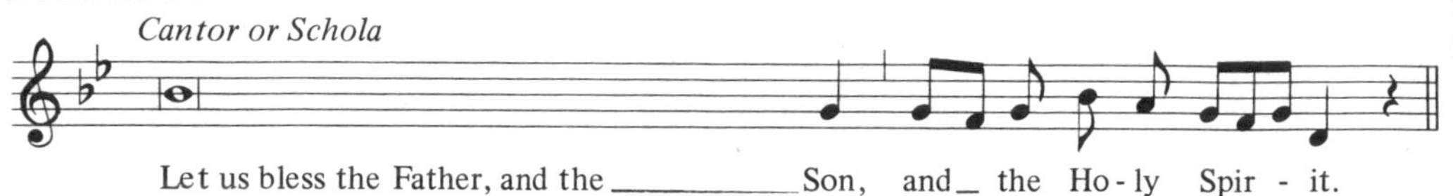
Cantor or Schola
Let us bless the Father, and the Son, and the Ho - ly Spir - it.

All
Let us praise and ex - alt him a - bove all for - ev - er.

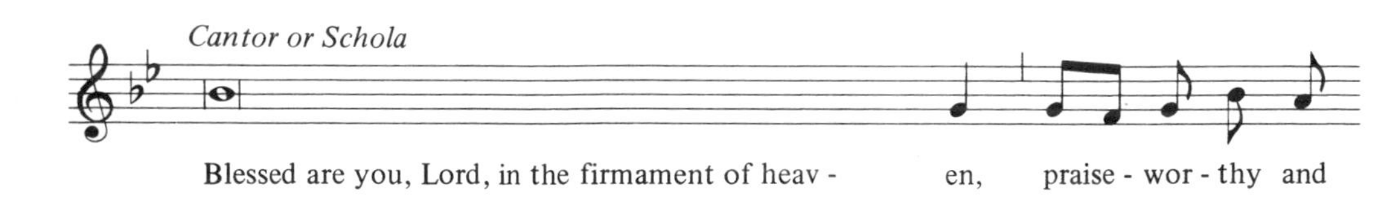
Cantor or Schola
Blessed are you, Lord, in the firmament of heav - en, praise - wor - thy and

All
glo - rious. And ex - alt - ed a - bove all for ev - er.

Ps. 149
Sing to the Lord a New Song

ANTIPHON: We praise your glorious name, O Lord, our God

I. *Cantor or Schola* II. *All*
T. 3a
We praise your glo - rious name, O Lord, our God.

PSALM 149: 1-6.

Sing to the Lord a new song,
    In the assembly of the faithful sing his praise.
Let Israel rejoice in its maker,
    Let Zion's sons exult in their king.

All repeat ANTIPHON

Let them praise his name with dancing
    And make music with timbrel and harp.
For the Lord takes delight in his people.
    With salvation he crowns the poor.

All repeat ANTIPHON

Let the faithful rejoice in their glory,
    Shout for joy and take their rest.
Let the praise of God be on their lips.
    And a two edged-sword in their hand.

All repeat ANTIPHON

DOXOLOGY
Glory to the Father, and to the Son,
    And to the Holy Spirit:
As it was in the beginning, is now,
    And will be forever. Amen.

All repeat ANTIPHON

Readings

SUNDAY *Revelation 7:9-12*

I saw before me a huge crowd which no one could count from every nation and race, people and tongue. They stood before the throne and the Lamb, dressed in long white robes and holding palm branches in their hands. They cried out in a loud voice, "Salvation is from our God, who is seated on the throne, and from the Lamb!" All the angels who were standing around the throne and the elders and the four living creatures fell down before the throne to worship God. They said: "Amen! Praise and glory, wisdom and thanksgiving and honor, power and might, to our God forever and ever. Amen!"

MONDAY *2 Thessalonians 3:10b-13*

Anyone who would not work should not eat. We hear that some of you are unruly, not keeping busy but acting like busybodies. We enjoin all such, and we urge them strongly in the Lord Jesus Christ, to earn the food they eat by working quietly. You must never grow weary of doing what is right.

TUESDAY *Romans 13:11-14*

You know the time in which we are living. It is now the hour for you to wake from sleep, for our salvation is closer than when we first accepted the faith. The night is far spent; the day draws near. Let us cast off deeds of darkness and put on the armor of light. Let us live honorably as in daylight; not in carousing and drunkenness, not in sexual excess and lust, not in quarreling and jealousy. Rather, put on the Lord Jesus Christ and make no provision for the desires of the flesh.

WEDNESDAY *Tobit 4:15a. 16a. 18a. 19*

Do to no one what you yourself dislike. Give to the hungry some of your bread, and to the naked some of your clothing. Seek counsel from every wise man. At all times bless the Lord God, and ask him to make all your paths straight and to grant success to all your endeavors and plans.

THURSDAY *Isaiah 66:1-2*

Thus says the Lord: The heavens are my throne, and the earth is my footstool. What kind of house can you build for me; what is to be my resting place? My hand made all these things when all of them came to be, says the Lord. This is the one whom I approve: the lowly and afflicted man who trembles at my word.

FRIDAY *Ephesians 4:29-32*

Never let evil talk pass your lips; say only the good things men need to hear, things that will really help them. Do nothing that will sadden the Holy Spirit with whom you were sealed against the day of redemption. Get rid of all bitterness, all passion and anger, harsh words, slander, and malice of every kind. In place of these, be kind to one another, compassionate, and mutually forgiving, just as God has forgiven you in Christ.

SATURDAY *2 Peter 1:10-11*

Be solicitous to make your call and election permanent, brothers; surely those who do so will never be lost. On the contrary, your entry into the everlasting kingdom of our Lord and Savior Jesus Christ will be richly provided for.

Responsory **486**

Cantor or Schola
Christ,_ Son of the liv - ing God,_ have mer - cy on_ us.
All
Christ,_ Son of the liv - ing God,_ have mer - cy on_ us.
Cantor or Schola
You are seat - ed at the right_ hand of the Fa - ther.
All
Have mer - cy on_ us.
DOXOLOGY
Cantor or Schola
Glo - ry to the Fa - ther, and to_ the Son, and to the Ho - ly Spir - it.
All
Christ,_ Son of the liv - ing God,_ have mer - cy on_ us.

487 Blessed Be the Lord, the God of Israel

Canticle of Zechariah

SEASONAL ANTIPHONS
A Ordinary Time
Let us serve_ the Lord in ho - li - ness all the days_ of our life.___
B Advent
Come_ and set___ us free, Lord God of power_ and might.
C Christmastide
Glo - ry to God in the high - est, and peace_ to his peo - ple on earth.
D Lent
Lord,_ by your Ho - ly Cross you have re - deemed___ the world.
E Eastertide
The Lord is ris - en from the tomb. Al - le - lu - ia!
F Pentecost
The Spir - it of the Lord_ has filled the whole_ world. Al - le -

lu - ia! Al - le - lu - ia!

LUKE 1: 68–79.

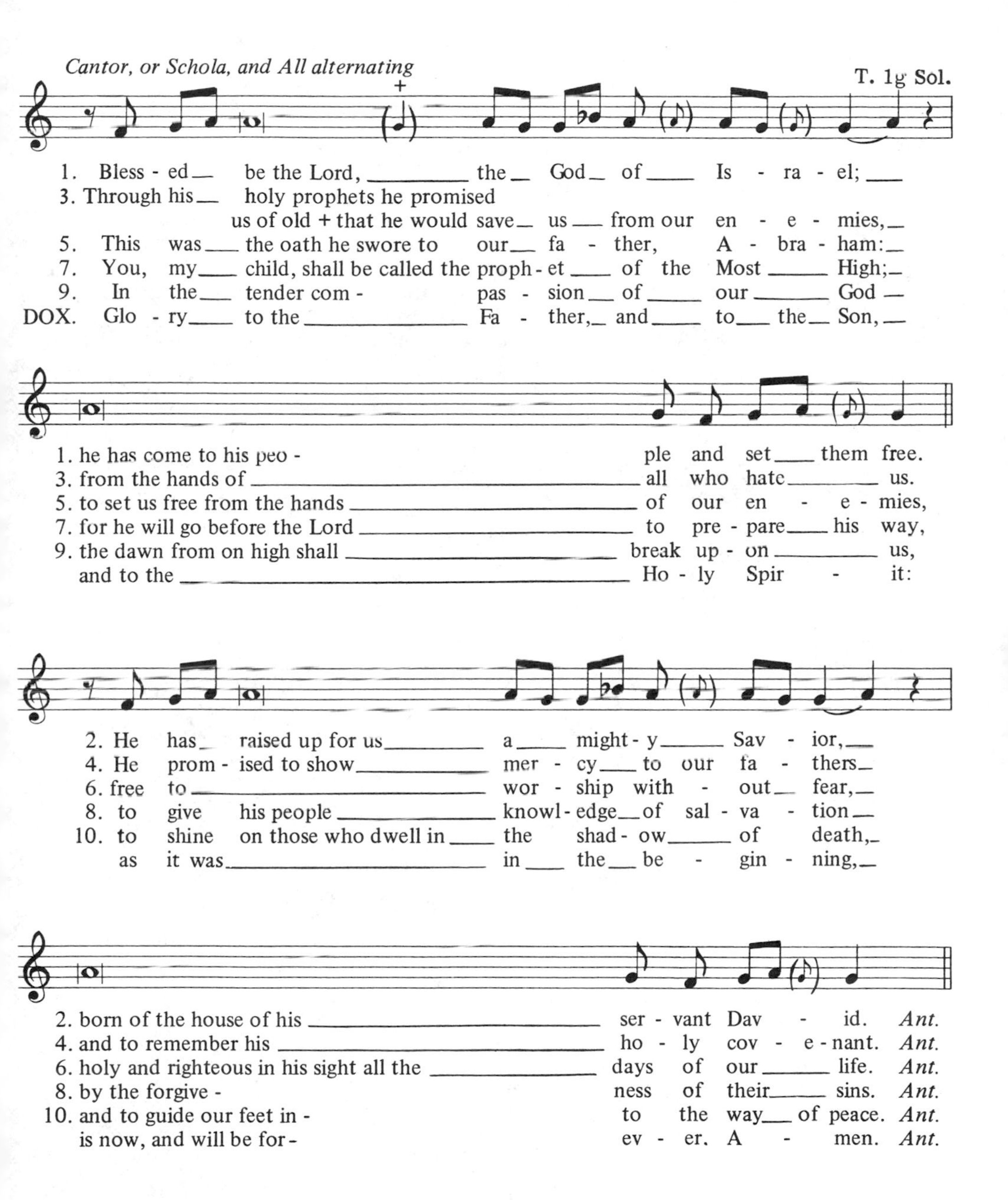
Cantor, or Schola, and All alternating
T. 1g Sol.
1. Bless - ed be the Lord, the God of Is - ra - el;
3. Through his holy prophets he promised
us of old + that he would save us from our en - e - mies,
5. This was the oath he swore to our fa - ther, A - bra - ham:
7. You, my child, shall be called the proph - et of the Most High;
9. In the tender com - pas - sion of our God
DOX. Glo - ry to the Fa - ther, and to the Son,
1. he has come to his peo - ple and set them free.
3. from the hands of all who hate us.
5. to set us free from the hands of our en - e - mies,
7. for he will go before the Lord to pre - pare his way,
9. the dawn from on high shall break up - on us,
and to the Ho - ly Spir - it:
2. He has raised up for us a might - y Sav - ior,
4. He prom - ised to show mer - cy to our fa - thers
6. free to wor - ship with - out fear,
8. to give his people knowl - edge of sal - va - tion
10. to shine on those who dwell in the shad - ow of death,
as it was in the be - gin - ning,
2. born of the house of his ser - vant Dav - id. Ant.
4. and to remember his ho - ly cov - e - nant. Ant.
6. holy and righteous in his sight all the days of our life. Ant.
8. by the forgive - ness of their sins. Ant.
10. and to guide our feet in - to the way of peace. Ant.
is now, and will be for - ev - er. A - men. Ant.

INTERCESSIONS

THE LORD'S PRAYER *See* ORDER OF MASS *(Omit Embolism)*

488 Dismissal

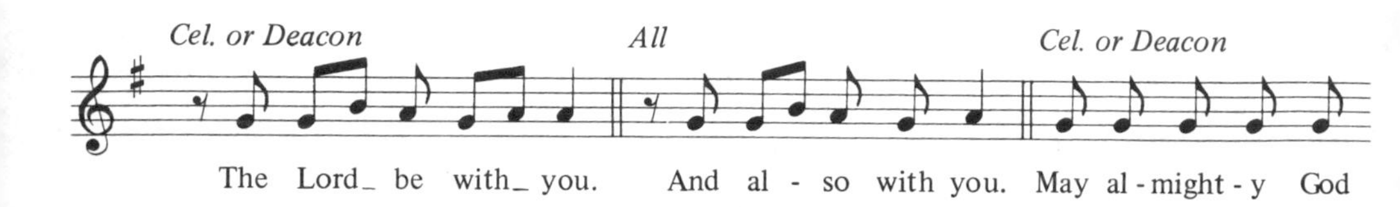
Cel. or Deacon
All
Cel. or Deacon
The Lord_ be with_ you. And al - so with you. May al - might - y God

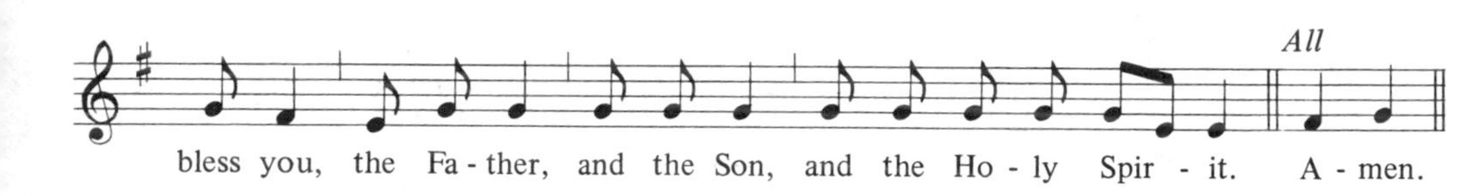
All
bless you, the Fa - ther, and the Son, and the Ho - ly Spir - it. A - men.

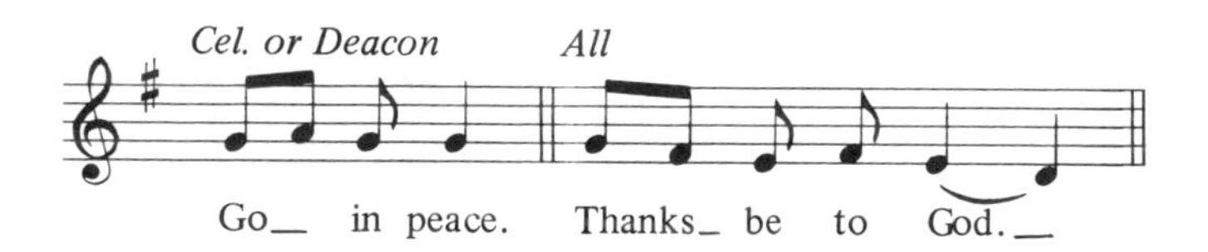
Cel. or Deacon
All
Go_ in peace. Thanks_ be to God._

In the absence of Celebrant or Deacon, conclude as follows - Leader

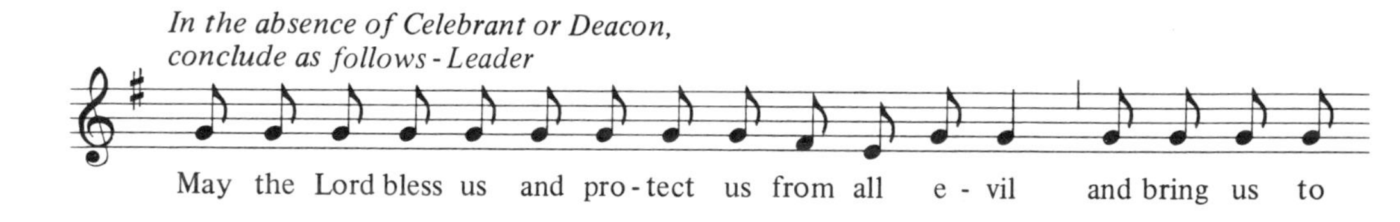
May the Lord bless us and pro - tect us from all e - vil and bring us to

All
ev - er - last - ing life. A - men.

SERVICE OF LIGHT

A Musical Form of Evening Prayer

489

Order of Service

I. THANKSGIVING FOR LIGHT

Procession with candle and opening versicle and response

HYMN: O RADIANT LIGHT

Preface of Thanksgiving for light

II. PENITENTIAL SERVICE

PSALM 141 and antiphon
See HYMN No. 251 for paraphrase of PSALM 141 for alternate setting

Collect at option of celebrant

III. PSALMODY

PSALM 23 and antiphon

Collect at option of celebrant

IV. SCRIPTURE READING AND HOMILY

Option of celebrant
May vary according to season, solemnity or feast

V. NEW TESTAMENT CANTICLE – CANTICLE OF MARY

See Nos. 508, 513 or 514 for CANTICLE OF SIMEON which may be substituted for CANTICLE OF MARY depending on feast or time of day

VI. INTERCESSIONS

May vary at the option of the celebrant or assistant

VII. THE LORD'S PRAYER

See Nos. 30, 31 or 69 (PATER NOSTER) omit Embolism

VIII. BLESSING AND DISMISSAL

IX. RECESSIONAL HYMN

SERVICE OF LIGHT

A Musical Form of Evening Prayer

490 Thanksgiving for Light

All STAND Procession with candle

Celebrant Je - sus Christ is the light of the world.
All A light that no dark - ness can ex - tin - guish.

491 O Radiant Light

Plainsong *Te lucis ante terminum*

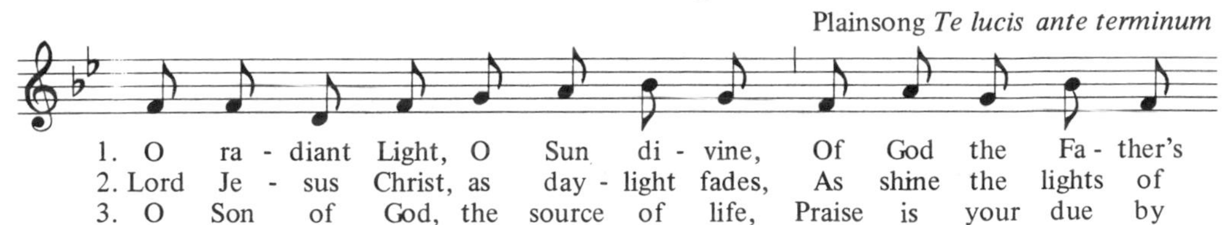
1. O ra - diant Light, O Sun di - vine, Of God the Fa - ther's
2. Lord Je - sus Christ, as day - light fades, As shine the lights of
3. O Son of God, the source of life, Praise is your due by

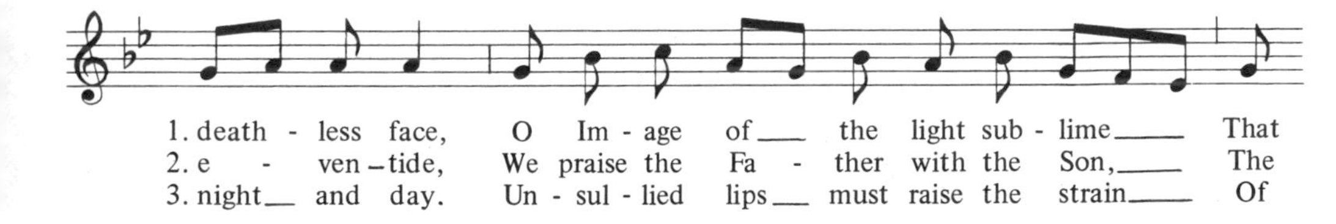
1. death - less face, O Im - age of the light sub - lime That
2. e - ven – tide, We praise the Fa - ther with the Son, The
3. night and day. Un - sul - lied lips must raise the strain Of

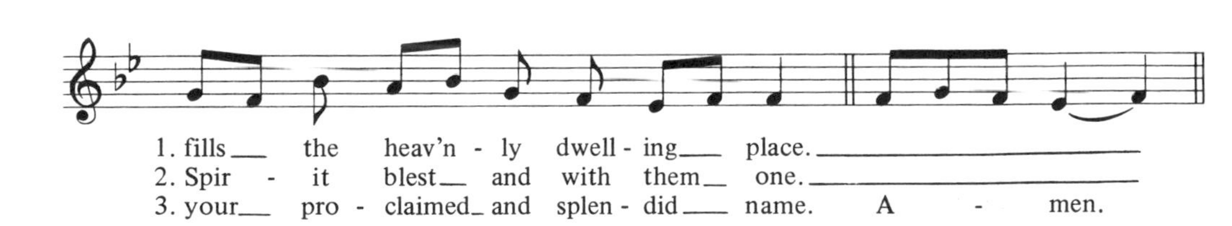
1. fills the heav'n - ly dwell - ing place.
2. Spir - it blest and with them one.
3. your pro - claimed and splen - did name. A - men.

Preface of Thanksgiving for Light

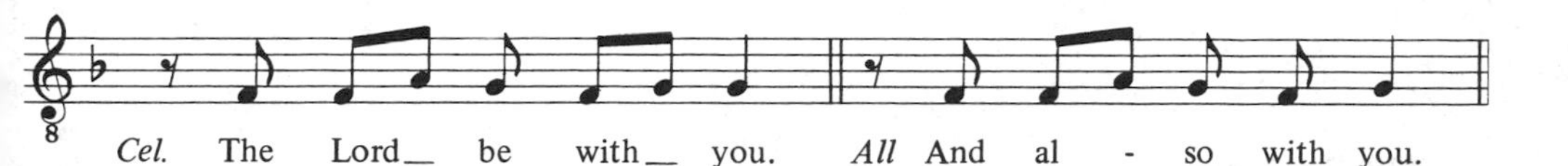
Cel. The Lord be with you. All And al - so with you.

Cel. Lift up your hearts. All We lift them up to the Lord. Cel. Let us

give thanks to the Lord our God. All It is right to give him thanks and praise.

PRAYER OF THANKSGIVING FOR LIGHT

Cel.: We praise and thank you, O God, through your Son Jesus Christ, our Lord, through whom you have enlightened us, by revealing the light that never fades. Night is falling and day's allotted span draws to a close. The daylight which you created for our pleasure has fully satisfied us; and yet, of your free gift, now the evening lights do not fail us. We praise you and glorify you through your Son, Jesus Christ, our Lord; through him be glory, power and honor to you and the

Ho - ly Spir - it, now and al - ways and for - ev - er.

RESPONSE I
All A - men.
or
RESPONSE II
All A - men.
or
RESPONSE III
All A - men, a - men.

PENITENTIAL SERVICE

An Evening Prayer for Forgiveness

493 Ps. 141 Lord, Place a Guard at My Mouth

ANTIPHON: Receive my prayers as incense

All STAND

I *Cantor or Schola* II *All*

Re - ceive my prayers as in - cense, my up - lift - ed hands as an eve-ning of - f'ring.

PSALM 141: 3.4.5.8.9.10.
Cantor and Schola (or People) alternating
T. Per.
+
1. Lord, place ______ a guard at MY mouth, a sentry at the door of MY lips.__

2. —— Keep me from wanting to do wrong, + or to join evil *ones in their* WICK-ed-ness.
May I never take part *in* THEIR feasts. *(Antiphon)*

3. A good man may punish me and reprimand me in kindness, + but I will not let an
e-*vil man a*-NOINT my head,
because I am always praying against *his* E-vil deeds.

4. ____ But I, Lord God, *keep trust-ing* IN you;
I seek your protection; do *not* LET me die. *(Antiphon)*

5. Pro - tect me from the traps they have set for me, + from the snares of *those e-vil* DO-ers.
May the wicked fall into their own traps while I *go* BY un-harmed.

DOX. Give _ praise to the Father, the Son and *the Ho-ly* SPIR-it,
both now and forev-*er*. A-men. *(Antiphon)*

Flex +
do wrong, or. . .
kind - ness, but. . .
set for me, from. . .
COLLECT
Celebrant Let us pray. . .
All A - men.

Ps. 23
The Lord Is My Shepherd

494

ANTIPHON: The Lord shepherds his flock

All SIT

I *Cantor or Schola* II *All*
T. 4E
The Lord shep-herds his flock and watch - es all the night.

PSALM 23:1-6

Cantor and Schola (or People) alternating
T. 4E
1. The Lord is *my* SHEP - herd; I have *ev-'ry-thing* I need.

2. He lets me *rest in* GREEN grass
and leads me to quiet *pools of fresh* WA-ter. *(Antiphon)*

3. He *gives me* NEW strength.
He guides me in the right way, *as he has* PROM-ised.

4. Even if that way goes through the deepest darkness,+
I will not be afraid, Lord, because *you are* WITH me;
your shepherd's *rod and staff* KEEP me safe. *(Antiphon)*

5. You pre - pare a banquet for me,+ where all my ene-*mies can* SEE me;
you welcome me by pouring ointment on my head
and fill-*ing my cup* TO the brim.

6. Certainly your goodness and love will be with me as *long as* I live;
and your house will be *my home for*-EV-er. *(Antiphon)*

DOX. Give praise to the Father, the Son and the *Ho-ly* SPIR-it,
now and *for-ev-er.* Amen. *(Antiphon)*

Flex +
dark-ness, I...
for me, where...

COLLECT *(See preceding psalm)*

Scripture Reading and Homily

SIT. A period of silent reflection precedes the homily. On special days a second reading might be appropriate.

Canticle

495

Canticle of Mary

Magnificat

ANTIPHON: My soul rejoices in my God

STAND

I *Cantor or Schola* II *All*

My soul re - joic - es in my God.

LUKE 1:46-55

Cantor or Schola (or People) alternating T. 8G Sol.

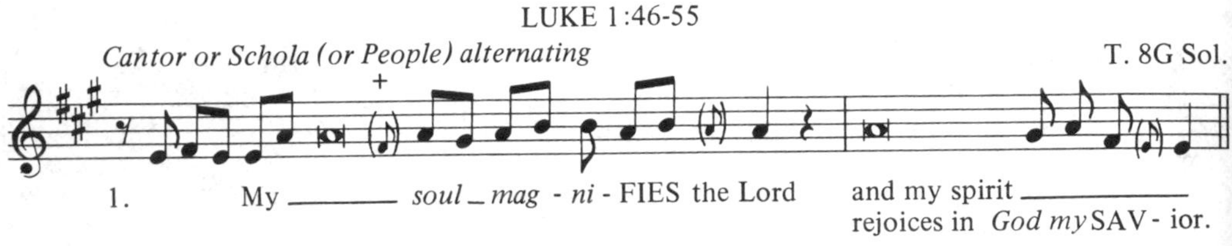
1. My *soul mag - ni* - FIES the Lord
and my spirit
rejoices in *God my* SAV - ior.

2. For he has regarded the lowliness *of his hand*-MAID-en;
for behold, henceforth all generations will *call me* BLESS-ed. *(Antiphon)*

3. For he who is mighty *has done great* THINGS for me,
and *ho-ly* IS his name.

4. And his mer-cy is *on those who* FEAR him
from generation to *gen-er*-A-tion. *(Antiphon)*

5. He has shown strength with his arm,+he has confused
the *proud in their* IN-most thoughts;
he has put down the mighty from their thrones/
and exalted *those of* LOW de-gree.

6. He has filled the *hun-gry with* GOOD things
and the rich he has sent *emp-ty* A-way. *(Antiphon)*

7. He has helped *Is-rael, his* SER-vant,
in remembrance *of his* MER-cy.

8. As he prom-*ised to our* FA-thers,
to Abraham and his *seed for*-EV-er. *(Antiphon)*

DOX. Give praise to the Father, the Son and *the Ho-ly* SPIR-it,
now *and for*-EV-er. *(Antiphon)*

Flex +
his arm, he.

Intercessions **496**

STAND. The Assistant Minister, or Cantor, sings the petitions and All respond.

1. Help and save us. . . . . Let us pray to the Lord. *All* Lord, hear our prayer.
2. That this whole evening. . . .
3. For an angel of peace. . . . .
4. For the forgiveness. . . . . . .
5. For that is good. . . . .
6. For peace and repentence. . .
7. For a Christian end. . . . . . .
8. As we call. . . . . To you, O Lord.

CONCLUDING PRAYER

Celebrant Morning, noon and night. . . . . Christ our Lord. *All* A - men.

The Lord's Prayer **497**

Cel. Let us pray with confidence to the Fa - ther in the words our Savior gave __ us.

All Our Fa - ther who art in heav - en, hal-lowed be thy name; thy king - dom come;

thy will be done on earth as it is in heav - en. Give us this day our dai-ly bread;

and for-give us our tres-pass-es as we for-give those who tres-pass a-gainst_ us;

and lead us not in-to temp-ta-tion, but de-liv-er us from e-vil.

For the king-dom, the power and the glo-ry are yours, now and for-ev-er.

498 Blessing and Dismissal

Assistant Bow down your heads to the Lord.

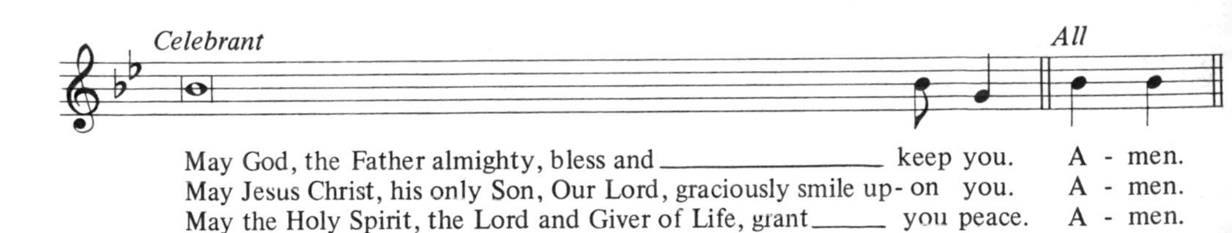
Celebrant
All
May God, the Father almighty, bless and ______ keep you. A-men.
May Jesus Christ, his only Son, Our Lord, graciously smile up-on you. A-men.
May the Holy Spirit, the Lord and Giver of Life, grant ______ you peace. A-men.

RECESSIONAL HYMN

NIGHT PRAYER
Office of Compline

499

Order of Service

OPENING INVOCATION	O GOD, COME TO MY ASSISTANCE *See* Nos. 1 and 2 from ORDER OF MASS for alternate setting
PENITENTIAL RITE	With I CONFESS
HYMN	NOW WITH THE FAST DEPARTING LIGHT Alternate text: ALL PRAISE TO YOU, O GOD, THIS NIGHT
PSALMODY	PSALM 91 and antiphons BE MY REFUGE *Ordinary time* ALLELUIA *Eastertide* Alternate psalmody PSALM 4 and 134 and antiphons IN THE SILENT HOURS *Ordinary time* ALLELUIA *Eastertide*
READINGS	
RESPONSORY	INTO YOUR HANDS *Ordinary time* THIS IS THE DAY *Eastertide*
CANTICLE OF SIMEON	LORD, YOU HAVE DISMISSED YOUR SERVANT IN PEACE and antiphon PROTECT US
PRAYERS	One is given for Sunday and each weekday Alternate prayers at the discretion of the leader
BLESSING AND CONCLUSION	
ANTIPHON OF THE BLESSED VIRGIN MARY	

500 Opening Invocation*

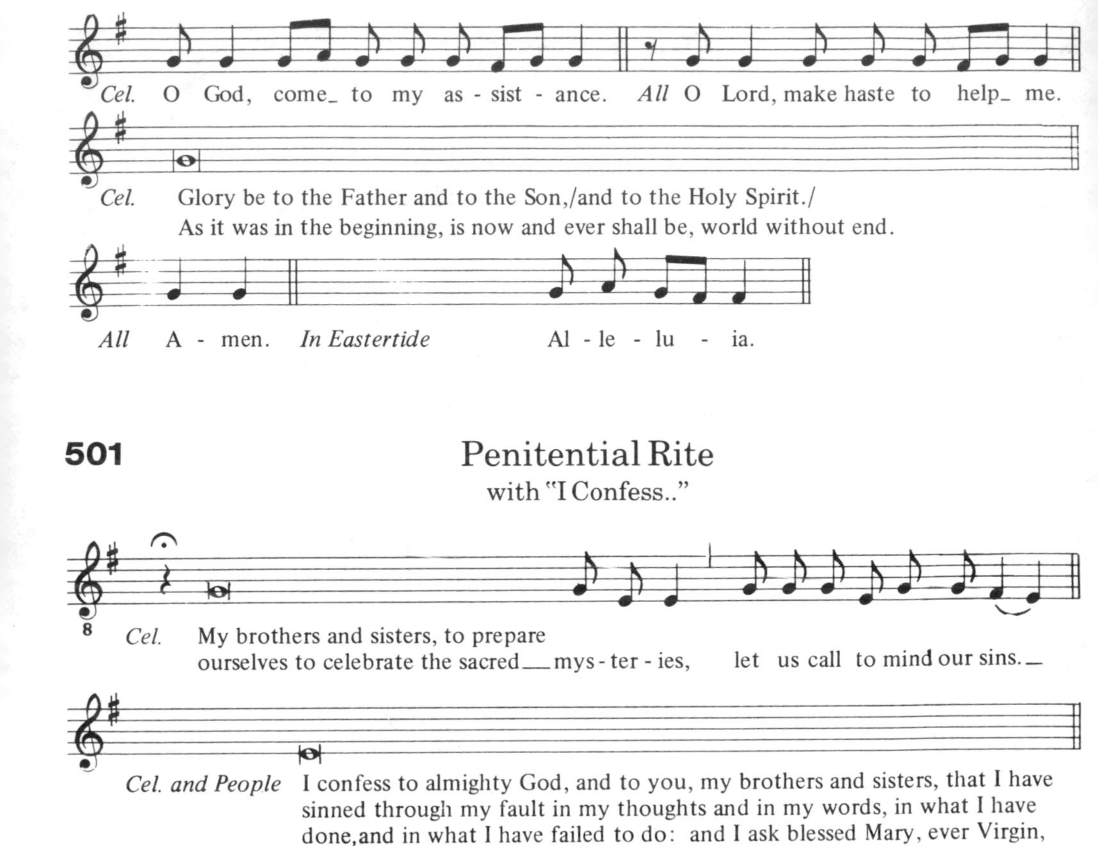
Cel. O God, come to my as - sist - ance. All O Lord, make haste to help me.
Cel. Glory be to the Father and to the Son,/and to the Holy Spirit./
As it was in the beginning, is now and ever shall be, world without end.
All A - men. In Eastertide Al - le - lu - ia.

501 Penitential Rite

with "I Confess.."

Cel. My brothers and sisters, to prepare ourselves to celebrate the sacred mys - ter - ies, let us call to mind our sins.

Cel. and People I confess to almighty God, and to you, my brothers and sisters, that I have sinned through my fault in my thoughts and in my words, in what I have done, and in what I have failed to do: and I ask blessed Mary, ever Virgin, all the angels and saints, and you, my brothers and sisters, to pray for me to the Lord our God.

Cel. May al-might - y God have mer - cy on us, for - give us our sins, and

bring us to ev - er - last - ing life. All A - men.

*For alternate OPENING INVOCATION, use NOS. 1 and 2, from "Order of Mass."

Now with the Fast Departing Light

502

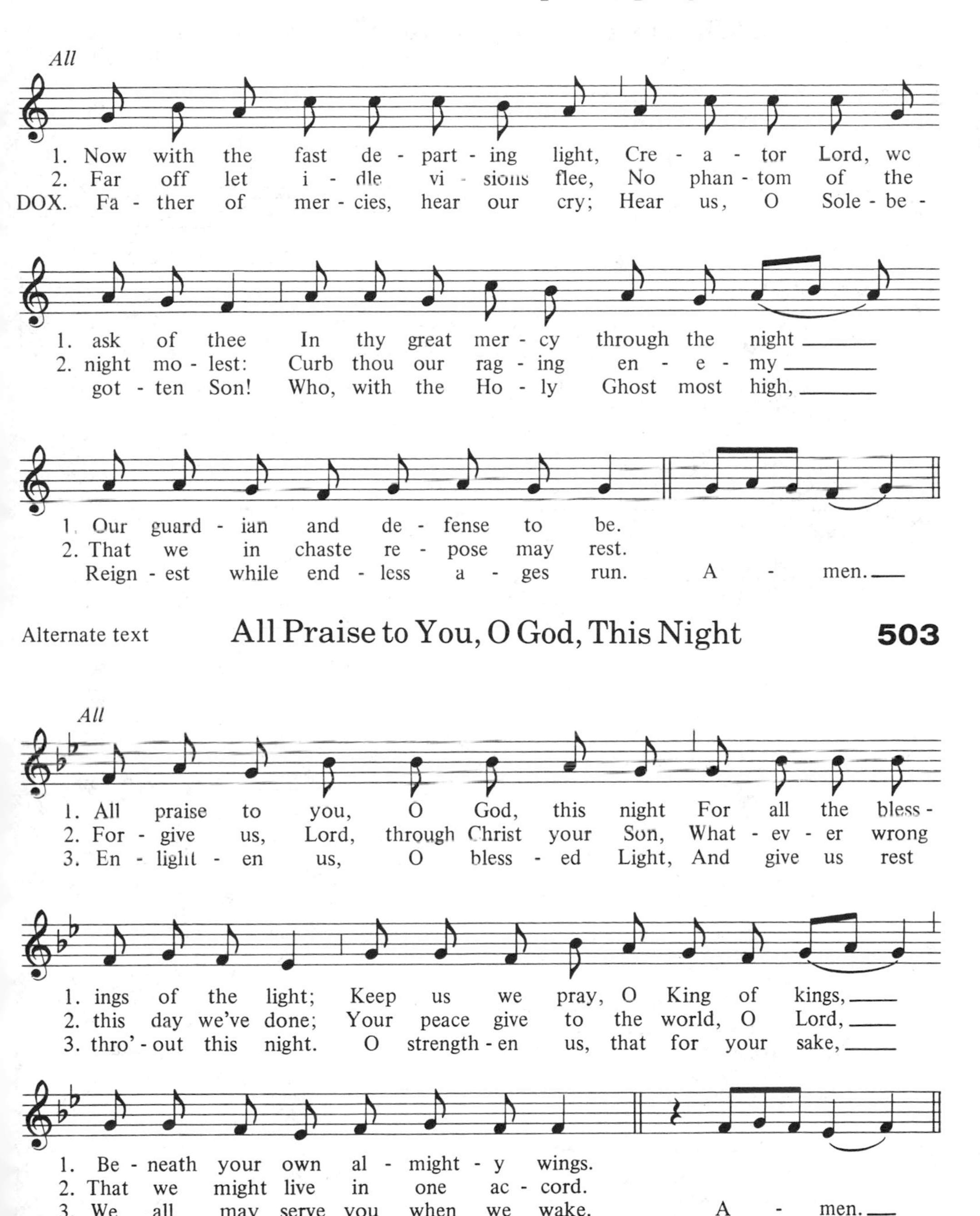
All
1. Now with the fast de - part - ing light, Cre - a - tor Lord, we
2. Far off let i - dle vi - sions flee, No phan - tom of the
DOX. Fa - ther of mer - cies, hear our cry; Hear us, O Sole - be -
1. ask of thee In thy great mer - cy through the night
2. night mo - lest: Curb thou our rag - ing en - e - my
got - ten Son! Who, with the Ho - ly Ghost most high,
1. Our guard - ian and de - fense to be.
2. That we in chaste re - pose may rest.
Reign - est while end - less a - ges run. A - men.
Alternate text
All Praise to You, O God, This Night
503
All
1. All praise to you, O God, this night For all the bless -
2. For - give us, Lord, through Christ your Son, What - ev - er wrong
3. En - light - en us, O bless - ed Light, And give us rest
1. ings of the light; Keep us we pray, O King of kings,
2. this day we've done; Your peace give to the world, O Lord,
3. thro' - out this night. O strength - en us, that for your sake,
1. Be - neath your own al - might - y wings.
2. That we might live in one ac - cord.
3. We all may serve you when we wake. A - men.

Text: *Te lucis ante terminum,* anon. Office Hymn trans. T. Ken, +1711, alt.
Tune: *Te lucis ante terminum.* Plainchant, Mode 8. Acc. T. M.

Ps. 91

504 You Who Dwell in the Shelter of the Most High

ANTIPHONS: A Be my refuge and my strength, O Lord
B Alleluia-Eastertide

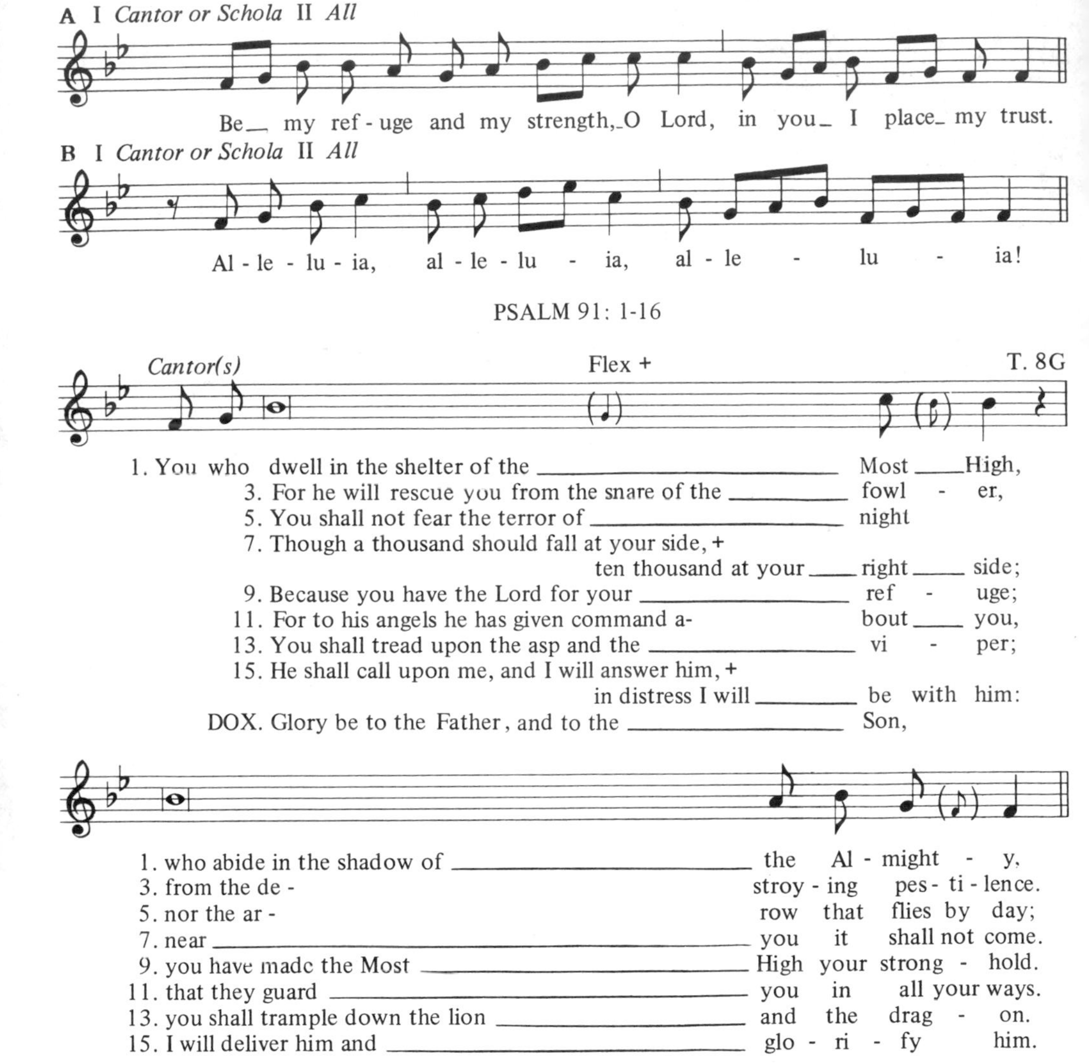
A I *Cantor or Schola* II *All*
Be my ref - uge and my strength, O Lord, in you I place my trust.
B I *Cantor or Schola* II *All*
Al - le - lu - ia, al - le - lu - ia, al - le - lu - ia!
PSALM 91: 1-16
Cantor(s)
Flex +
T. 8G
1. You who dwell in the shelter of the Most High,
3. For he will rescue you from the snare of the fowl - er,
5. You shall not fear the terror of night
7. Though a thousand should fall at your side, +
ten thousand at your right side;
9. Because you have the Lord for your ref - uge;
11. For to his angels he has given command a- bout you,
13. You shall tread upon the asp and the vi - per;
15. He shall call upon me, and I will answer him, +
in distress I will be with him:
DOX. Glory be to the Father, and to the Son,
1. who abide in the shadow of the Al - might - y,
3. from the de - stroy - ing pes - ti - lence.
5. nor the ar - row that flies by day;
7. near you it shall not come.
9. you have made the Most High your strong - hold.
11. that they guard you in all your ways.
13. you shall trample down the lion and the drag - on.
15. I will deliver him and glo - ri - fy him.
and to the Ho - ly Spir - it.

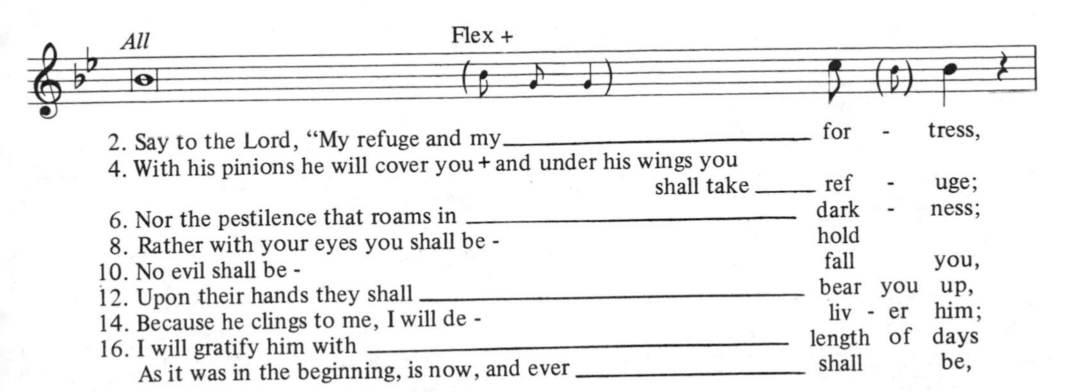
All
Flex +
2. Say to the Lord, "My refuge and my ___ for - tress,
4. With his pinions he will cover you + and under his wings you shall take ___ ref - uge;
6. Nor the pestilence that roams in ___ dark - ness;
8. Rather with your eyes you shall be - hold
10. No evil shall be - fall you,
12. Upon their hands they shall ___ bear you up,
14. Because he clings to me, I will de - liv - er him;
16. I will gratify him with ___ length of days
As it was in the beginning, is now, and ever ___ shall be,

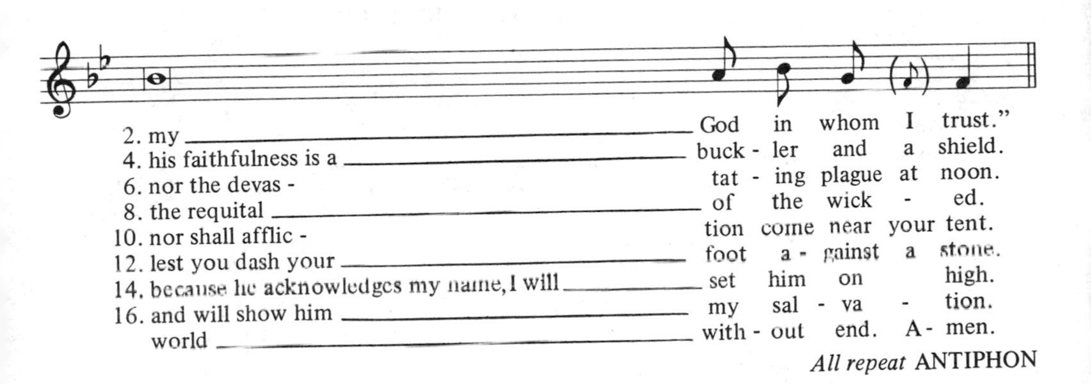
2. my ___ God in whom I trust."
4. his faithfulness is a ___ buck - ler and a shield.
6. nor the devas - tat - ing plague at noon.
8. the requital ___ of the wick - ed.
10. nor shall afflic - tion come near your tent.
12. lest you dash your ___ foot a - gainst a stone.
14. because he acknowledges my name, I will ___ set him on high.
16. and will show him ___ my sal - va - tion.
world ___ with - out end. A - men.
All repeat ANTIPHON

ALTERNATE PSALMODY

505 Ps. 4 When I Call, Answer Me
Ps. 134 O Come, Bless the Lord

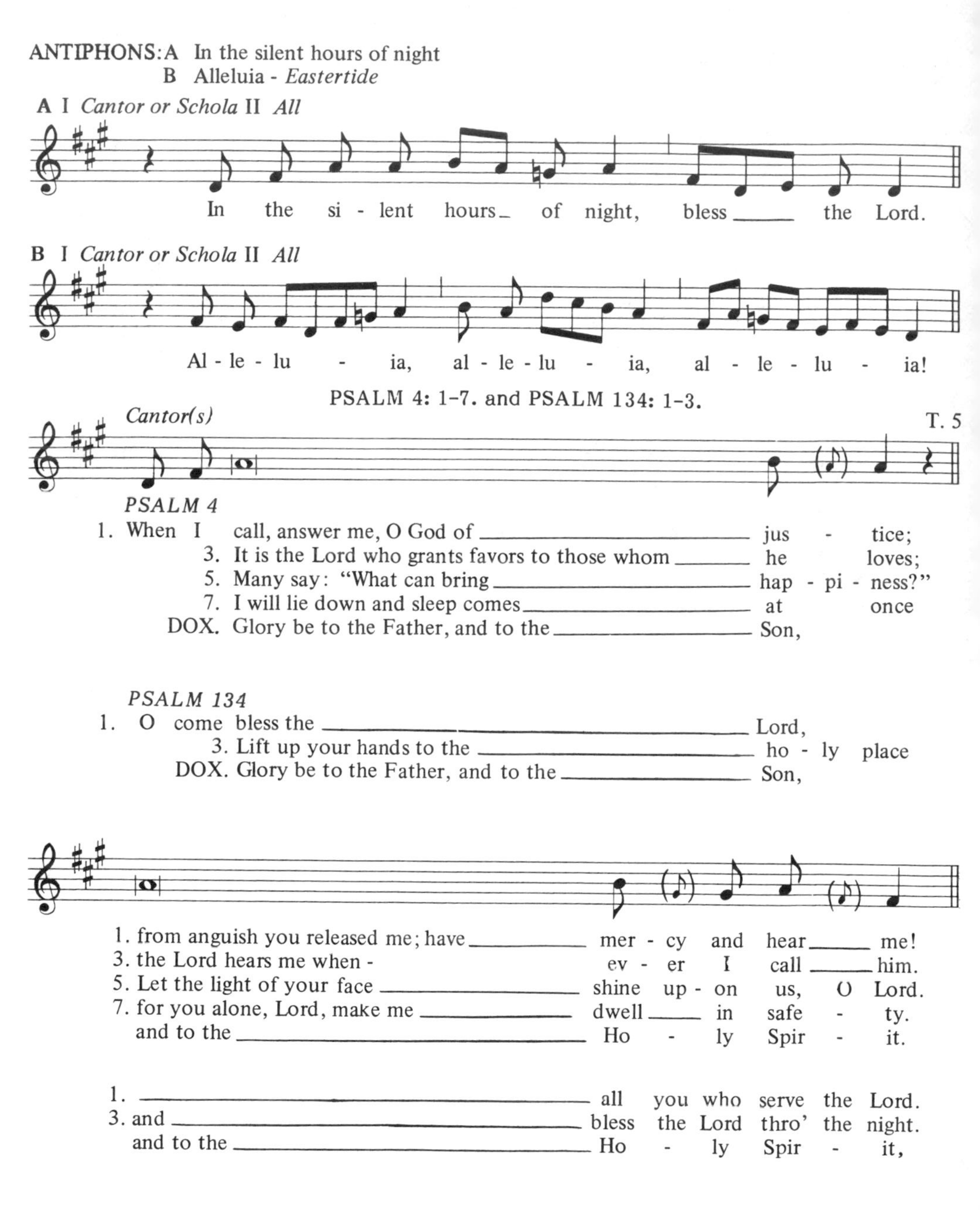

ANTIPHONS: A In the silent hours of night
B Alleluia - Eastertide
A I Cantor or Schola II All
In the si - lent hours of night, bless the Lord.
B I Cantor or Schola II All
Al - le - lu - ia, al - le - lu - ia, al - le - lu - ia!
PSALM 4: 1–7. and PSALM 134: 1–3.
Cantor(s)
T. 5
PSALM 4
1. When I call, answer me, O God of jus - tice;
3. It is the Lord who grants favors to those whom he loves;
5. Many say: "What can bring hap - pi - ness?"
7. I will lie down and sleep comes at once
DOX. Glory be to the Father, and to the Son,
PSALM 134
1. O come bless the Lord,
3. Lift up your hands to the ho - ly place
DOX. Glory be to the Father, and to the Son,
1. from anguish you released me; have mer - cy and hear me!
3. the Lord hears me when - ev - er I call him.
5. Let the light of your face shine up - on us, O Lord.
7. for you alone, Lord, make me dwell in safe - ty.
and to the Ho - ly Spir - it.
1. all you who serve the Lord.
3. and bless the Lord thro' the night.
and to the Ho - ly Spir - it,

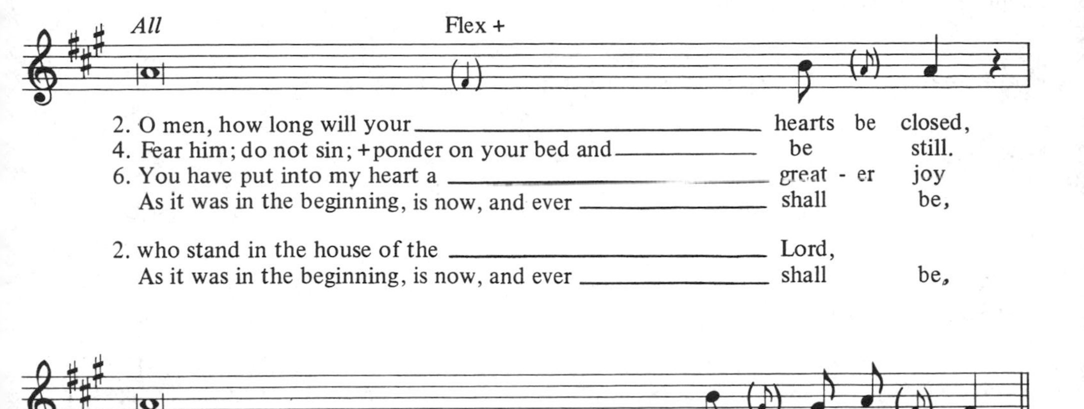
All
Flex +
2. O men, how long will your hearts be closed,
4. Fear him; do not sin; +ponder on your bed and be still.
6. You have put into my heart a great - er joy
As it was in the beginning, is now, and ever shall be,
2. who stand in the house of the Lord,
As it was in the beginning, is now, and ever shall be,

2. will you love what is futile and seek what is false?
4. Trust in the Lord and make jus - tice your sac - ri - fice.
6. than they have from abundance of corn and new wine.
world with-out end. A - men.

All repeat ANTIPHON

2. in the courts of the house of our God.
world with-out end. A - men.

All repeat ANTIPHON

Readings **506**

Sunday Revelation 22:4-5

They shall see the Lord face to face and bear his name on their foreheads. The night shall be no more. They will need no light from lamps or the sun, for the Lord God shall give them light, and they shall reign forever.

Monday I Thessalonians 5:9-10

God has destined us for acquiring salvation through our Lord Jesus Christ. He died for us, that all of us, whether awake or asleep, together might live with him.

Tuesday I Peter 5:8-9a

Stay sober and alert. Your opponent the devil is prowling like a roaring lion looking for someone to devour. Resist him, solid in your faith.

Wednesday Ephesians 4:26-27

If you are angry, let it be without sin. The sun must not go down on your wrath; do not give the devil a chance to work on you.

Thursday I Thessalonians 5:23

May the God of peace make you perfect in holiness. May he preserve you whole and entire, spirit, soul, and body, irreproachable at the coming of our Lord Jesus Christ.

Friday Jeremiah 14:9a

You are in our midst, O Lord, your name we bear; do not forsake us, O Lord, our God!

Saturday Deuteronomy 6:4-7

Hear, O Israel! The Lord is our God, the Lord alone! Therefore, you shall love the Lord, your God, with all your heart, and with all your soul, and with all your strength. Take to heart these words which I enjoin on you today. Drill them into your children. Speak of them at home and abroad, whether you are busy or at rest.

507 Responsory

A Into your hands - *During the year*
B This is the day - *Eastertide* *See* Psalm 118, Nos. 450 or 451

I *Cantor* II *All*

In - to your_ hands,_ O Lord,_ I com - mend_ my spir - it.
C. You_ have re - deemed_us, Lord, God_of truth._ All I com-mend_my spir-it.

C. Glo-ry be to the Fa - ther, and to_ the Son, and to the Ho - ly Ghost._

All In - to your_ hands,_O Lord,_ I com-mend_ my spir - it.

Lord, You Have Dismissed Your Servant in Peace **508**

ANTIPHON: Protect us, Lord

Canticle of Simeon

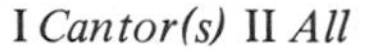
I Cantor(s) II All

Pro - tect _ us, Lord, while _ we are a - wake, and keep _ us while _ we

sleep, _ that we may wake _ with Christ _ and _ rest _ in peace.

LUKE 2:29-32

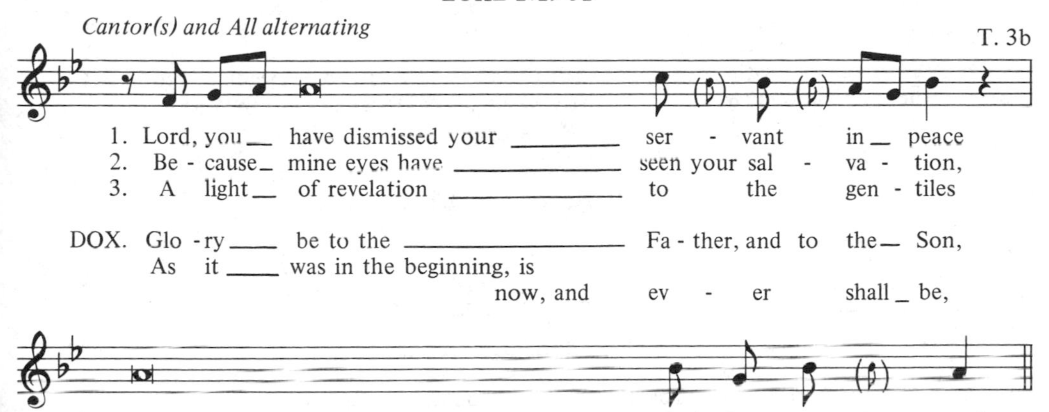
Cantor(s) and All alternating
T. 3b
1. Lord, you _ have dismissed your _ ser - vant in _ peace
2. Be - cause _ mine eyes have _ seen your sal - va - tion,
3. A light _ of revelation _ to the gen - tiles
DOX. Glo - ry _ be to the _ Fa - ther, and to the _ Son,
As it _ was in the beginning, is now, and ev - er shall _ be,
1. ac - cord - ing to your word,
2. which you have prepared before the _ face of all peo - ples,
3. and the glory of your _ peo - ple Is - ra - el.
and _ to the Ho - ly Ghost,
world with - out end. A - men.

All repeat ANTIPHON

Prayers **509**

Sunday

Lord, we beg you to visit this house and banish from it all the deadly power of the enemy. May your holy angels dwell here to keep us in peace, and may your blessing be upon us always. We ask this through Christ our Lord. Amen.

Monday

Lord, give our bodies restful sleep and let the work we have done today bear fruit in eternal life. We ask this through Christ our Lord. Amen.

Tuesday

Lord, fill us this night with your radiance. May we sleep in peace and rise with joy to welcome the light of a new day in your name. We ask this through Christ our Lord. Amen.

Wednesday

Lord Jesus Christ, you have given your followers an example of gentleness and humility, a task that is easy, a burden that is light. Accept the prayers and work of this day, and give us the rest that will strengthen us to render more faithful service to you who live and reign forever and ever. Amen.

Thursday

Lord God, send peaceful sleep to refresh our tired bodies. May your help always renew us and keep us strong in your service. We ask this through Christ our Lord. Amen.

Friday

All powerful God, keep us united with your Son in his death and burial so that we may rise to new life with him, who lives and reigns forever and ever. Amen.

Saturday

Lord, be with us throughout this night. When day comes we rise from sleep to rejoice in the resurrection of your Christ, who lives and reigns forever and ever. Amen.

510 Blessing and Conclusion

Leader

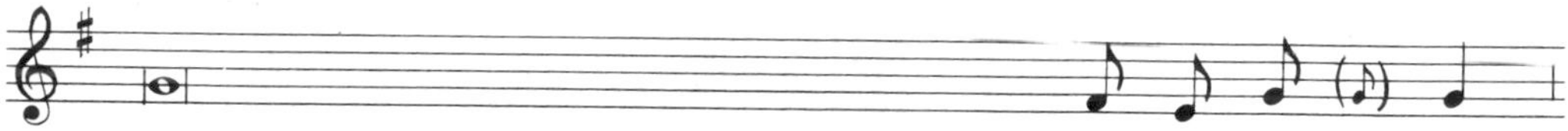

May the all-powerful Lord grant ______ us a rest - ful night

Optional May the Lord make his face to ______ shine up - on us,
May the almighty and merciful Lord, Father, Son and Ho - ly Spir - it,

After each blessing

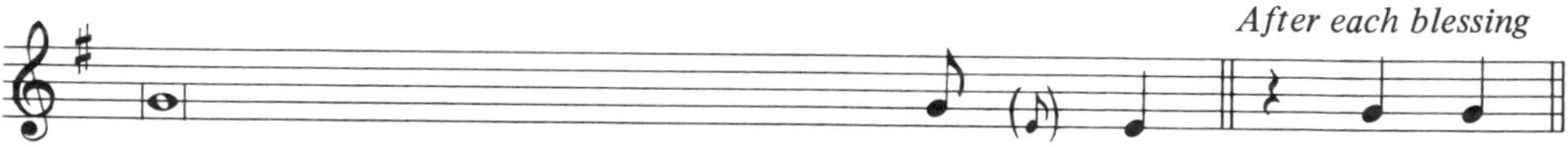

and a ______ peace - ful death. *All* A - men.

and may he be gracious ______ to us.
bless and ______ keep us.

Antiphons of the Blessed Virgin Mary

No. 219 ADVENT	Loving Mother of Our Savior	*Alma Redemptoris Mater*
No. 172 LENT	Hail Mary, Queen of Heav'n	*Ave Regina Caelorum*
No. 220 EASTERTIDE	Mary, Queen of Heav'n	*Regina Caeli*
No. 171 ORDINARY TIME	Hail, O Holy Queen	*Salve Regina*

Rite of Blessing of Candles and Procession

Order of Service

A. All hold unlighted candles until the Celebrant arrives at the place where the blessing will take place (not the sanctuary, but in some other place, for example, outside the church, in the school, in the middle aisle, in a side chapel, etc.). When he reaches the place, the Cantor, or Schola, and all sing:

Behold, the Lord Will Come with Power **512**

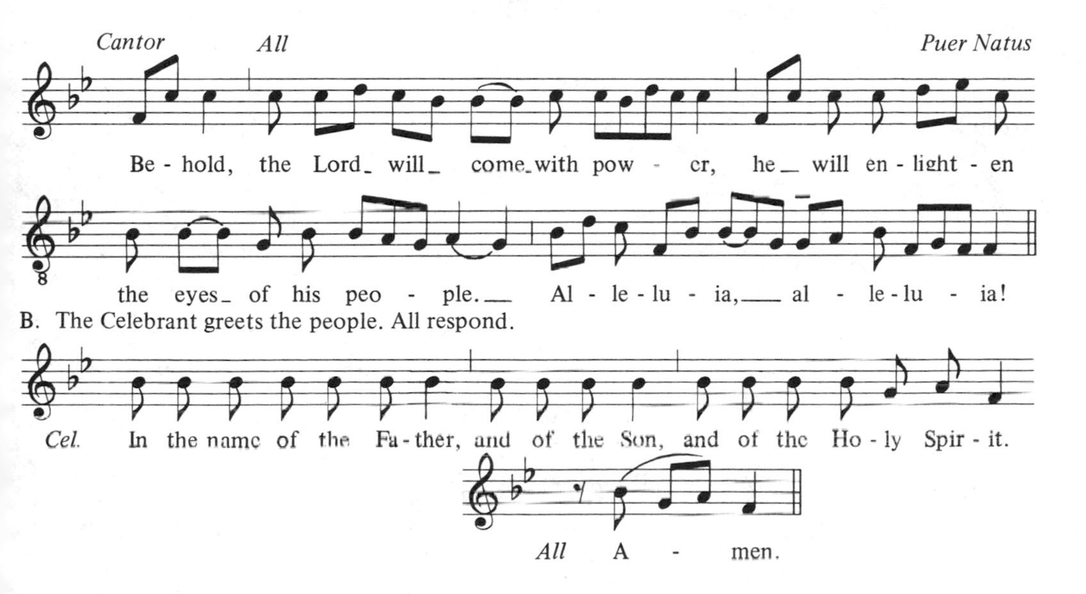
Cantor
All
Puer Natus
Be - hold, the Lord_ will_ come_with pow - er, he_ will en - light - en
the eyes_ of his peo - ple._ Al - le - lu - ia,_ al - le - lu - ia!
B. The Celebrant greets the people. All respond.
Cel. In the name of the Fa - ther, and of the Son, and of the Ho - ly Spir - it.
All A - men.

Cel. The grace and peace of God our Fa - ther and the Lord Je - sus Christ_
be_ with you.

All And al - so_ with you.

Celebrant announces the feast and comments briefly on its meaning.

Celebrant blesses the candles. *All* Amen.

C. Candles are lit. Celebrant takes a lighted candle and intones the words:

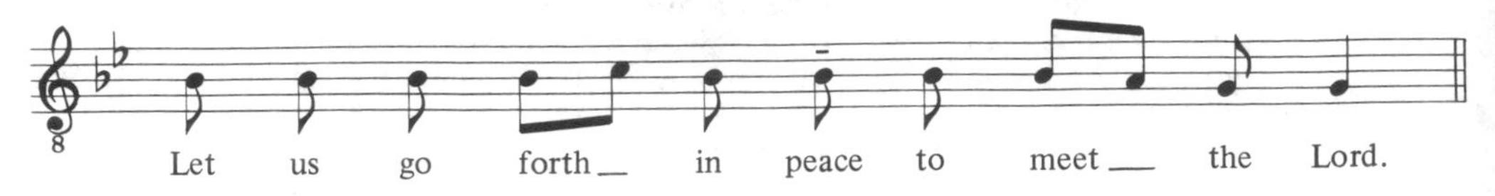
Let us go forth __ in peace to meet __ the Lord.

D. The procession begins. During this action one of the following is sung:

513 Now, Master, You Can Dismiss Your Servant in Peace

Canticle of Simeon

ANTIPHON A light of revelation to the gentiles

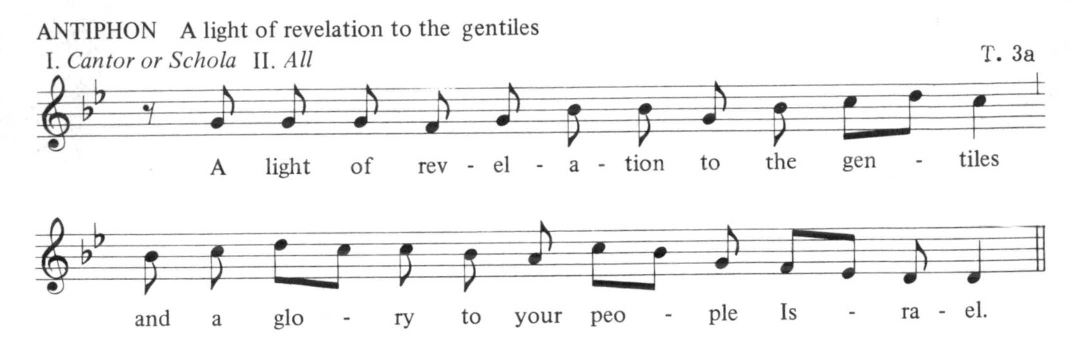
I. *Cantor or Schola* II. *All*
T. 3a
A light of rev - el - a - tion to the gen - tiles
and a glo - ry to your peo - ple Is - ra - el.

LUKE 2: 29–32.

Now, Master, you can dismiss your servant in peace;
You have fulfilled your word.

All repeat ANTIPHON

For my eyes have witnessed your saving deed
Displayed for all the peoples to see.

All repeat ANTIPHON

A revealing light to the gentiles,
The glory of your people Israel.

All repeat ANTIPHON

DOXOLOGY
Glory to the Father, and to the Son
And to the Holy Ghost.
As it was in the beginning, is now,
and ever shall be,
World without end. Amen.

All repeat ANTIPHON

Nunc Dimittis

514

Canticle of Simeon
Alternate Setting

ANTIPHON : Lumen ad revelationem gentium

T. 8G

Lu - men ad re - ve - la - ti - ó - nem gén - ti - um,

et ___ gló - ri - am ___ ple - bis tu - ae Is - ra - el.

LUKE 2: 29-32

Nunc dimittis servum tuum, Domine,
Secundum verbum tuum in pace:

All repeat ANTIPHON

Quia viderunt oculi mei
Salutare tuum.

All repeat ANTIPHON

Quod parasti
ante faciem omnium populorum.

All repeat ANTIPHON

DOX. Gloria Patri, et Filio,
Et Spiritui Sancto.
Sicut erat in principio et nunc, et semper,
Et in saecula saeculorum. Amen.

All repeat ANTIPHON

I. ENTRANCE RITE

E. As the Celebrant enters the church or sanctuary, one of the following may be sung:

No. 103 ALL CREATURES OF OUR GOD AND KING
No. 130 CHRIST IS THE WORLD'S LIGHT
No. 181 HAIL TO THE LORD'S ANOINTED
No. 205 JOY TO THE WORLD

F. The Celebrant venerates the altar with incense and goes to the chair. The Glory to God and Opening Prayer follow immediately.

Omit Penitential rite

II. LITURGY OF THE WORD

A. No. 10 ORDER OF MASS

B. Responsorial psalm. One of the following is suggested:

No. 379 HERE, LORD, ARE YOUR PEOPLE and PSALM 24 (I)
No. 432 ALL THE ENDS OF THE EARTH HAVE SEEN THE SALVATION BY OUR GOD and PSALM 98 (I)

C. Gospel acclamation

No. 94 ORDER OF MASS

The candles are extinguished

III. LITURGY OF THE EUCHARIST

A. Presentation of gifts. One of the following is suggested:

No. 196 IN HIS TEMPLE, NOW BEHOLD HIM
No. 209 LET ALL MORTAL FLESH KEEP SILENCE

B. Eucharistic prayer

No. 16 ORDER OF MASS

IV. RECESSION

One of the following is suggested:

No. 204 JESUS, NAME OF WONDROUS LOVE
No. 205 JOY TO THE WORLD
No. 333 TO THE NAME OF OUR SALVATION

515

ASH WEDNESDAY

Rite of Blessing and Imposition of Ashes

Order of Service

WITHIN MASS

I. ENTRANCE RITE

A. Entrance hymn accompanies the procession of ministers to the sanctuary. One of the following may be sung:
No. 153 FATHER ALMIGHTY, POUR ON US THY BLESSING
No. 165 GOD IS MY STRONG SALVATION

B. Greeting by the celebrant
No. 1 ORDER OF MASS

C. Opening prayer chanted by the celebrant
Omit Penitential rite

II. LITURGY OF THE WORD

A. First Scripture reading: Joel 2: 12-18.

B. Responsorial Psalm

Nos. 400 or 401 HAVE MERCY ON ME, O LORD, IN YOUR GOODNESS and PSALM 51

C. Second Scripture reading: 2 Corinthians 5: 20. 21. 6: 1. 2.

D. Gospel acclamation. One of the following may be used:

Nos. 87, 88, 89 or 90 Verse for Ash Wednesday

E. Gospel reading: Matthew 6: 1-6. 16-18.

F. Homily

III. BLESSING AND IMPOSITION OF ASHES

A. The celebrant chants or recites the prayer. All respond: Amen.

B. Celebrant blesses the ashes with holy water in silence.

C. The people come forward to receive the ashes. During this ceremony, one of the following may be sung:

No. 215 LORD, THOU HAST SEARCHED ME
No. 246 O LAMB OF GOD, ALL HOLY

IV. GENERAL INTERCESSIONS

Prayers are chanted according to formulae.

No. 14 ORDER OF MASS

V. LITURGY OF THE EUCHARIST

No. 16 ORDER OF MASS

VI. COMMUNION RITE

No. 30 ORDER OF MASS

VII. RECESSIONAL HYMN

No. 207 LIFT HIGH THE CROSS

OUTSIDE OF MASS

RITE OF BLESSING AND IMPOSITION OF ASHES

I. II. III. IV. and VII. as above

Omit Nos. V. and VI.

516

Passion Sunday

Commemoration of the Lord's Entrance into Jerusalem

I. THE PROCESSION

A The people receive their palm or other branches as they assemble.

B Organ plays quietly while the clergy process to the place where the blessing will take place, whether this be out-of-doors, in a separate chapel, in the rear of the church, or in the cross-aisle of the church.

C When the procession has arrived at the appointed place, the following may be sung:

517

Hosanna Filio David

Gregorian

Ho-sán - na Fí - li - o Da-vid: be - ne-dí - ctus
Trans. Hosanna to the Son of David: blessed is he
qui ve - nit in nó - mi - ne Dó - mi - ni. Rex Is -
who comes in the name of the Lord. King of Israel:
ra - el: Ho-sán - na in ex - cel - sis.
Hosanna in the highest.

Text: Passion Sunday Liturgy.
Tune: *Hosanna*, Plainchant, Mode 7.

D. Celebrant gives a brief instruction

II. BLESSING OF THE BRANCHES

A. Celebrant chants prayer to which all respond: Amen

Celebrant sprinkles the branches in silence

B. Celebrant reads or chants the gospel. If chanted, the responses are as follows:

Nos. 10-11, or 60-61 ORDER OF MASS

C. Celebrant gives a brief homily

D. After the homily, the Celebrant chants:

Let us go forth__ in peace to meet__ the Lord.

III. PROCESSION

A. As the procession moves toward the sanctuary where the celebration of Mass will take place, the people and choir sing one of the following:

No. 105 ALL GLORY, LAUD AND HONOR
No. 336 TO JESUS CHRIST, OUR SOV'REIGN KING

B. When Celebrant arrives in sanctuary, he venerates and incenses the altar. He proceeds immediately to the chair. He chants the opening prayer. People respond as usual: Amen.

Greeting and Penitential Rite are omitted

IV. LITURGY OF THE WORD

A. First Scripture reading: Isaiah 50:4-7

B. Responsory

Ps. 22 All You Who See Me Scoff at Me

518

ANTIPHON: My God, my God, why have you forsaken me?

I. *Cantor or Schola* II. *All*

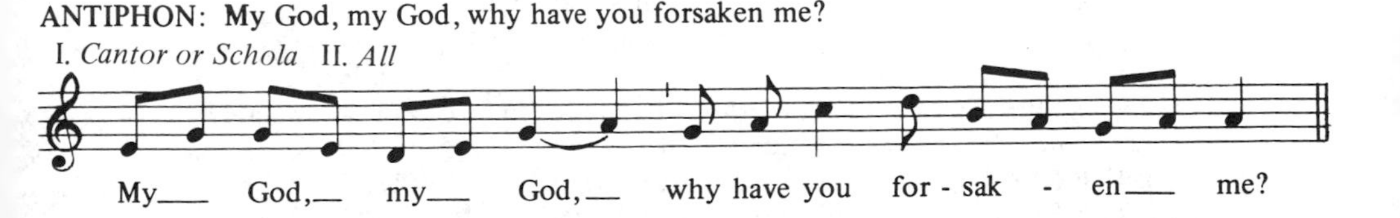
My__ God,__ my__ God,__ why have you for - sak - en__ me?

PSALM 22: 8-9. 17-18a. 19-20. 23-24.

All you who see me scoff at me;
They mock me with parted lips, they wag their heads:
"He relied on the Lord; let him deliver him,
Let him rescue him if he loves him."
All repeat ANTIPHON

Indeed, many dogs surround me,
A pack of evildoers closes in upon me;
They have pierced my hands and feet;
I can count all my bones.
All repeat ANTIPHON

They divide my garments among them,
And for my vesture they cast lots.
But you, O Lord, be not far from me;
O my help, hasten to aid me.
All repeat ANTIPHON

I will proclaim your name to my brethren;
In the midst of the assembly I will praise you:
"You who fear the Lord, praise him;
All you descendants of Jacob, give glory to him."
All repeat ANTIPHON

C. Second Scripture reading: St. Paul to the Philippians 2:5-11

D. Gospel acclamation: *See also* Nos. 87-90

519 Christ Became Obedient for Us

Gospel Acclamation for Passion Sunday and Holy Week

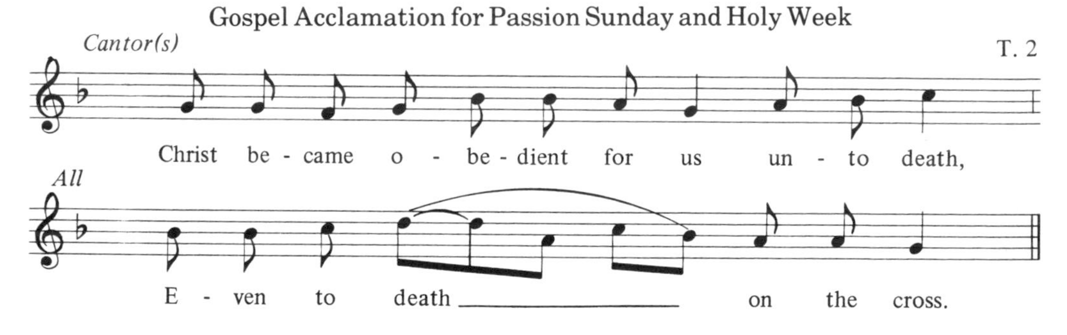
Cantor(s)
T. 2
Christ be - came o - be - dient for us un - to death,
All
E - ven to death on the cross.

PHILIPPIANS 2:8-9

Because of this, God highly exalted him
And bestowed on him the name that is above ev'ry other name:
Cantor(s) Christ became. . .
All Even to death. . .

E. The Passion of Our Lord is chanted by three deacons or three cantors as available. The parts assigned to the crowd are sung by all.

No. 520 THE PASSION OF OUR LORD ACCORDING TO MATTHEW (Year A)
No. 521 THE PASSION OF OUR LORD ACCORDING TO MARK (Year B)
No. 522 THE PASSION OF OUR LORD ACCORDING TO LUKE (Year C)

The Passion of Our Lord Jesus Christ According to Matthew

520

Narrator The Passion of our Lord Jesus Christ according to Matthew. One of the Twelve whose name was Judas Iscariot went off to the chief priests and said,

Speaker "What are you willing to give me if I hand Jesus over to you?"

N. They paid him thirty pieces of silver, and from that time on he kept looking for an opportunity to hand him over. On the first day of the feast of Unleavened Bread, the disciples came to Jesus and said,

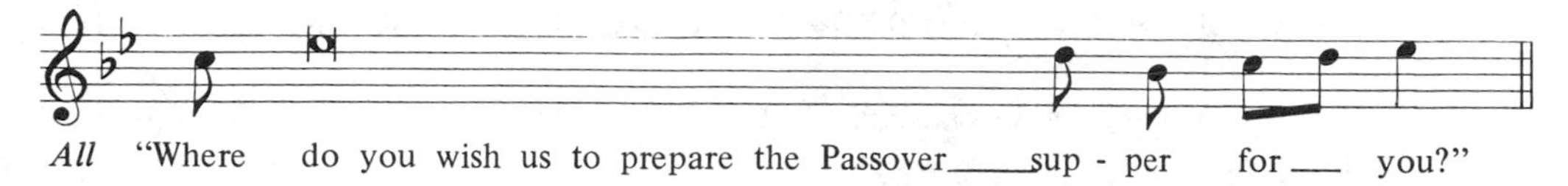
All "Where do you wish us to prepare the Passover___sup - per for___ you?"

N. He said,

Jesus "Go to this man in the city and tell him, 'The Teacher says, My appointed time draws near. I am to celebrate the Passover with my disciples in your house'."

N. The disciples then did as Jesus had ordered and prepared the Passover Supper. When it grew dark he reclined at table with the Twelve. In the course of the meal, he said,

J. "I give you my word, one of you is about to betray me."

N. Distressed at this, they began to say to him one after another,

All "Sure - ly it is not I,___ Lord?"

N. He replied,

J. "The man who has dipped his hand into the dish with me is the one who will hand me over. The Son of Man is departing, as Scripture says of him, but woe to that man by whom the Son of Man is betrayed. Better for him if he had never been born."

N. Then Judas, his betrayer, spoke:

S. "Surely it is not I, Rabbi?"

N. Jesus answered,

J. "It is you who have said it."

N. During the meal Jesus took bread, blessed it, broke it, and gave it to his disciples, saying:

J. "Take this and eat it. This is my body."

N. Then he took a cup, gave thanks, and gave it to them, saying:

J. "All of you must drink from it, for this is my blood, the blood of the covenant, to be poured out in behalf of many for the forgiveness of sins. I tell you, I will not drink this fruit of the vine from now until the day I drink new wine with you in my Father's reign."

N. Then, after singing songs of praise, they walked out to the Mount of Olives. Jesus then said to them,

J. "Tonight your faith in me will be shaken, for Scripture has it: 'I will strike the shepherd and the sheep of the flock will be dispersed.' But after I am raised up, I will go to Galilee ahead of you."

N. Peter responded,

S. "Though all may have their faith in you shaken, mine will never be shaken!"

N. Jesus said to him,

J. "I give you my word, before the cock crows tonight you will deny me three times."

N. Peter replied,

S. "Even though I have to die with you, I will never disown you."

N. And all the other disciples said the same. Then Jesus went with them to a place called Gethsemane. He said to his disciples,

J. "Stay here while I go over there and pray."

N. He took along Peter and Zebedee's two sons, and began to experience sorrow and distress. Then he said to them,

J. "My heart is nearly broken with sorrow. Remain here and stay awake with me."

N. He advanced a little and fell prostrate in prayer.

J. "My Father, if it is possible, let this cup pass by me. Still, let it be as you would have it, not as I."

N. When he returned to his disciples, he found them asleep. He said to Peter,

J. "So you could not stay awake with me for even an hour? Be on guard and pray that you may not undergo trial. The spirit is willing, but nature is weak."

N. Withdrawing a second time, he began to pray:

J. "My Father, if this cannot pass me by without my drinking it, your will be done!"

N. Once more, on his return, he found them asleep; they could not keep their eyes open. He left them again, withdrew somewhat, and began to pray a third time, saying the same words as before. Finally he returned to his disciples and said to them,

J. "Sleep on now. Enjoy your rest! The hour is on us when the Son of Man is to be handed over to the power of evil men. Get up! Let us be on our way! See, my betrayer is here."

N. While he was still speaking, Judas, one of the Twelve, arrived accompanied by a great crowd with swords and clubs. They had been sent by the chief priests and elders of the people. His betrayer had arranged to give them a signal, saying,

S. "The man I shall embrace is the one; take hold of him."

N. He immediately went over to Jesus, embraced him and said:

S. "Peace, Rabbi!"

N. Jesus answered,

J. "Do what you are here for, Friend!"

N. At that moment they stepped forward to lay hands on Jesus and arrested him. Suddenly one of those who accompanied Jesus put his hand to his sword, drew it, and slashed at the high priest's servant, cutting off his ear. Jesus said to him:

J. "Put back your sword where it belongs. Those who use the sword are sooner or later destroyed by it. Do you not suppose that I can call on my Father to provide at a moment's notice more than twelve legions of angels? But then how would the Scriptures be fulfilled which say it must happen this way?"

N. At that very time Jesus said to the crowd:

J. "Am I a brigand, that you have come armed with swords and clubs to arrest me? From day to day I sat teaching in the temple precincts, yet you never arrested me. Nonetheless, all this has happened in fulfillment of the writings of the prophets."

N. Then all the disciples deserted him and fled. Those who had apprehended Jesus led him off to Caiaphas the high priest, where the scribes and the elders were convened. Peter kept following him at a distance as far as the high priest's residence. Going inside, he sat down with the guards to see the outcome. The chief priests, with the whole Sanhedrin, were busy trying to obtain false testimony against Jesus so that they might put him to death. They discovered none, despite the many false witnesses who took the stand. Finally, two came forward who stated:

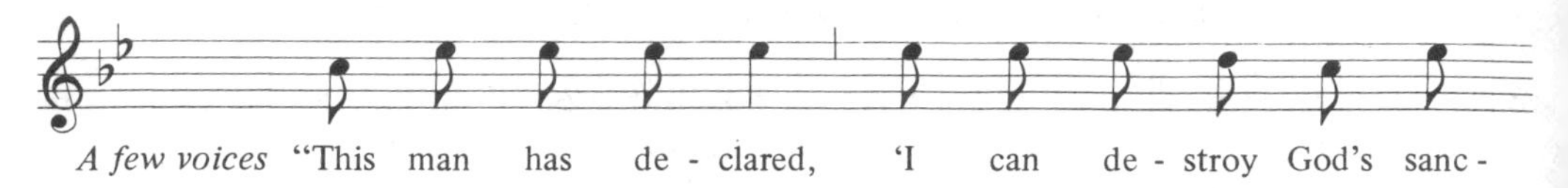
A few voices "This man has de - clared, 'I can de - stroy God's sanc -

tu - ary and re - build it in three days'."

N. The high priest rose to his feet and addressed him:

S. "Have you no answer to the testimony leveled against you?"

N. But Jesus remained silent. The high priest then said to him:

S. "I order you to tell us under oath before the living God whether you are the Messiah, the Son of God."

N. Jesus answered,

J. "It is you who say it. But I tell you this: Soon you will see the Son of Man seated at the right hand of the Power and coming on the clouds of heaven."

N. At this the high priest tore his robes:

S. "He has blasphemed! What further need have we of witnesses? Remember, you have heard the blasphemy. What is your verdict?"

N. They answered:

All "He de - serves death!"

N. Then they began to spit in his face and hit him. Others slapped him, saying:

All "Play the proph - et for us, Mes - si - ah! Who struck you?"

N. Then Peter was sitting in the courtyard when one of the serving girls came over to him and said:

S. "You too were with Jesus the Galilean."

N. He denied it in front of everyone:

S. "I don't know what you are talking about!"

N. When he went out to the gate, another girl saw him and said to those nearby,

S. "This man was with Jesus the Nazorean."

N. Again he denied it with an oath:

S. "I don't know the man!"

N. A little while later some bystanders came over to Peter and said,

All "You are cer - tain - ly one of them! E - ven your ac - cent gives you a - way!"

N. At that he began cursing and swore,

S. "I don't even know the man!"

N. Just then a rooster began to crow, and Peter remembered the prediction Jesus had made: "Before the rooster crows you will three times disown me." He went out and began to weep bitterly. At daybreak all the chief priests and elders of the people took formal action against Jesus to put him to death. They bound him and led him away to be handed over to the procurator, Pilate. Then Judas, who had handed him over, seeing that Jesus had been condemned, began to regret his action deeply. He took the thirty pieces of silver back to the chief priests and elders and said:

S. "I did wrong to deliver up an innocent man!"

N. They retorted,

All "What is that to us? It is your af - fair!"

N. So Judas flung the money into the temple and left. He went off and hanged himself. The chief priests picked up the silver, observing,

St. Matthew - Passion No. 520

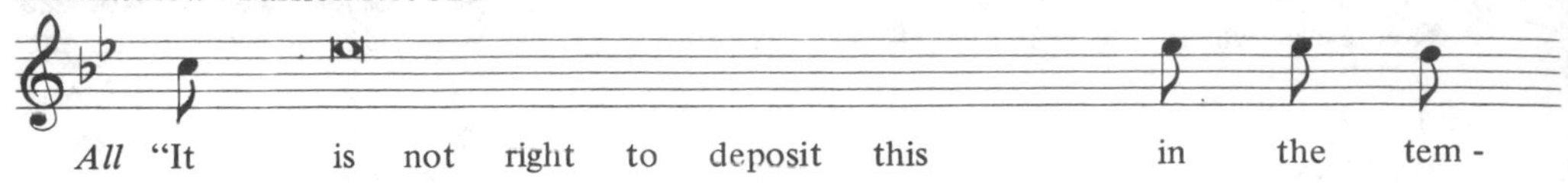
All "It is not right to deposit this in the tem -

ple trea - sur - y since it is blood mon - ey."

N. After consultation, they used it to buy the potter's field as a cemetery for foreigners. That is why that field, even today, is called Blood Field. On that occasion what was said by Jeremiah the prophet was fulfilled: "They took the thirty pieces of silver, the value of a man with a price on his head, a price set by the Israelites, and they paid it out for the potter's field just as the Lord had commanded me."

**N.* Jesus was arraigned before the procurator, Pontius Pilate, who questioned him:

S. "Are you the King of the Jews?"

N. Jesus responded,

J. "As you say."

N. Yet when he was accused by the chief priests and elders, he made no reply. Then Pilate said to him,

S. "Surely you hear how many charges they bring against you."

N. He did not answer him on a single count, much to the procurator's surprise. Now on the occasion of a festival the procurator was accustomed to release one prisoner, whom the crowd would designate. They had at the time a notorious prisoner named Barabbas. Since they were already assembled, Pilate said to them,

S. "Which one do you wish me to release for you, Barabbas or Jesus, the so-called Messiah?"

N. He knew, of course, that it was out of jealousy that they had handed him over. While he was still presiding on the bench, his wife sent him a message: "Do not interfere in the case of that holy man. I had a dream about him today which has greatly upset me."

N. Meanwhile, the chief priests and elders convinced the crowd that they should ask for Barabbas and have Jesus put to death. So when the procurator asked them,

S. "Which one do you wish me to release for you?"

---

*Here begins the short form.

N. They said,

All "Bar - ab - bas!"

N. Pilate said to them,

S. "Then what am I to do with Jesus, the so-called Messiah?"

N. They all cried,

All "Cru - ci - fy him!"

N. He said,

S. "Why, what crime has he committed?"

N. But they only shouted the louder,

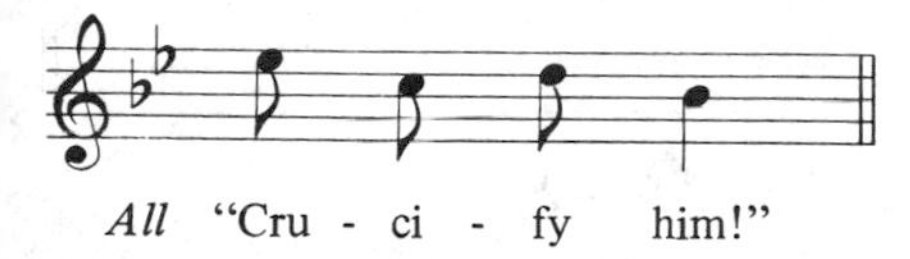
All "Cru - ci - fy him!"

N. Pilate finally realized that he was making no impression and that a riot was breaking out instead. He called for water and washed his hands in front of the crowd, declaring as he did so,

S. "I am innocent of the blood of this just man. The responsibility is yours."

N. The whole people said in reply,

All "Let his blood be on us and on our chil - dren."

N. At that, he released Barabbas to them. Jesus, however, he first had scourged; then he handed him over to be crucified. The procurator's soldiers took Jesus inside the praetorium and collected the whole cohort around him. They stripped off his clothes and wrapped him in a scarlet military cloak. Weaving a crown of thorns, they fixed it on his head, and stuck a reed in his right hand. Then they began to mock him by dropping to their knees before him, saying,

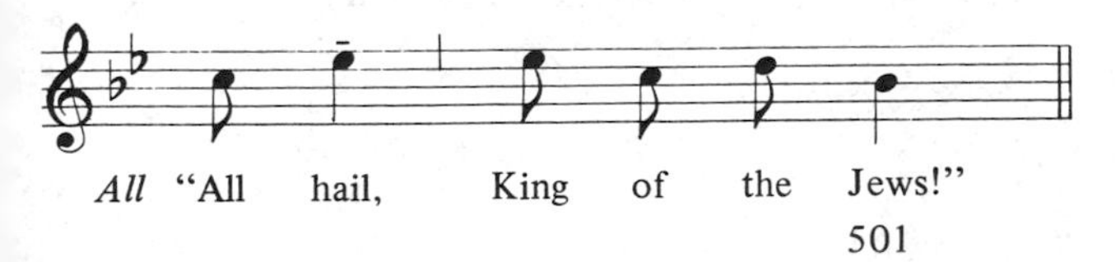
All "All hail, King of the Jews!"

N. They also spat at him. Afterward they took hold of the reed and kept striking him on the head. Finally, when they had finished making a fool of him, they stripped him of the cloak, dressed him in his own clothes, and led him off to crucifixion. On their way they met a Cyrenian named Simon. This man they pressed into service to carry the cross. Upon arriving at a site called Golgotha (a name which means Skull Place), they gave him a drink of wine flavored with gall, which he tasted but refused to drink. When they had crucified him they divided his clothes among them by casting lots; then they sat down there and kept watch over him. Above his head they had put the charge against him in writing: "This is Jesus, King of the Jews." Two insurgents were crucified along with him, one at his right and one at his left. People going by kept insulting him, tossing their heads and saying:

All "So you are the one who was going to de - stroy the tem - ple and
re - build it in three_ days! Save your - self, why don't you?
Come down from that cross if you are God's Son!"
N. The chief priests, the scribes and the elders also joined in the jeering:
All "He saved others but he cannot save him - self! So he's the
King of Is - ra - el! Let's see him come down from that cross, and then
we will be - lieve. He re - lied on God; let God res - cue him now
if he wants_ to. Af - ter all, he claimed, 'I am God's Son'."

N. The insurgents who had been crucified with him kept taunting him in the same way. From noon onward, there was darkness over the whole land until midafternoon. Then toward midafternoon Jesus cried out in a loud tone,

J. "Eli, Eli, lama sabachthani?"

N. That is, "My God, my God, why have you forsaken me?" This made some of the bystanders who heard it remark,

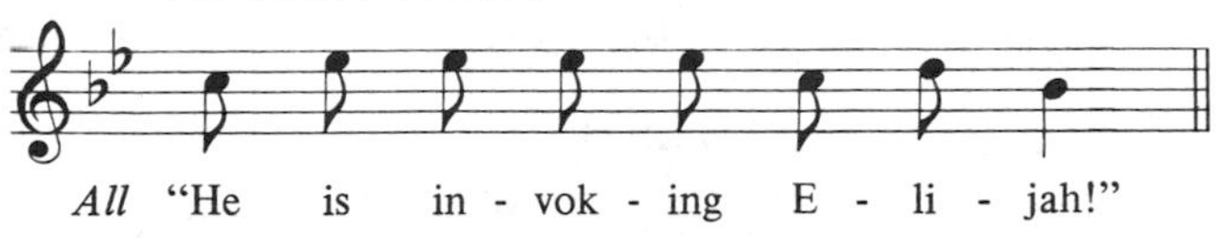
All "He is in - vok - ing E - li - jah!"

N. Immediately one of them ran off and got a sponge. He soaked it in cheap wine, and sticking it on a reed, tried to make him drink.

N. Meanwhile, the rest said,

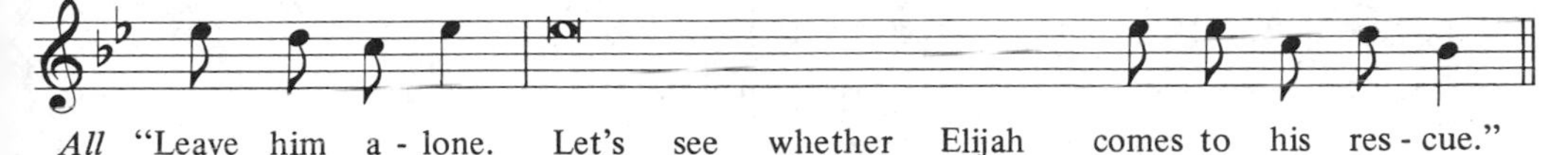
All "Leave him a - lone. Let's see whether Elijah comes to his res - cue."

N. Once again Jesus cried out in a loud voice and gave up his spirit.

(Kneel and pause)

N. Suddenly the curtain of the sanctuary was torn in two from top to bottom. The earth quaked, boulders split, tombs opened. Many bodies of saints who had fallen asleep were raised. After Jesus' resurrection they came forth from their tombs and entered the holy city and appeared to many. The centurion and his men who were keeping watch over Jesus were terror-stricken at seeing the earthquake and all that was happening, and said:

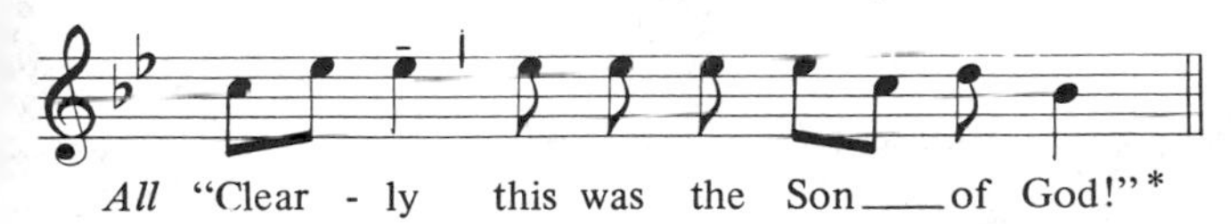
All "Clear - ly this was the Son ___ of God!"*

N. Many women were present looking on from a distance. They had followed Jesus from Galilee to attend to his needs. Among them were Mary Magdalene, and Mary, the mother of James and Joseph, and the mother of Zebedee's sons. When evening fell, a wealthy man from Arimathea arrived, Joseph by name. He was another of Jesus' disciples, and had gone to request the body of Jesus. Thereupon Pilate issued an order for its release. Taking the body, Joseph wrapped it in fresh linen and laid it in his own new tomb which had been hewn from a formation of rock. Then he rolled a huge stone across the entrance and went away. But Mary Magdalene and the other Mary remained sitting there facing the tomb. The next day, the one following the Day of Preparation, the chief priests and the Pharisees called at Pilate's residence, saying:

---

*Here ends the short form. Narrator adds: This is the gospel of the Lord.

All "Sir, we have recalled that that impostor while he was still alive
made the claim, 'Af - ter three days I will rise.' You should issue
an order having the tomb kept un - der sur - veil - lance un - til the third day.
Oth - er - wise, his disciples may go and steal him and
tell the peo - ple, 'He has been raised from the dead!'
This fi - nal im - pos - ture would be worse than the first."

N. Pilate told them,

S. "You have a guard. Go and secure the tomb as best you can."

N. So they went and kept it under surveillance of the guard, after fixing a seal to the stone.

This is the gospel of the Lord.

The Mass continues.

The Passion of Our Lord Jesus Christ According to Mark

521

Narrator The Passion of our Lord Jesus Christ according to Mark.

The feasts of Passover and Unleavened Bread were to be observed in two days' time, and therefore the chief priests and scribes began to look for a way to arrest Jesus by some trick and kill him. Yet they pointed out,

All "Not dur - ing the fes - ti - val, or the peo - ple may ri - ot."

N. When Jesus was in Bethany reclining at table in the house of Simon the leper, a woman entered carrying an alabaster jar of perfume made from expensive aromatic nard. Breaking the jar, she began to pour the perfume on his head. Some were saying to themselves indignantly:

All "What is the point of this extravagant waste of per - fume?
It could have been sold for over three hun - dred
sil - ver piec - es and the mon - ey giv - en to the poor."

N. They were infuriated at her. But Jesus said:

Jesus "Let her alone. Why do you criticize her? She has done me a kindness. The poor you will always have with you and you can be generous with them whenever you wish, but you will not always have me. She has done what she could. By perfuming my body she is anticipating its preparation for burial. I assure you, wherever the good news is proclaimed throughout the world, what she has done will be told in her memory."

N. Then Judas Iscariot, one of the Twelve, went off to the chief priests to hand Jesus over to them. Hearing what he had to say, they were jubilant and promised to give him money. He for his part kept looking for an opportune way to hand him over. On the first day of Unleavened Bread, when it was customary to sacrifice the paschal lamb, his disciples said to him,

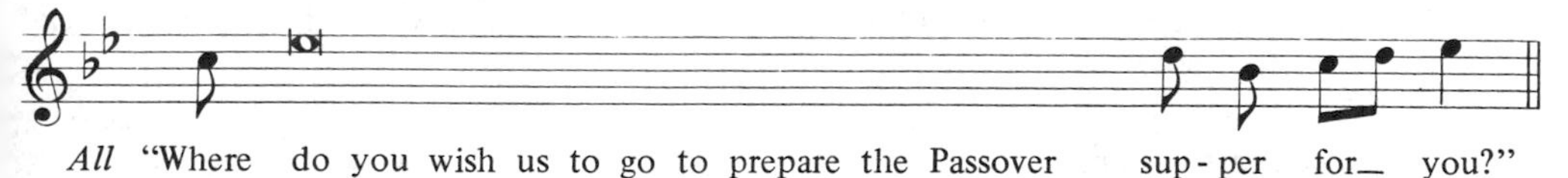
All "Where do you wish us to go to prepare the Passover sup - per for_ you?"

N. He sent two of his disciples with these instructions:

J. "Go into the city and you will come upon a man carrying a water jar. Follow him. Whatever house he enters, say to the owner, 'The Teacher asks, Where is my guest room where I may eat the Passover with my disciples?' Then he will show you an upstairs room, spacious, furnished, and all in order. That is the place you are to get ready for us."

N. The disciples went off. When they reached the city they found it just as he had told them, and they prepared the Passover supper. As it grew dark, he arrived with the Twelve. They reclined at table, and in the course of the meal Jesus said,

J. "I give you my word, one of you is about to betray me, yes, one who is eating with me."

N. They began to say to him sorrowfully, one by one,

All "Sure - ly not — I!"

N. He said,

J. "It is one of the Twelve–a man who dips into the dish with me. The Son of Man is going the way the Scripture tells of him. Still, accursed be that man by whom the Son of Man is betrayed. It were better for him had he never been born."

N. During the meal he took bread, blessed and broke it, and gave it to them saying:

J. "Take this. This is my body."

N. He likewise took a cup, gave thanks and passed it to them, and they all drank from it. He said to them:

J. "This is my blood, the blood of the covenant, to be poured out on behalf of many. I solemnly assure you, I will never again drink of the fruit of the vine until the day when I drink it in the reign of God."

N. After singing songs of praise, they walked out to the Mount of Olives. Jesus then said to them:

J. "Your faith in me will be shaken, for Scripture has it, 'I will strike the shepherd and the sheep will be dispersed.' But after I am raised up, I will go to Galilee ahead of you."

N. Peter said to him,

Speaker "Even though all are shaken in faith, it will not be that way with me."

N. Jesus answered,

J. "I give you my assurance, this very night before the cock crows twice, you will deny me three times."

N. But Peter kept reasserting vehemently,

S. "Even if I have to die with you, I will not disown you."

N. They all said the same. They went then to a place named Gethsemane. He said to his disciples,

J. "Sit down here while I pray."

N. At the same time he took along with him Peter, James and John. Then he began to be filled with fear and distress. He said to them,

J. "My heart is filled with sorrow to the point of death. Remain here and stay awake."

N. He advanced a little and fell to the ground, praying that if it were possible this hour might pass him by. He kept saying,

J. "Abba, O Father, you have the power to do all things. Take this cup away from me. But let it be as you would have it, not as I."

N. When he returned, he found them asleep. He said to Peter,

J. "Asleep, Simon? You could not stay awake for even an hour? Be on guard and pray that you may not be put to the test. The spirit is willing but nature is weak."

N. Going back again he began to pray in the same words. Once again he found them asleep on his return. They could not keep their eyes open, nor did they know what to say to him. He returned a third time and said to them,

J. "Still sleeping? Still taking your ease? It will have to do. The hour is on us. You will see that the Son of Man is to be handed over into the clutches of evil men. Rouse yourselves and come along. See! My betrayer is near."

N. Even while he was speaking, Judas, one of the Twelve, made his appearance accompanied by a crowd with swords and clubs; these people had been sent by the chief priests, the scribes, and the elders. The betrayer had arranged a signal for them, saying:

S. "The man I shall embrace is the one; arrest him and lead him away, taking every precaution."

N. He then went directly over to him, embraced him and said,

S. "Rabbi!"

N. At this they laid hands on him and arrested him. One of the bystanders drew his sword and struck the high priest's slave, cutting off his ear. Addressing himself to them, Jesus said:

J. "You have come out to arrest me, armed with swords and clubs as if against a brigand. I was within your reach daily, teaching in the temple precincts, yet you never arrested me. But now, so that the Scriptures may be fulfilled. . ."

N. With that, all deserted him and fled. There was a young man following him who was covered with nothing but a linen cloth. As they seized him he left the cloth behind and ran off naked. Then they led Jesus off to the high priest, and all the chief priests, the elders and the scribes came together. Peter followed him at a distance right into the high priest's court-yard, where he found a seat with the temple guard and began to warm himself at the fire. The chief priests with the whole Sanhedrin were busy soliciting testimony against Jesus that would lead to his death, but they could not find any. Many spoke out against him falsely under oath but their testimony did not agree. Some, for instance, on taking the stand, testified falsely by alleging:

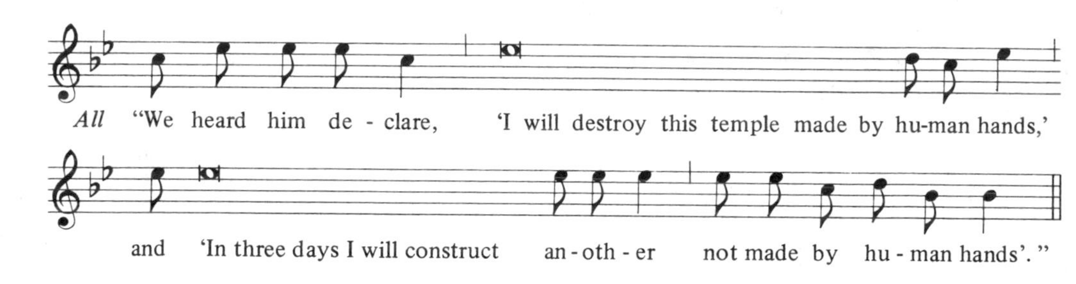
All "We heard him de - clare, 'I will destroy this temple made by hu-man hands,'
and 'In three days I will construct an - oth - er not made by hu - man hands'."

N. Even so, their testimony did not agree.

N. The high priest rose to his feet before the court and began to interrogate Jesus:

S. "Have you no answer to what these men testify against you?"

N. But Jesus remained silent; he made no reply. Once again the high priest interrogated him:

S. "Are you the Messiah, the Son of the Blessed One?"

N. Then Jesus answered:

J. "I am; and you will see the Son of Man seated at the right hand of the Power and coming with the clouds of heaven."

N. At that, the high priest tore his robes and said:

S. "What further need do we have of witnesses? You have heard the blasphemy. What is your verdict?"

N. They all concurred in the verdict "guilty", with its sentence of death. Some of them then began to spit on him. They blindfolded him and hit him, while the officers manhandled him, saying:

All "Play the proph - et!"

N. While Peter was down in the courtyard, one of the servant girls of the high priest came along. When she noticed Peter warming himself, she looked more closely at him and said:

S. "You too were with Jesus of Nazareth."

N. But he denied it:

S. "I don't know what you are talking about! What are you getting at?"

N. Then he went out into the gateway. At that moment a rooster crowed. The servant girl, keeping an eye on him, started again to tell the bystanders:

S. "This man is one of them."

N. Once again he denied it. A little later the bystanders said to Peter once more:

S. "You are certainly one of them! You're a Galilean, are you not?"

N. He began to curse and to swear,

S. "I don't even know the man you are talking about!"

N. Just then a second cockcrow was heard and Peter recalled the prediction Jesus had made to him, "Before the cock crows twice you will disown me three times." He broke down and began to cry. *As soon as it was daybreak the chief priests, with the elders and scribes (that is, the whole Sanhedrin), reached a decision. They bound Jesus, led him away, and handed him over to Pilate. Pilate interrogated him:

S. "Are you the King of the Jews?"

N. Jesus replied:

J. "You are the one who is saying it."

*Here begins the short form.

N. The chief priests, meanwhile, brought many accusations against him. Pilate interrogated him again:

S. "Surely you have some answer? See how many accusations they are leveling against you."

N. But greatly to Pilate's surprise, Jesus made no further response. Now on the occasion of a festival he would release for them one prisoner, any man they asked for. There was a prisoner named Barabbas jailed along with the rebels who had committed murder in the uprising. When the crowd came up to press their demand that he honor the custom, Pilate rejoined,

S. "Do you want me to release the King of the Jews for you?"

N. He was aware, of course, that it was out of jealousy that the chief priests had handed him over. Meanwhile, the chief priests incited the crowd to have him release Barabbas instead. Again Pilate asked them,

S. "What am I to do with the man you call the King of the Jews?"

N. They shouted back,

All "Cru - ci - fy him!"

N. Pilate protested,

S. "Why? What crime has he committed?"

N. They only shouted the louder,

All "Cru - ci - fy him!"

N. So Pilate, who wished to satisfy the crowd, released Barabbas to them; and after he had had Jesus scourged, he handed him over to be crucified. The soldiers now led Jesus away into the hall known as the praetorium; at the same time they assembled the whole cohort. They dressed him in royal purple, then wove a crown of thorns and put it on him, and began to salute him,

All "All hail! King of the Jews!"

N. Continually striking Jesus on the head with a reed and spitting at him, they genuflected before him and pretended to pay him homage. When they had finished mocking him, they stripped him of the purple, dressed him in his own clothes and led him out to crucify him. A man named Simon of Cyrene, the father of Alexander and Rufus, was coming in from the fields and they pressed him into service to carry the cross. When they brought Jesus to the site of Golgotha (which means Skull Place), they tried to give him wine drugged with myrrh, but he would not take it. Then they crucified him and divided up his garments by rolling dice for them to see what each should take. It was about nine in the morning when they crucified him. The inscription proclaiming his offense read, "The King of the Jews." With him they crucified two insurgents, one at his right and one at his left. People going by kept insulting him, tossing their heads and saying:

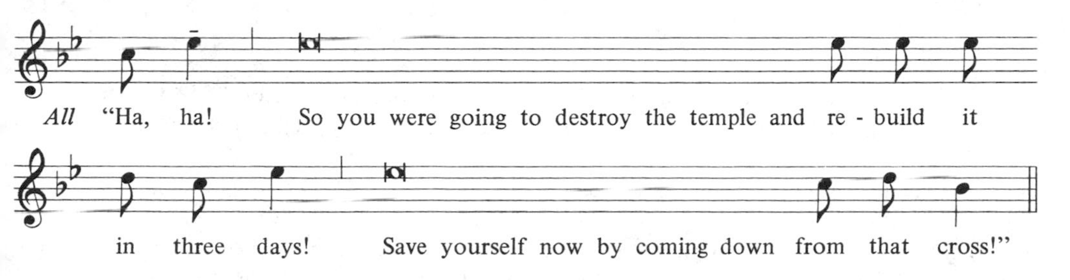
All "Ha, ha! So you were going to destroy the temple and re - build it
in three days! Save yourself now by coming down from that cross!"

N. The chief priests and the scribes also joined in and jeered:

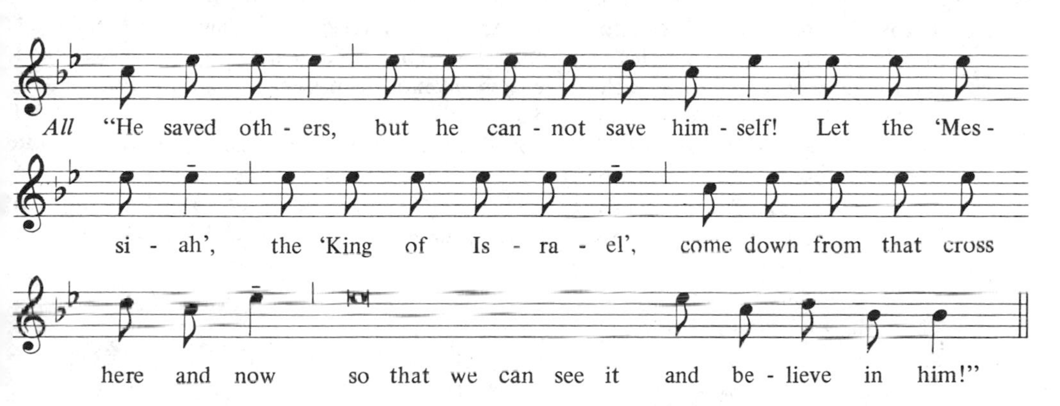
All "He saved oth - ers, but he can - not save him - self! Let the 'Mes -
si - ah', the 'King of Is - ra - el', come down from that cross
here and now so that we can see it and be - lieve in him!"

N. The men who had been crucified with him likewise kept taunting him. When noon came, darkness fell on the whole countryside and lasted until midafternoon. At that time Jesus cried in a loud voice,

J. "Eloi, Eloi, lama sabachthani?"

N. Which means, "My God, my God, why have you forsaken me?" A few bystanders who heard it remarked,

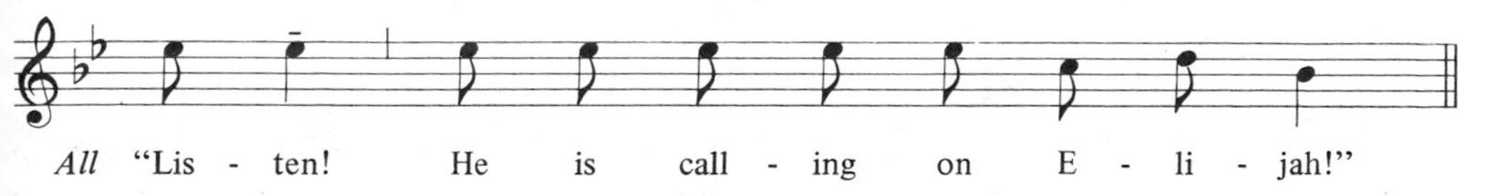
All "Lis - ten! He is call - ing on E - li - jah!"

N. Someone ran off, and soaking a sponge in sour wine, stuck it on a reed to try to make him drink. The man said,

S. "Now let's see whether Elijah comes to take him down."

N. Then Jesus, uttering a loud cry, breathed his last.

(Kneel and pause. Narrator continues.)

At that moment the curtain in the sanctuary was torn in two from top to bottom. The centurion who stood guard over him, on seeing the manner of his death, declared:

S. "Clearly this man was the Son of God!" *

N. There were also women present looking on from a distance. Among them were Mary Magdalene, Mary the mother of James the younger and Joses, and Salome. These women had followed Jesus when he was in Galilee and attended to his needs. There were also many others who had come up with him to Jerusalem. As it grew dark (it was Preparation Day, that is, the eve of the sabbath), Joseph of Arimathea arrived – a distinguished member of the Sanhedrin. He was another who looked forward to the reign of God. He was bold enough to seek an audience with Pilate, and urgently requested the body of Jesus. Pilate was surprised that Jesus should have died so soon. He summoned the centurion and inquired whether Jesus was already dead. Learning from him that he was dead, Pilate released the corpse to Joseph. Then, having bought a linen shroud, Joseph took him down, wrapped him in the linen, and laid him in a tomb which had been cut out of rock. Finally he rolled a stone across the entrance of the tomb. Meanwhile, Mary Magdalene and Mary, the mother of Joses, observed where he had been laid.

This is the gospel of the Lord.

---

*Here ends the short form. Narrator adds: This is the gospel of the Lord.

The Mass continues.

The Passion of Our Lord Jesus Christ According to Luke

Narrator The Passion of our Lord Jesus Christ according to Luke.

When the hour arrived, Jesus took his place at table, and the apostles with him. He said to them:

Jesus "I have greatly desired to eat this Passover with you before I suffer. I tell you, I will not eat again until it is fulfilled in the kingdom of God."

N. Then taking a cup, he offered a blessing in thanks and said:

J. "Take this and divide it among you; I tell you, from now on I will not drink of the fruit of the vine until the coming of the reign of God."

N. Then taking bread and giving thanks, he broke it and gave it to them, saying:

J. "This is my body to be given for you. Do this as a remembrance of me."

N. He did the same with the cup after eating, saying as he did so:

J. "This cup is the new covenant in my blood, which will be shed for you. And yet the hand of my betrayer is with me at this table. The Son of Man is following out his appointed course, but woe to that man by whom he is betrayed."

N. Then they began to dispute among themselves as to which of them would do such a deed. A dispute arose among them about who should be regarded as the greatest. He said,

J. "Earthly kings lord it over their people. Those who exercise authority over them are called their benefactors. Yet it cannot be that way with you. Let the greater among you be as the junior, the leader as the servant. Who, in fact, is the greater–he who reclines at the table or he who serves the meal? Is it not the one who reclines at table? Yet I am in your midst as the one who serves you. You are the ones who have stood loyally by me in my temptations. I for my part assign to you the dominion my Father has assigned to me. In my kingdom, you will eat and drink at my table, and you will sit on thrones judging the twelve tribes of Israel. Simon, Simon! Remember that Satan has asked for you, to sift you all like wheat. But I have prayed for you that your faith may never fail. You in turn must strengthen your brothers."

N. Peter said to him,

Speaker "Lord, at your side I am prepared to face imprisonment and death itself."

N. Jesus replied,

J. "I tell you, Peter, the rooster will not crow today until you have three times denied that you know me."

N. He asked them,

J. "When I sent you on mission without purse or traveling bag or sandals, were you in need of anything?"

N. They replied,

All "Not___ a thing."

N. He said to them,

J. "Now, however, the man who has a purse must carry it; the same with the traveling bag. And the man without a sword must sell his coat and buy one. It is written in Scripture, 'He was counted among the wicked,' and this, I tell you, must come to be fulfilled in me. All that has to do with me approaches its climax."

N. They said,

All "Lord, here are two swords!"

N. He answered,

J. "Enough."

N. Then he went out and made his way, as was his custom, to the Mount of Olives; his disciples accompanied him. On reaching the place he said to them,

J. "Pray that you may not be put to the test."

N. He withdrew from them about a stone's throw, then went down on his knees and prayed in these words:

J. "Father, if it is your will, take this cup from me; yet not my will but yours be done."

N. An angel then appeared to him from heaven to strengthen him. In his anguish he prayed with all the greater intensity, and his sweat became like drops of blood falling to the ground. Then he rose from prayer and came to his disciples, only to find them asleep, exhausted with grief. He said to them,

J. "Why are you sleeping? Wake up, and pray that you may not be subjected to the trial."

N. While he was still speaking, a crowd came, led by the man named Judas, one of the Twelve. He approached Jesus to embrace him. Jesus said to him,

J. "Judas, would you betray the Son of Man with a kiss?"

N. When the companions of Jesus saw what was going to happen, they said,

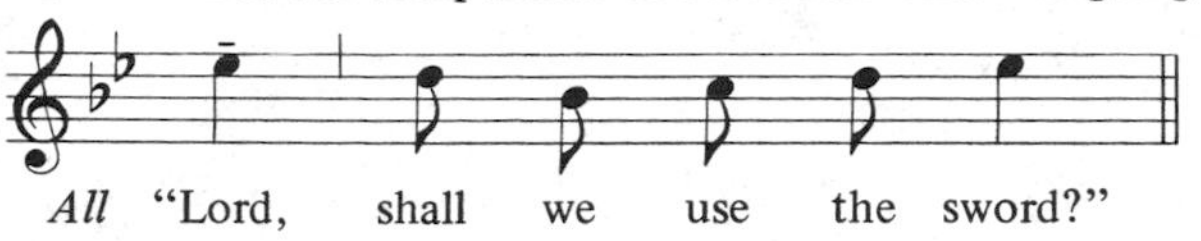

All "Lord, shall we use the sword?"

N. One of them went so far as to strike the high priest's servant and cut off his right ear. In answer to their question, Jesus said:

J. "Enough!"

N. Then he touched the ear and healed the man. But to those who had come out against him—the chief priests, the chiefs of the temple guard, and the ancients—Jesus said:

J. "Am I a criminal that you come out after me armed with swords and clubs? When I was with you day after day in the temple you never raised a hand against me. But this is your hour—the triumph of darkness!"

N. They led him away under arrest and brought him to the house of the high priest, while Peter followed at a distance. Later they lighted a fire in the middle of the courtyard and were sitting beside it, and Peter sat among them. A servant girl saw him sitting in the light of the fire. She gazed at him intently, then said:

S. "This man was with him."

N. He denied the fact, saying:

S. "Woman, I do not know him."

N. A little while later someone else saw him and said,

S. "You also are one of them."

N. But Peter said,

S. "No, sir, not I!"

N. About an hour after that, another spoke more insistently:

S. "This man was certainly with him, for he is a Galilean."

N. Peter responded,

S. "My friend, I do not know what you are talking about."

N. At the very moment he was saying this, a rooster crowed. The Lord turned around and looked at Peter, and Peter remembered the word that the Lord had spoken to him, "Before the rooster crows today, you will deny me three times." He went out and wept bitterly.

Meanwhile the men guarding Jesus amused themselves at his expense. They blindfolded him first, slapped him, and then taunted him:

All "Play the proph - et: which one struck_ you?"

N. And they directed many other insulting words at him. At daybreak, the elders of the people, the chief priests, and the scribes assembled again. Once they had brought him before their council, they said:

All "Tell us, are you the Mes - si - ah?"

N. He replied,

J. "If I tell you, you will not believe me, and if I question you, you will not answer. This much only will I say: 'From now on, the Son of Man will have his seat at the right hand of the Power of God'."

N. They asked in chorus,

All "So you are the Son of God?"

N. He answered,

J. "It is you who say I am."

N. They said,

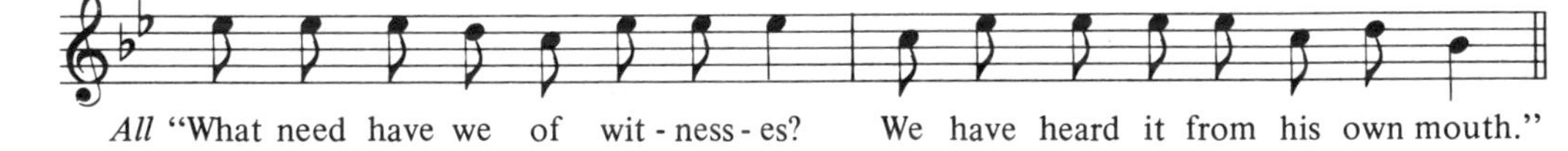
All "What need have we of wit - ness - es? We have heard it from his own mouth."

**N.* Then the entire assembly rose up and led him before Pilate. They started his prosecution by saying,

---

*Here begins the short form.

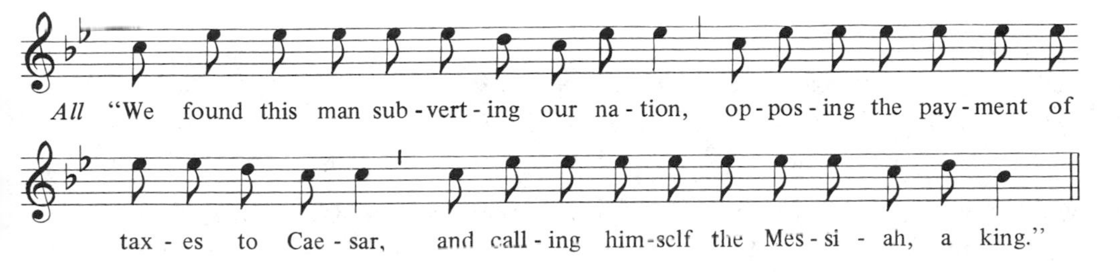
All "We found this man sub - vert - ing our na - tion, op - pos - ing the pay - ment of
tax - es to Cae - sar, and call - ing him - self the Mes - si - ah, a king."

N. Pilate asked him,

S. "Are you the King of the Jews?"

N. He answered,

J. "That is your term."

N. Pilate reported to the chief priests and the crowds,

S. "I do not find a case against this man."

N. But they insisted,

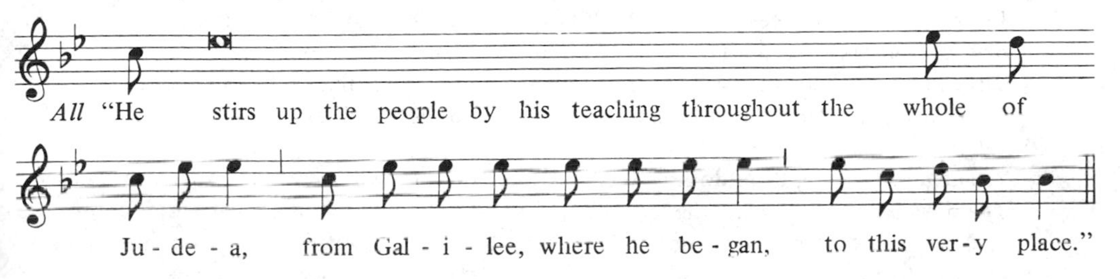
All "He stirs up the people by his teaching throughout the whole of
Ju - de - a, from Gal - i - lee, where he be - gan, to this ver - y place."

N. On hearing this Pilate asked if the man was a Galilean; and when he learned that he was under Herod's jurisdiction, he sent him to Herod, who also happened to be in Jerusalem at the time. Herod was extremely pleased to see Jesus. From the reports about him he had wanted for a long time to see him, and he was hoping to see him work some miracle. He questioned Jesus at considerable length, but Jesus made no answer. The chief priests and scribes were at hand to accuse him vehemently. Herod and his guards then treated him with contempt and insult, after which they put a magnificent robe on him and sent him back to Pilate. Herod and Pilate, who had previously been set against each other, became friends from that day. Pilate then called together the chief priests, the ruling class, and the people, and said to them:

S. "You have brought this man before me as one who subverts the people. I have examined him in your presence and have no charge against him arising from your allegations. Neither has Herod, who therefore has sent him back to us; obviously this man has done nothing to deserve death. Therefore I mean to release him, once I have taught him a lesson."

N. The whole crowd cried out,

All "A - way with this man; re - lease Bar - ab - bas for us!"

N. This Barabbas had been thrown in prison for causing an uprising in the city, and for murder. Pilate addressed them again, for he wanted Jesus to be the one he released. But they shouted back,

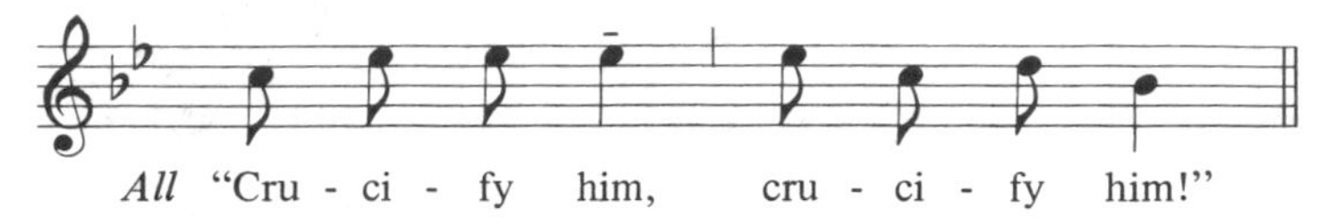
All "Cru - ci - fy him, cru - ci - fy him!"

N. He said to them for the third time,

S. "What wrong is this man guilty of? I have not discovered anything about him deserving of the death penalty. I will therefore chastise him and release him."

N. But they demanded with loud cries that he be crucified, and their shouts increased in violence. Pilate then decreed that what they demanded should be done. He released the one they asked for, who had been thrown in prison for insurrection and murder, and delivered Jesus up to their wishes. As they led him away, they laid hold of one Simon the Cyrenean, who was coming in from the fields. They put a crossbeam on Simon's shoulder for him to carry along behind Jesus. A great crowd of people followed him, including women who beat their breasts and lamented over him. Jesus turned to them and said:

J. "Daughters of Jerusalem, do not weep for me. Weep for yourselves and for your children. The days are coming when they will say, 'Happy are the sterile, the wombs that never bore and the breasts that never nursed.' Then they will begin saying to the mountains, 'Fall on us,' and to the hills 'Cover us.' If they do these things in the green wood, what will happen in the dry?"

N. Two others who were criminals were led along with him to be crucified. When they came to Skull Place, as it was called, they crucified him there and the criminals as well, one on his right and the other on his left. Jesus said,

J. "Father, forgive them; they do not know what they are doing."

N. They divided his garments, rolling dice for them. The people stood there watching and the leaders kept jeering at him saying,

All "He saved oth - ers; let him save himself if he is the
Mes - si - ah of God, the cho - sen one."

N. The soldiers also made fun of him, coming forward to offer him their sour wine and saying:

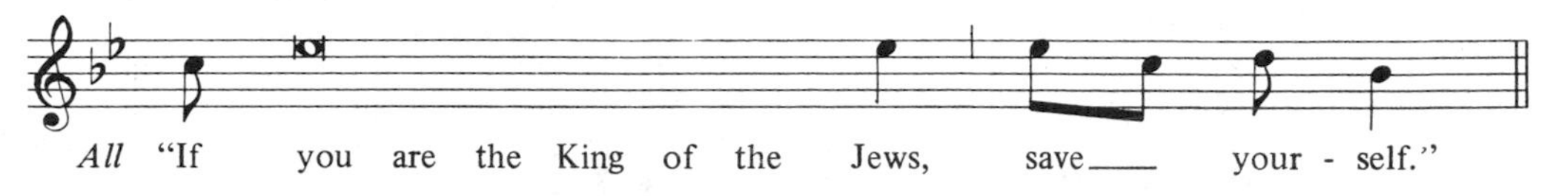
All "If you are the King of the Jews, save___ your - self."

N. There was an inscription over his head: "This is the King of the Jews." One of the criminals hanging in crucifixion blasphemed him,

S. "Aren't you the Messiah? Then save yourself and us."

N. But the other one rebuked him:

S. "Have you no fear of God, seeing you are under the same sentence? We deserve it, after all. We are only paying the price for what we've done, but this man has done nothing wrong."

N. Then he said,

S. "Jesus, remember me when you enter upon your reign."

N. And Jesus replied,

J. "I assure you: this day you will be with me in paradise."

N. It was now around midday, and darkness came over the whole land until midafternoon with an eclipse of the sun. The curtain in the sanctuary was torn in two. Jesus uttered a loud cry and said,

J. "Father, into your hands I commend my spirit."

N. After he said this, he expired.

(Kneel and pause.)

N. The centurion, upon seeing what had happened, gave glory to God by saying,

S. "Surely, this was an innocent man."

N. After the crowd assembled for this spectacle witnessed what had happened, they went home, beating their breasts. All his friends and the women who had accompanied him from Galilee were standing at a distance watching everything.* There was a man named Joseph, an upright and holy member of the Sanhedrin, who had not been associated with their plan or their action. He was from Arimathea, a Jewish town, and he looked expectantly for the reign of God. This man approached Pilate with a request for Jesus' body. He took it down, wrapped it in fine linen, and laid it in a tomb hewn out of the rock, in which no one had yet been buried. That was the Day of Preparation, and the sabbath was about to begin. The women who had come with him from Galilee followed along. They saw the tomb and how his body was buried. Then they went back home to prepare spices and perfumes. They observed the sabbath as a day of rest, in accordance with the law.

This is the gospel of the Lord.

*Here ends the short form. Narrator adds: This is the gospel of the Lord.

F. Homily

G. Profession of faith

No. 62 CREDO III
No. 12 or 13 PROFESSION OF FAITH

H. General intercessions

No. 14 ORDER OF MASS

V. LITURGY OF THE EUCHARIST

A. Presentation of gifts. During this action one of the following may be sung:

No. 198 JESU, JOY AND TREASURE

No. 330 THINK OF THE SON OF GOD

B. Mass proceeds as usual.

See 16 *ff* ORDER OF MASS

VI. COMMUNION AND DISMISSAL

A. During the distribution of holy communion, one of the following may be sung:

No. 164 GODHEAD HERE IN HIDING
No. 199 JESU, JOY OF MAN'S DESIRING
No. 298 SING, MY TONGUE, THE SAVIOR'S GLORY

B. Postcommunion prayer and dismissal

See ORDER OF MASS

C. Recessional hymn

No. 248 O SACRED HEAD SURROUNDED

HOLY THURSDAY

Evening Mass of the Lord's Supper
Order of Service

I. ENTRANCE RITE

A. The entrance procession. One of the following is suggested:

No. 217 LORD, WHO AT YOUR FIRST EUCHARIST DID PRAY
No. 298 SING, MY TONGUE, THE SAVIOR'S GLORY

B. Greeting and Penitential Rite

Nos. 1-3 ORDER OF MASS

C. GLORIA is intoned and sung. During the singing of the GLORIA the bells are rung and thereafter remain silent until the Easter Vigil, unless otherwise indicated by the bishop(s).

Nos. 7 or 8 ORDER OF MASS
No. 55 GLORIA (Gregorian Mass VIII)
Nos. 44, or 49 GLORY TO GOD IN THE HIGHEST

D. Opening prayer by celebrant. All respond: Amen.

II. LITURGY OF THE WORD

A. First reading: Exodus 12: 1-8. 11-14

B. Responsorial psalm:

No. 445 THE CUP OF BLESSING and PSALM 116

C. Second reading: 1 Corinthians 11: 23-26

D. Gospel acclamation. One of the acclamations for Holy Thursday may be used:

Nos. 87, 88, 89, or 90 ORDER OF MASS

E. Gospel: John 13: 1-15

F. Homily

G. Washing of the feet. During this action one of the following may be used:

No. 351 WHERE ABIDETH CHARITY AND LOVE
No. 563 IMITATING CHRIST'S HUMILITY

H. General intercessions:

No. 14 ORDER OF MASS

III. LITURGY OF THE EUCHARIST

A. Presentation of the gifts. One of the following is suggested:

No. 198 JESU, JOY AND TREASURE
No. 199 JESU, JOY OF MAN'S DESIRING

B. Prayer over the gifts and eucharistic prayer

Nos. 16-19 ORDER OF MASS

IV. COMMUNION AND DISMISSAL

A. The Lord's Prayer

Nos. 30, 31, or 69 ORDER OF MASS

B. After the embrace of peace, one of the following is suggested:

No. 32 or 33 LAMB OF GOD
No. 246 O LAMB OF GOD, ALL HOLY
No. 71 AGNUS DEI IX
No. 79 AGNUS DEI XVIII

C. During the distribution of communion, one of the following may be used:

No. 164 GODHEAD HERE IN HIDING
No. 139 COME, TAKE THE BODY OF THE SAVIOR

D. As a meditation after communion, one of the following responsive readings is suggested:

No. 570 ODE OF TRUST
No. 591 WE ARE GOD'S CHILDREN

E. Prayer after communion by the celebrant. All respond: Amen.

V. TRANSFER OF HOLY EUCHARIST

A. During the procession, verses 1 to 4 inclusive of either of the following hymns are repeated until the celebrant and ministers reach the altar of reposition. Then verses 5 and 6 are sung:

No. 228 NOW MY TONGUE, THE MYST'RY TELLING
No. 275 PANGE LINGUA

B. After a period of silent adoration, the celebrant and ministers return to the sacristy.

Note: There is no recessional hymn

Holy Thursday-Chrism Mass

524

I. ENTRANCE RITE

A. Procession of priests and bishop. Suggested hymn:
No. 346 WE LOVE YOUR TEMPLE, LORD

B. Greeting and Penitential Rite.
Nos. 1-3 ORDER OF MASS

C. GLORIA is intoned and sung:
Nos. 7 or 8 ORDER OF MASS
No. 55 GLORIA (Gregorian Mass VIII)
Nos. 44 or 49 GLORY TO GOD IN THE HIGHEST

D. Opening prayer by the bishop to which all respond: Amen.

II. LITURGY OF THE WORD

A. First reading: Is. 61: 1-3a. 6a. 8b-9.

B. Responsorial psalm:
No. 421 I WILL SING THE GOODNESS OF THE LORD with PSALM 89

C. Second reading: Rev. 1: 5-8.

D. Gospel acclamation. One of the acclamations may be used:
Nos. 87-90 ORDER OF MASS

E. Gospel: Luke 4: 16-21.

F. Homily and renewal of commitment to priestly service

G. Prayers of intercession by bishop to which all respond:
Lord Jesus Christ, hear us and answer our prayer.
At the conclusion all respond: Amen.

H. Procession with the oils. The hymn O REDEEMER *(see below)* is sung or:
No. 596 FATHER, LORD OF EARTH AND HEAVEN
No. 597 LORD, YOU GIVE THE GREAT COMMISSION

III. LITURGY OF THE EUCHARIST

ORDER OF MASS

IV. COMMUNION AND DISMISSAL

ORDER OF MASS

A period of silence may be observed after communion, or a psalm of praise may be sung.

At the recession verses from O REDEEMER may be sung or an appropriate hymn:

No. 160 FORTH IN THE PEACE OF CHRIST WE GO

525 O Redeemer, Receive the Song

ANTIPHON

I. Cantor or Schola II. All
O Re - deem - er, re - ceive_the song_of those who sing_your praise.

1. A tree made fruitful by the fostering light of the sun
   brought forth oil that it might be blessed.
   Humbly we bring it to the Savior of the world.

2. In your kindness, O King of the eternal homeland,
   Consecrate this oil of olives as a sign of life,
   a safeguard against the demon.

All repeat ANTIPHON

3. May both men and women be made new by being anointed
   with the chrism;
   And may the wound to their glorious dignity be healed.

4. Our minds being made clean at the sacred font,
   let our sins be put to flight.
   May holy gifts be lavished on those whose foreheads
   are anointed.

All repeat ANTIPHON

5. You who were born from the heart of the Father,
   and did fill the womb of the Virgin,
   Grant light for those who share in the chrism and
   put an end to death.

6. May this day be a festival for us forever and ever.
   May it not grow old with time, and may it be made
   holy with worthy praise.

All repeat ANTIPHON

Good Friday
ORDER OF SERVICE
Celebration of the Lord's Passion

526

I. LITURGY OF THE WORD

A Procession takes place in silence

B Opening prayer by the Celebrant to which all respond: Amen

C First reading: Isaiah 51:13-53:12

D Responsory

Ps. 31
In You, O Lord, I Take Refuge

527

ANTIPHON: Father, I put my life in your hands

Joseph Policelli

T. 4g
Fa - ther, I put my life in your hands.

PSALM 31: 2-3a. 3b. 6. 12-13. 15-16. 17. 25.

1. In you, O Lord, I take refuge; let me never be put to shame.
   In your justice rescue me.
   Into your hands I commend my spirit;
   You will redeem me, O Lord, O faithful God.
   All repeat ANTIPHON

2. For all my foes I am an object of reproach, a laughing stock
   to my neighbors, and a dread to my friends;
   They who see me abroad flee from me.
   I am forgotten like the unremembered dead;
   I am like a dish that is broken.
   All repeat ANTIPHON

3. But my trust is in you, O Lord;
   I say, "You are my God."
   In your hands is my destiny; rescue me from the clutches
   of my enemies
   And my persecutors.
   All repeat ANTIPHON

4. Let your face shine upon your servant;
   Save me in your kindness.
   Take courage and be stouthearted,
   All you who hope in the Lord.
   All repeat ANTIPHON

E Second reading: St. Paul to the Hebrews 4: 14-16. 5: 7-9

F Gospel acclamation

528 Christ Became Obedient for Us

Gospel Acclamation for Passion Sunday and Holy Week

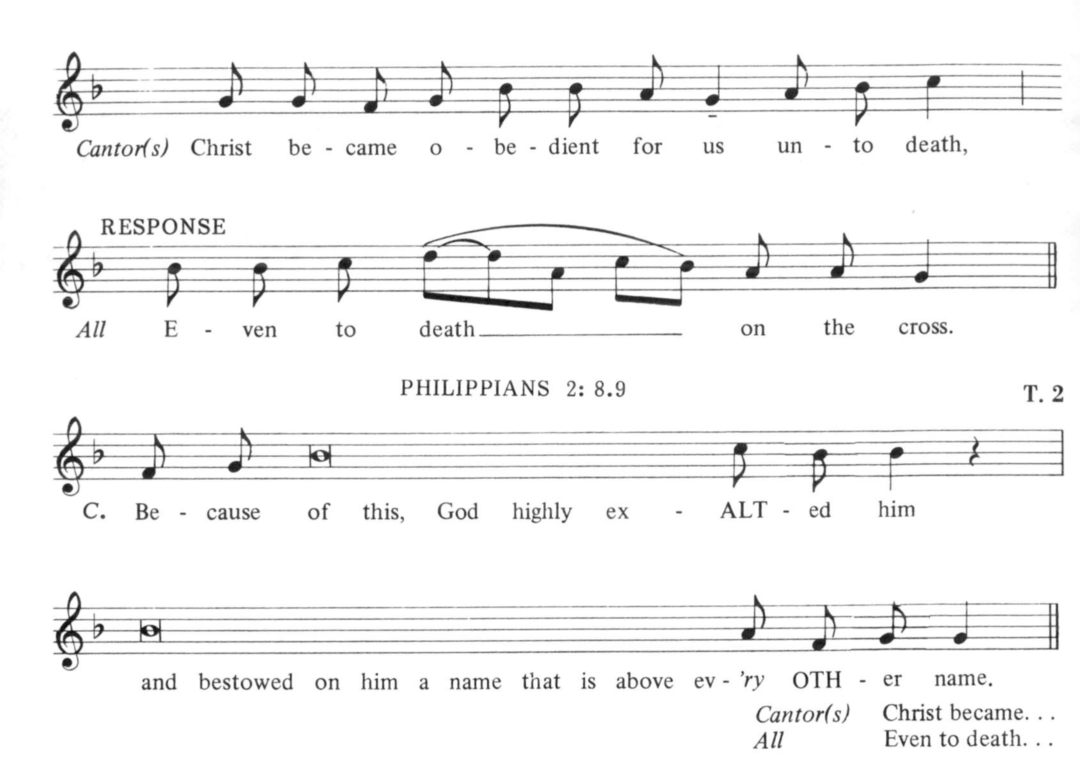
Cantor(s) Christ be - came o - be - dient for us un - to death,
RESPONSE
All E - ven to death on the cross.
PHILIPPIANS 2: 8.9
T. 2
C. Be - cause of this, God highly ex - ALT - ed him
and bestowed on him a name that is above ev - 'ry OTH - er name.
Cantor(s) Christ became. . .
All Even to death. . .

G The Passion of Our Lord chanted by three deacons or three cantors as available. Parts assigned to the crowd are sung by All. *(See next page)*

The Passion of Our Lord Jesus Christ According to John

Narrator The Passion of our Lord Jesus Christ according to John.

Jesus went out with his disciples across the Kidron valley. There was a garden there, and he and his disciples entered it. The place was familiar to Judas as well, the one who was to hand him over, because Jesus had often met there with his disciples. Judas took the cohort as well as guards supplied by the chief priests and the Pharisees, and came there with lanterns, torches and weapons. Jesus, aware of all that would happen to him, stepped forward and said to them,

Jesus "Who is it you want?"

N. They replied,

All "Je - sus the Naz - o - re - an."

N. He answered,

J. "I am he."

N. Now Judas, the one who was to hand him over, was right there with them. As Jesus said to them, "I am he," they retreated slightly and fell to the ground. Jesus put the question to them again,

J. "Who is it you want?"

N. They repeated,

All "Je - sus the Naz - o - re - an."

N. Jesus said,

J. "I have told you, I am he. If I am the one you want, let these men go."

N. This was to fulfill what he had said, "I have not lost one of those you gave me." Then Simon Peter, who had a sword, drew it and struck the slave of the high priest, severing his right ear. The slave's name was Malchus. At that Jesus said to Peter,

J. "Put your sword back in its sheath. Am I not to drink the cup the Father has given me?"

N. Then the soldiers of the cohort, their tribune, and the Jewish guards arrested Jesus and bound him. They led him first to Annas, the father-in-law of Caiaphas who was high priest that year. It was Caiaphas who had proposed to the Jews the advantage of having one man die for the people. Simon Peter, in company with another disciple, kept following Jesus closely. This disciple, who was known to the high priest, stayed with Jesus as far as the high priest's courtyard, while Peter was left standing at the gate. The disciplc known to the high priest came out and spoke to the woman at the gate, and then brought Peter in. This servant girl who kept the gate said to Peter,

Speaker "Aren't you one of this man's followers?"

N. He replied,

S. "No, not I."

N. Now the night was cold, and the servants and the guards who were standing around had made a charcoal fire to warm themselves by. Peter joined them and stood there warming himself. The high priest questioned Jesus, first about his disciples, then about his teaching. Jesus answered by saying:

J. "I have spoken publicly to any who would listen. I always taught in a synagogue or in the temple area where all the Jews come together. There was nothing secret about anything I said. Why do you question me? Question those who heard me when I spoke. It should be obvious they will know what I said."

N. At this reply, one of the guards who was standing nearby gave Jesus a sharp blow on the face. He said,

S. "Is that any way to answer the high priest?"

N. Jesus replied,

J. "If I said anything wrong produce the evidence, but if I spoke the truth why hit me?"

N. Annas next sent him, bound, to the high priest Caiaphas. All through this, Simon Peter had been standing there warming himself. They said to him,

All "Are you not a dis - ci - ple of his?"

N. He denied it, saying:

S. "I am not!"

N. One of the high priest's slaves – as it happened, a relative of the man whose ear Peter had severed – insisted,

S. "But did I not see you with him in the garden?"

N. Peter denied it again. At that moment a cock began to crow. At daybreak they brought

Jesus from Caiaphas to the praetorium. They did not enter the praetorium themselves, for they had to avoid ritual impurity if they were to eat the Passover supper. Pilate came out to them. He demanded,

S. "What accusation do you bring against this man?"

N. They retorted,

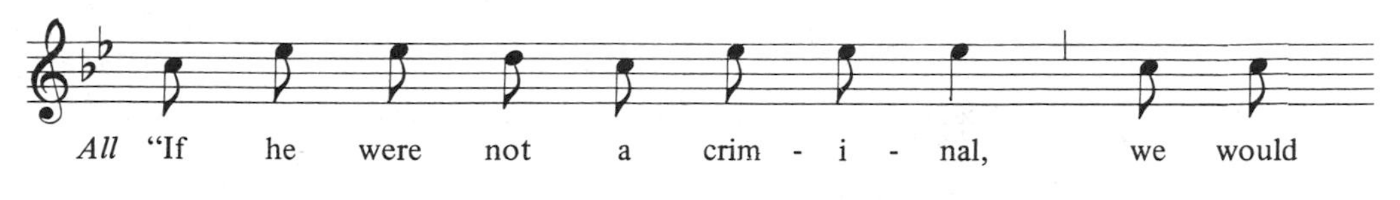
All "If he were not a crim - i - nal, we would

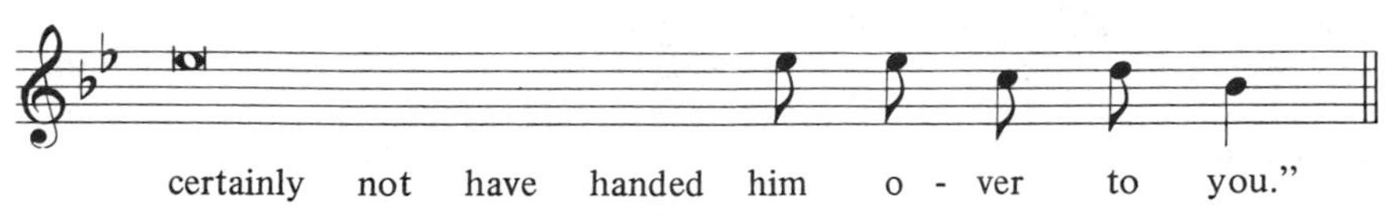
certainly not have handed him o - ver to you."

N. At this Pilate said,

S. "Why do you not take him and pass judgment on him according to your law?"

N. The Jews answered,

All "We may not put an - y - one to death."

N. This was to fulfill what Jesus had said, indicating the sort of death he would die. Pilate went back into the praetorium and summoned Jesus. He asked him,

S. "Are you the King of the Jews?"

N. Jesus answered,

J. "Are you saying this on your own, or have others been telling you about me?"

N. Pilate retorted,

S. "I am no Jew! It is your own people and the chief priests who have handed you over to me. What have you done?"

N. Jesus answered:

J. "My kingdom does not belong to this world. If my kingdom were of this world, my subjects would be fighting to save me from being handed over to the Jews. As it is, my kingdom is not here."

N. At this Pilate said to him,

S. "So, then, you are a king?"

N. Jesus replied:

J. "It is you who say I am a king. The reason I was born, the reason why I came into the world, is to testify to the truth. Anyone committed to the truth hears my voice."

N. Pilate said to him,

S. "Truth! What does that mean?"

N. After this remark, Pilate went out again to the Jews and told them:

S. "Speaking for myself, I find no case against this man. Recall your custom whereby I release to you someone at Passover time. Do you want me to release to you the King of the Jews?"

N. They shouted back,

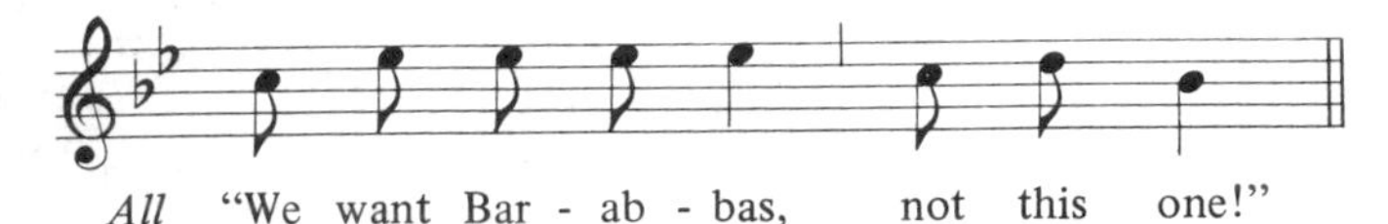
All "We want Bar - ab - bas, not this one!"

N. Barabbas was an insurrectionist. Pilate's next move was to take Jesus and have him scourged. The soldiers then wove a crown of thorns and fixed it on his head, throwing around his shoulders a cloak of royal purple. Repeatedly they came up to him and said, slapping his face as they did so,

All "All hail, King of the Jews!"

N. Pilate went out a second time and said to the crowd:

S. "Observe what I do. I am going to bring him out to you to make you realize that I find no case against him."

N. When Jesus came out wearing the crown of thorns and the purple cloak, Pilate said to them,

S. "Look at the man!"

N. As soon as the chief priests and the temple guards saw him, they shouted,

All "Cru - ci - fy him! Cru - ci - fy him!"

N. Pilate said,

S. "Take him and crucify him yourselves; I find no case against him."

N. The Jews responded,

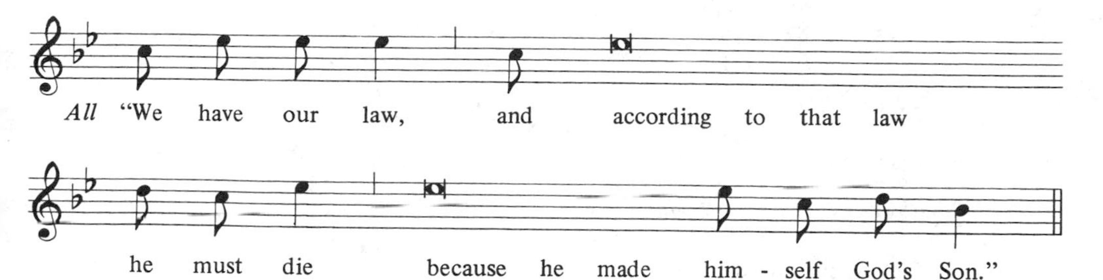
All "We have our law, and according to that law
he must die because he made him - self God's Son."

N. When Pilate heard this kind of talk, he was more afraid than ever. Going back into the praetorium, he said to Jesus,

S. "Where do you come from?"

N. Jesus would not give him any answer. Pilate asked him,

S. "Do you refuse to speak to me? Do you not know that I have the power to release you and the power to crucify you?"

N. Jesus answered:

J. "You would have no power over me whatever unless it were given you from above. That is why he who handed me over to you is guilty of the greater sin."

N. After this, Pilate was eager to release him, but the Jews shouted,

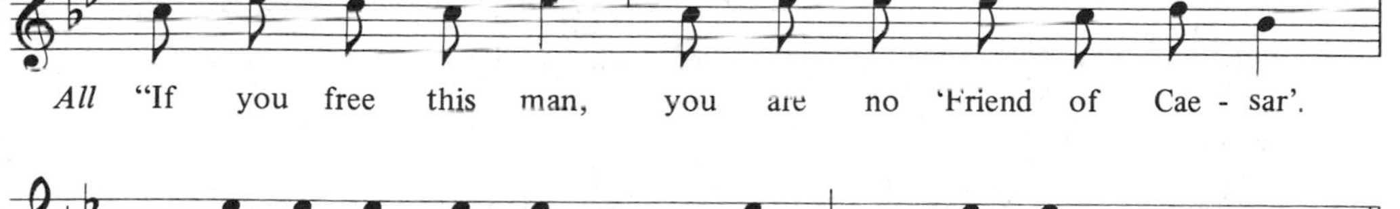
All "If you free this man, you are no 'Friend of Cae - sar'.

An - y - one who makes him - self a king be - comes Cae - sar's · ri - val."

N. Pilate heard what they were saying, then brought Jesus outside and took a seat on a judge's bench at the place called the Stone Pavement- Gabbatha in Hebrew. It was the Preparation Day for Passover, and the hour was about noon. He said to the Jews,

S. "Look at your king!"

N. At this they shouted,

All "A - way with him! A - way with him! Cru - ci - fy him!"

N. Pilate exclaimed,

S. "What! Shall I crucify your king?"

N. The chief priests replied,

All "We have no king but Cae - sar."

N. In the end, Pilate handed Jesus over to be crucified. Jesus was led away, and carrying the cross by himself, went out to what is called the Place of the Skull (in Hebrew, Golgotha). There they crucified him, and two others with him: one on either side, Jesus in the middle. Pilate had an inscription placed on the cross which read, "Jesus the Nazorean, the King of the Jews." This inscription, in Hebrew, Latin and Greek, was read by many of the Jews, since the place where Jesus was crucified was near the city. The chief priests of the Jews tried to tell Pilate,

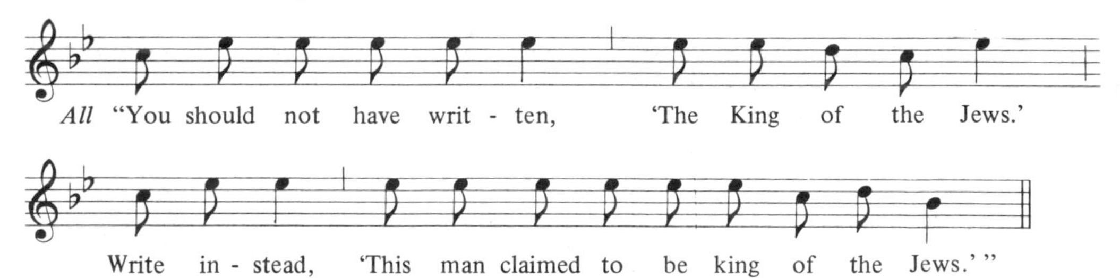
All "You should not have writ - ten, 'The King of the Jews.'
Write in - stead, 'This man claimed to be king of the Jews.' "

N. Pilate answered,

S. "What I have written, I have written."

N. After the soldiers had crucified Jesus, they took his garments and divided them four ways, one for each soldier. There was also his tunic, but this tunic was woven in one piece from top to bottom and had no seam. They said to each other,

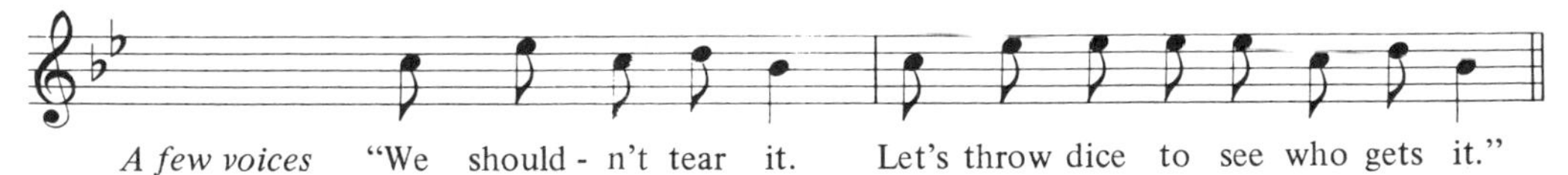
A few voices "We should - n't tear it. Let's throw dice to see who gets it."

N. The purpose of this was to have the Scripture fulfilled: "They divided my garments among them; for my clothing they cast lots." And this was what the soldiers did. Near the cross of Jesus there stood his mother, his mother's sister, Mary the wife of Clopas, and Mary Magdalene. Seeing his mother there with the disciple whom he loved, Jesus said to his mother,

J. "Woman, there is your son."

N. In turn he said to the disciple,

J. "There is your mother."

N. From that hour onward, the disciple took her into his care. After that, Jesus, realizing that everything was now finished, to bring the Scripture to fulfillment, said,

J. "I am thirsty."

N. There was a jar there, full of common wine. They stuck a sponge soaked in this wine on some hyssop, and raised it to his lips. When Jesus took the wine, he said,

J. "Now it is finished."

N. Then he bowed his head, and delivered over his spirit.

(Kneel and pause)

N. Since it was the Preparation Day the Jews did not want to have the bodies left on the cross during the sabbath, for that sabbath was a solemn feast day. They asked Pilate that the legs be broken and the bodies be taken away. Accordingly, the soldiers came and broke the legs of the men crucified with Jesus, first of one, then of the other. When they came to Jesus and saw that he was already dead, they did not break his legs. One of the soldiers ran a lance into his side, and immediately blood and water flowed out. This testimony has been given by an eyewitness, and his testimony is true. He tells what he knows is true, so that you may believe. These events took place for the fulfillment of Scripture: "Break none of his bones." There is still another Scripture passage which says: "They shall look on him whom they have pierced."

Afterward, Joseph of Arimathea, a disciple of Jesus, although a secret one for fear of the Jews, asked Pilate's permission to remove Jesus' body. Pilate granted it, so they came and took the body away. Nicodemus, the man who had first come to Jesus at night, likewise came, bringing a mixture of myrrh and aloes which weighed about a hundred pounds. They took Jesus' body, and in accordance with Jewish burial custom, bound it up in wrappings of cloth with perfumed oils. In the place where he had been crucified there was a garden, and in the garden a new tomb in which no one had ever been laid. Because of the Jewish Preparation Day they laid Jesus there, for the tomb was close at hand.

This is the gospel of the Lord.

H. Homily

I. General Intercessions. Response to all prayers is either: Amen; or as at No. 8 ORDER OF MASS

II. VENERATION OF THE CROSS

A. During the showing of the Cross, one of the following is sung three times with a prearranged interval between each repetition:

530 Behold the Wood of the Cross

Good Friday-for the Showing of the Cross

I.
Cel. This_ is the wood_ of the cross, on which_hung the Sav - ior
of_ the world._ All Come, _ let us wor - ship.

II.
Cel. This_ is the wood_ of the cross, on which_ hung the Sav - ior
of_ the world._ All Come, _ let us wor - ship.

III.
Cel. This_ is the wood_ of the cross, on which_hung the Sav - ior
of_ the world._ All Come, _ let us wor - ship.

B. During the veneration of the Cross, one of the following may be sung:

O My People

531

Lamentation for Good Friday

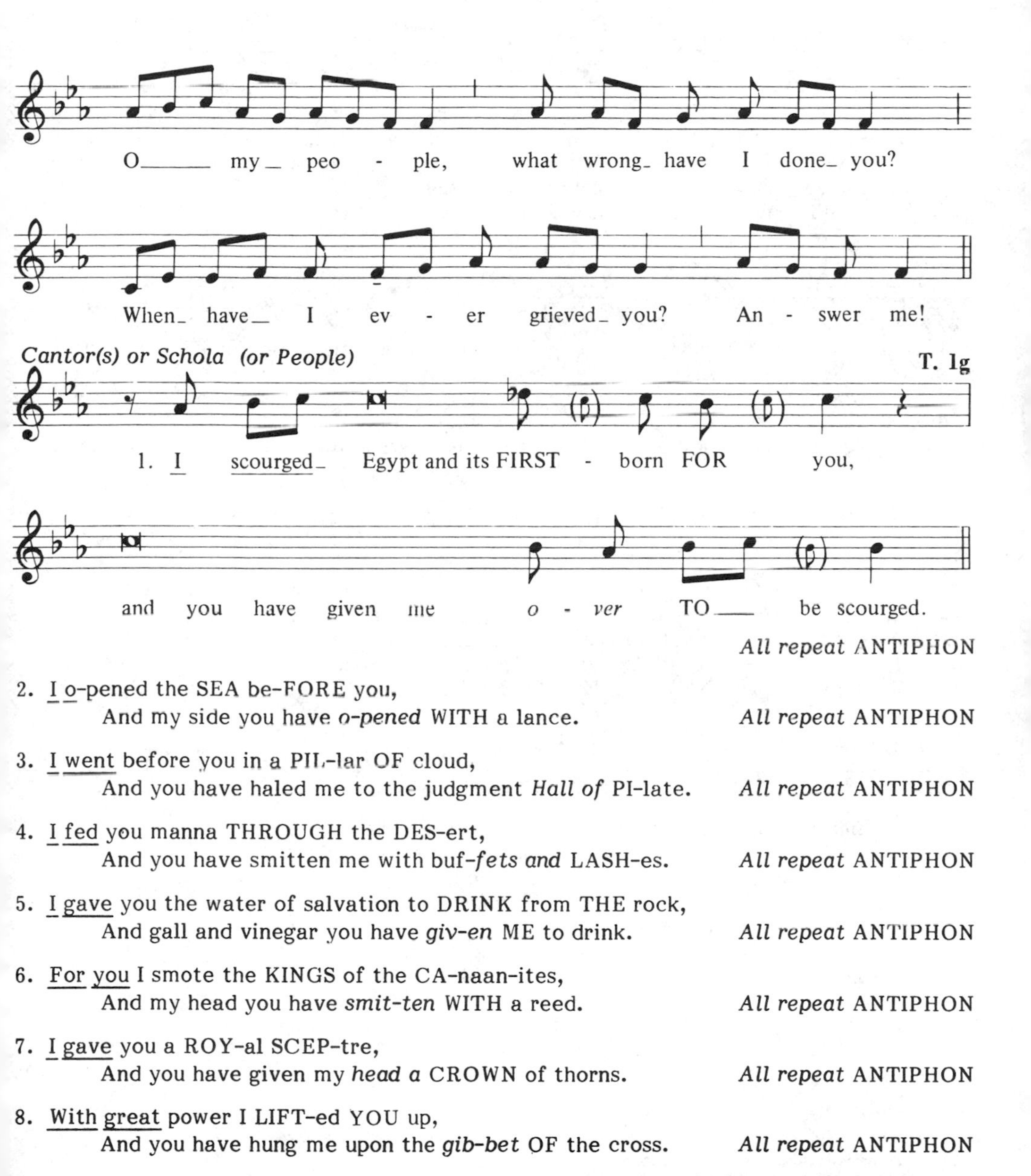
O my peo - ple, what wrong have I done you?
When have I ev - er grieved you? An - swer me!
Cantor(s) or Schola (or People)
T. 1g
1. I scourged Egypt and its FIRST - born FOR you,
and you have given me o - ver TO be scourged.

All repeat ANTIPHON

2. I o-pened the SEA be-FORE you,
   And my side you have *o-pened* WITH a lance. — *All repeat* ANTIPHON

3. I went before you in a PIL-lar OF cloud,
   And you have haled me to the judgment *Hall of* PI-late. — *All repeat* ANTIPHON

4. I fed you manna THROUGH the DES-ert,
   And you have smitten me with buf-*fets and* LASH-es. — *All repeat* ANTIPHON

5. I gave you the water of salvation to DRINK from THE rock,
   And gall and vinegar you have *giv-en* ME to drink. — *All repeat* ANTIPHON

6. For you I smote the KINGS of the CA-naan-ites,
   And my head you have *smit-ten* WITH a reed. — *All repeat* ANTIPHON

7. I gave you a ROY-al SCEP-tre,
   And you have given my *head a* CROWN of thorns. — *All repeat* ANTIPHON

8. With great power I LIFT-ed YOU up,
   And you have hung me upon the *gib-bet* OF the cross. — *All repeat* ANTIPHON

532 Faithful Cross-Sing, My Tongue

Choir FAITHFUL CROSS, O tree of beauty,
Noble tree, O tree divine,
Not a grove on earth can show us
Such a leaf and flow'r as thine.

SWEET THE NAILS and sweet the wood,
Laden with so sweet a load.

All *Gregorian Chant*

1. Sing, my tongue, the ___ Sav - ior's glo - ry; tell ___ his tri -
2. Eat - ing of the ___ tree for - bid - den, man ___ had sunk
3. Such the or - der ___ God ap - point - ed, when ___ for sin
4. So when now at ___ length the full - ness of ___ the sa -
5. All with - in a ___ low - ly man - ger, lo, ___ a ten -

1. umph far and wide; ___ Tell a - loud the fa - mous sto - ry
2. in Sa - tan's snare, ___ When our pit - y - ing Cre - a - tor
3. he would a - tone; ___ To the ser - pent thus op - pos - ing
4. cred time drew nigh, ___ Then the Son, the world's Cre - a - tor,
5. der babe he lies! ___ See his gen - tle Vir - gin Moth - er

1. of his bod - y cru - ci - fied; ___ How up - on the cross a
2. did this sec - ond tree pre - pare; ___ Des - tined, man - y a - ges
3. schemes yet deep - er than his own; ___ Thence the rem - e - dy pro -
4. left his Fa - ther's throne on high; ___ From a Vir - gin womb ap -
5. lull to sleep his in - fant cries! ___ While the limbs of God in -

1. vic - tim, van - quish - ing in ___ death ___ he died.
(Schola: Sweet the nails. .)
2. la - ter, that first e - vil ___ to ___ re - pair.
(Schola: Faithful cross. .)
3. cur - ing, whence the fa - tal ___ wound ___ had come.
(Schola: Sweet the nails. .)
4. pear - ing, clothed in our mor - tal - i - ty.
(Schola: Faithful cross. .)
5. car - nate round with swath - ing ___ bands ___ she ties.
(Schola: Sweet the nails. .) . . . (A - men. ___)

Text: St. Thomas Aquinas, +1274. Trans. anon.
Tune: *Pange lingua sacramentum.* Plainchant, Mode 3.

6. Thus did Christ to perfect manhood
    In our mortal flesh attain;
  Then of his free choice he goeth
    to a death of bitter pain;
  And as a lamb upon the altar
    of the cross, for us is slain.

(Schola: Faithful cross. .)

7. Lo, with gall his thirst he quenches!
    See the thorns upon his brow!
  Nails, his tender flesh are rending!
    See, his side is open now!
  Whence, to cleanse the whole creation,
    streams of blood and water flow.

(Schola: Sweet the nails. .)

8. Lofty tree, bend down thy branches,
    to embrace thy sacred load;
  Oh, relax the native tension
    of that all too rigid wood;
  Gently, gently bear the members
    of thy dying King and God.

(Schola: Faithful cross. .)

9. Tree, which solely wast found worthy
    the world's great victim to sustain,
  Harbor from the raging tempest,
    ark that saved the world again,
  Tree, with sacred blood anointed
    of the Lamb for sinners slain!

(Schola: Sweet the nails. .)

CONCLUSION – *Never omitted*

10. Blessing, honor everlasting,
    to th'immortal Deity;
  To the Father, Son and Spirit,
    equal praises ever be;
  Glory through the earth and heaven
    (to) Trinity in Unity. Amen.

(Schola: Faithful cross. .)
Sweet the nails. .)

N. B. Underlined syllables have two notes of the melody.

III. HOLY COMMUNION

A No. 30 or 31 OUR FATHER
No. 69 PATER NOSTER

B During the distribution of communion, the following, or suitable motets by the choir, may be sung:

No. 330 THINK OF THE SON OF GOD
No. 227 NOW, HIS YEARS OF LIFE PERFECTED

C Celebrant chants prayer after communion and prayer over the people.

All Amen.

Note: There is no recessional hymn.

533 Easter Vigil

Evening Vigil of the Resurrection
Order of Service

I. SERVICE OF LIGHT

A. Procession of ministers to front door or cross aisle of the church takes place in silence.

B. Instruction and blessing of fire. People respond to prayers: Amen.

C. Inscribing and lighting Easter candle.

D. Candlelight procession. Deacon, carrying the Easter candle while processing toward the altar, stops and chants three times on a higher pitch each time one of the following:

Deacon Lu - men Chri - sti. *All* De - o gra - ti - as.
OR:
Deacon Light_ of ___ Christ.___ *All* Thanks_ be to God.___

E. Deacon chants the Easter proclamation (Exultet). During the course of the proclamation he chants the introduction to the Eucharistic prayer.

No. 17 ORDER OF MASS (also Nos. 18, 19, 65)

At the end, all respond Amen as given at:

No. 27 ORDER OF MASS (also Nos. 28, 29, 68)

Candles are extinguished

II. LITURGY OF THE WORD

A. Instruction and first reading: Genesis 1.

Responsory: No. 438 SEND FORTH YOUR SPIRIT, LORD and PSALM 104 (I)
Celebrant chants prayer after each response. People answer: Amen.

B. Second reading: Genesis 22.

Responsory:

No. 368 KEEP ME SAFE, O GOD and PSALM 16

C. Third reading: Exodus 14-15.
Responsory: No. 474 I WILL SING TO THE LORD and EXODUS 15 (Moses' Canticle)

D. Fourth reading: Isaiah 14.

Responsory: No. 387 I WILL PRAISE and PSALM 30

E. Fifth reading: Isaiah 55.

Responsory: No. 476 WITH JOY YOU WILL DRAW WATER and ISAIAH 12

F. Sixth reading: Baruch 3.

Responsory: No. 371 or 372 LORD, YOU HAVE THE WORDS OF EVERLASTING LIFE and PSALM 19

G. Seventh reading: Ezekiel 36.

Responsory: No. 396 AS THE DEER and PSALM 42-43

H. GLORY TO GOD

No. 8 ORDER OF MASS or one of the following: No. 7, 44, 49, 55, 77, or 82
The church bells are rung during the singing of the hymn.

I. Prayer. All respond: Amen.

J. Epistle: Romans 6: 3-11.

K. Gospel acclamation.
No. 450 ALLELUIA and PSALM 118 may be used, or:

Alleluia **534**

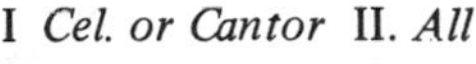
I *Cel. or Cantor* II. *All*

Al - le - lu - ia.

L. GOSPEL (Mark 16). Chanted responses given at:

Nos. 10-11 ORDER OF MASS

M. HOMILY

III. LITURGY OF BAPTISM

A. Instruction by celebrant. Litany follows immediately.

535 Litany of the Saints

PART I

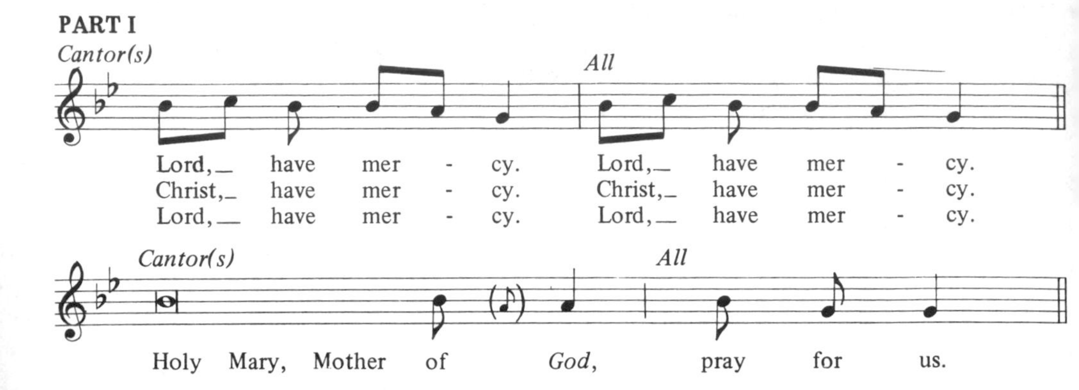
Cantor(s)
All
Lord,_ have mer - cy. Lord,_ have mer - cy.
Christ,_ have mer - cy. Christ,_ have mer - cy.
Lord,_ have mer - cy. Lord,_ have mer - cy.
Cantor(s)
All
Holy Mary, Mother of God, pray for us.

Saint Mi-chael,
Holy Angels of God,
Saint John the Bap-tist,
Saint Jo-seph,
Saints Peter and Paul,
Saint An-drew,
Saint John,
Saint James,
Saint Matthi-as,
Saint Mary Mag-dalene,
Saint Ste-phen,
Saint Igna-tius,
Saint Law-rence,
Saints Perpetua and Felic-ity,
Saint Ag-nes,
Saint Greg-ory,
Saint Augus-tine,
Saint Athana-sius,
Saint Bas-il,
Saint Mar-tin,
Saint Ben-edict,
Saint Ber-nard,
Saints Francis and Dom-inic,
Saint Francis Xa-vier,
Saint John Vian-ney,
Saint Cather-ine,
Saint There-sa,*

All holy men and wom-en,

* Names of the patron saint(s) of the church, of the localities and of the baptismal candidates may be added after tha Saint Theresa.

PART II

Cantor(s)

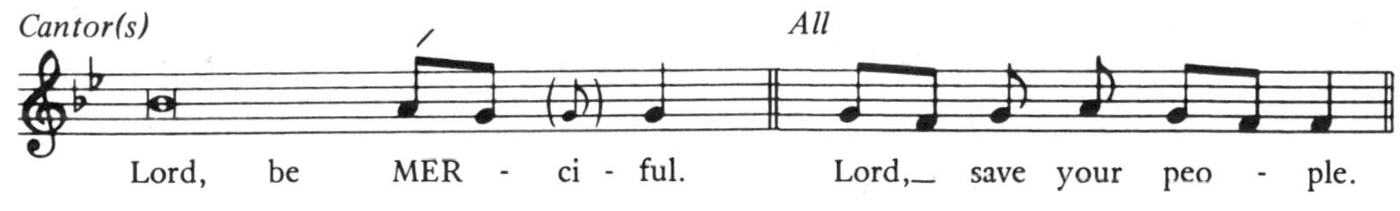
All
Lord, be MER - ci - ful. Lord,_ save your peo - ple.

From all E-vil,
From EV-'ry sin,
From ever-LAST-ing death,
By your coming AS man,
By your death and rising to a NEW life,
By your gift of the Holy SPIR-it,

PART III

Cantor(s)
All
Be merciful to us SIN - ners,
Lord, hear our prayer.

For the ordination of deacons, priests and the consecration of a bishop

Guide and protect *your* HO-ly Church,
Keep the pope and all the clergy in faithful ser-*vice* TO your Church,
Bring all peoples together *in* TRUST and peace,
Strengthen us in *your* SER-vice,

For Holy Orders - several candidates

Bless *these* CHO-sen men,
Bless these chosen men and make *them* HO-ly,
Bless these chosen men, make them holy, and consecrate them for their sa-*cred* DU-ties,

For a single ordination or consecration

Bless *this* CHO-sen man
Bless this chosen man and make *him* HO-ly,
Bless this chosen man, make him holy, and consecrate him for his sa-*cred* DU-ties,

For the Sacrament of Initiation (Baptism)

By the grace of baptism give new life to *these* CHO-sen ones,

For the blessing of the font (Easter Vigil) if there are no candidates

By your grace bless this font where your children *will* BE re-born,

Jesus, Son of *the* LIV-ing God,

Cantor(s)
All
Christ, hear us.
Christ, hear us.
Cantor(s)
All
Lord Je - sus, hear our prayer.
Lord Je - sus, hear our prayer.

B. Blessing of the water. At the end of the prayer all respond: Amen. The acclamation follows immediately.

No. 307 SPRINGS OF WATER - Antiphon only: I *Cantor(s)* II *All*

C. Instruction. Renewal of baptismal promises, baptisms and confirmations (if any) take place here. People respond to all prayers: Amen.

D. As the celebrant sprinkles the people with holy water, all sing:

No. 312 THE CHURCH'S ONE FOUNDATION, verses 1 and 2

Extinguish candles after the hymn.

E. General intercessions

No. 14 ORDER OF MASS

F. Presentation of gifts

No. 358 YE SONS AND DAUGHTERS OF THE LORD

IV. LITURGY OF THE EUCHARIST

Nos. 16-29 ORDER OF MASS

V. COMMUNION AND DISMISSAL

A. Nos. 30-38 ORDER OF MASS. One or more of the following hymns, psalms, or readings may be used for communion:

No. 145 CROWN HIM WITH MANY CROWNS
No. 434 ALLELUIA and PSALM 98(III)
No. 432 ALL THE ENDS OF THE EARTH HAVE SEEN and PSALM 98(I)
No. 568 LIGHT CONQUERS DARKNESS (Odes of Solomon XV)
No. 569 NEW HEAVEN AND NEW EARTH (Revelation 21-22)
No. 572 PRAISE AND THANKSGIVING FOR NEW LIFE AND HOPE THROUGH THE RESURRECTION OF JESUS (1 Peter 1: 3-9)
No. 39A ITE MISSA EST
No. 39 THE MASS IS ENDED

B. Recessional hymn. One of the following may be used:

No. 131 CHRIST THE LORD IS RIS'N TODAY!
No. 201 JESUS CHRIST IS RIS'N TODAY

Order of Service

Note: The selection and use of music may vary according to circumstances and the needs of the people. The titles given below are intended merely as guides in preparing the program for the ceremony.

I. RECEPTION OF CANDIDATES FOR BAPTISM

A. The organ plays while the people assemble.

B. An entrance hymn may be sung during the procession of the ministers to the place of greeting. One of the following is suggested:

No. 279 PRAISE, MY SOUL, THE KING OF HEAVEN
No. 255 O MY SOUL, BLESS GOD THE FATHER
No. 436 BLESS THE LORD and PSALM 103(1)

C. Greeting by the celebrant

D. Questioning of parents

E. Welcome into the church community

II. CELEBRATION OF GOD'S WORD

A. Procession to where the reading will take place. During this action one of the following may be sung:

No. 165 GOD IS MY STRONG SALVATION
No. 346 WE LOVE YOUR TEMPLE, LORD
No. 381 TO YOU DO I LIFT UP MY SOUL and PSALM 25(I)

B. Scripture reading

C. Responsorial psalm

No. 396 AS THE DEER LONGS FOR RUNNING WATER and PSALMS 42-43
No. 371 LORD, YOU HAVE THE WORDS OF EVERLASTING LIFE and PSALM 19(I)
Adults No. 400 REMEMBER YOUR LOVE and PSALM 51(1)
Children No. 384 BE ATTENTIVE, O LORD and PSALM 27(I)

D. Gospel acclamation

Outside Lent No. 95 ALLELUIA and verse for baptism
During Lent No. 90A Lenten acclamation and verse for baptism

E. Gospel reading

F. Prayer of the faithful

No. 14A or B or No. 63 ORDER OF MASS

G. Litany of the Saints

No. 535 LITANY OF THE SAINTS - Part I only

H. Prayer of exorcism

I. Anounting before baptism

III. CELEBRATION OF THE SACRAMENT

A. Procession to the font. During this action the following may be sung

No. 476 WITH JOY YOU WILL DRAW WATER and ISAIAH 12

B. Prayer at the font

C. Blessing and invocation of God over the baptismal water

D. Renunciation of Satan and profession of faith

E. The Baptism. During this action a short acclamation may be sung:

No. 307 SPRINGS OF WATER

F. Anointing with the chrism

G. Clothing with white garment

H. Lighting candle

I. Ephpheta, i. e., prayer over the ears and mouth

IV. CONCLUSION

A. Procession to the altar. During this action the following may be sung:

No. 452 HOW BLESSED ARE THEY and PSALM 119(I)

B. The Lord's Prayer

Nos. 30, 31, or 69 ORDER OF MASS

C. The blessing

D. Hymn of thanksgiving

No. 477 MY SOUL REJOICES and MAGNIFICAT
No. 230 or 231 NOW THANK WE ALL OUR GOD

E. Organ postlude

Order of Service

Note: The selection and use of music may vary according to circumstances and the needs of the people. The titles given below are intended merely as guides in preparing the program for the ceremony.

I. ENTRANCE RITE

A. The organ plays while the people assemble.

B. The entrance hymn may be sung during the procession of the bishop and ministers to the sanctuary:

No. 362 YOU CALLED ME, FATHER, BY MY NAME
No. 312 THE CHURCH'S ONE FOUNDATION

C. Sign of the Cross and Greeting

Nos. 1 and 2 ORDER OF MASS

D. Penitential Rite

No. 3 or 4 ORDER OF MASS

E. Glory to God *Omit during Lent.*

No. 7, 8, 44, 49, 55, 77, or 82 ORDER OF MASS

F. Opening prayer. All respond: Amen.

II. LITURGY OF THE WORD

A. First Scripture reading

B. Responsorial psalm. One of the following may be sung:

Nos. 428, 429, or 430 SING A NEW SONG TO THE LORD and PSALM 96(II), (III), or (IV)
No. 375 IN THE ASSEMBLY OF YOUR PEOPLE and PSALM 22(II)
No. 439 THE SPIRIT OF GOD IS UPON ME and PSALM 104
No. 377 I AM THE GOOD SHEPHERD and PSALM 23

C. Second Scripture reading

D. Gospel acclamation

Outside Lent No. 95 ALLELUIA and verse for Confirmation
During Lent No. 90A Acclamation for Lent and verse for Confirmation

E. Gospel reading

III. CELEBRATION OF THE SACRAMENT

A. Presentation of candidates

B. Homily given by the bishop

C. Renewal of baptismal promises

D. Imposition of hands. The bishop chants or recites a prayer to which all respond:

Bishop My dear friends. . . . . . through Christ our Lord.

All Amen.

E. Anointing of each candidate by the bishop. During this action, one of the following may be sung:

No. 135 COME, HOLY GHOST, CREATOR BLEST
No. 187 HOLY SPIRIT, COME AND SHINE
No. 340 VENI CREATOR SPIRITUS

F. General intercessions

No. 14 THE ORDER OF MASS

Note: The PROFESSION OF FAITH *is omitted*

IV. LITURGY OF THE EUCHARIST

A. During the presentation of the gifts, one of the following may be sung:

No. 268 O WORSHIP THE KING
No. 234 O BE JOYFUL IN THE LORD
No. 470 I WILL PRAISE YOUR NAME FOREVER and PSALM 145 (II)

B. Prayer over the gifts

All respond Amen

C. Preface responses and eucharistic prayer

Nos. 17-29 THE ORDER OF MASS, or 65-68

V. COMMUNION RITE

A. Nos. 30-33 THE ORDER OF MASS, or 69-71

B. Communion song during the distribution of Holy Communion:

No. 198 JESU, JOY OF MAN'S DESIRING
No. 211 LIFT UP YOUR HEADS, YE MIGHTY GATES
No. 324 THE KING OF LOVE MY SHEPHERD IS

C. Communion meditation. One of the following responsive readings is suggested:

No. 555 CHRISTIAN WITNESS (Ephesians 6)
No. 557 DUTIES TOWARD GOD (Sirach 2)
No. 578 THE BEATITUDES (Matthew 5)
No. 586 THE REWARD OF JUSTICE (Book of Wisdom 1)

The organ plays softly during the readings.

VI. BLESSING AND CONCLUSION

A. Bishop chants or recites prayers. People respond to each: Amen.

B. Bishop chants the blessing.

No. 37 (English) or 74 (Latin) ORDER OF MASS

C. Concluding hymn. One of the following is suggested:

No. 188 HOLY SPIRIT, EVER DWELLING
No. 100 A MIGHTY FORTRESS IS OUR GOD

D. Organ postlude

THE RITE OF CONFIRMATION OUTSIDE OF MASS

Same as above with some omissions. See below for suggested outline

I. ENTRANCE RITE. *Omit* D. *and* E. *Otherwise as given*

II. LITURGY OF THE WORD. *As given*

III. CELEBRATION OF THE SACRAMENT. *As given*

IV. LITURGY OF THE EUCHARIST. *Omit*

V. COMMUNION RITE. *Omit all except* OUR FATHER. *See* Nos. 30, 31, *or* 69

VI. BLESSING - PRAYER OVER THE PEOPLE. *As given*

Order of Service

I. GREETING TO MOURNERS

A. The organ plays while the people assemble
B. The organ plays while the ministers and celebrant process from the sacristy to place where the formal greeting will be given near the front door of the church
C. Celebrant chants or reads the greeting

No. 1 ORDER OF MASS

D. Celebrant chants prayer

People respond Amen

II. ENTRANCE RITE

A. At the conclusion of the greeting, the celebrant proceeds toward the altar. He is followed by the ministers and the pall bearers.

During this action the people are invited to join the cantor, or schola, in singing the processional hymn. One of the following is suggested:

No. 540 REQUIEM AETERNAM (Gregorian Requiem) - Introit - Kyrie
No. 157 FOR ALL THE SAINTS
No. 207 LIFT HIGH THE CROSS
No. 241 O GOD, OUR HELP IN AGES PAST
No. 539 SAINTS OF GOD *See below*

539 Saints of God

T.M.

Cantor or Choir
Saints of God, come_ to his her aid! Come_ to meet him, her, an - gels

All
of the Lord! Re-ceive his/her soul and pre-sent him/her to God
Cantor or Choir
the Most High. May Christ who called you take you to him-self;
All
may an-gels lead you to A-bra-ham's side. Re-ceive his/her soul
Cantor or Choir
and pre-sent him/her to God, the Most High. Give him/her e-ter-nal
rest, O Lord, and may your light shine on him/her for-ev-er.
All
Re-ceive his/her soul and pre-sent him/her to God the Most High.

540

Requiem Aeternam

Introit and Kyrie

Gregorian "Requiem"

Ré - qui - em* ae - tér - nam do - na e - is
Dó - mi - ne: et lux per - pé -
tu - a lú - ce - at e - is.
Ps. 65 (64)
Te de - cet hy - mnus De - us in Si - on, et ti - bi red - dé - tur
vo - tum in Je - rú - sa - lem:* ex - aú - di o - ra - ti - ó - nem me - am,
ad te o - mnis ca - ro vé - ni - et. Ré - qui - em

Ký - ri - e, e - lé - i - son.
Chri - ste, e - lé - i - son.
Ký - ri - e, e - lé - i - son.
Ký - ri - e, e - lé - i - son.

B. Celebrant chants the opening prayer. *All respond* Amen.

III. LITURGY OF THE WORD

A. Following the first Scripture reading, a psalm with an appropriate antiphon, or a psalm hymn may be sung. Whenever possible the people are invited to take part in this sung response to the reading. One of the following may be substituted for No. 541 on the next page:

No. 241 O GOD, OUR HELP IN AGES PAST
No. 165 GOD IS MY STRONG SALVATION
No. 384 BE ATTENTIVE and PSALM 27(I)
No. 396 THOUGH I WALK IN A DEATH-DARK VALLEY and PSALMS 42-43
No. 445 I SHALL WALK BEFORE THE LORD and PSALM 116(II)
No. 460 WITH THE LORD THERE IS MERCY and PSALM 130

Eternal Rest *Cantor and Schola* **541**

B. Before the Gospel reading, an acclamation is sung by all

542 Gospel Acclamations

Outside of Lent

Cantor sings ALLELUIA All repeat

T. 6
Al - le - lu - ia, al - le - lu - ia, al - le - lu - ia.

During Lent

T. 2
Praise and hon - or to you, Lord Je - sus Christ.

One of the following verses may be sung:

The Lord said: I am the ressurrection and the life,
He who believes in me will not die forever.

The souls of the just are in the hands of God.
They seemed in the view of the foolish to be dead, but they are in peace.

Blessed are the dead who die in the Lord, may they rest from their labors
For they take their works with them.

C. After the homily, the Prayers of the Faithful are either recited or chanted. If sung, one of the following may be used:

No. 14 or No. 63 ORDER OF MASS

IV. LITURGY OF THE EUCHARIST

A. During the presentation of the gifts, No. 543 on the next page may be sung, or one of the following:

No. 101 ACCEPT, ALMIGHTY FATHER
No. 121 BE THOU MY VISION
No. 216 LORD, THOU HAST SEARCHED ME
No. 306 SPIRIT SEEKING LIGHT AND BEAUTY

Pie Jesu

Gabriel Fauré *(For Cantor or Schola only)*

543

Pie Jesu, Domine, dona eis requiem sempiternam
(Loving Jesus, Lord, grant them rest eternal)

B. Celebrant chants prayer over the gifts. All respond: Amen.

C. Liturgy of the Eucharist continues as usual.
Nos. 17-29 ORDER OF MASS

V. COMMUNION RITE

A. Nos. 30-33 ORDER OF MASS

B. During the distribution of communion, No. 544 or 555 given below may be used, or one of the following may be sung:
No. 209 LET ALL MORTAL FLESH KEEP SILENCE
No. 324 THE KING OF LOVE MY SHEPHERD IS
No. 391 or 392 TASTE AND SEE and PSALM 34
No. 418 YOU OPEN YOUR HAND and PSALM 84(II)

May Light Eternal

Theodore Marier *(For Cantor or Schola only)*

544

May light eternal shine upon them, O Lord: with your saints forever, for you are merciful. Eternal rest grant unto them, O Lord, and let perpetual light shine upon them. With your saints forever, for you are merciful.

545

Ps. 23 (22)
Dominus Pascit Me

ANTIPHON: Lux aeterna (Es. 4:2, 35)

Gregorian "Requiem Mass"

Lux ae - tér - na lú - ce - at e - is, Dó - mi - ne,
May perpetual light shine upon them, O Lord,
cum san - ctis tu - is in ae - tér - num, qui - a pi - us es.
with your saints forever, for you are merciful.

PSALM 23 (22): 1-9

Dóminus pascit me; nihil mihi deest;
In páscuis viréntibus cubáre me facit.
Ad aquas, ubi quiéscam, condúcit me.
Réficit ánimam meam.

All repeat ANTIPHON

Dedúcit me per sémitas rectas
Propter nomen suum.
Etsi incédam in valle tenebrósa,
Non timébo mala, quia mecum es.

All repeat ANTIPHON

Virga tua et báculus tuus:
Haec me consolántur.
Paras mihi mensam
Spectántibus adversáriis meis;

All repeat ANTIPHON

Inúngis óleo caput meum;
Calix meus ubérimus est.
Benígnitas et grátia me sequéntur
Cunctis diébus vitae meae.

All repeat ANTIPHON

Et habitábo in domo Dómini
In longíssima témpora.

All repeat ANTIPHON

Glória Patri, et Fílio,
Et Spirítui Sancto.
Sicut erat in princípio, et nunc et semper,
Et in saécula saeculórum. Amen.

All repeat ANTIPHON

For translation of psalm, see No. 376

C. Celebrant chants communion oration

All respond Amen

VI. FINAL COMMENDATION AFTER MASS

A. The celebrant and ministers proceed to the bier. The celebrant chants the prayer. During the sprinkling with holy water and incensation, the following may be sung or:

No. 539 SAINTS OF GOD

I Believe That My Redeemer Lives **546**

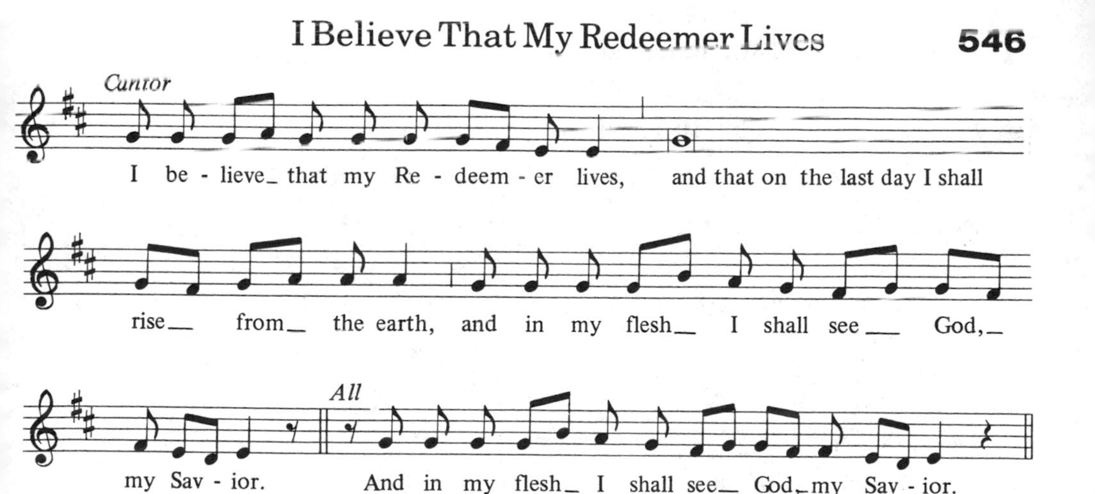
Cantor
I be - lieve_ that my Re - deem - er lives, and that on the last day I shall
rise__ from__ the earth, and in my flesh__ I shall see__ God,__
my Sav - ior.
All
And in my flesh_ I shall see__ God,_my Sav - ior.

Cont'd on next page

Cantor
It will not be some other be - ing, but I my - self who see him:
my own eyes shall gaze on him:
All
And in my flesh I shall see God, my Sav - ior.
Cantor
This hope of mine, I cher - ish in my heart.
All
And in my flesh I shall see God, my Sav - ior.
Cantor
I be - lieve that my Re - deem - er lives, and that on the last day I shall rise from the earth,
All
and in my flesh I shall see God, my Sav - ior.

B At the conclusion of the responsory, the Celebrant may chant the following:

547 Invocations of the Litany

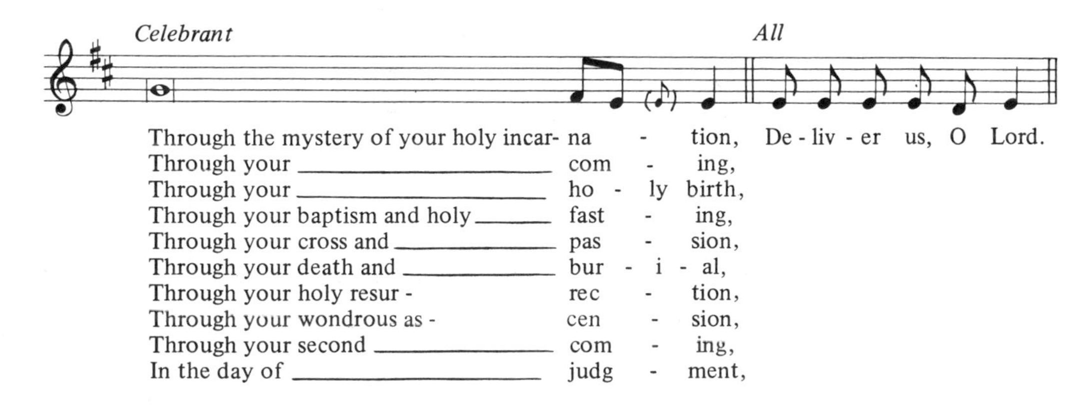
Celebrant
All
Through the mystery of your holy incar- na - tion, De - liv - er us, O Lord.
Through your com - ing,
Through your ho - ly birth,
Through your baptism and holy fast - ing,
Through your cross and pas - sion,
Through your death and bur - i - al,
Through your holy resur - rec - tion,
Through your wondrous as - cen - sion,
Through your second com - ing,
In the day of judg - ment,

C. Concluding prayer is chanted by celebrant. *All respond:* Amen.

D. During the recession, one of the following may be sung:

Outside of Lent

No. 204 JESUS, NAME OF WONDROUS LOVE
No. 157 FOR ALL THE SAINTS

During Lent

No. 207 LIFT HIGH THE CROSS

Any time

No. 539 SAINTS OF GOD
No. 548 IN PARADISUM
No. 549 MAY THE ANGELS

In Paradisum 548

See next page for translation of Latin text

In pa - ra - dí-sum de - dú - cant te an - gé - li In tu - o ad - vén - tu
su - scí - pi - ant te már - ty - res, et per - dú - cant te in ci - vi -
tá - tem san - ctam Je - rú - sa - lem. Cho - rus an - ge -
ló - rum te su - scí - pi - at, et cum Lá - za - ro quon -
dam páu - pe - re ae - tér - nam há - be - as ré - qui - em.

549 May the Angels

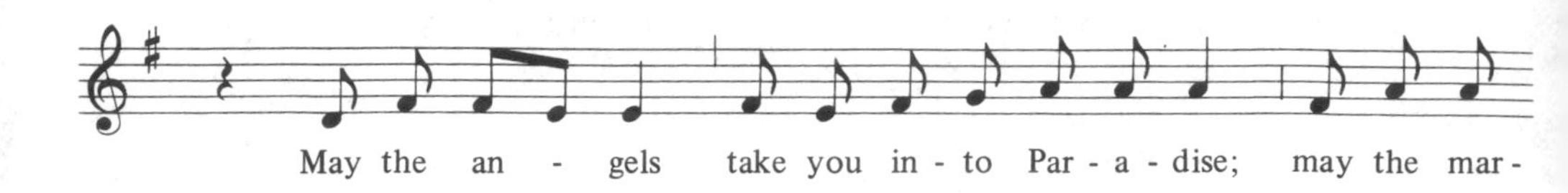
May the an - gels take you in - to Par - a - dise; may the mar -

tyrs come to wel-come you ___ on your way, and lead you in - to the

ho - ly ___ cit - y, Je - ru - sa - lem. May the choir ___

of an - gels wel - come you, and with La - za - rus who once was poor,

may you have ev - er - last — - — ing ___ rest.

See INDEX No. 610 *under* "Ordination" - Religious Professions *for additional hymns*

I. ENTRANCE RITE

- A. Organ prelude
- B. Entrance hymn - No. 103 ALL CREATURES OF OUR GOD AND KING
  - No. 218 LORD, WHO HAST MADE US FOR THINE OWN
  - No. 110 ALLELUIA, ALLELUIA! SING A NEW SONG TO THE LORD
  - No. 597 LORD, YOU GIVE THE GREAT COMMISSION.
- C. Greeting and penitential rite
  - *See* ORDER OF MASS - English or Latin
- D. Glory to God *See* ORDER OF MASS - English or Latin
- E. Opening Prayer *Bishop* Let us pray. . . . forever and ever.
  - *All* Amen.

II. LITURGY OF THE WORD

- A. First reading *See* LECTIONARY No. 769
- B. Responsorial psalm *One of the following is suggested.*
  - No. 428 GO FORTH INTO THE WORLD and PSALM 96 (II)
  - No. 441 YOU ARE A PRIEST FOREVER and PSALM 110
  - No. 445 THE CUP OF BLESSING or I SHALL WALK BEFORE THE LORD and PSALM 116 (II)
- C. Second reading *See* LECTIONARY No. 770
- D. Gospel acclamation

Outside of Lent	*During Lent*
No. 92 with Verse 3 or 4	Nos. 87 to 90 *inclusive*
No. 95 - *under* Holy Orders	LENT V (BC) "The Lord says. . ."

- E. Gospel reading *See* LECTIONARY No. 773

III. LITURGY OF ORDINATION

- A. Calling of candidates
- B. Presentation of candidates
- C. Election by the bishop and consent of the people
  - *All* Thanks be to God.
  - *Applause according to local custom*
- D. Homily
- E. Commitment to celibacy *Only for deacons who are preparing for ordination to the priesthood*
- F. Examination of candidates
- G. Promise of obedience
- H. Invitation to prayer and Litany of the Saints *See* No. 535
- I. Laying on of hands *Action done in silence*
- J. Prayer of consecration
  - *Bishop* Let us pray. . . .
  - *All* Amen. *See* ORDER OF MASS No. 27, 28, or 29
- K. *For deacons only* Investiture with stole and dalmatic

ANTIPHON Blessed are they who dwell in your house *with*
PSALM 84 (I) *See* No. 418

I. *Cantor or Schola* II. *All*

Bless - ed are they who dwell _ in your house, _ O _ Lord. _

L. *For deacons only* Presentation of the Book of the Gospels
M. *For deacons only* Sign of peace
ANTIPHON: If anyone serves me *with* PSALM 146 *See* No. 471

I. *Cantor or Schola* II. *All*

If an-y-one serves_ me, says_ the Lord, my Fa-ther in heav-en will hear_ him.

N. *For priests only* Investiture with stole and chasuble

Ps. 110

551 Dixit Dominus Domino Meo

I. *Cantor or Schola* II. *All* T. 8G

Ju - rá - vit Dó - mi-nus et non pae - ni - té - bit e - um.
The Lord has sworn *and will not change his mind.*

Tu_ es sa - cér - dos in ae - tér - num.
You are a priest forever.

PSALM 110: 1. 5.*

Dixit Dóminus Dómino meo;
Sede a dextris meis.
Jurávit Dóminus non paenitébit eum.
Tu es sacérdos in aetérnum secúndum
órdinem Melchísedech.
All repeat ANTIPHON

DOX. Glória Patri, et Fílio,
Et Spirítui Sancto.
Sicut erat in princípio, et nunc, et semper.
Et in saécula saeculórum. Amen.
All repeat ANTIPHON

**Psalm 109 in Latin Psalter*
N. B. *For English translation* *see* No. 441

O. *For priests only* Anointing of hands
No. 340 VENI CREATOR SPIRITUS
No. 135 COME, HOLY GHOST
No. 441 YOU ARE A PRIEST FOREVER and PSALM 110

P. *For priests only* Presentation of gifts
N. B. *In the Rite of Ordination of Priests, the gifts are brought up at this time and not later*
No. 347 WE REJOICE, GOD'S HOLY PEOPLE
See INDEX No. 610 *under* Presentation of Gifts *for additional hymns*

Q. *For priests only* Sign of peace
No. 394 I COME TO DO YOUR WILL, LORD and PSALM 40
or antiphon and psalm given below

ANTIPHON: You are my friends *with* PSALM 100 *See* No.435

I. *Cantor or Schola* II. *All*

You_ are my friends,_ says _ the Lord, If __ you do what I __ com-mand you.

IV. LITURGY OF THE EUCHARIST
A. Preparation of gifts *Only for Rite of Ordination of Deacons*
No. 347 WE REJOICE, GOD'S HOLY PEOPLE
See INDEX No. 610 *under* Presentation of Gifts *for additional hymns*
B. Prayer over the gifts
Bishop O Lord, . . . *All* Amen
C. Eucharistic prayer *See* ORDER OF MASS - English or Latin

V. COMMUNION RITE *See* ORDER OF MASS - Latin or English
A. The Lord's Prayer
B. Lamb of God
C. Communion meditation
D. Prayer after communion

VI. CONCLUDING RITE
A. Blessing of the bishop by the newly ordained *According to local custom*
B. Blessing and dismissal *See* ORDER OF MASS - Latin or English
C. Recessional hymn
No. 597 LORD, YOU GIVE THE GREAT COMMISSION
No. 230, 231 NOW THANK WE ALL OUR GOD
No. 107 ALL PEOPLE THAT ON EARTH DO DWELL
See INDEX No. 610 *under Thanksgiving*
D. Organ postlude

Order of Service

For alternate hymn settings, see INDEX No. 610 *under* Repentance, God's Mercy, Thanksgiving

I. ENTRANCE RITE
- A. Organ Prelude
- B. Entrance hymn. The following is suggested:
  No. 153 FATHER ALMIGHTY, POUR ON US THY BLESSING
- C. Sign of the cross and greeting
  Nos. 1-2, or Nos. 51-52 ORDER OF MASS
- D. Opening prayer

II. LITURGY OF THE WORD
- A. First reading: *See* LECTIONARY No. 886
- B. Responsorial psalm. One of the following is suggested:
  No. 383 AND FORGIVE ALL OUR SINS, O LORD and PSALM 24(III)
  No. 389 LORD, FORGIVE THE WRONG I HAVE DONE and PSALM 32
  No. 400 REMEMBER YOUR LOVE and PSALM 51(I)
  No. 420 YOU, O LORD, ARE GOOD AND FORGIVING and PSALM 86
  No. 460 WITH THE LORD THERE IS MERCY and PSALM 130
- C. Second reading: *See* LECTIONARY No. 887
- D. Gospel acclamation
  Outside of Lent No. 93 ORDER OF MASS Sentence No. 1
  During Lent Nos. 87-90 ORDER OF MASS Sentence for Ash Wednesday
- E. Gospel: *See* LECTIONARY No. 890
- F. Homily

III. LITURGY OF RECONCILIATION
- A. Examination of conscience
- B. Act of repentance and general confession
  No. 4 ORDER OF MASS
- C. Prayers of the faithful
- D. Individual confession and absolution. On Ash Wednesday, after receiving absolution, it is appropriate for all to come forward for the imposition of ashes-a sign of public penance-and to place a spoonful of incense on the burning coals of the thurible.
- E. Proclamation of praise for God's mercy. One of the following is suggested:
  No. 107 ALL PEOPLE THAT ON EARTH DO DWELL
  No. 230 or 231 NOW THANK WE ALL OUR GOD
  No. 202 or 203 JOYFUL, JOYFUL WE ADORE THEE
  No. 259 O PRAISE YE THE LORD
  No. 310 TELL HIS PRAISE IN SONG AND STORY

IV. CONCLUDING RITE
- A. Concluding prayer, blessing and dismissal
- B. Organ postlude

Order of Service

I. ENTRANCE RITE
- A. Organ prelude
- B. Processional hymn. *See* INDEX No. 610 *under* Praise
- C. Greeting and opening prayer

II. LITURGY OF THE WORD
- A. Scripture reading: 1 Samuel 3: 1-10
- B. Responsorial psalm
  No. 394 I COME TO DO YOUR WILL, LORD and PSALM 40
- C. Gospel acclamation
  Nos. 85-98 ORDER OF MASS
- D. Gospel: John 15: 1-8
- E. Homily

III. RITE OF INVESTITURE
- A. Blessing of surplices, crosses and hymnals

V. Our help is in the name of the Lord. *R.* Who made heaven and earth.
V. The Lord be with you. *R.* And also with you.
Celebrant Let us pray. O God, by whose word all things are made holy, pour out your blessings on these crosses, surplices and hymnals. Grant that whoever uses them in accordance with your holy will, your law, and with a spirit of thanksgiving may experience, by your power, health in body and protection in soul as he invokes your most holy Name. We ask this through Christ our Lord.
All respond Amen. *Celebrant sprinkles the surplices, crosses and hymnals with holy water*

- B. Presentation of choristers

Choirmaster Reverend Father, we ask that you invest and bless these choristers here present *(announces all names)*as members of the *(name of choir).* They have shown such zeal for the service of Christ that they have proved themselves worthy of this honor.
Celebrant God be praised. Bring the choristers forward.

Choristers form in rows in the sanctuary

- C. *Celebrant* My dear choristers, do you promise to serve Christ, our King, by attending faithfully and punctually all classes, rehearsals and services required of you, as long as you remain choristers in good standing in the *(name of choir)*?

Choristers Yes, with the grace of God, I will.
Celebrant Will you respect and obey those who are set over you and keep all the rules of the choir?
Choristers Yes, with the grace of God, I will.
Celebrant Let us pray. *Extends his hands over the choristers and continues.* O Lord, God almighty, behold and sanctify these your servants. Keep them in the holy fellowship of your saints through the mercy and loving kindness of your only begotten Son, Jesus Christ, who lives in unity with the Holy Spirit, and reigns as King forever.
All respond Amen.

Choristers come one by one to the celebrant. Each kneels before him, places his right hand in that of the celebrant, and says:

Chorister I consecrate my voice to God, to sing his praises and to proclaim his glory; and I promise to keep my heart and tongue pure so that I may always praise him more worthily.

Celebrant then invests each chorister with surplice and cross saying to each:

(Name. .), receive this surplice. Wear it with love and reverence before the altar of God that you may be found worthy to be numbered among the choirs of angels and saints. *Chorister* Amen.

Celebrant continues Receive this cross. Whenever you place it about your neck, keep in mind that it is the sign of your salvation and final victory. In the name of the Father, and of the Son, and of the Holy Spirit. *Chorister* Amen.

Celebrant continues Receive this book. May the inspired songs found in its pages help you to lift your heart and mind to God when you sing your praises to him. *Chorister* Amen.

After the last chorister has been invested, the choristers stand and sing REPLEATUR OS MEUM *as given on the next page. All respond* Amen.

Celebrant blesses the choristers, making the sign of the cross over them saying:

May God bless you and may he be the keeper of your hearts and minds, in the name of the Father, and of the Son, and of the Holy Spirit.

All Amen.

Celebrant then sprinkles the choristers with holy water. They process to the choir stalls singing:

No. 208 LET ALL THINGS NOW LIVING Verses 1 and 4

D. Anthem sung by choir

E. Prayers of the faithful

No. 14, 15, or 63 ORDER OF MASS

IV. CONCLUDING RITE

A. Dismissal and blessing

No. 34, 35, or 73 ORDER OF MASS

B. Recessional hymn

No. 207 LIFT HIGH THE CROSS

C. Organ postlude

Repleatur

For Choir Investiture

Re - ple - á - tur os me-um lau-de tu - a ut pos-sim can - tá - re;
Let my mouth be filled with your praise that I may be able to sing;

gau - dé-bunt lá - bi - a me - a dum can - tá-ve - ro ti - bi.
my lips shall rejoice when I shall sing to thee.

ORATION

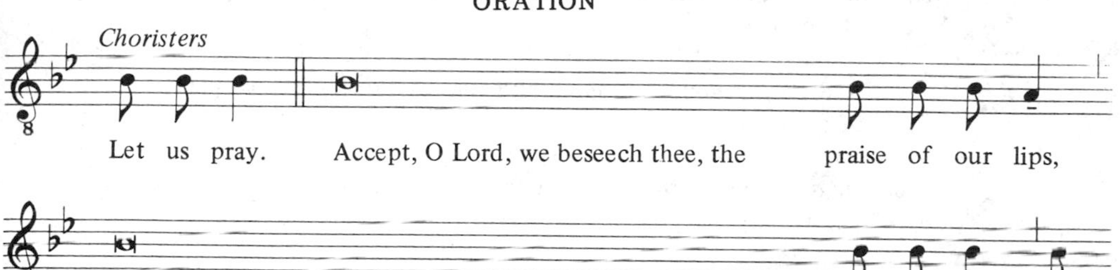
Choristers
Let us pray. Accept, O Lord, we beseech thee, the praise of our lips,
and through the intercession of thy saints Pius, Gregory and Cae - cil - ia, grant

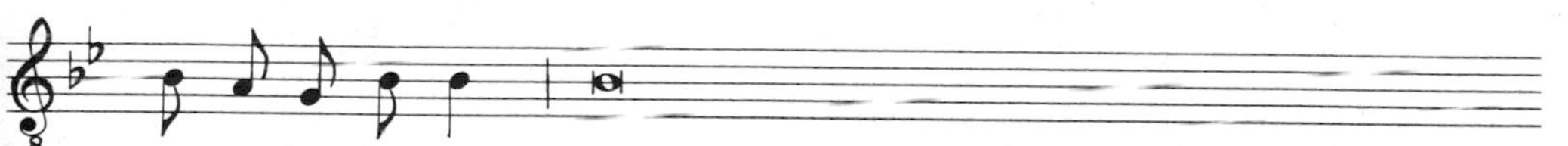
us in thy mer - cy, that the praises we offer thee during our pilgrimage here

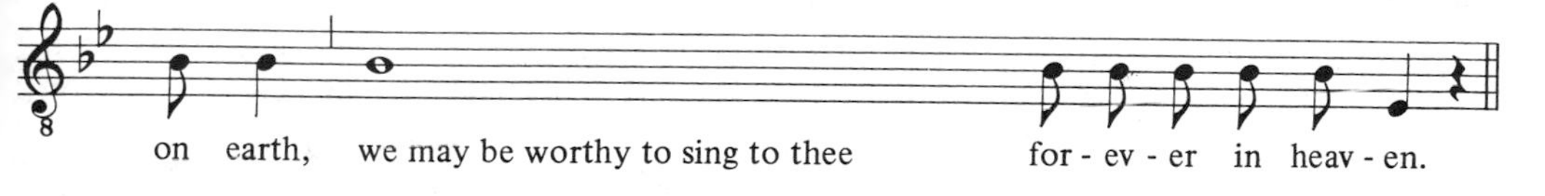
on earth, we may be worthy to sing to thee for - ev - er in heav - en.

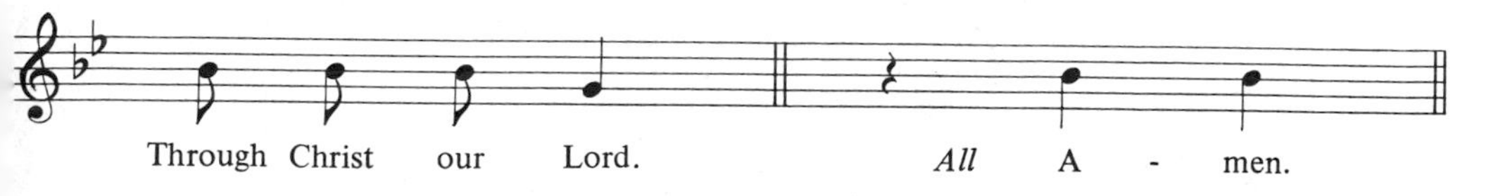
Through Christ our Lord. All A - men.

Text: Anon.
Tune: Plainchant, Mode 5.

555 Christian Witness

Ephesians 6:10-17.

Brethren, be strengthened in the Lord and in the might of his power.

> Put on the armor of God, that you may be able to stand against the wiles of the devil.

For our wrestling is not against flesh and blood, but against the Principalities and the Powers, against the world-rulers of this darkness, against the spiritual forces of wickedness on high.

> Therefore take up the armor of God, that you may be able to resist in the evil day, and stand in all things perfect.

Stand, therefore, having girded your loins with truth, and having put on the breastplate of justice,

> And having your feet shod with the readiness of the gospel of peace,

In all things taking up the shield of faith, with which you may be able to quench all the fiery darts of the most wicked one.

> And take unto you the helmet of salvation and the sword of the spirit, that is, the word of God.

Courage In Trial

Job 11: 7 - 19.

Can you penetrate the designs of God? Dare you vie with the perfection of the Almighty?

It is higher than the heavens; what can you do?
It is deeper than the nether world; what can you know?

It is longer than the earth in measure, and broader than the sea.

If he seize and imprison or call to judgment, who then can say him nay?

For he knows the worthlessness of men and sees iniquity; will he then ignore it?

Will empty man then gain understanding, and the wild jackass be made docile?

If you set your heart aright and stretch out your hands toward him,

If you remove all iniquity from your conduct, and let not injustice dwell in your tent,

Surely then you may lift up your face in innocence; you may stand firm and unafraid.

For then you shall forget your misery, or recall it like waters that have ebbed away.

Then your life shall be brighter than the noonday; its gloom shall become as the morning,

And you shall be secure, because there is hope; you shall look around you and lie down in safety,

And you shall take your rest with none to disturb.

557 Duties Toward God

Sirach 2: 1 - 9. 11.

When you come to serve the Lord, prepare yourself for trials.

Be sincere of heart and steadfast, undisturbed in time of adversity.

Cling to him, forsake him not; thus will your future be great.

Accept whatever befalls you; in crushing misfortune be patient;

For in fire gold is tested, and worthy men in the crucible of humiliation.

Trust God and he will help you; make straight your ways and hope in him.

You who fear the Lord, wait for his mercy, turn not away lest you fall.

You who fear the Lord, trust him, and your reward will not be lost.

You who fear the Lord, hope for good things, for lasting joy and mercy.

Compassionate and merciful is the Lord; he forgives sins, he saves in time of trouble.

Friendship of God

John 15: 1 - 15.

"I am the true vine, and my Father is the vine-dresser.

> Every branch in me that bears no fruit he will take away; and every branch that bears fruit he will cleanse, that it may bear more fruit.

You are already clean because of the word that I have spoken to you.

> Abide in me, and I in you. As the branch cannot bear fruit of itself unless it remain on the vine, so neither can you unless you abide in me.

I am the vine, you are the branches. He who abides in me, and I in him, he bears much fruit: for without me you can do nothing.

> If anyone does not abide in me, he shall be cast outside as the branch and wither; and they shall gather them up and cast them into the fire, and they shall burn.

If you abide in me, and if my words abide in you, ask whatever you will and it shall be done to you.

> In this is my Father glorified, that you may bear much fruit, and become my disciples.

As the Father has loved me, I also have loved you. Abide in my love.

> If you keep my commandments you will abide in my love, as I also have kept my Father's commandments, and abide in his love.

These things I have spoken to you that my joy may be in you, and that your joy may be made full.

This is my commandment, that you love one another as I have loved you.

Greater love than this no one has, that one lay down his life for his friends.

You are my friends if you do the things I command you.

No longer do I call you servants, because the servant does not know what his master does.

But I have called you friends, because all things that I have heard from my Father I have made known to you."

559 Emmanuel - God with Us

Isaiah 9: 1. 5. 6.

The people who walked in darkness have seen a great light;
Upon those who dwelt in the land of gloom a light has shone.

For a child is born to us, a son is given to us; upon his shoulder dominion rests.

They name him Wonder-Counselor, God-Hero, Father-Forever, Prince of Peace.

His dominion is vast and forever peaceful, from David's throne, and over his kingdom,

Which he confirms and sustains by judgment and justice, both now and forever.

Endurance Through Faith in God

560

James 1: 4 - 8. 12. 13. 17 - 20.

Let patience have its perfect work, that you may be perfect and entire, lacking nothing.

> But if any of you is wanting in wisdom, let him ask it of God, who gives abundantly to all men, and does not reproach; and it will be given to him.

But let him ask with faith, without hestitaion. For he who hesitates is like a wave of the sea, driven and carried about by the wind.

> Therefore, let not such a one think that he will receive anything from the Lord, being a double-minded man, unstable in all his ways.

Blessed is the man who endures temptation; for when he has been tried, he will receive the crown of life which God has promised to those who love him.

> Let no man say when he is tempted, that he is tempted by God; for God is no tempter to evil, and he himself tempts no one.

Every good gift and every perfect gift is from above, coming down from the Father of Lights, with whom there is no change, nor shadow of alteration.

> Of his own will he has begotten us by the word of truth, that we might be, as it were, the firstfruits of his creatures.

You know this, my beloved brethren. But let every man be swift to hear, slow to speak, and slow to wrath.

> For the wrath of man does not work the justice of God.

561 Fraternal Charity

Romans 12: 4. 5. 9 - 12. 20. 21.

For just as in one body we have many members, yet all members have not the same function.

So we, the many, are one body in Christ, but severally members one of another.

Let love be without pretense. Hate what is evil, hold to what is good.

Love one another with fraternal charity, outdo one another in showing honor.

Be not slothful in zeal; be fervent in spirit, serving the Lord, rejoicing in hope.

Be patient in tribulation, persevering in prayer.

Share the needs of the saints, practising hospitality.

Bless those who persecute you; bless and do not curse.

Rejoice with those who rejoice; weep with those who weep.

Be of one mind towards one another. Do not set your mind on high things but condescend to the lowly.

Be not wise in your own conceits. To no man render evil for evil, but provide good things not only in the sight of God, but also in the sight of all men.

But if thy enemy is hungry, give him food; if he is thirsty, give him drink; for by so doing thou wilt heap coals of fire upon his head.

Be not overcome by evil, but overcome evil with good.

God's Love for Us

1 John 4: 7. 9. 11. 12. 17 - 21.

Beloved, let us love one another, for love is from God. And everyone who loves is born of God, and knows God.

In this has the love of God been shown in our case, that God has sent his only-begotten Son into the world that we may live through him.

Beloved, if God has so loved us, we also ought to love one another.

No one has ever seen God. If we love one another, God abides in us and his love is perfected in us.

In this is love perfected with us, that we may have confidence in the day of judgment; because as he is, even so are we also in this world.

There is no fear in love; but perfect love casts out fear, because fear brings punishment. And he who fears is not perfected in love.

Let us therefore love, because God first loved us.

If anyone says, "I love God," and hates his brother, he is a liar.

For how can he who does not love his brother, whom he sees, love God, whom he does not see?

And this commandment we have from him, that he who loves God should love his brother also.

563

Imitating Christ's Humility

Philippians 2: 1 - 11.

If, therefore, there is any comfort in Christ, any encouragement from charity, any fellowship in the Spirit, any feelings of mercy,

Fill up my joy by thinking alike, having the same charity, with one soul and one mind.

Do nothing out of contentiousness or out of vainglory, but in humility let each one regard the others as his superiors,

Each one looking not to his own interests but to those of others.

Have this mind in you which was also in Christ Jesus,

Who though he was by nature God, did not consider being equal to God a thing to be clung to,

But emptied himself, taking the nature of a slave and being made like unto men.

And appearing in the form of a man, he humbled himself, becoming obedient to death, even to death on a cross.

Therefore God also has exalted him and bestowed upon him the name that is above every name,

So that at the name of Jesus every knee should bend, of those in heaven, on earth and under the earth,

And every tongue should confess that the Lord Jesus Christ is in the glory of God the Father.

Hymn of the Incarnation

The Odes of Solomon No. VII

The Lord has become like me,
in order that I might receive him;
He has reckoned like myself
in order that I might put him on;
And I trembled not when I saw him,
because he was gracious to me:

Like my nature he became
that I might learn from him,
And like my form,
that I might not turn back from him.

The Father has given the Word of knowledge
to be seen by those who belong to him,
That they may recognize him who made them,
and not suppose that they came of themselves:

For knowledge he has appointed as his way,
he has widened and extended it;
He has brought it to all perfection,
and has set over it the footprints of his light;
And I walked therein
from the beginning even to the end.

For by him was the path of knowledge made,
and it rested in the Son.

And the Most High shall be known in his saints
to proclaim the good news to those who have Songs of the Lord's coming,
That they may go forth to meet him,
and may sing to him with joy and the harp of many voices,

The seers shall come before him
        and they shall be seen before him;

And they shall praise the Lord for his love:
        because he is near and beholds:

And hatred shall be taken from the earth,
        and along with jealousy it shall be drowned:

For ignorance has been destroyed,
        because the knowledge of the Lord has arrived.

They who make songs
        shall sing the grace of the Lord Most High;
And they shall bring their songs,
        and their heart shall be like the day:
        and like the excellent beauty of the Lord their pleasant song.

And there shall neither be anything that breathes without
        knowledge, nor any that is without speech:
For he has given a mouth to his creation,
        to open the voice of the mouth towards him, to praise him.

(ALL:)
        O confess his power,
            and show forth his grace!

Love - the Greatest Commandment

1 Corinthians 13.

And I point out to you a yet more excellent way. If I should speak with the tongues of men and of angels, but do not have charity, I have become as sounding brass or a tinkling cymbal.

> And if I have prophecy and know all mysteries and all knowledge, and if I have all faith so as to remove mountains, yet do not have charity, I am nothing.

And if I distribute all my goods to feed the poor, and if I deliver my body to be burned, yet do not have charity, it profits me nothing.

> Charity is patient, is kind; charity does not envy, is not pretentious, is not puffed up.

Is not ambitious, is not self-seeking, is not provoked;

> Thinks no evil, does not rejoice over wickedness, but rejoices with the truth;

Bears with all things, believes all things, hopes all things, endures all things.

> Charity never fails, whereas prophecies will disappear, and tongues will cease, and knowledge will be destroyed.

For we know in part and we prophesy in part;

> But when that which is perfect has come, that which is imperfect will be done away with.

When I was a child, I spoke as a child, I felt as a child, I thought as a child. Now that I have become a man, I have put away the things of a child.

We see now through a mirror in an obscure manner, but then face to face. Now I know in part, but then I shall know even as I have been known.

So there abide faith, hope and charity, these three; but the greatest of these is charity.

566 Joy and Peace

Philippians 4: 4 - 9.

Rejoice in the Lord always; again I say, rejoice.

Let your moderation be known to all men. The Lord is near.

Have no anxiety, but in every prayer and supplication with thanksgiving let your petitions be made known to God.

And may the peace of God which surpasses all understanding guard your hearts and your minds in Christ Jesus.

For the rest, brethren, whatever things are true, whatever honorable, whatever just, whatever holy, whatever lovable, whatever of good repute,

If there be any virtue, if anything worthy of praise, think upon these things.

And what you have learned and received and heard and seen in me, these things practise. And the God of peace will be with you.

Invitation to Grace

Isaiah 55: 1. 6. 10 - 13.

All you who are thirsty, come to the water!

Seek the Lord while he may be found, call him while he is near.

For just as from the heavens the rain and snow come down and do not return there till they have watered the earth, making it fertile and fruitful,

Giving seed to him who sows and bread to him who eats,

So shall my word be that goes forth from my mouth; it shall not return to me void, but shall do my will, achieving the end for which I sent it.

Yes, in joy you shall depart, in peace you shall be brought back;

Mountains and hills shall break out in song before you, and all the trees of the countryside shall clap their hands.

In place of the thornbush, the cypress shall grow, instead of nettles, the myrtle.

This shall be to the Lord's renown, an everlasting imperishable sign.

568 Light Conquers Darkness

Odes of Solomon No. XV

As the sun is the joy to them who seek for its daybreak,
so is my joy to the Lord;
Because he is my Sun and his rays have made me rise up,
and his light has dispelled all darkness from my face.

In him I have acquired eyes
and have seen his holy day;
Ears have become mine,
and I have heard his truth.

The thought of knowledge has been mine,
and I have been delighted through the Lord.

The way of error I have left, and have walked towards him,
and have received from him salvation beyond measure.

And according to his bounty he has given to me,
and according to his excellent beauty he has made me.

I have put on incorruption through his Name,
and have put off corruption by his grace.

Death has been destroyed before his face,
and Sheol has been abolished by his word;

And there has gone up deathless life in the land of the Lord,
and it has been made known to all his faithful,

(ALL:)
and has been given without measure to all who trust in him.

New Heaven and New Earth

Revelation 21: 1 - 7. 22. 1. 3. 5.

And I saw a new heaven and a new earth. For the first heaven and the first earth passed away and the sea was no more.

> And I saw the holy city, New Jerusalem, coming down out of heaven from God, made ready as a bride adorned for her husband.

And I heard a loud voice from the throne saying, "Behold the dwelling of God is with men, and he will dwell with them.

> And they will be his people, and God himself will be with them as their God.

And God will wipe away every tear from their eyes. And death shall be no more;

> Neither shall there be mourning, nor crying, nor pain any more, for the former things have passed away."

And he who was sitting on the throne said, "Behold, I make all things new!"

> And he said, "Write, for these words are trustworthy and true."

And he said to me, "It is done! I am the Alpha and the Omega, the beginning and the end. To him who thirsts I will give of the fountain of the water of life freely."

> And he showed me a river of the water of life, clear as crystal, coming forth from the throne of God and of the Lamb.

And night shall be no more, and they shall have no need of light of lamp, or light of sun, for the Lord God will shed light upon them;

> And they shall reign forever and ever.

570 Ode of Trust

The Odes of Solomon No. V

I will give thanks unto you, O Lord,
        because I love you;
O Most High, you will not forsake me,
        for you are my hope:
Freely I have received your grace,
        I shall live thereby.

My persecutors will come
        and not see me:
A cloud of darkness shall fall upon their eyes;
        and an air of thick gloom shall darken them;
And they shall have no light to see,
        that they may not take hold upon me.

Let their counsel become powerless,
        and what they have cunningly devised
        let it return upon their own heads;
For they have devised a counsel,
        and it did not succeed;
They have prepared themselves for evil,
        and were found to be empty.

For my hope is upon the Lord,
        and I will not fear;
And because the Lord is my salvation,
        I will not fear:

And he is as a garland upon my head,
        and I shall not be moved;
Even if everything should be shaken,
        I stand firm;
And if all things visible should perish,
        I shall not die:

(ALL:)
        Because the Lord is with me,
                and I am with him.

Power of the Creator to Save His People

Isaiah 40: 12 - 14. 28 - 29. 31.

Who has cupped in his hands the waters of the sea, and marked off the heavens with a span?

Who has held in a measure the dust of the earth, weighed the mountains in scales and the hills in a balance?

Who has directed the spirit of the Lord, or has instructed him as his counselor:

Whom did he consult to gain knowledge?

Who taught him the path of judgment, or showed him the way of understanding?

Do you not know or have you not heard?

The Lord is the eternal God, creator of the ends of the earth.

He does not faint nor grow weary, and his knowledge is beyond scrutiny.

He gives strength to the fainting; for the weak he makes vigor abound.

They that hope in the Lord will renew their strength,
They will soar as with eagles' wings;

They will run and not grow weary, walk and not grow faint.

572 Praise and Thanksgiving for New Life and Hope Through the Resurrection of Jesus

1 Peter 1: 3 - 9.

Blessed be the God and Father of our Lord Jesus Christ, who according to his great mercy has begotten us again, through the resurrection of Jesus Christ from the dead,

> Unto a living hope, unto an incorruptible inheritance – undefiled and unfading, reserved for you in heaven.

By the power of God you are guarded through faith for salvation, which is ready to be revealed in the last time.

> Over this you rejoice: though now for a little while, if need be, you are made sorrowful by various trials,

That the temper of your faith – more precious by far than gold which is tried by firc –

> May be found unto praise and glory and honor at the revelation of Jesus Christ.

Him, though you have not seen, you love.

> In him, though you do not see him, yet believing, you exult with a joy unspeakable and triumphant;

Receiving, as the final issue of your faith, the salvation of your souls.

Promise of Salvation

573

Isaiah 40: 1 - 5. 9 - 11.

Comfort, give comfort to my people, says your God.

Speak tenderly to Jerusalem, and proclaim to her that her service is at an end, her guilt is expiated.

Indeed, she has received from the hand of the Lord double for all her sins.

A voice cries out: In the desert prepare the way of the Lord! Make straight in the wasteland a highway for our God!

Every valley shall be filled in, every mountain and hill shall be made low;

The rugged land shall be made a plain, the rough country, a broad valley.

Then the glory of the Lord shall be revealed, and all mankind shall see it together; for the mouth of the Lord has spoken.

Go up onto a high mountain, Zion, herald of glad tidings;

Cry out at the top of your voice, Jerusalem, herald of good news!

Fear not to cry out and say to the cities of Judah: Here is your God!

Here comes with power the Lord God, who rules by his strong arm;

Here is his reward with him, his recompense before him.

Like a shepherd he feeds his flock; in his arms he gathers the lambs,

Carrying them in his bosom, and leading the ewes with care.

574

Practice of Virtue

Colossians 3: 12 - 17.

Put on therefore, as God's chosen ones, holy and beloved, a heart of mercy, kindness, humility, meekness, patience.

> Bear with one another and forgive one another, if anyone has a grievance against any other; even as the Lord has forgiven you, so else do you forgive.

But above all these things have charity, which is the bond of perfection.

> And may the peace of Christ reign in your hearts; unto that peace, indeed, you were called in one body.

Show yourselves thankful. Let the word of Christ dwell in you abundantly;

> In all wisdom teach and admonish one another by hymns, psalms and spiritual canticles, singing in your hearts to God by his grace .

Whatever you do in word or in work, do all in the name of the Lord Jesus, giving thanks to God the Father through him.

Prologue of St. John Gospel

John 1: 1 - 14.

In the beginning was the Word, and the Word was with God: and the Word was God.

He was in the beginning with God.

All things were made through him, and without him was made nothing that has been made.

In him was life, and the life was the light of men.

And the light shines in the darkness; and the darkness grasped it not.

There was a man, one sent from God, whose name was John.

This man came as a witness, to bear witness concerning the light, that all might believe through him.

He was not himself the light, but was to bear witness to the light.

It was the true light that enlightens every man who comes into the world.

He was in the world, and the world was made through him, and the world knew him not.

He came unto his own, and his own received him not.

But to as many as received him he gave the power of becoming sons of God; to those who believe in his name.

Who were born not of blood, nor of the will of flesh, nor of the will of man, but of God.

And the Word was made flesh, and dwelt among us. And we saw his glory – glory as of the only begotten of the Father – full of grace and truth.

Continued on next page

576 Response to God's Gifts

James 1: 22 - 27.

Be doers of the word, and not hearers only, deceiving yourselves.

For if anyone is a hearer of the word, and not a doer, he is like a man looking at his natural face in a mirror:

For he looks at himself and goes away, and presently he forgets what kind of man he is.

But he who has looked carefully into the perfect law of liberty and has remained in it,

Not becoming a forgetful hearer but a doer of the work, shall be blessed in his deed.

And if anyone thinks himself to be religious, not restraining his tongue but deceiving his own heart, that man's religion is vain.

Religion pure and undefiled before God the Father is this: to give aid to orphans and widows in their tribulation, and to keep oneself unspotted from this world.

Suffering and Triumph of the Servant of the Lord 577

Isaiah 53.

Who would believe what we have heard? To whom has the arm of the Lord been revealed?

He grew up like a sapling before him, like a shoot from the parched earth;

There was in him no stately bearing to make us look at him, nor appearance that would attract us to him.

He was spurned and avoided by men, a man of suffering, accustomed to infirmity,

One of those from whom men hide their faces, spurned, and we held him in no esteem.

Yet it was our infirmities that he bore, our sufferings that he endured,

While we thought of him as stricken, as one smitten by God and afflicted.

But he was pierced for our offenses; crushed for our sins;

Upon him was the chastisement that makes us whole, by his stripes we were healed.

We had all gone astray like sheep, each following his own way;

But the Lord laid upon him the guilt of us all.

Though he was harshly treated, he submitted and opened not his mouth:

Like a lamb led to the slaughter or a sheep before the shearers, he was silent and opened not his mouth.

> Oppressed and condemned, he was taken away, and who would have thought any more of his destiny?

When he was cut off from the land of the living, and smitten for the sin of his people,

> A grave was assigned him among the wicked and a burial place with evildoers,

Though he had done no wrong nor spoken any falsehood.

> If he gives his life as an offering for sin, he shall see his descendants in a long life,

And the will of the Lord shall be accomplished through him.

> Because of his affliction he shall see the light in fullness of days;

Through his suffering, my servant shall justify many, and their guilt he shall bear.

> Therefore I will give him his portion among the great, and he shall divide the spoils with the mighty,

Because he surrendered himself to death and was counted among the wicked;

> And he shall take away the sins of many, and win pardon for their offenses.

The Beatitudes

Matthew 5: 3 - 12.

Blessed are the poor in spirit, for theirs is the kingdom of heaven.

Blessed are the meek, for they shall possess the earth.

Blessed are they who mourn, for they shall be comforted.

Blessed are they who hunger and thirst for justice, for they shall be satisfied.

Blessed are the merciful, for they shall obtain mercy.

Blessed are the clean of heart, for they shall see God.

Blessed are the peacemakers, for they shall be called children of God.

Blessed are they who suffer persecution for justice' sake, for theirs is the kingdom of heaven.

Blessed are you when men reproach you, and persecute you, and, speaking falsely, say all manner of evil against you, for my sake. Rejoice and exult, because your reward is great in heaven; for so did they persecute the prophets who were before you.

579 The Benedictus

Luke 1: 68 - 79.

Blessed be the Lord, the God of Israel, because he has visited and wrought redemption for his people,

And has raised up a horn of salvation for us, in the house of David his servant,

As he promised through the mouth of his holy ones, the prophets from of old;

Salvation from our enemies, and from the hand of all who hate us,

To show mercy to our forefathers and to be mindful of his holy covenant,

Of the oath that he swore to Abraham our father, that he would grant us,

That delivered from the hand of our enemies, we would serve him without fear,

In holiness and justice before him all our days.

And thou, child, shalt be called the prophet of the Most High, for thou shalt go before the face of the Lord to prepare his ways,

To give to his people knowledge of salvation through forgiveness of their sins,

Because of the loving-kindness of our God, wherewith the Orient from on high has visited us,

To shine on those who sit in darkness and in the shadow of death, to guide our feet into the way of peace.

The Disciple Speaks

The Odes of Solomon No. XIV

As the eyes of a son are to his father,
so are my eyes, O Lord, at all times towards you.

Turn not from me your mercies, O Lord,
and take not from me your kindness.

Stretch out to me, O Lord, at all times your right hand,
and be my guide, even unto the end,
according to your good pleasure,

Let me be well-pleasing before you,
because of your glory, and because of your Name.

Let me be preserved from evil,
and let your meekness, O Lord, abide with me,
and the fruits of your love.

Teach me the psalms of your truth,
that I may bring forth fruit in you;

And open to me the harp of the Holy Spirit,
that with all its notes I may praise you, O Lord.

And, according to the multitude of your tender mercies,
so you shall give to me.

The Hidden Counsel of God: On Suffering

Wisdom 3: 1 - 3. 5 - 7. 9.

But the souls of the just are in the hand of God, and no torment shall touch them.

> They seemed, in the view of the foolish, to be dead; and their passing away an affliction and their going forth from us, utter destruction. But they are in peace.

Chastised a little, they shall be greatly blessed, because God tried them and found them worthy of himself.

> As gold in the furnace, he proved them, and as sacrificial offerings he took them to himself.

In the time of their visitation they shall shine, and shall dart about as sparks through stubble;

> Those who trust in him shall understand truth, and the faithful shall abide with him in love;

Because grace and mercy are with his holy ones, and his care is with his elect.

The Praises of the Word in Creation

The Odes of Solomon XVI

As the work of the farmer is the plowshare,
and the work of the steersman is the guiding of the ship,
So also my work is the psalm of the Lord,
my craft and my occupation are in his praises:
Because his love has nourished my heart,
And even to my lips, his fruits he poured out.

For my love is the Lord,
and therefore I will sing to him;
For I am made strong in his praise,
and I have faith in him.

I will open my mouth,
and his Spirit will utter in me
the glory of the Lord and his beauty;
The work of his hands and the operation of his fingers,
the multitude of his mercies and the strength of his Word.

For the Word of the Lord searches out all things,
both the invisible and that which reveals his thought;
For the eye sees his works,
and the ear hears his thoughts.

He spread out the earth and he settled the waters in the sea;
he measured the heavens and fixed the stars;
And he established the creation and set it up;
and he rested from his works.

And created things run their courses, and do their works,
and they know not how to stand and be idle;
and his heavenly hosts are subject to his Word.

The treasure-chamber of the light is the sun,
and the treasury of the darkness is the night;
And he made the sun for the day that it may be bright,
but night brings darkness over the face of the land;
and their alterations one to the other speak the beauty of God.

And there is nothing that is without the Lord;
for he was before anything came into being.

And the worlds were made by his Word,
and by the thought of his heart.

(ALL:)
Glory and honor to his Name!

583

The Fountains of the Savior

The Odes of Solomon XXX

Fill waters for yourselves from the living fountain of the Lord,
for it is opened to you;
And come, all you thirsty, and take the draft;
and rest by the fountain of the Lord.

For fair it is and pure,
and it gives rest to the soul.

Much more pleasant are its waters than honey;
and the honeycomb of bees is not to be compared with it.

For it flows forth from the lips of the Lord,
and from the heart of the Lord is its name.

And it came infinitely and invisibly,
and until it was given in the midst they did not know it.

Blessed are they who have drunk therefrom,
and have found rest thereby.

The Last Discourse of Jesus

John 14: 1 - 4. 16 - 20. 27.

"Let not your heart be troubled. You believe in God, believe also in me.

In my Father's house there are many mansions. Were it not so, I should have told you, because I go to prepare a place for you.

And if I go and prepare a place for you, I am coming again, and I will take you to myself; that where I am, there you also may be.

And where I go you know, and the way you know.

And I will ask the Father and he will give you another Advocate to dwell with you forever,

The Spirit of truth whom the world cannot receive, because it neither sees him nor knows him.

But you shall know him, because he will dwell with you, and be in you.

I will not leave you orphans; I will come to you.

Yet a little while and the world no longer sees me. But you see me, for I live and you shall live.

In that day you will know that I am in my Father, and you in me, and I in you.

Peace I leave with you, my peace I give to you; not as the world gives do I give to you. Do not let your heart be troubled, or be afraid."

585

The Promise of a Messiah

Isaiah 11:1-5, 9.

A shoot shall sprout from the stump of Jesse, and from his roots a bud shall blossom.

The spirit of the Lord shall rest upon him: a spirit of wisdom and of understanding,

A spirit of counsel and of strength, a spirit of knowledge and of fear of the Lord,

And his delight shall be the fear of the Lord.

Not by appearance shall he judge, nor by hearsay shall he decide,

But he shall judge the poor with justice, and decide aright for the land's afflicted.

He shall strike the ruthless with the rod of his mouth, and with thc breath of his lips he shall slay the wicked.

Justice shall be the band about his waist, and faithfulness a belt upon his hips.

There shall be no harm or ruin on all my holy mountain; for as water fills the sea, the earth shall be filled with knowledge of the Lord.

The Reward of Justice

Wisdom 1: 1 - 7.

Love justice, you who judge the earth; think of the Lord in goodness and seek him in integrity of heart;

> Because he is found by those who test him not, and he manifests himself to those who do not disbelieve him.

For perverse counsels separate a man from God, and his power, put to proof, rebukes the foolhardy;

> Because into a soul that plots evil wisdom enters not, nor dwells she in a body under debt of sin.

For the holy spirit of discipline flees deceit and withdraws from senseless counsels; and when injustice occurs it is rebuked.

> For wisdom is a kindly spirit, yet she acquits not the blasphemer of his guilty lips;

Because God is the witness of his inmost self and the sure observer of his heart and the listener of his tongue.

> For the spirit of the Lord fills the world, is all-embracing, and knows what man says.

587 The Ten Commandments

Exodus 20; 1. 3 - 5a. 7. 8. 12a.

Then God delivered all these commandments: I, the Lord, am your God. You shall not have other gods beside me.

You shall not carve idols for yourselves in the shape of anything in the sky above or on the earth below or in the waters beneath the earth;

You shall not bow down before them or worship them.

You shall not take the name of the Lord, your God, in vain.

Remember to keep holy the sabbath day.

Honor your father and mother.

You shall not kill.

You shall not commit adultery.

You shall not steal.

You shall not bear false witness against your neighbor.

You shall not covet your neighbor's house. You shall not covet your neighbor's wife, nor anything that belongs to him.

True Happiness

588

Psalm 1: 1 - 6.

Happy the man who follows not the counsel of the wicked nor walks in the way of sinners, nor sits in the company of the insolent,

> But delights in the law of the Lord and meditates on his law day and night.

He is like a tree planted near running water, that yields its fruit in due season, and whose leaves never fade. Whatever he does prospers.

> Not so the wicked, not so; they are like chaff which the wind drives away.

Therefore in judgment the wicked shall not stand, nor shall sinners, in the assembly of the just.

> For the Lord watches over the way of the just, but the way of the wicked vanishes.

589 Unity in the Mystical Body

Ephesians 4: 1 - 7. 11 - 13. 31. 32.

I, therefore, the prisoner in the Lord, exhort you to walk in a manner worthy of the calling with which you were called,

With all humility and meekness, with patience, bearing with one another in love,

Careful to preserve the unity of the Spirit in the bond of peace:

One body and one Spirit, even as you were called in one hope of your calling;

One Lord, one faith, one Baptism;

One God and Father of all, who is above all, and throughout all, and in us all.

But to each one of us grace was given according to the measure of Christ's bestowal.

He himself gave some men as apostles, and some as prophets, others again as evangelists, and others as pastors and teachers,

In order to perfect the saints for a work of ministry, for building up the body of Christ,

Until we all attain to the unity of the faith and of the deep knowledge of the Son of God, to perfect manhood, to the mature measure of the fullness of Christ.

Let all bitterness, and wrath, and indignation, and clamor, and reviling, be removed from you, along with all malice.

On the contrary, be kind to one another, and merciful, generously forgiving one another, as also God in Christ has generously forgiven you.

Wisdom and Understanding

Job 28: Selected Verses

Whence comes wisdom, and where is the place of understanding?

It is hid from the eyes of any beast; from the birds of the air it is concealed.

The path to it no bird of prey knows, nor has the hawk's eye seen that path.

The proud beasts have not trodden it, nor has the lion gone that way.

The abyss declares, "It is not in me"; and the sea says, "I have it not."

Abaddon and Death say, "Only by rumor have we heard of it."

God knows the way to it; it is he who is familiar with its place.

For he beholds the ends of the earth and sees all that is under the heavens.

He has set a boundary for the darkness; to the farthest confines he penetrates.

He sets his hand to the flinty rock, and overturns the mountains at their foundations.

He splits the channels in the rocks; his eyes behold all that is precious.

Continued on next page

He probes the wellsprings of the streams, and brings hidden things to light.

He has weighed out the wind and fixed the scope of the waters;

When he made rules for the rain and a path for the thunderbolts,

Then he saw wisdom and appraised it, gave it its setting, knew it through and through.

And to man he said: Behold, the fear of the Lord is wisdom; and avoiding evil is understanding.

We are God's Children

1 John 3: 1 - 3. 18 - 24.

Behold what manner of love the Father has bestowed upon us, that we should be called children of God; and such we are.

This is why the world does not know us, because it did not know him.

Beloved, now we are the children of God, and it has not yet appeared what we shall be. We know that, when he appears, we shall be like to him, for we shall see him just as he is.

And everyone who has this hope in him makes himself holy, just as he also is holy.

My dear children, let us not live in word, neither with the tongue, but in deed and in truth.

In this we know that we are of the truth, and in his sight we set our hearts at rest,

Because if our heart blames us, God is greater than our heart and knows all things.

Beloved, if our heart does not condemn us, we have confidence towards God,

And whatever we ask, we shall receive from him, because we keep his commandments and do those things that are pleasing in his sight.

And this is his commandment, that we should believe in the name of his Son, Jesus Christ, and love one another, even as he gave us commandment.

And he who keeps his commandments abides in God, and God in him.

And in this we know that he abides in us, by the Spirit whom he has given us.

592 Truth Speaks Inwardly

The Following of Christ

That the truth speaks inwardly without the sound of words.

The children of Israel said of old to Moses: "Speak thou to us, and we will hear. Let not the Lord speak to us lest we die." *(Exod. 20, 19)*

I do not pray thus, O Lord, I do not pray thus; but with the prophet Samuel, I humbly say: "Speak, Lord, for Thy servant heareth."

And let not Moses speak to me nor any of the prophets; but do You speak to me, Lord God, You who inspire and enlighten all the prophets.

For You alone can fully instruct me without them; but they can accomplish nothing without You.

They may utter fine words, but they cannot give the spirit; they say beautiful things, but when You are silent they cannot inflame the heart.

They teach us the letter; but You unfold its meaning.

They bring forth spiritual mysteries; but You impart the understanding of their secret.

They teach the commandments; but You give grace and strength to observe them.

They show the way; but You give strength to follow it.

They work only outwardly; but You teach and enlighten the heart.

They water the plants outwardly; but You give them fruitfulness.

They cry with words; but You give understanding to the hearing.

Therefore, let not Moses speak to me, but do You speak to me, O Lord my God, Eternal Truth, lest I die and remain unfruitful if I am admonished only outwardly and am not inflamed within;

Lest it turn to my damnation, if I hear the word of God and do not fulfill it; if I know the word of God and do not love it; if I believe the word of God and do not keep it.

Therefore, "Speak, O Lord, for Thy servant heareth"; Thou hast the words of eternal life." *(John 6, 69)*

Speak within me for some comfort of my soul, and for a complete amendment of my life, and for Your eternal praise and honor. Amen.

An Invitation to the Lord's Table

The Following of Christ

Come to Me, all you that labor and are burdened, and I will refresh you, says the Lord. *(Matt. XI, 28)*

The bread that I will give is My flesh, for the life of the world. *(John VI, 52)*

Take you and eat: This is My Body, which shall be delivered for you. This do for the commemoration of Me. *(I Cor. XI, 14)*

He that eats My flesh and drinks My blood abides in Me and I in him. *(John VI, 57)*

Come to My table, you are called and invited.

Come to Me now and despise Me not, lest you be despised by Me hereafter, lest you may have to hear then the words: Depart from Me. *(Matt. XXV, 41)*

Come to Me who love you from the heart, and who out of love for you have paid the price. It is good to come to My inn; all is paid and settled; be cheerful and happy at My expense.

Enter freely, not only you, but come to Me, all of you, cleric and lay, good and bad, poor and rich.

No matter who you are, come to Me, all of you who labor in the work of penance, who are heavily troubled with temptations; come and I will refresh you and take away the burden of your temptations.

I will feed you with My sacred Body and refresh you with My Blood; I will cheer you and comfort you, so that you may forget all your woes and sorrows.

Come to Me, especially all of you who lead a sinful life and are overladen with guilt.

Be converted and come to Me with all your heart. *(Joel II, 12)*

For My Father has not sent Me to judge the world, but to save the world. *(John XII, 47)*

And therefore, fear Me not, come all of you without exception.

I will gladly forgive your sins. I will remit the punishment you have deserved, for My Father has committed all judgment to Me. *(John V, 22)*

Come then to Me. I will refresh you with My own self. I will give you My Flesh to eat and My Blood to drink. Eat and drink and be filled, My dearest children!

Incline your ears and hearken to Me and receive Me. *(Ps. XLIV, 11)*

Forget your people and your father's house. *(Ps. XLIV, 11)*

Forget the world and forsake all that is in the world.

Abandon your former sinful life and cling to me.

Place your faith, your hope, your comfort and your life in Me.

And then shall I, your Lord, your God, your Spouse, desire your beauty and unite you unto Me. *(Ps. XLIV, 12)*

Hear the voice of your Lord today, wait not till tomorrow; and harden not your hearts. *(Ps. XCIV, 8)*

Hear your Saviour Who has made you for Himself, that you might enjoy Him forever; Who has bought you with a great price, that He might possess you as His own. *(I Cor. VI, 20)*

Come! I will give Myself to you as food for your soul and as an eternal reward.

594 The Brave Flags of Our King

Vexilla Regis

The brave flags of our King unfold
 The dazzling riddle of the Cross:
Our King on whom all life depends
 Bore death that life might have no end.

Heart severed by the murderous wedge
 Of the thong-driven soldier's lance,
He poured out floods of water and blood
 To wash the filth off us of sins.

That noble tree, shot through with light,
 Fall-red with coins of kingly blood,
Was deemed the fittest of its stock
 To touch the flesh in which God stood.

O Cross, our sole and only hope,
 Now Passiontide has come again,
Enlarge with grace all good men's scope
 And free our souls enslaved by sin.

O Spring of Healing, Trinity,
 Let each soul praise you in its way.
On those your cross brought victory
 Lavish the price beyond all pay.

Trans. by William Alfred

Alleluia, Veni Sancte Spiritus

595

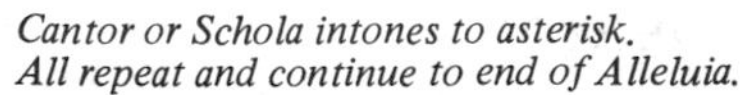

Cantor or Schola intones to asterisk.
All repeat and continue to end of Alleluia.

Pentecost Sunday

Al - le - lu - ia.*

Cantor(s) or Schola
Ve - ni San-cte Spí -

- ri - tus, re-ple tu-ó - rum cor-da fi-dé - li - um:

et tu-i a - mó - - - - - - -

All
- - - ris in e - is i - gnem* ac - cén - de.

All: Alleluia

Text: Anon.
Tune: Plainchant, Mode 2.

596

Father, Lord of Earth and Heaven

1. Fa - ther, Lord of earth and heav - en, God the ho - ly, God the strong,
2. Christ, our king, our priest, our proph - et, Sealed as God's_be - lov - ed Son,
3. Priest of heav - en, send your Spir - it, Ho - ly priest-hood's ho - ly seal;
4. Give us joy, O Ho - ly Spir - it, Joy that once_on Christ you shed;

1. Bless these gifts with grace and heal - ing, King to whom_all gifts be - long.
2. With your chrism a - noint your peo - ple, Make them ho - ly, keep them one.
3. Bless this oil by which, Good Shep - herd, Cho - sen shep - herds you re - veal.
4. Send us out as God's true ser - vants, One with Christ,_our glo - rious end.

1. Christ, our lead - er, sin - gle - hand - ed You have brought us vic - to - ry;
2. Christ, our light, our joy, our_ glo - ry, Strength - en us with heav'n-ly grace;
3. Christ, our heal - er, in your_ mer - cy Raise us up and make us whole;
4. Be a - mong us, God our_ Fa - ther, Be a - mong us, God the Son,

1. Bless this oil_ to keep your peo - ple Strong and watch - ful,_ bold and free.
2. Build us as_ your ho - ly tem - ple, God the Spir - it's_ dwell-ing place.
3. Bless this oil_ to bring your peo - ple Health of bod - y,_ peace of soul.
4. Be a - mong_us, Ho - ly Spir - it; Dwell with - in_ us,_ make us one.

Text: J. Quinn, S. J.,
Tune: *Sunrise*, "Trier Gesangbuch", 1695.

Lord, You Give the Great Commission 597

1. Lord, you give the great com-mis - sion: "Heal the sick and_ preach the word."
2. Lord, you call us to your ser - vice: "In my name bap - tize and teach."
3. Lord, you make the com - mon ho - ly, "This my bod - y,__ this my blood."
4. Lord, you bless with words as - sur - ing: "I am with you_ to the end."

1. Lest the Church ne - glect its mis - sion And the gos - pel go un - heard,
2. That the world may trust your prom - ise, Life a - bun - dant meant for each,
3. Let your priests for earth's true glo - ry, Dai - ly lift life heav - en - ward,
4. Faith and hope and love re - stor - ing, May we serve as you in - tend,

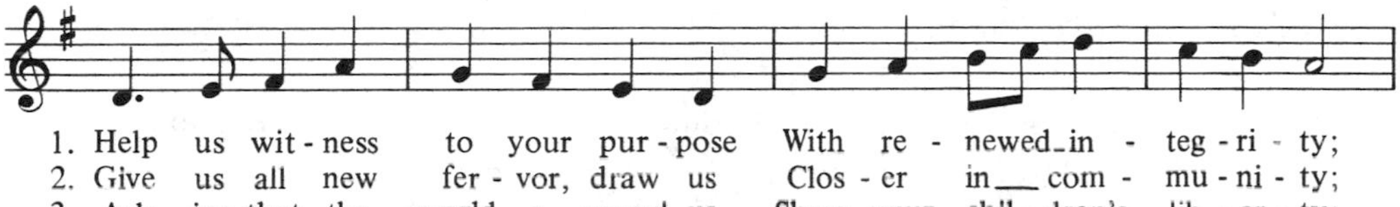

1. Help us wit - ness to your pur - pose With re - newed_in - teg - ri - ty;
2. Give us all new fer - vor, draw us Clos - er in__ com - mu - ni - ty;
3. Ask - ing that the world a - round us Share your chil - dren's lib - er - ty;
4. And, a - mid the cares that claim us, Hold in mind_ e - ter - ni - ty;

1.-4. With the Spir - it's gifts em-power us For the work of min - is - try.

Tune: *Rex Gloriae,* H. Smart, +1879.

We Believe *For Choir only* 598

INDICES

599. . . . . Responsorial Psalms and Antiphons for: ABC Yearly Liturgical Cycles: All Sundays and Solemnities with Selected Appropriate Hymns — *See* Choir Edition

600. . . . . Proper of Saints: All Solemnities, Feasts and Memorials — *See* Choir Edition

601. . . . . Weekday Liturgical Cycles — *See* Choir Edition

602. . . . . Common, Ritual Masses, Masses for Various Occasions, Votive Masses — *See* Choir Edition

603. . . . . Numerical List of Psalms, Antiphons and Psalm Hymns — *See* pages 613-622

604. . . . . Alphabetical List of Hymn Tunes — *See* pages 623-624

605. . . . . Metrical Index of Hymn Tunes — *See* Choir Edition

606A. . . . Gregorian Chants — *See* Choir Edition

606B. . . . Psalm Tones by Modes and Endings — *See* Choir Edition

607. . . . . Readings from Scripture and Other Sources — *See* page 625

608. . . . . Authors, Translators and Text Sources — *See* Choir Edition

609. . . . . Composers, Arrangers and Music Sources — *See* Choir Edition

610. . . . . Topical Index of Seasonal Hymns and Uses — *See* Choir Edition

611. . . . . Alphabetical List of Antiphons, Responses, Responsories, Refrains, Canticles, and Invitatories — *See* Choir Edition

612. . . . . Alphabetical List of First Lines of Hymns and Common Titles — *See* pages 626-628

1 **Happy Are They Who Follow Not the Counsel of the Wicked** 363
Happy are they who hope in the Lord

4 **O My Just God, When I Call, Answer Me** 364
O Lord, let your face shine on us

4 **When I Call Answer Me** 505
A: In the silent hours of night
B: Alleluia (Eastertide)

8 **When I Behold Your Heavens** 365
O Lord, our God, how wonderful your name
O How Glorious, Full of Wonder 243

13 **But I Have Trusted in Thy Steadfast Love** 366
With delight I rejoice in the Lord

15 **They Who Walk Blamelessly** 367
They who do justice will live

16 **Keep Me, O God, for in You I Take Refuge** 368
A: You are my inheritance, O Lord
B: Lord, you will show us the path of life
C: Keep me safe, O God, you are my hope

17 **Hear, O Lord, a Just Cause** 369
O Lord, when your glory appears

18 **I Love You, O Lord, My Strength** 370
I Love you, O Lord, my strength

19(I) **The Law of the Lord Is Perfect** 371
Lord, you have the words of everlasting life
The Perfect Law of God 327

19(II) **The Law of the Lord Is Perfect** 372
A: You, Lord, have the words of everlasting life
B: Your words, Lord, are spirit and life
The Perfect Law of God 327

19(III) **The Heavens Declare the Glory of God** 373
A: Their message goes out to all the earth
B: The precepts of the Lord give joy to the heart
The Perfect Law of God 327

22(I) **All You Who See Me Scoff at Me** 374
My God, my God, why have you forsaken me?
My God, My God, O Hear My Plea 225

22(II) **I Will Fulfill My Vows** 375
In the assembly of your people, I will praise you, Lord
My God, My God, O Hear My Plea 225

22 **All You Who See Me Scoff at Me** 518
My God, my God, why have you forsaken me?

23(I) **The Lord Is My Shepherd** **376**
A: The Lord is my shepherd
B: I shall live in the house of the Lord
The King of Love My Shepherd Is 324

23(II) **The Lord Is My Shepherd** **377**
I am the Good Shepherd
The King of Love My Shepherd Is 324

23(III) **Dominus Pascit Me** **378**
Panem caeli dedit eis: Alleluia
The King of Love My Shepherd Is 324

23 **The Lord Is My Shepherd** **494**
The Lord shepherds his flock

23 **Dominus Pascit Me** **545**
Lux aeterna (Es. 4: 2,35)

24(I) **The Lord's Are the Earth and Its Fullness** **379**
A: Let the Lord enter
B: Here, Lord, are your people

24(II) **Lift up Your Heads, O Gates** **380**
Who is the King of glory?

25(I) **Make Known Your Ways to Me, O Lord** **381**
A: To you do I lift up my soul
B: Teach me your ways, O Lord
To You I Lift My Soul 337

25(II) **Make Known Your Ways to Me, O Lord** **382**
A: Your ways, Lord, are love and truth
B: Remember your mercies, Lord
To You I Lift My Soul 337

25(III) **To You, O Lord, I Lift Up My Soul** **383**
And forgive all our sins, O Lord
To You I Lift My Soul 337

27(I) **The Lord Is My Light and My Salvation** **384**
A: I believe that I shall see the good things of the Lord
B: The Lord is my light and my salvation
C: Be attentive, O Lord, to my prayer
God Is My Strong Salvation 165
Safe in the Hands of God 291

27(II) **The Lord Is My Light and My Salvation** **385**
Response: The Lord is near to those who call on him
God Is My Strong Salvation 165
Safe in the Hands of God 291

29 **Declare to the Lord, O Daughters and Sons of God** **386**
Response: Alleluia

Psalm	Title	No.
30	**I Will Extol You, O Lord**	387
	I will praise you, Lord, for you have rescued me	
31	**In You, O Lord, I Take My Refuge**	388
	A: Father, I put my life in your hands	
	B: Lord, be my rock of safety	
32	**Happy Are They Whose Sins Are Forgiven**	389
	A: Lord, forgive the wrong I have done	
	B: I turn to you, Lord, in time of trouble	
33	**Upright Is the Word of the Lord**	390
	A: O how blessed the people	
	B: Lord, let your mercy be on us	
	Rejoice, All Peoples, in the Lord 288	
34(I)	**I Will Bless the Lord at All Times**	391
	A: Taste and see the goodness of the Lord	
	B: I will bless the Lord at all times	
	O Taste and See That God Is Good 265	
	Tell His Praise in Song and Story 310	
34(II)	**I Will Bless the Lord at All Times**	392
	A: The Lord hears the cry of the poor	
	B: Taste and see the goodness of the Lord	
	O Taste and See That God Is Good 265	
	Tell His Praise in Song and Story 310	
34(III)	**I Will Bless the Lord at All Times**	393
	The angel of the Lord will rescue those who fear him	
	O Taste and See That God Is Good 265	
	Tell His Praise in Song and Story 310	
36	*High In The Heavens, Eternal God* 184	
40	**For the Lord I Waited Patiently**	394
	A: I come to do your will, Lord	
	B: Lord, come to my aid	
41	**Happy Are They Who Have Regard for the Lowly**	395
	Lord, heal my soul, for I have sinned against you	
42-43	**My Soul Thirsts for God**	396
	A: Though I walk in a death-dark valley	
	B: As the deer longs for running water	
45	**My Heart Overflows with a Goodly Theme**	397
	A: The queen stands at your right hand	
	B: The bridegroom is here	
47	**All You Peoples, Clap Your Hands**	398
	God mounts his throne amid shouts of joy	
	All Nations, Clap Your Hands 106	
50	**God the Lord Has Spoken**	399
	To the upright I will show the saving power of God	

51(I) **Have Mercy on Me, O God, in Your Goodness** 400
Remember your love and have mercy on me
God of All Mercy, Lord Above 168
51(II) **Have Mercy on Me, O God, in Your Goodness** 401
A: Create a clean heart in me, O God
B: I shall arise and return to my father
God of All Mercy, Lord Above 168
54 **O God, by Your Name Save Me** 402
The Lord upholds my life
62 **Only in God Is My Soul at Rest** 403
Rest in God alone, O my soul
63 **O God, You Are My God Whom I Seek** 404
My soul is thirsting for you, O Lord, my God
O Lord, You Are My God 253
63 **O God, You Are My God** 482
As the morning breaks, I look for you, O God
65 **O God, in Zion People Must Praise You** 405
The seed that falls on good ground
To Bless the Earth 332
66 **Shout to God with Joy, All the World** 406
Response: Give him glorious praise
All Ye Peoples, Bless the Lord 109
67 **May God Have Pity on Us** 407
A: O God, let all the nations praise you
B: May God bless us in his mercy
God of Mercy, God of Grace 169
68 **The Just Rejoice** 408
O God, in your goodness
69 **I Pray to You for the Time of Your Favor, O Lord** 409
A: In your great love, Lord, answer me
B: Turn to the Lord in your need
71 **In You, O Lord, I Take Refuge** 410
A: I will sing of your salvation
B: Since my mother's womb, you have been my strength
72 **O God, with Your Judgment Endow the King** 411
A: Ev'ry nation on earth will serve him
B: Justice shall flourish in his time
Hail to the Lord's Anointed 181

78(I) **What We Have Heard and Know** 412
The Lord gave them bread from heaven
O Praise Our Great and Gracious Lord 258
78(II) **Give Ear, O My People, to My Teaching** 413
Do not forget the works of the Lord
O Praise Our Great and Gracious Lord 258
80(I) **Give Ear, O Shepherd of Israel** 414
Response: Lord, mighty God
80(II) **From Egypt You Took a Vine** 415
The vineyard of the Lord is the house of Israel
81 **Take Up a Melody and Sound the Timbrel** 416
Sing with joy to God, our help
84(I) **How Lovely Is Your Dwelling Place** 417
Response: I Long for the house of the Lord
84(II) **How Lovely Is Your Dwelling Place** 418
You open your hand and fill ev'ry creature
85 **I Will Hear What the Lord God Proclaims** 419
A: O Lord, come let us see your kindness
B: Grant peace, O Lord, to all who wait for you
Come, Show Us Your Salvation, Lord 138
86 **You, O Lord, Are Good and Forgiving** 420
You, O Lord, are good and forgiving
89 **I Will Sing of Your Steadfast Love** 421
A: I will sing the goodness of the Lord
B: The son of David will live forever
90 **O Lord, You Have Been Our Refuge** 422
A: In ev'ry age, O Lord, you have been our refuge
B: Fill us with your love, O Lord
C: Lord, give success to the work of our hands
O God, Our Help in Ages Past 241
91 **You Who Dwell in the Shelter of the Most High** 423
A: When I am troubled, Lord, be my refuge
B: He has placed his angels over you.
Within the shelter of the Lord 353
91 **You Who Dwell in the Shelter of the Most High** 504
A: Be my refuge and my strength, O Lord (During Lent and Ordinary Time)
B: Alleluia (During Eastertide)
92 **It Is Good to Give Thanks to the Lord** 424
O Lord, it is good to give thanks and sing your praise, Most High

93 **The Lord is King** **425**
Christ, Lord of Glory
95 **Come, Let Us Sing Joyfully to the Lord** **426**
A: If today you hear his voice, harden not your hearts
B: Let us come before the Lord and praise him
Come, Let Us Sing Unto the Lord 137
To God with Gladness Sing 335
95 **Come, Let Us Sing to the Lord** **480**
Ordinary Time: Come let us sing to the Lord,
the rock of our salvation
Advent: Come let us worship the Lord,
the King who is to come
Christmas: Christ is born for us; come,
let us adore him
Lent: Come, let us worship Christ the Lord,
who for our sake endured
temptation and suffering
Easter: The Lord is risen, Alleluia!
Pentecost: Come let us adore Christ
the Lord, who promised
the Holy Spirit on his people. Alleluia!
96(I) **Sing to the Lord a New Song** **427**
A: Today is born our savior, Christ the Lord
B: Proclaim his marvelous deeds to all the nations
96(II) **Sing to the Lord a New Song** **428**
A: Go forth into the world and teach all nations
B: Give to the Lord glory and honor
96(III) **Sing to the Lord, O Bless His Name** **429**
Sing a new song to the Lord
96(IV) **Sing to the Lord, O Bless His Name** **430**
Response: Alleluia
97 **The Lord is King** **431**
A: A light will shine on us this day
B: The Lord is king, the most high over all the earth
C: Let the good rejoice in the Lord
98(I) **Sing to the Lord a New Song** **432**
All the ends of the earth
Alleluia, Alleluia! Sing a New Song to the Lord 110
Joy to the World 205
98(II) **Sing to the Lord a New Song** **433**
A: The Lord has revealed to the nations
B: The Lord comes to rule the world with justice
Alleluia, Alleluia! Sing a New Song to the Lord 110
Joy to the World 205

98(III) **Sing to the Lord a New Song** **434**

Response: Alleluia

Alleluia, Alleluia! Sing a New Song to the Lord 110

Joy to the World 205

100 **Sing with Joy to the Lord, All Ye Lands** **435**

A: We are his people

B: Sing with joy to the Lord, all ye lands

You are my friends 551

All People That on Earth Do Dwell 107

O Be Joyful in the Lord 234

Sing, All Creation 296

103(I) **Bless the Lord, O My Soul** **436**

A: Bless the Lord, O my soul

B: The Lord is kind and merciful

O My Soul, Bless God the Father 255

Praise, My Soul, The King of Heaven 279

Rejoice, My Soul, and Bless the Lord 286

103(II) **Bless the Lord, O My Soul** **437**

The Lord has set his throne in heaven

O My Soul, Bless God the Father 255

Praise, My Soul, the King of Heaven 279

Rejoice, My Soul, and Bless the Lord 286

104(I) **Bless the Lord, O My Soul** **438**

Send forth your Spirit, Lord (Easter Vigil)

Send Forth from the Heav'ns 292

O Worship the King 268

104(II) **Bless the Lord, O My Soul** **439**

A: Send forth your Spirit, Lord

(Pentecost - Holy Spirit - Confirmation)

B: The Spirit of God is upon me

(Alternate setting for Confirmation)

Send Forth from the Heav'ns 292

O Worship the King 268

104(III) **Bless the Lord, O My Soul** **439A**

Send forth your Spirit, Lord

Send Forth from the Heav'ns 292

O Worship the King 268

107 **They Who Sailed the Sea in Ships** **440**

Give thanks to the Lord, his love is everlasting

110 **The Lord Says to My Lord** **441**

Response: You are a priest forever in the line of Melchizedek

•110 **Dixit Dominus Domino Meo** 551
Juravit Dominus
112 **Happy Are They Who Fear the Lord** 442
A: The just one is a light in darkness to the upright
B: Happy are they who fear the Lord
C: Happy are they who are merciful
113 **Praise the Lord, You His Servants** 443
A: Praise the Lord who lifts up the poor
B: The Lord will give him a seat
with the leaders of his people
C: Blessed be the name of the Lord forever
116(I) **What Shall I Render to the Lord** 444
A: Gracious is the Lord and just
B: I will take the cup of salvation
What Shall I Render to the Lord? 349
116(II) **I Love the Lord** 445
A: The cup of blessing
B: I shall walk before the Lord
What Shall I Render to the Lord? 349
••117(I) **All You Nations, Praise the Lord** 446
Go out to all the world
••117(II) **Laudate Dominum** 447
Alleluia
••117(III) **Laudate Dominum, Omnes Gentes** 448
A: Adoremus in aeternum
B: Attende, Domine
••117(IV) **Laudate Dominum, Omnes Gentes** 449
A: Rorate caeli
B: Cor Jesu
118(I) **Give Thanks to the Lord for He Is Good** 450
A: Alleluia
B: Give thanks to the Lord for he is good
C: The stone rejected by the builders
D: This is the day the Lord has made
This Is the Day the Lord Created 329
118(II) **Give Thanks to the Lord for He Is Good** 451
This is the day the Lord has made
This Is the Day the Lord Created 329
119(I) **How Blessed Are They** 452
How blessed are they who walk in the law of the Lord

• *No. 109 in Latin Vulgate*
•• *No. 116 in Latin Vulgate*

119(II) **How Blessed Are They** **453**
I love your commands, O Lord, my God
121 **I Lift up My Eyes Toward the Mountains** **454**
Our help is from the Lord who made heav'n and earth
122 **I Rejoiced Because They Said to Me** **455**
We will go up to the house of the Lord
123 **To You I Lift Up My Eyes** **456**
Our eyes are fixed on the Lord, pleading for his mercy
124 **If It Had Not Been the Lord** **457**
Our soul has escaped like a bird from the hunter's net
126 **When the Lord Brought Back the Captives** **458**
A: The Lord has done great things for us
B: Those who sow in tears shall reap in joy
128 **Happy Are You Who Fear the Lord** **459**
A: Happy are you who fear the Lord
B: May the Lord bless us all the days of our lives
130 **Out of the Depths I Cry to You** **460**
A: With the Lord there is mercy
B: I hope in the Lord and I trust in his word
Out of the Depths, to You, O Lord, We Cry 277
131 **My Heart Is Not Proud, O Lord** **461**
In you, O Lord, I have found my peace
132 **Lo, We Heard of It in Ephrathah** **462**
A: Lord, go up to the place of your rest
B: God will give him the throne of David, his father
How Good a Thing It Is 186
134 **Come, Bless the Lord** **505**
A: In the silent hours of night
B: Alleluia (Eastertide)
136(I) **Give Thanks to the Lord for He Is Good** **463**
Refrains: His love is everlasting
For his mercy endures forever
Give Thanks to God for He Is Good 162
136(II) **Give Thanks to the Lord for He Is Good** **464**
Refrains: His love is everlasting
For his mercy endures forever
Give Thanks to God for He Is Good 162
137 **By the Streams of Babylon** **465**
Let my tongue be silenced
138(I) **I Will Give Thanks to You** **466**
A: Lord, I thank you for your faithfulness and love
B: In the sight of the angels
With All My Powers of Heart and Tongue 352

138(II) **I Will Give Thanks to You** **467**
A: Lord, your love is eternal
B: Lord, on the day I called for help
With All My Powers of Heart and Tongue 352

139 **O Lord, You Have Probed Me** **468**
A: I give you thanks
B: Guide me, O Lord, along the everlasting way
Lord, Thou Hast Searched Me 216

141 **Lord, Place a Guard at My Mouth** **493**
Receive my prayers as incense
Lord, Make Haste to Hear My Cry 251

145(I) **I Will Extol You, O My God and King** **469**
A: You open your hand to feed us, Lord
B: The Lord is compassionate
O Lord, You Are My God and King 252

145(II) **I Will Extol You, O My God and King** **470**
A: I will praise your name forever
B: Your friends tell the glory of your kingship, Lord
O Lord, You Are My God and King 252

146 **Forever the Lord God Keeps His Faith** **471**
A: Lord, Come and Save us
B: Praise the Lord, O my soul
C: Happy the poor in spirit

147(I) **Praise the Lord for He Is Good** **472**
A: The Word of God became man and lived among us
B: Praise the Lord, Jerusalem

147(II) **Praise the Lord for He Is Good** **473**
Praise the Lord, who heals the brokenhearted

148 *Let the Whole Creation Cry* 210
Lord, Who Hast Made Us For Thine Own 218
Praise the Lord, Ye Heav'ns Adore Him 282

149 **Sing to the Lord a New Song** **484**
We praise your glorious name

150 *O Praise Ye the Lord* 259
Praise the Lord, His Glories Show 280
Praise the Lord Who Reigns Above 281

A solis ortus cardine 264
Adeste fideles 102, 235
Adoro te 164
Agincourt 319, 328
Alberta 253, 277
Allein Gott 104
America 222
Amor 293
Andernach 141, 160, 161
Angel's Song 239, 263, 309
Anima Christi 305
Antioch 205
Ar hyd y nos 146, 159
Ashgrove 208
Attende Domine 250
Augustine 206
Aurelia 312
Aurora caelum 225
Austria 202, 214, 302
Ave Maria 117
Ave Verum 118
Aylesbury 125, 186

Branle de l'official 151
Bryn myrddin 110

Cantique 226
Cheshire 223
Chislehurst 109, 149
Christe sanctorum 155, 278
Christi munera 238
Christus der ist mein Leben 165, 332
Christus Rex(1) 129
Christus Rex(2) 336
Coelites plaudant 273, 296
Creator alme siderum 147, 260
Crucifer 207

Darmstadt 346
Darwall's 148th 120, 290, 335, 356
Den des Vaters Sinn geboren 108
Desrocquettes 121
Deus tuorum militum 266, 267
Diademata 145
Divine Praises 122
Divinum mysterium 269
Dix 114, 158
Domnach Trionide 306
Down Ampney 133
Dundee 242, 265

Ein' feste Burg 100
Eisenach 134, 321
Ellacombe 197, 287, 316
Emendar 330
Ermuntre dich 126

Ferial Day 136
Festgesang 182
Finest Wheat 360
Finlay 234
Fontes aquarum 307
Forest Green 249
Franconia 123
Freu dich sehr 144, 233
Freuen wir uns all in ein 190, 343, 353

Gaudeamus pariter 131, 204, 280
Gerontius 224, 314
Gloria 113
Gott des Himmels und der Erden 124, 154

Hanover 268, 292
Herzliebster Jesu 153
Hyfrydol 112, 140, 282
Hymn to Joy 203, 215, 303

In Adventu 325
In Babilone 166, 175, 188, 243
In dulci jubilo 195
Irby 270

Je sais, Vierge Marie 331
Jesu dulcis memoria 247, 251
Jesu meine Freude 198
Jesus Christ unser Herre 181

King's Weston 116
Kremser 344

Laetatus 354
Lauda anima 196, 279
Lauda Sion 150
Laudate Dominum 259, 357
Laudes 281
Leoni 320, 327
Liebster Jesu 355
Llanfair 176, 210
Lobe den Herrn 283, 284
London New 288
Lourdes Hymn 193

Love Unknown 337, 345
Lucis Creator optime 262
Lyra Davidica 201

Macht hoch die Tür 211
Mainz(1) 115
Mainz(2) 163
Materna 232
McGrath 285
Meinen Jesum lass ich nicht 298
Merton 183
Mount Auburn 135
Munich 101, 274

Narenza 334
National Hymn 167
Nicaea 185
Northbrook 286
Nos respectu gratiae 297
Nun danket 230, 231
Nun danket all und bringet Ehr 213, 137, 237

O filii et filiae 358
O Lamm Gottes unschuldig 246
Offeramus 347
Old 130th 142
Old 81st 194
Old Hundredth 107, 245

Pange lingua 228, 275, 532A
Passion Chorale 248
Pastor bonus 294
Pearsall 326
Personent Hodie 272
Picardy 209
Pleading Savior 299
Puer Natus in Bethlehem 99
Puer nobis 138, 350

Ratisbon 132, 169
Regent Square 128, 333
Rendez à Dieu 156, 329
Rex Gloriae 148, 174, 597
Rockport 258
Rottenburg 352
Rustington 111, 310

Safe in the Hands 291
Salve feste dies 178, 179
Salve Regina 170
Salzburg 173, 300
Sandringham 257
Schönster Herr Jesu 139
Scientia salutis 130
Sedulius 323
Sei Lob und Ehr' 315
Sine nomine 157
Slane 127
Song 1 217
Song 22 311
St. Anne 241, 362
St. Catherine 152
St. Columba 324
St. Flavian 212
St. Francis 103
St. George's Windsor 143
St. Patrick's Breastplate 189
St. Theodolph 105
St. Thomas New 106
St. Thomas Old 200
Stille Nacht 295
Sunrise 255, 596

Tallis' Canon 244, 252
Te Deum 180
Te Deum laudamus 361
Te lucis ante terminum(1) 240, 348, 481
Te lucis ante terminum(2) 491
Te lucis ante terminum(3) 502, 503
Terry 177
The First Nowell 318
The King's Majesty 168, 216, 317
Tregaron 192, 322
Trinitas 289
Truro 184

Ubi caritas 351
Une jeune puçelle 339

Veni Creator 340
Veni Emmanuel 236
Veni Sancte Spiritus 187, 341
Victimae paschali 342
Vigiles et sancti 218, 313, 359

Wachet auf 338
Wareham 254, 261, 349
Was Gott tut das ist wohlgetan 162, 301
Wen nur den lieben Gott 191
Werde munter mein Gemüthe 199
Wie schön leuchtet der Morgenstern 256
Winchester New 271

Colossians 3:12-17.	574	Practice of Virtues
1 Corinthians 13.	565	Love - the Greatest Commandment
Deuteronomy 6:4-7.	506	Saturday (Night Prayer)
Ephesians 4:1-7.11-13.31.32.	589	Unity in the Mystical Body
Ephesians 4:26-27.	506	Wednesday (Night Prayer)
Ephesians 4:29-32.	485	Friday (Morning Prayer)
Ephesians 6:10-17.	555	Christian Witness
Exodus 20:1.3-5a.7.8.12a.	587	The Ten Commandments
Isaiah 11:1-5.9.	585	The Promise of a Messiah
Isaiah 40:1-5.9-11.	573	Promise of Salvation
Isaiah 40:12-14.28-29.31.	571	Power of the Creator to Save His People
Isaiah 53.	577	Suffering and Triumph of the Servant of the Lord
Isaiah 55:1.6.10-13.	565	Invitation to Grace
Isaiah 66:1-2.	485	Thursday (Morning Prayer)
Isaiah 9:1.5.6.	559	Emmanuel - God with Us
James 1:22-27.	576	Response to God's Gifts
James 1:4-8.12.13.17-20.	560	Endurance Through Faith In God
Jeremiah 14:9a.	506	Friday (Night Prayer)
Job 11:7-19.	556	Courage in Trial
Job 28: Selected Verses.	590	Wisdom and Understanding
1 John 3:1-3.18-24.	591	We Are God's Children
1 John 4:7.9.11-12.17-21.	562	God's Love for Us
John 14:1-4.16-20.27.	584	The Last Discourse of Jesus
John 15:1-15.	558	Friendship of God
John 1:1-14.	575	Prologue of St. John Gospel
Luke 1:68-79.	579	The Benedictus
Matthew 5:3-12.	578	The Beatitudes
Odes of Solomon No. V.	570	Ode of Trust
Odes of Solomon No. VII.	564	Hymn of the Incarnation
Odes of Solomon No. XIV.	580	The Disciple Speaks
Odes of Solomon No. XV.	568	Light Conquers Darkness
Odes of Solomon No. XVI.	582	The Praises of the Word in Creation
Odes of Solomon No. XXX.	583	The Fountains of the Savior
1 Peter 1:3-9.	572	Praise and Thanksgiving for New Life and Hope Through the Resurrection of Jesus
1 Peter 5:8-9a.	506	Tuesday (Night Prayer)
2 Peter 1:10-11.	485	Saturday (Morning Prayer)
Philippians 2:1-11.	563	Imitating Christ's Humility
Philippians 4:4-9.	566	Joy and Peace
Psalm 1:1-6.	588	True Happiness
Revelation 21:1-7. 22:1.3-5.	569	New Heaven and New Earth
Revelation 22:4-5.	506	Sunday (Night Prayer)
Revelation 7:9-12.	485	Sunday (Morning Prayer)
Romans 12:4.5.9-12.20.21.	561	Fraternal Charity
Romans 13:11-14.	485	Tuesday (Morning Prayer)
Sirach 2:1-9.11.	557	Duties Toward God
The Following of Christ	592	Truth Speaks Inwardly
The Following of Christ	593	An Invitation to the Lord's Table
1 Thessalonians 5:23.	506	Thursday (Night Prayer)
1 Thessalonians 5:9-10.	506	Monday (Night Prayer)
2 Thessalonians 3:10b-13.	485	Monday (Morning Prayer)
Tobit 4:15a.16a.18a.19.	485	Wednesday (Morning Prayer)
Vexilla Regis	594	The Brave Flags of Our King
Wisdom 1:1-7.	586	The Reward of Justice
Wisdom 3:1-3.5-7.9.	581	The Hidden Counsel of God: On Suffering

HYMNS
First Lines and Common Titles

A Boy Is Born in Bethlehem 99
A Mighty Fortress Is Our God 100
Accept, Almighty Father 101
Adeste, Fideles 102
All Creatures of Our God and King 103
All Glory Be to God on High 104
All Glory, Laud and Honor 105
All Nations, Clap Your Hands (Ps. 47) 106
All People That on Earth Do Dwell (Ps. 100) 107
All Praise to You, O God, This Night 503
All Who Keep the Faith of Jesus 108
All Ye Peoples, Bless the Lord (Ps. 66) 109
Alleluia 308
Alleluia! Sing to Jesus 112
Alleluia! Sing to Jesus 111
Alleluia, Alleluia! Sing a New Song
to the Lord (Ps. 98) 110
Alma Redemptoris Mater 219
America 222
America the Beautiful 232
Angels We Have Heard on High 113
As with Gladness Men of Old 114
At the Cross Her Station Keeping 115
At the Name of Jesus 116
Ave Maria 117
Ave Regina Caelorum 172
Ave Verum Corpus 118

Baptized into Your Name Most Holy 119
Be Thou My Vision 121
Be Thou My Vision 121A
Before the Lord We Bow 120
Blessed Be God 122
Blest Are the Pure in Heart 123
Bread of Heav'n, on Thee We Feed 124
Break Forth, O Beauteous Heav'nly Light 126
Breathe on Me, Breath of God 125

Christ Be My Leader 127
Christ Is Made the Sure Foundation 128
Christ Is the World's Light 130
Christ, Lord of Glory 129
Christ the Lord Is Ris'n Today! 131
Christ, Whose Glory Fills the Skies 132
Come Down, O Love Divine 133
Come, Follow Me 134
Come, Holy Ghost, Creator Blest 135
Come, Holy Spirit, Ever One 136
Come, Let Us Sing unto the Lord (Ps. 95) 137
Come, Show Us Your Salvation, Lord (Ps. 85) 138
Come, Take the Body of the Savior 139
Come, Thou Long-Expected Jesus 140
Come, Thou Redeemer of the Earth 141
Come unto Me, Ye Weary 142
Come, Ye Thankful People, Come 143
Comfort, Comfort Ye, My People 144
Crown Him with Many Crowns 145

Day Is Done 146
Dear Maker of the Starry Skies 147
Dear Saint Joseph, Son of David 148
Ding, Dong! Merrily on High 151
Divine Praises 122

Easter Glory Fills the Sky! Alleluia! 149
Ecce Panis Angelorum 150

Faith of Our Fathers 152
Father Almighty, Pour on Us Thy Blessing 153
Father, Lord of Earth and Heaven 596
Father, Lord of Earth and Heaven 154
Father of Mercy, God of Consolation 155
Father, We Thank Thee 156
For All the Saints 157
For the Beauty of the Earth 158
For the Fruit of All Creation 159
Forth in the Peace of Christ We Go 160
Forth in Thy Name, O Lord 161

Gift of Finest Wheat 360
Give Thanks to God for He Is Good (Ps. 136) 162
God, Father, Praise and Glory 163
God Is My Strong Salvation (Ps. 27) 165
God of All Mercy, Lord Above (Ps. 51) 168
God of Gods, We Sound His Praises 166
God of Mercy, God of Grace (Ps. 67) 169
God of Our Fathers 167
Godhead Here in Hiding 164

Hail, Holy Queen 170
Hail Mary, Queen of Heav'n 172
Hail, O Holy Queen 171
Hail, O Once Despised Jesus! 175
Hail, O Once Despised Jesus! 174
Hail, Redeemer, King Divine! 173
Hail the Day That Sees Him Rise 176
Hail the Sign, the Cross of Jesus 177
Hail, This Festival Day! - Blessed
Virgin Mary 178
Hail, This Festival Day! - Christ
the King 179

Hail to the Lord's Anointed (Ps. 72) 181
Hark! A Herald Voice Is Sounding 183
Hark! The Herald Angels Sing 182
High in the Heav'ns, Eternal God (Ps. 36) 184
Holy God, We Praise Thy Name 180
Holy, Holy, Holy! 185
Holy Spirit, Come and Shine 187
Holy Spirit, Ever Dwelling 188
How Good a Thing It Is (Ps. 133) 186

I Clasp unto My Heart This Day 189
I Come with Joy to Meet the Lord 190
I Heard the Voice of Jesus Say 192
I Sing the Mighty Power of God 197
If Thou But Trust in God to Guide Thee 191
Immaculate Mary 193
In Christ There Is No East or West 194
In Dulci Jubilo 195
In His Temple Now Behold Him 196

Jesu, Joy and Treasure 198
Jesu, Joy of Man's Desiring 199
Jesus, Bread in Mercy Broken 200
Jesus Christ Is Ris'n Today 201
Jesus, Name of Wondrous Love 204
Joy to the World (Ps. 98) 205
Joyful, Joyful, We Adore Thee 202
Joyful, Joyful, We Adore Thee 203

Let All Mortal Flesh Keep Silence 209
Let All the World in Ev'ry Corner Sing 206
Let All Things Now Living 208
Let the Whole Creation Cry (Ps. 148) 210
Lift High the Cross 207
Lift up Your Heads, Ye Mighty Gates 211
Lord Jesus, as We Turn from Sin 213
Lord of Nations, God Eternal 214
Lord of Nations, God Eternal 215
Lord, Thou Hast Searched Me (Ps. 139) 216
Lord, Who at Your First Eucharist Did Pray 217
Lord, Who Hast Made Us for Thine Own (Ps. 148) 218
Lord, Who Throughout These Forty Days 212
Lord, You Give the Great Commission 597
Lorica of Saint Patrick 189
Lourdes Hymn 193
Loving Mother of Our Saviour 219

Magnificat 233
Mary the Dawn 221
Mary, Queen of Heav'n 220
My Country 'Tis of Thee 222
My God, Accept My Heart This Day 223
My God, How Wonderful You Are 224
My God, My God, O Hear My Plea (Ps. 22) 225

Now Fades All Earthly Splendor 226
Now, His Years of Life Perfected 227
Now My Tongue, the Myst'ry Telling 228
Now Thank We All Our God 230
Now Thank We All Our God 231
Now with the Fast Departing Light 502

O Be Glad, My Soul, Rejoice 233
O Be Joyful in the Lord (Ps. 100) 234
O Beautiful for Spacious Skies 232
O Come, All Ye Faithful 235
O Come, O Come, Emmanuel 236
O for a Thousand Tongues to Sing 237
O God, from Whom Mankind Derives Its Name 238
O God in Heav'n 239
O God of Light 240
O God of Light 481
O God, Our Help in Ages Past (Ps. 90) 241
O God, Unseen, Yet Ever Near 242
O Gracious Light 244
O Holy Spirit, Enter In 245
O How Glorious, Full of Wonder (Ps. 8) 243
O Jesus, in Thy Heart Divine 247
O Lamb of God, All Holy 246
O Little Town of Bethlehem 249
O Lord, Incline Thine Ear 250
O Lord, Make Haste to Hear My Cry (Ps. 141) 251
O Lord, You Are My God (Ps. 63) 253
O Lord, You Are My God and King (Ps. 145) 252
O Love of God, How Strong and True 254
O Morning Star, How Fair and Bright 256
O My Soul, Bless God the Father (Ps. 103) 255
O Perfect Love 257
O Praise Our Great and Gracious Lord (Ps. 78) 258
O Praise Ye the Lord (Ps. 150) 259
O Radiant Light 491
O Sacred Head Surrounded 248
O Salutaris Hostia 260
O Salutaris Hostia 261
O Saving Victim 260
O Saving Victim 261
O Splendor of Eternal Light 263
O Splendor of Eternal Light 262
O Sun of Justice, Fill Our Hearts 264
O Taste and See That God Is Good (Ps. 34) 265
O Thou, the Heav'ns' Eternal King 266
O Wondrous Sight, O Vision Fair 267
O Worship the King (Ps. 104) 268
Of the Father's Love Begotten 269
On Jordan's Bank 271
On This Day 272
Once in Royal David's City 270
Only-Begotten, Word of God Eternal 273

Our Father, We Have Wandered 274
Out of the Depths, to You, O Lord, We Cry (Ps. 130) 277

Pange Lingua - Tantum Ergo Sacramentum 275
Praise and Thanksgiving Be to God 278
Praise, My Soul, the King of Heaven (Ps. 103) 279
Praise the Lord Who Reigns Above (Ps. 150) 281
Praise the Lord, His Glories Show (Ps. 150) 280
Praise the Lord, Ye Heav'ns Adore Him (Ps. 148) 282
Praise to the Holiest 285
Praise to the Lord 284
Praise to the Lord 283

Regina Caeli, Laetare 220
Rejoice, All Peoples, in the Lord (Ps. 33) 288
Rejoice, My Soul, and Bless the Lord (Ps. 103) 286
Rejoice, Rejoice, Believers 287
Rejoice, the Lord Is King 290
Rejoice with Us in God the Trinity 289

Safe in the Hands of God (Ps. 27) 291
Salve Regina 171
Send Forth from the Heav'ns (Ps.104) 292
Set Her as a Seal upon Your Heart 293
Shepherd of Souls 294
Silent Night, Holy Night! 295
Sing, All Creation (Ps. 100) 296
Sing, My Tongue 532
Sing, My tongue, Thy Savior's Glory 298
Sing of Mary, Pure and Lowly 299
Sing of Christ, Proclaim His Glory 302
Sing of Christ, Proclaim His Glory 303
Sing Praise to God Who Reigns Above 301
Sion, at Thy Shining Gates 297
Songs of Thankfulness and Praise 300
Soul of Christ 304
Soul of My Savior 305
Spirit Seeking Light and Beauty 306
Spirit Seeking Light and Beauty 306A
Springs of Water, Bless the Lord
(Ps. 118 I Saw water) 307

Take Up Your Cross 309
Tantum Ergo Sacramentum - Pange Lingua 275
Te Deum 180
Te Deum 361
Tell His Praise in Song and Story (Ps. 34) 310
Tell Out, My Soul, the Greatness of the Lord 311
Th'Eternal Gifts of Christ the King 317
The Church Triumphant in Thy Love 314
The Church's One Foundation 312
The Clouds of Night Are Passed Away 313
The Day is Surely Drawing Near 315
The Day of Resurrection 316
The First Nowell 318
The Glory of These Forty Days 319
The God of Abraham Praise 320
The God Whom Earth and Sea and Sky 321
The Great Creator of the Worlds 322
The Great Forerunner of the Morn 323
The King of Love My Shepherd Is (Ps. 23) 324
The King Shall Come When Morning Dawns 325
The Lord Is King 326
The Perfect Law of God (Ps. 19) 327
The Royal Banners Forward Go 328
Therefore, We Before Him Bending 228
Therefore, We Before Him Bending 298
Think of the Son of God 330
This Is the Day the Lord Created (Ps. 118) 329
Thou Art the Star of Morning 331
To Bless the Earth (Ps. 65) 332
To Christ, the Prince of Peace 334
To God with Gladness Sing (Ps. 95) 335
To Jesus Christ, Our Sov'reign King 336
To the Name of Our Salvation 333
To You I Lift My Soul (Ps. 25) 337
'Twas in the Moon of Wintertime 339

Up, Awake, from Highest Steeple 338
Up, Awake, from Highest Steeple 338A

Veni Creator Spiritus 340
Veni Sancte Spiritus 341
Versicle - Response - Oration for Benediction 229
Versicle - Response - Oration for Benediction 276
Victimae Paschali Laudes 342

We Find Thee, Lord, in Others' Needs 343
We Gather Together 344
We Give Immortal Praise 345
We Love Your Temple, Lord 346
We Praise You, Father, for Your Gift 348
We Rejoice, God's Holy People 347
What Shall I Render to the Lord? (Ps. 116) 349
What Star is This? 350
Where Abideth Charity and Love 351
With All My Powers of Heart and Tongue (Ps. 138) 352
With Joy We Go up to the House of the Lord 354
Within the Shelter of the Lord (Ps. 91) 353
Word of God, Come Down on Earth 355

Ye Holy Angels Bright 356
Ye Servants of God, Your Master Proclaim 357
Ye Sons and Daughters of the Lord 358
Ye Watchers and Ye Holy Ones 359
You Are God: We Praise You 361
You Called Me, Father, by My Name 362
You Satisfy the Hungry Heart 360